Pangea: Paleoclimate, Tectonics, and Sedimentation During Accretion, Zenith, and Breakup of a Supercontinent

Edited by

George D. Klein
New Jersey Marine Sciences Consortium
Sandy Hook Field Station
Building #22
Fort Hancock, New Jersey 07732

SPECIAL PAPER
288

1994

Published by The Geological Society of America, Inc.
3300 Penrose Place, P.O. Box 9140, Boulder, Colorado 80301

Printed in U.S.A.

GSA Books Science Editor Richard A. Hoppin

Library of Congress Cataloging-in-Publication Data

Pangea : paleoclimate, tectonics, and sedimentation during accretion,
    zenith, and breakup of a supercontinent / edited by George D. Klein.
        p.   cm. — (Special paper ; 288)
    "Summarizes . . . papers presented during an international workshop
held in Lawrence, Kansas, in May 1992"—Pref.
    Includes bibliographical references and index.
    ISBN 0-8137-2288-8
    1. Pangaea (Geology)—Congresses.   I. Klein, George deVries,
1933–   . II. Series: Special papers (Geological Society of
America) ; 288.
    QE511.5.P355   1994
    551.7'2—dc20   93-49028
                                            CIP

Cover: Paleogeography of Kazanian (Late Permian; 255 Ma) showing high mountains
(dark brown), coastal plains (light brown), continental shelves (light blue), and deeper
oceans (dark blue). Color copy provided by Christopher R. Scotese.

10   9   8   7   6   5   4   3   2   1

Contents

Preface v

1. Introduction: Project PANGEA and Workshop Recommendations 1
  G. D. Klein and B. Beauchamp, with contributions by A. Baud,
  B. I. Chuvashov, O. R. Lopez-Gamundi, J. T. Parrish, C. A. Ross,
  P. A. Scholle, C. R. Scotese, and W. L. Watney

2. Pangea: Evolution of a Supercontinent and Its Consequences for Earth's
Paleoclimate and Sedimentary Environments 13
  J. J. Veevers

3. Pangean Climates 25
  T. J. Crowley

4. Idealized Pangean Climates: Sensitivity to Orbital Change 41
  J. E. Kutzbach

5. Phanerozoic CO$_2$ Levels and Global Temperatures Inferred
from Changing Paleogeography 57
  T. R. Worsley, T. L. Moore, C. M. Fraticelli, and C. R. Scotese

6. Orogenic Enhancement of Weathering and Continental Ice-Sheet
Initiation 75
  T. L. Moore and T. R. Worsley

7. General Circulation Model Simulations of Triassic Climates:
Preliminary Results 91
  K. M. Wilson, D. Pollard, W. W. Hay, S. L. Thompson, and C. N. Wold

8. Depiction of Modern and Pangean Deserts: Evaluation of GCM
Hydrological Diagnostics for Paleoclimate Studies 117
  M. A. Chandler

iii

9. *The Climatic Evolution of India and Australia from the Late Permian to Mid-Jurassic: A Comparison of Climate Model Results with the Geologic Record* 139
   P. J. Fawcett, E. J. Barron, V. D. Robison, and B. J. Katz

10. *Pangean Orogenic and Epeirogenic Uplifts and Their Possible Climatic Significance* 159
    G. M. Friedman

11. *The Breakup of Pangea and Its Impact on Climate: Consequences of Variscan-Alleghanide Orogenic Collapse* 169
    W. Manspeizer

12. *Turning Point in Pangean Environmental History at the Permian/Triassic (P/Tr) Boundary* 187
    J. J. Veevers, P. J. Conaghan, and S. E. Shaw

13. *Geologically Rapid Late Triassic Extinctions: Palynological Evidence from the Newark Supergroup* 197
    S. J. Fowell, B. Cornet, and P. E. Olsen

14. *The Carbon and Oxygen Isotope Record During the Evolution of Pangea: Carboniferous to Triassic* 207
    E. L. Grossman

15. *Permian Climatic Cooling in the Canadian Arctic* 229
    B. Beauchamp

16. *Pangean Shelf Carbonates: Controls and Paleoclimatic Significance of Permian and Triassic Reefs* 247
    E. Flügel

17. *Stratal Hierarchy and Sequence Stratigraphy—Middle Pennsylvanian, Southwestern Kansas, U.S.A.* 267
    J. C. Youle, W. L. Watney, and L. L. Lambert

Index 287

Preface

This special paper summarizes both invited and contributed papers presented during an international workshop held in Lawrence, Kansas, in May 1992, to define the research direction of Project PANGEA. Project PANGEA is the second research effort of the Global Sedimentary Geology Program (GSGP) of the International Union of Geological Sciences (IUGS). Project PANGEA is sponsored under the auspices of the IUGS.

Project PANGEA was approved by GSGP's executive committee during the summer of 1990 at the Nottingham (UK) International Congress of Sedimentology. The leadership for this project was changed in January 1991 at which time George D. Klein (then at the University of Illinois at Urbana-Champaign and Benoit Beauchamp (Geological Survey of Canada, Calgary) were asked by GSGP's director, Robert N. Ginsburg, to organize Project PANGEA and a workshop to plan the international research program for the project to assure its continuation. That workshop was held in Lawrence, Kansas, from May 22 through May 28, 1992. Most of the invited and contributed papers presented there are incorporated into this volume. The introductory chapter summarizes the recommendations of the various working groups that held sessions to plan their activities.

At this time, I express my deepest appreciation to the following individuals who reviewed manuscripts for this publication, some of whom reviewed more than one: Thomas J. Algeo, Thomas F. Anderson, Eric J. Barron, Robert A. Berner, Mark A. Chandler, Thomas J. Crowley, Gerald M. Friedman, Robert N. Ginsburg, Richard L. Hay, William T. Holser, Lee R. Kump, Warren Manspeizer, James R. Markello, Stephen Marshak, George T. Moore, Robert J. Oglesby, Ben A. Van der Pluijm, Gregory J. Retalleck, Alfred Traverse, J.G.C. Walker, Debra A. Willard, C. Pius Weibel, and Thomas R. Worsley. In particular, Thomas J. Crowley is thanked not only for reviewing three paleoclimate papers but also for recommending others to review manuscripts in paleoclimatology.

In addition, I thank once again the many financial sponsors who made the workshop possible. I thank the National Science Foundation (Project Grant EAR-91-17687), the division on Sedimentary Geology of the Geological Society of America (for providing four student grants), SEPM (Society for Sedimentary Geology), International Association of Sedimentologists, CHEVRON Oil Field Research Co., and Allen Press for their support. I also express my appreciation to Thomas A. Ovenshine of the International Division of the U.S. Geological Survey for providing travel authorizations in and round-trip travel to the United States for two Russian participants. Without their support, the workshop would not have taken place.

Finally, I thank Robert N. Ginsburg for his guidance, advice, and support, and the International Union of Geological Sciences for its sponsorship.

G. D. Klein
Fort Hancock, New Jersey
March 25, 1993

Geological Society of America
Special Paper 288
1994

Introduction: Project Pangea and workshop recommendations

George D. Klein
New Jersey Marine Sciences Consortium, Building #22, Fort Hancock, New Jersey 07732
Benoit Beauchamp
Institute of Sedimentary and Petroleum Geology, Geological Survey of Canada, 3303 33rd Street NW, Calgary,
*   Alberta, T2L 2A7, Canada*
With contributions by:
Aymon Baud
Musee Geologique, UNIL-BFSH 2, CH-1015 Lausanne, Switzerland
Boris I. Chuvashov
Institute of Geology and Geochemistry, Academy of Sciences, Uralian Branch, Pochtovyi per 7, 62009 Cateriniburg, Russia
Oscar R. Lopez-Gamundi
Frontier Exploration–South America, Texaco, 4800 Fourace Place, Bellaire, Texas 77401-2324
Judith T. Parrish
Department of Geosciences, Gould-Simpson Building 77, University of Arizona, Tucson, Arizona 85721
Charles A. Ross
Geostrat Consultants, 600 Highland Drive, Bellingham, Washington 98225-6410
Peter A. Scholle
Department of Geological Sciences, Heroy Building, Southern Methodist University, Dallas, Texas 75275
Christopher R. Scotese
Department of Geology, University of Texas at Arlington, P.O. Boz 19049, Arlington, Texas 76019
W. Lynn Watney
Kansas Geological Survey, 1930 Constant Avenue, Lawrence, Kansas 66047-2598

PREAMBLE

A major number of problems concerning the nature and consequences of natural or anthropogenic environmental change can be solved only by the geological sciences. Many of these problems require separation of first-order driving mechanisms from background processes. Long-term as well as short-term variations during geological time in the numerical magnitudes of different environmental parameters are not well understood, however. The maximum and minimum rates of environmental change that occurred during geological time also remain unknown, and their global as well as local scale and consequences are poorly understood.

To address these problems and correlate them to current environmental concerns, an intensive study of the sedimentary record is mandatory because that record is the only source from which critical data can be obtained. Additional data are needed to calibrate the sedimentary record in terms of first-order processes characteristic of Earth as a planet. These include both mantle-driven processes (intrinsic) that drive plate tectonics, including the assembly and breakup of supercontinents, and solar-driven processes (extrinsic) that influence long-term and short-term climatic changes, such as advance and retreat of continental glaciers, changes in upwelling cycles, changes in monsoonal climate patterns, and desertification. Study of the sedimentary record involves examining the preservation of both intrinsically controlled and extrinsically controlled depositional events during Earth's history. Expressed in another way, the sedimentary record can be viewed as a strip-chart recording of the intrinsic and extrinsic record of Earth history.

Among the most spectacular manifestations of concurrent intrinsic and extrinsic changes are the assembly of the supercontinent Pangea during late Paleozoic and early Mesozoic time and its subsequent breakup and dispersal during latest Triassic and earliest to middle Jurassic time that led to the present-day disposition of continents. Thus studies of Pangea's sedimentary record to determine long-term and short-term magnitudes of environmental changes must involve multidisciplinary aspects of geodynamics and climate modeling. This

Klein, G. D., and Beauchamp, B., 1994, Introduction: Project Pangea and workshop recommendations, *in* Klein, G. D., ed., Pangea: Paleoclimate, Tectonics, and Sedimentation During Accretion, Zenith, and Breakup of a Supercontinent: Boulder, Colorado, Geological Society of America Special Paper 288.

volume focuses on the current state of the art of research about these changes during the evolution of Pangea.

Many major resources are known to occur within the stratigraphic record represented by the 145-m.y. record of Pangea. These include extensive source beds and reservoirs of petroleum and natural gas, coal, evaporites including potash, and phosphate deposits. Their occurrences appear to be controlled in part by the mantle-driven tectonic history of Pangea, whereas other occurrences can be attributed to solar-driven climatic change and associated changes in oceanic circulation and upwelling. An intensive study of the sedimentary rock record of Pangea will improve prediction of occurrences of these resources and establishment of their origin.

This volume focuses on the sedimentary record associated with the evolution of the supercontinent Pangea. The chapters represent state-of-the-art research summaries of what is known and what work is expected in the future relevant to the changing role of paleoclimate on the sedimentary record during the accretion, zenith, and breakup of a supercontinent. These papers were presented during an international workshop held in Lawrence, Kansas, in May 1992 to define the research direction of Project Pangea, the second research effort of the Global Sedimentary Geology Program (GSGP) of the International Union of Geological Sciences (IUGS).

Project Pangea focuses on the most recent time of supercontinent accretion and dispersal when continents merged toward a geoid low, and much of Pangea's climate appeared to be disposed in an icehouse mode. The accretion and dispersal of Pangea are the most recent examples of a recurring long-term global cyclic phenomenon. The 145-m.y. interval of Pangeas's history, however, was characterized by considerable climatic variability that belies the broad-scale icehouse climate suggested for times of supercontinent development. Consequently, Pangea's sedimentary record represents an ideal interval during Earth history from which to evaluate the processes and magnitude of environmental variability and develop a predictive rationale for evaluating current global environmental concerns. Study of Pangeas's sedimentary record is justified further as a baseline for study of intrinsic and extrinsic processes and effects associated with Precambrian supercontinents and of the history of continental growth and evolution because that record can present maximum and minimum values of the qualitative and quantitative variability of climatic-driven processes on the sedimentary record.

RESEARCH PROBLEMS

The following research problems were identified as potential salient components in Project Pangea during preliminary planning prior to the Project Pangea Workshop held in Lawrence, Kansas, from May 23 through 28, 1992. These initial problem sets included:

1. What is the causal connection between large-scale global climatic change, such as the icehouse-greenhouse change and the history of flux of CO_2 from the mantle? To what extent is that climatic change providing a signal of intrinsic, mantle-driven processes influencing climatic change both for the long term and the short term?

2. What is the record of variation of oxygen, sulphur, strontium, and carbon isotopic composition of seawater during Pennsylvanian, Permian, Triassic, and Jurassic time? How does this record constrain paleoclimatic models calibrated from the sedimentary record?

3. What was the role of astronomical forcing factors (Milankovitch orbital parameters) in driving solar-driven climatic change, and how complete is the record of such deposition that is preserved in cyclic sequence such as the famous cyclothems of the Pennsylvanian or the lacustrine cycles of the Triassic? Is this forcing dominant or subordinate? What is their record of preservation of forcing factors in both cyclic and noncyclic stratigraphic sequences? What short-term, intrinsically forced, tectonic processes can mimic, mask, or override the preservation record of astronomical forcing?

4. What mechanism controls relative changes in sea level that existed at time scales ranging from glacial (tens of thousands of years), to intermediate (one to 10 million years), to changes in seafloor spreading rates (tens of millions of years)? To what extent are these changes representative of convergence and separation of intrinsic and extrinsic forcing factors?

5. What does widespread occurrence of Permo-Triassic evaporites indicate about global climatic change during development of the supercontinent Pangea? How did storage of large quantities of salt in Permo-Triassic basins modify oceanic chemistry? To what extent did such evaporation develop a more brackish global ocean, and to what extent did such a chemical change contribute to late Permian extinctions?

6. What are the structure, strength, and effect of both intrinsically forced and extrinsically forced climatic change on the preservation, life history, and evolution of terrestrial and marine flora and fauna? What are the consequences of climatic changes on the distribution, deposition, and preservation of petroleum and metalliferous source beds? How did these climatic changes influence the distribution of warm- and cold-climate coals? Of evaporites? Of phosphates? What specific combination of intrinsic and/or extrinsic processes favored the deposition and preservation of glacial sedimentary facies? How did these changes influence the history of sea level during the accretion, zenith, and dispersal of Pangea?

7. What combination of intrinsic and extrinsic forcing factors influenced the variability of Permo-Triassic reef facies? How did these forcing factors influence the temporal distribution and evolutionary history of the reef facies? What was the rate of change in evolution and facies style of these reefs, and how can they be compared to different Holocene reef communities?

8. What are the combined or separated intrinsic and extrinsic forcing factors that produced profound biological changes during the Permo-Triassic? What were the driving

forces that caused rapid change (collapse?) of existing ecosystems? Were the causes extraterrestrial or mantle driven?

9. How do changing continental paleoposition, paleoclimates, and sea-level change influence the evolutionary record of continental flora and fauna during the accretion, zenith, and dispersal of Pangea? How did changing paleogeography influence paleobiogeography during the history of Pangea? What were the dynamics of floral and faunal replacement and the evolution of terrestrial ecosystems? How did these changes in terrrestrial life history interface with changes in marine life history? What do associated paleobiogeographic changes indicate about the magnitude and rate of climatic change?

WORKSHOP ACTIVITIES

An international workshop, from May 23 through 28, 1992, was held to organize the research effort for Project Pangea, which is the second project sponsored by the GSGP, a commission of the IUGS. The goal of the workshop was to recommend international and multidisciplinary research objectives within the framework of Project Pangea.

Principal objectives for Project Pangea are to (1) understand global processes, their magnitude and temporal variations during the time of accretion, zenith, and breakup of the supercontinent Pangea; (2) examine the global sedimentary record and variability from the base of the Pennsylvanian (Middle Carboniferous) through the Middle Jurassic; (3) determine the cause and nature of climate variability during Pangea's existence; and (4) determine the causes of Permo-Triassic and Triassic-Jurassic extinctions. However, during the workshop it became clear that the major objective for Project Pangea that is expected to lead to new, significant, and different results is *paleoclimate modeling and geological verification of such models.*

The Project Pangea workshop itself was organized into an opening plenary session of invited papers, a special plenary session on Paleoclimate Modeling, and breakout sessions by the working groups who formulated recommendations for research as well as hosted sessions of short contributed papers.

The opening plenary session on Sunday, May 24, 1992, consisted of the following invited talks:

George D. Klein, U.S.A.—Project Pangea: Goals and developments; tectonic-climatic discrimination of cyclic deposition.

John J. Veevers, Australia—Pangea: Evolution of a supercontinent and its consequences for Earth's paleoclimate and sedimentary environments.

Thomas J. Crowley, U.S.A.—Pangean paleoclimates.

George T. Moore, D. N. Hayashida, C. A. Ross, and S. R. Jacobson, U.S.A.—The paleoclimate of Pangea during its formation (Late Permian) and disintegration (Late Jurassic).

Jane Francis, UK—Paleoclimates of Pangea (geological evidence).

Martin A. Perlmutter and M. D. Matthews, U.S.A.—Global cyclostratigraphy: Depositional response to climate change and basin evolution.

Ethan L. Grossman, U.S.A.—The stable isotope record during the evolution of Pangea: Progress and prospects.

John J. Veevers and S. E. Shaw, Australia—Turning point in Pangean environmental history at or about the Permian/Triassic boundary.

Sarah Fowell, U.S.A.—Late Triassic palynofloral evolutions and climate cyclicity, eastern North America.

Benoit Beauchamp, Canada—Carboniferous to Triassic tectono-climatic evolution of northern Pangea.

Erik Flugel, Germany—Pangean shelf carbonates: Controls of Permian and Triassic reef and platform development.

Aymon Baud, Switzerland—Late Permian to Late Triassic of the Tethys: Existing problems, new facts, and theories—a review.

To assist in developing synergism between sedimentary geology and paleoclimate modeling, a separate special plenary session dealt with paleoclimate modeling and model-geological observations and comparisons. Organized by Dr. Bette Otto-Bleisner and Mark Chandler, both of the U.S.A., this session not only included the following presentations but also brought together the paleoclimate modeling community with the sedimentary geological community for the first time.

Chris R. Scotese and Jan Golonka, U.S.A.—Phanerozoic paleogeographic maps.

Malcolm I. Ross, C. R. Scotese, A. J. Boucot, Chen Xu, and Anne Raymond, U.S.A.—Late Carboniferous climatic simulation using a simple parametric climate model.

John E. Kutzbach and A. M. Ziegler, U.S.A.—Numerical simulation of the climate of Pangea—Late Carboniferous climatic simulation using a simple parametric climate model.

Eric D. Gyllenhaal and A. M. Ziegler, U.S.A.—Comparisons of lithologic and paleobotanical data with predictions of atmospheric general circulation models: Examples from the Late Permian.

Starley L. Thompson, David Pollard, W. W. Hay, and Kevin Wilson, U.S.A.—Simulations of Triassic climate using a global circulation climate model.

Peter J. Fawcett and Eric J Barron, U.S.A.—The climatic evolution of India and Australia from the Late Permian to Jurassic: A comparison of climate model results with the geologic record.

Bruce W. Sellwood, P. Valdes, and G. Price, UK—Climate modeling in the Jurassic: GCM predictions in comparison with the geological data base.

Mark Chandler, U.S.A.—Pangean climate of the early Jurassic: GCM simulations, the paleoclimate record climate feedbacks, and increased heat transport.

Robert J. Oglesby, U.S.A.—Modeling the effects of orbital insolation changes on pre-Pleistocene climates and sedimentary cycles.

Thomas R. Worsley, T. L. Moore, C. R. Scotese, and Carmen M. Fraticelli, U.S.A.—Phanerozoic paleoceanography and global climate.

The final closing plenary session on May 27 consisted of presentations of recommendations from each working group for future research activities within Project Pangea. These are summarized in the sections that follow.

WORKSHOP RECOMMENDATIONS

Project Pangea was originally organized into five working groups, but it became clear during the workshop that the working group structure needed some revision and reorganization. Principal recommendations of the new working groups (by name) are summarized below.

Working group 1: Paleoclimate (Judith T. Parrish, U.S.A. chair)

The scientific rationale for pursuing modeling studies of paleoclimate is twofold. For climatologists, such studies provide opportunities for testing the sensitivity of climate models to changing, realistic boundary conditions. Pangea represented an extreme paleogeography with an associated possible extreme climate regime. Successful simulation of this extreme climate would demonstrate robustness of the climate models. For geologists, modeling studies enhance understanding of the effects of climate on the geological record, especially sedimentation, diagenesis, evolution, extinction, and biogeography. Climatic models also may provide a global framework within which the relatively scattered data on paleoclimate might be interpreted.

WG-1 participants observed that first-order agreement was achieved when comparing the results of all climate models that were applied to Pangea. Thus, future work should focus on climate forcing and response. Three general and overlapping recommendations of areas of future research were offered: (1) specific studies of critical paleoclimatic processes, (2) model-model comparisons, and (3) data and model-data comparisons. Although geological participation is critical for the third recommendations, cooperation with other working groups is needed in *all* these areas of research.

Critical paleoclimatic processes. WG-1 recommended that whenever possible, the climate modeling research community should target critical climatic processes for treatment with sensitivity tests. Sensitivity tests are successive model runs in which one or two variables are changed. The test permits analysis of model behavior and helps identify processes that are particularly important for climate, given certain starting conditions (such as paleogeography). Critical climatic processes already identified as appropriate for such treatment are (1) ocean heat transport/sea surface temperature (OHT/SST), (2) orbital variability, (3) CO_2, (4) paleogeography, especially topography and sea level, and (5) ice. Currently, OHT/SST are either computed or specified but in both cases are artificially constrained.

WG-1 recommended minimizing the constraints as well as conducting sensitivity tests. Model results already suggest that climate may be very sensitive to topography, and thus WG-1 recommended that WG-2 emphasize determining not only the distribution of highlands but also their altitudes and topographic profiles.

The most complete climate models are those that couple the oceans and atmosphere. Creating coupled ocean-atmosphere models is currently a major effort in climatology, but such models are still relatively undeveloped. Nevertheless, WG-1 foresees the possibility that such models will become available during the lifetime of Project Pangea, and thus recommended as a long-term goal the creation of paleogeographic models of paleobathymetry that will permit effective study of deep-ocean circulation.

Model-model comparisons. WG-1 recommended that, when presenting results in published papers, climate modelers specifically address differences among various models because these differences are important for interpreting the geological record. Geologists are not equipped by training to interpret differences in model results and thus depend on expertise of climate modelers to make those interpretations. To facilitate comparisons, WG-1 recommended that whenever possible, the modeling community use some boundary conditions in common. Specifically, WG-1 recommended using common values of (1) percent change in solar constant, (2) rotation rates, (3) for the present, CO2 values from the Berner curve, (4) seasonal, rather than perpetual, models, and (5) values for orbital parameters, that is, eccentricity = 0 and perihelion = 0. Additionally, WG-1 recommended that climate modelers address both interannual variability and long-term planetary averages. A long-term goal of WG-1 is to produce a document comparing model results and discussing the implications of model results from interpretation of paleoclimates.

Data and model-data comparisons. WG-1 strongly supported efforts within WG-3 to gain participation of experts on various paleoclimate indicators to facilitate compilation of data in a manner exploiting the full potential of the geological record. WG-1 supports ongoing efforts to calibrate sedimentological and paleontological indicators using modern climate. Additional, WG-1 recommended collection of data in such a manner as to capture the full range of variability of each modeled interval to more effectively tie the geological record into model runs that examine climatic maxima and minima with respect to, for instance, orbital parameters and sea level.

WG-1 identified three major problems worthy of particular attention and requiring geological data. These problems (and some of the required data) are: (1) strong winter cooling and extreme seasonality of temperature in the Southern Hemisphere (paleobotanical and other biotic data, sedimentary evidence of freezing, soil isotopes, moisture estimates); (2) CO_2 (proxy data for CO_2—for example, isotopes in paleosols and marine organic carbon); and (3) tropical and polar sea surface temperatures (isotopes, Sr/Ca paleothermometer). Because, for example, coals are not precise rainfall indicators but rather indicate water table levels, WG-1 advised that both modelers and geologists must be critical in interpretations of moisture balance in their models and that model outputs must be compared with appropriate data.

WG-1 also discussed targeting specific time slices. WG-1 concluded that their model studies should focus on time slices proposed by WG-2 and WG-3 because their criteria for chosing time slices are the same criteria WG-1 would use, namely data availability. Modeling studies are still experimental, so much studies require the best data available for distinguishing among results of various sensitivity tests.

WG-1 observed that the number of modeling studies of Pangea indicates that these intervals present problems that are inherently of interest to modelers. Geological expertise is essential to these studies for identifying important aspects of the problem of Pangean climates.

Working group 2: Plate tectonics and paleogeography (Christopher R. Scotese, U.S.A. chair)

The principal goal of WG-2 is to produce large-scale paleogeographic maps illustrating the distribution of mountains, land, shallow oceans, and deep ocean basins for five time intervals during the history of Pangea—namely, the latest Carboniferous to earliest Permian (Stephanian-Autunian), Late Permian (Kazanian), earliest Triassic (Scythian), Late Triassic (Karnian), and early Jurassic (Pliensbachian). Preliminary versions of these maps would be distributed to other working groups and would serve as base maps on which biogeographic, oceanographic, economic, sedimentological, and paleoclimatic data could be compiled. Besides the five detailed paleogeographic maps, WG-2 will produce approximately 15 plate tectonic base maps (one for each stage from the Late Carboniferous through the Middle Jurassic). Figures 1 through 8 show paleogeographic base maps for use by Project Pangea scientists.

Final versions of these maps would show the distribution of mountains, land, and sea as well as active plate boundaries and major structural features, major lithofacies, significant accessory lithofacies (reefs, coal, evaporites), important paleogeographic features (lakes, major rivers, impact sites), political boundaries and modern geographic features for reference, and an index map providing sources of information displayed on the maps. All this information would be compiled on a set of present-day base maps (Mercator projection, 1:10,000,000) and then digitized and replotted on reconstructed base maps at the preferred publication scale of 1:20,000,000.

WG-2 formed nine regional panels (Table 1) to compile the information for these maps. Panel coordinators will compile the paleogeographic information for each time slice. The Paleomap Project, University of Texas at Arlington, will provide the present-day base maps, coordinate digital compilation of the paleogeography, and produce the final reconstructions.

Working group 3: Global synchroneity of the sedimentary record (Benoit Beauchamp, Canada, and P. A. Scholle, U.S.A, co-chairs)

WG-3 proposed two major recommendations:

Recommendation 1. To scrutinize in great detail the sedimentary record of three time slices during the history of Pangea. These time slices are Moscovian (305–315 Ma), Kazanian (264–269 Ma), and Carnian (220–228 Ma). The goal in analyzing these time slices is to compile an inventory of the

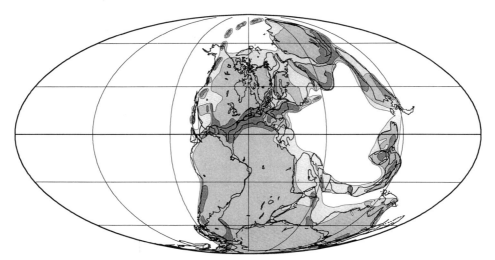

Figure 1. Paleogeographic map, Late Carboniferous (Westphalian), 306 Ma. (When citing this map, please cite it as follows: Scotese, C. R., 1994, Late Carboniferous paleogeographic map, *in* Klein, G. D., ed., Pangea: Paleoclimate, Tectonics, and Sedimentation During Accretion, Zenith, and Breakup of a Supercontinent: Boulder, Colorado, Geological Society of America Special Paper 288.)

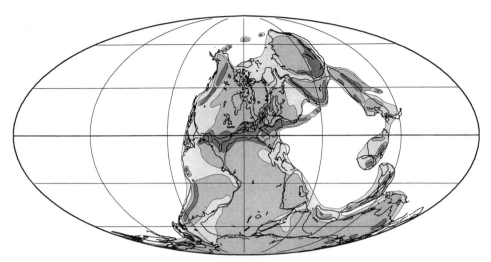

Figure 2. Paleogeographic map, Early Permian (Artinskian), 277 Ma. (When citing this map, please cite it as follows: Scotese, C. R., 1994, Early Permian paleogeographic map, *in* Klein, G. D., ed., Pangea: Paleoclimate, Tectonics, and Sedimentation During Accretion, Zenith, and Breakup of a Supercontinent: Boulder, Colorado, Geological Society of America Special Paper 288.)

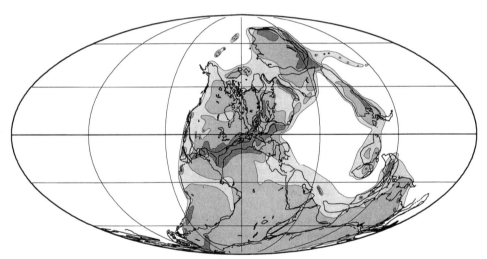

Figure 3. Paleogeographic map, Late Permian (Kazanian), 255 Ma. (When citing this map, please cite it as follows: Scotese, C. R., 1994, Late Permian paleogeographic map, *in* Klein, G. D., ed., Pangea: Paleoclimate, Tectonics, and Sedimentation During Accretion, Zenith, and Breakup of a Supercontinent: Boulder, Colorado, Geological Society of America Special Paper 288.)

total spectrum of marine and nonmarine climate-sensitive facies in order to reconstruct the global paleoclimatic-environmental setting for each time scale and to provide a standardized set of data to other specialists, especially climate modelers and paleogeographers.

Data to be compiled by WG-3 will comprise both published and newly acquired data. Data collection, where possible, will be completed in digital format, through expert systems and questionnaires. A basic set of background information will accompany each data entry. This basic informa-

tion will provide stratigraphic data, geographic data (present longitude and latitude, volume), detailed lithofacies and thickness, tectonic setting, vertical and lateral variability (eustatic, tectonics, or climatic changes), and fossil content.

Specific climatic indicators to be catalogued include:

Exposure-related features. Calcrete (pedogenic and nonpedogenic), paleosols, karst, bauxites and related deposits, red beds.

Glacial deposits. Terrestrial (all types), marine, glendonites.

Eolian deposits. Sand seas (dune deposits), eolian dust.

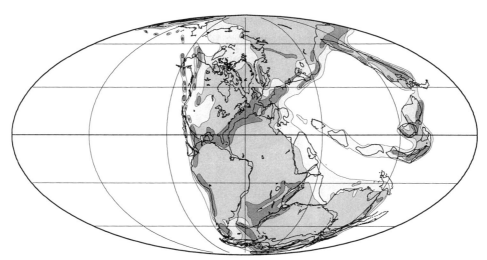

Figure 4. Paleogeographic map, Early Triassic (Induan), 242 Ma. (When citing this map, please cite it as follows: Scotese, C. R., 1994, Early Triassic paleogeographic map, *in* Klein, G. D., ed., Pangea: Paleoclimate, Tectonics, and Sedimentation During Accretion, Zenith, and Breakup of a Supercontinent: Boulder, Colorado, Geological Society of America Special Paper 288.)

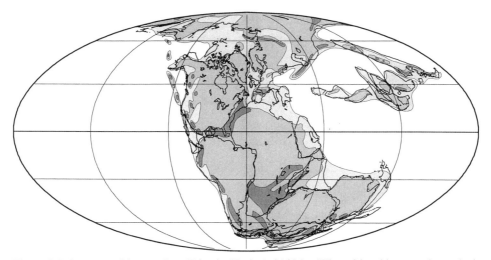

Figure 5. Paleogeographic map, Late Triassic (Norian), 216 Ma. (When citing this map, please cite it as follows: Scotese, C. R., 1994, Late Triassic paleogeographic map, *in* Klein, G. D., ed., Pangea: Paleoclimate, Tectonics, and Sedimentation During Accretion, Zenith, and Breakup of a Supercontinent: Boulder, Colorado, Geological Society of America Special Paper 288.)

Lacustrine deposits. General lake sediments, tufa sand travertines.

Coals and organic matter. Coal types, organic geochemistry of marine sediments.

Fluvial/deltaic deposits. Stream types, flow regimes/gradients.

Evaporites. Terrestrial (salina/lacustrine), marine minor versus extensive occurrences.

Reefs. Distinction of types with possible paleolatitudinal sensitivity.

Bioclastic limestone/skeletal associations. Latitudinal changes in faunal/skeletal assemblages.

Other carbonate. Original mineralogy of micrites; original mineralogy and distribution of ooids; original mineralogy and distribution of marine cements; diagenetic patterns in carbonate rocks as paleoclimate indicators (hardgrounds, intensity of meteoric alteration, cyclicity of alteration).

Silica deposits. Bedded chert, nonbedded deposits, association with other deposit types.

Phosphorite deposits. Major deposits, inventory of lower-

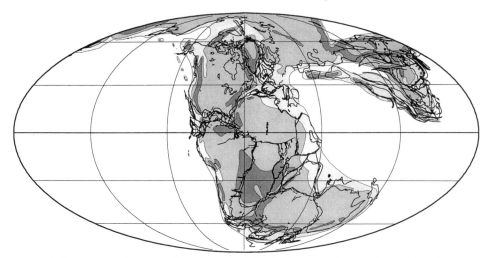

Figure 6. Paleogeographic map, Early Jurassic (Pliensbachian), 195 Ma. (When citing this map, please cite it as follows: Scotese, C. R., 1994, Early Jurassic paleogeographic map, *in* Klein, G. D., ed., Pangea: Paleoclimate, Tectonics, and Sedimentation During Accretion, Zenith, and Breakup of a Supercontinent: Boulder, Colorado, Geological Society of America Special Paper 288.)

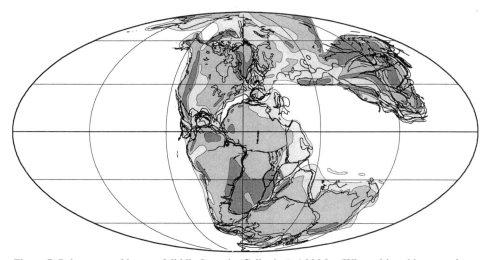

Figure 7. Paleogeographic map, Middle Jurassic (Callovian), 166 Ma. (When citing this map, please cite it as follows: Scotese, C. R., 1994, Middle Jurassic paleogeographic map, *in* Klein, G. D., ed., Pangea: Paleoclimate, Tectonics, and Sedimentation During Accretion, Zenith, and Breakup of a Supercontinent: Boulder, Colorado, Geological Society of America Special Paper 288.)

concentration deposits, identification of upwelling zones.

Iron-bearing mineral deposits. Glauconite, chamosite, oolitic ironstone.

Shales. Clay mineralogy, distinction of primary versus diagenetic assemblages.

Isotope geochemistry. Oxygen and carbon on brachiopods; other oxygen and carbon studies (whole rock, phosphates, water), sulfur on carbonates and evaporites, strontium, stratigraphic (secular) versus regional/climatic variations.

Paleobiogeography, paleocology, paleocommunities. Nonmarine (plants, tetrapods, and other vertebrates, trace fos-

sils), marine (biogeographic patterns of marine organisms; trace fossils [burrows/borings]; determination of paleo-oxygenation levels [laminae/bioturbation patterns]).

Recommendation 2. To examine the global sedimentary record of a long-ranging interval of Pangea's history to establish links between such seemingly unrelated, yet often synchronous, aspects of the geological record as climatic evolution, sequence boundaries, biogeography, tectonic shifts, and extraterrestrial impacts. This part of Project Pangea will examine Pangea as a highly interactive and dynamic system characterized by long periods of stability in the atmosphere,

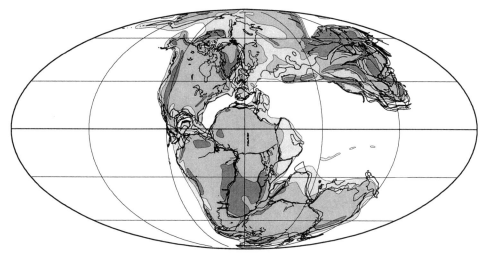

Figure 8. Paleogeographic map, Late Jurassic (Tithonian), 152 Ma. (When citing this map, please cite it as follows: Scotese, C. R., 1994, Late Jurassic paleogeographic map, *in* Klein, G. D., ed., Pangea: Paleoclimate, Tectonics, and Sedimentation During Accretion, Zenith, and Breakup of a Supercontinent: Boulder, Colorado, Geological Society of America Special Paper 288.)

TABLE 1. PALEOGEOGRAPHIC REGIONAL PANELS AND COORDINATORS, WG-2

Geographic Region	Coordinator
1. Gondwana	J. J. Veevers, Australia
2. Southeast Asia	Ian Metcalfe, Australia; Dietrich Helmcke, Germany
3. China	Wang Hongshen, Xu Xiaosong, Wang Chengshan, People's Republic of China
4. Former U.S.S.R.	A. Egorov, L. Natapov, V. Kazmin, Russia
5. North Europe	P. A. Ziegler, Switzerland
6. Tethys	J. Dercourte, France; A. Baud, Switzerland
7. North Atlantic Margins	W. Manspeizer, U.S.A.
8. Western North America	D. B. Rowley, U.S.A.
9. North American Arctic	Benoit Beauchamp, Canada

biosphere, hydrosphere, and lithosphere—a stability that was, from time to time, disturbed by geologically rapid shifts of global magnitude. To achieve this goal, one major time interval ranging from the Kazanian through and including the Norian was selected for global analysis.

The Kazanian-Norian interval was selected for two reasons. First, this time interval encompasses two time slices selected for detailed analysis per recommendation 1. Second, this time interval straddles the Permian-Triassic boundary, perhaps the culmination of the greatest global environmental perturbation of earth history.

A first step toward achieving the goals of this project will be to examine the Kazanian through Norian worldwide distribution of reefs, lacustrine carbonates, paleosols, biotic assemblages, carbonate mineralogy, phosphates, and carbon isotopes. The data recovered through this "pilot project" will be integrated in a time scale that will also display known sequence boundaries, climatic shifts, tectonic events, and episodes of volcanism. Ultimately, participants in Project Pangea will be able to rank chronostratigraphic boundaries based on the magnitude of tectonic, climatic, and depositional shifts observed across them. In a later stage, the project will expand to include a much broader base of Kazanian through Norian data.

Working group 4: Stratigraphic constraints on global synchroneity (C. A. Ross, U.S.A., and Aymon Baud, Switzerland, co-chairs)

The major problem addressed by WG-4 was the establishment of a detailed time-stratigraphic correlation baseline for the time interval during which Pangea evolved (Middle Carboniferous through Middle Jurassic). For this particular time interval, only three solid radiometric dates are available to define chronostratigraphic boundaries. WG-4 tentatively proposes a stratigraphic chart and time scale (Fig. 9) for the Middle Phanerozoic to establish where stratigraphic problems exist.

WG-4 recommended the following program of research to complete the major gaps in establishing reliable temporal constraints: (1) biostratigraphic studies to globally calibrate zonal schemes for correlation, (2) event stratigraphy to piece together provincial groupings known to occur in Middle Permian rocks; (3) Establishment of a sequence stratigraphy correlated to the global standard section and correlation of sequence boundaries with volcanic ash fall events for

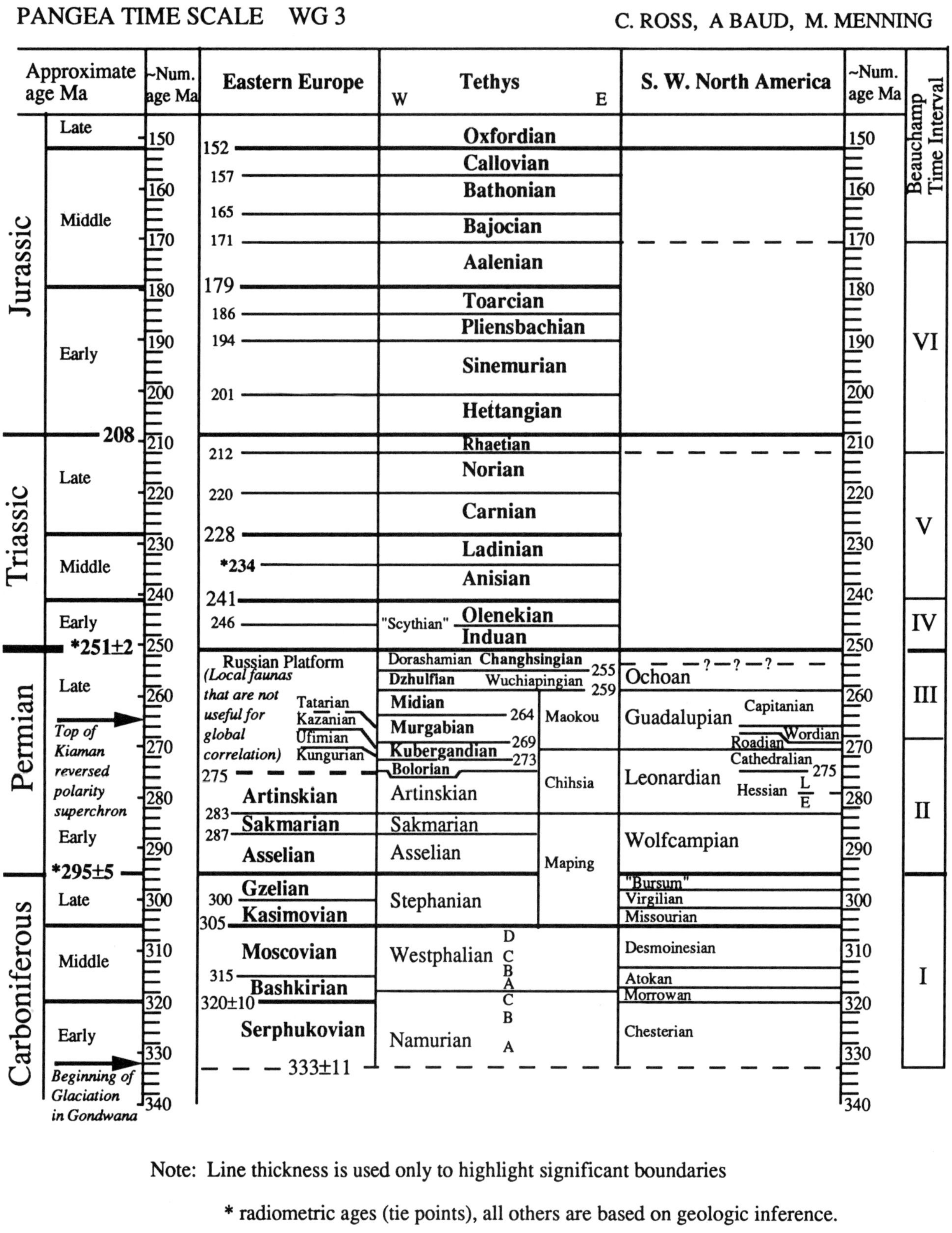

PANGEA TIME SCALE   WG 3   C. ROSS, A BAUD, M. MENNING

Approximate age Ma	~Num. age Ma	Eastern Europe	Tethys (W — E)	S. W. North America	~Num. age Ma	Beauchamp Time Interval
Jurassic — Late	150 / 152		Oxfordian		150	
Jurassic — Middle	157 / 160 / 165 / 170 / 171		Callovian		160	
			Bathonian			
			Bajocian		170	
			Aalenian			
Jurassic — Early	179 / 180 / 186 / 190 / 194 / 200 / 201		Toarcian		180	VI
			Pliensbachian		190	
			Sinemurian		200	
			Hettangian			
208	210 / 212		Rhaetian		210	
Triassic — Late	220		Norian		220	V
	228		Carnian			
Triassic — Middle	230 / *234		Ladinian		230	
	240 / 241		Anisian		240	
Triassic — Early	246	"Scythian"	Olenekian			IV
*251±2	250		Induan		250	

Russian Platform (Local faunas that are not useful for global correlation)

Approximate age Ma	~Num. age Ma	Eastern Europe	Tethys (W)	Tethys (E)	S. W. North America	~Num. age Ma	Interval
Permian — Late	260		Dorashamian / Changhsingian — 255		Ochoan		III
			Dzhulfian / Wuchiapingian — 259			260	
		Tatarian	Midian — 264	Maokou	Guadalupian — Capitanian		
		Kazanian	Murgabian — 269		Roadian / Wordian	270	
Top of Kiaman reversed polarity superchron	270	Ufimian	Kubergandian — 273		Cathedralian — 275		
		Kungurian	Bolorian	Chihsia	Leonardian — Hessian L/E		II
Permian — Early	275 / 280	Artinskian	Artinskian			280	
	283	Sakmarian	Sakmarian		Wolfcampian		
	287 / 290	Asselian	Asselian	Maping		290	
*295±5							
Carboniferous — Late	300	Gzelian — 300	Stephanian		"Bursum" / Virgilian	300	I
	305	Kasimovian — 305			Missourian		
Carboniferous — Middle	310	Moscovian	Westphalian D/C/B/A		Desmoinesian	310	
	315 / 320	Bashkirian	Westphalian C/B		Atokan / Morrowan	320	
	320±10						
Carboniferous — Early	330	Serphukovian	Namurian B/A		Chesterian	330	
Beginning of Glaciation in Gondwana	340	— 333±11				340	

Note: Line thickness is used only to highlight significant boundaries

* radiometric ages (tie points), all others are based on geologic inference.

Figure 9. Tentative Project Pangea Time Scale prepared by C. A. Ross, A. Baud, and M Menning on behalf of WG-3 (drafted by John O. Garbisch). Asterisks indicate radiometric ages (tie points); all other ages are based on geologic inference.

geochronological calibration; (4) a systematic program of radiometric dating to tie in with recommendations 1 and 3; (5) a program of paleomagnetic stratigraphy to tie in with recommendations 1, 3, and 4; and (6) an overall interdisciplinary chronostratigraphic approach combining all correlation techniques so that the mid-Phanerozoic time scale represented by the evolution of Pangea is adequately constrained as a baseline for paleoclimatic and paleographic studies.

In addition, WG-4 recommended a detailed analysis, integrating a variety of data emerging from WG-1, 2, and 3, to address the issue of the nature of the timing and causes of extinction.

Working group 5: Resources (W. L. Watney, U.S.A., B I. Chuvashov, Russia, Oscar R. Lopez-Gamundi, Argentina and U.S.A.)

WG-5 recognized that its activities are likely to overlap with other working groups. Thus it will focus on the same time slices as proposed by WG-2 and WG-4. WG-5 chose to investigate characteristics of important resources associated with Pangea and to improve the precision and accuracy of information on controlling processes, including climate, that are suited for simulation modeling and improving resource prediction.

WG-5's objectives included one that was short term—to constrain understanding of known resources (i.e., inventory and location—and one that was long term—to provide more refined process parameters for use in increasingly refined models, including climate, stratigraphic, and sedimentological simulations.

Knowing more about the details of selected resources, including their occurrence in space and time, may eventually pride other diagnostic characteristics of climate unknown to us today. For instance, known characteristics and distributional patterns of lacustrine source rocks in rift basins may further establish links to larger-scale climate and paleogeographic factors that are currently being modeled.

Certain thematic projects related to resource inventories and prediction are recommended. They include:

Theme 1. Paleoclimatic controls on the spatial and temporal occurrence of suboxic and anoxic sediments:

Project A: Phosphorites. Inventory phosphorite occurrences in Carboniferous and Permian. Investigate relationship between (1) maximum phosphorite deposition and occurrences leading to climax event, (2) changes in ocean circulation and upwelling systems during the formation of Pangea, and (3) glacio-eustatic control of phosphate events. Case studies would include the Permian Phosphoria rock complex of the Rocky Mountains, North America, and Late Carboniferous to Early Permian phosphorites in Cis-Uralalian region of Russia. COORDINATORS: Jorg Trappe (Germany), Boris I. Chuvashov (Russia).

Project B: Black shales (source rocks). Inventory occurrences in the Westphalian and Stephanian because of longer trend of black shales in Euro-American. The entire Permian organic-rich, high-latitude shales from Gondwana also are excellent candidates for inventory. The goal would be to investigate (1) the origin and nature (temporal and spatial distribution) of black shales and relationship of formation and character to glacio-eustasy, (2) stratigraphic correlation of black shales over Pangea (in progress), and (3) independent, interdisciplinary means to evaluate accumulation rates, sources of organic matter, modes of preservation of organic matter, and contribution and nature of organic productivity. Case studies include the organic-rich algal shales from high paleolatitudinal sites in Gondwana (Early Permian to early Late Permian) and evaluation of black shales from low paleolatitudes of Euroamerica that contain terrestrial organic matter and considerable ranges in total organic carbon and constituent organic and inorganic compounds, and the use of these shales as keys to correlate individual eustatic events over widespread areas of Pangea. COORDINATORS: Oscar R. Lopez-Gamundi (Argentina and U.S.A.), W. Lynn Watney (U.S.A.).

Project C: Occurrence of source rocks and possibly source-reservoir systems associated with Triassic-Jurassic rifting related to breakup of Pangea. This project would focus on Triassic-Jurassic rocks of eastern North America, Greenland, and the North Sea that were related to tectonic-structural evolution and paleoclimate and on nonmarine grabens containing synrift lacustrine source rocks in portions of Gondwana related to the Paleo-Pacific margins that were related to a global transtensional event. COORDINATORS: Marty Perlmutter, Warren Manspeizer (both of the U.S.A).

Theme 2. Paleoclimatic controls on the spatial and temporal occurrences of potential hydrocarbon reservoirs. This theme would focus on the occurrence and types of carbonate rocks that may serve as hydrocarbon reservoirs in strategic time intervals and sites in Pangea. Time intervals suggested included the Westphalian and Moscovian.

The approach to be taken includes (1) short-term inventory of occurrences; (2) establishment of multiscale facies architecture of carbonate buildups and surrounding strata, evaluation of influence of paleotectonic setting, paleoclimate, and glacio-eustasy, and characterization of unusual occurrences of key relationships critical to climate assessment (such as climatic occurrences of reefs; and (3) possible integration through quantitative modeling for improved prediction.

Case studies include the carbonates deposited along the Paleo-Tethyan shelves during the Permian, possibly late Carboniferous. COORDINATOR: W. Lynn Watney, Marty Perlmutter (both from U.S.A.).

Theme 3. Paleoclimatic controls on the spatial and temporal occurrence of low-latitude versus high-latitude coals. Based on compilation of coal beds and related facies to date, it is advised that a few localities of temperate coals be selected and compared with Tethyan coals. Temperate coals should be compared to peats presently forming in cold regions. This new model stresses the temperate, postglacial climatic conditions under which coals of Australia, South Africa, India, and South America were formed in contrast to the better-known Euroamerican model in which coals are associated with humid, low paleolatitude settings. These models need to be tested and refined through balanced sampling across Pangea. Coordination with the U.S. Geological Survey's Predictive Stratigraphic Analysis (PSA) with its focus on coal resources is recommended.

COORDINATOR: Oscar R. Lopez-Gamundi (Argentina and U.S.A.).

Theme 4. Metallic mineral resources. A recommendation from the plenary closing session reported that significant metallic mineral deposits are known from many of the sediment types associated with Pangea. A global perspective to their occurrence needs to be made. Manganese ores, particularly significant occurrences in the Urals, were considered.

COORDINATORS: W. Lynn Watney (U.S.A.), B. I. Chuvashov (Russia).

Working group 6: Biogeography and extinction (David J. Bottjer, U.S.A.) and Jane Francis, UK, co-chairs)

This working group was proposed and developed during the closing plenary session, and thus it did not meet formally during the workshop. Initial plans include organizing research projects to investigate the two major Pangean mass extinctions at the Permian-Triassic and Triassic-Jurassic boundaries. Future discussions will prioritize some possible biogeographic research projects.

Working group 7: Synthesis (George D. Klein, U.S.A. chair)

This working group will come more into the forefront as Project Pangea develops. Workshop activities consisted of coordinating communication between other working groups and focusing on issues that were significant but that may have failed to attract sufficient attention.

Among items of significance that were reviewed are the following: (1) data quality needs to be controlled; all observations are to be recorded on present-day longitude and latitude so as to assure transfer to paleogeographic base maps. (2) A need was expressed for study of metaliferous sediments, and WG-5 is following up on it (3) Paleotopographic studies need to be simulated. Mass-balancing of sediment volumes to paleotopography needs to be factored in to assure relevant paleoclimatic modeling. (4) A strong geochronological effort needs to be established within the framework of WG-4. (5) Final compilation of paleogeographic maps, sedimentary data, and model simulations is expected to be the final product of the efforts of Project Pangea to calibrate, sedimentologically, paleoclimate simulations.

ACKNOWLEDGMENTS

The Project Pangea Workshop was funded by grants and gifts from the National Science Foundation (Award EAR-91-17687), the U.S. Geological Survey, the Division on Sedimentary Geology of the Geological Society of America, SEPM (Society for Sedimentary Geology), International Association of Sedimentologists, Chevron Oil Field Research Corp., and Allen Press, Inc. Christopher R. Scotese and the Paleomap Project of the International Lithosphere Program provided the paleogeographic maps shown in Figures 1 through 8. Users of these maps are requested to reference them as shown in the caption for Figure 1. We acknowledge with gratitude the drafting of Figure 9 by John O. Garbisch.

MANUSCRIPT ACCEPTED BY THE SOCIETY MAY 14, 1993

Geological Society of America
Special Paper 288
1994

Pangea: Evolution of a supercontinent and its consequences for Earth's paleoclimate and sedimentary environments

J. J. Veevers
Australian Plate Research Group, School of Earth Sciences, Macquarie University, North Ryde, NSW 2109, Australia

ABSTRACT

During its life span from mid-Carboniferous (320 Ma) merger to mid-Jurassic (160 Ma) initial breakup, Pangea comprised two contrasting sedimentary provinces: (1) an emergent southern (Gondwanaland) province, with no more than 15% of the landmass covered by the sea, dominated by nonmarine facies, and (2) a submergent northern or Laurasian province, 25% or more covered by the sea, dominated by marine facies. This contrast arose from the unequal size of Pangea's original components. The 100-million-km^2 area of Paleozoic Gondwanaland, which generated a large heat anomaly in and beneath the lithosphere, dwarfed the 30-million-km^2 area of Laurentia and was 10 times the size of the two Chinese microplates. Pangea inherited the contrast and maintained it by the growth of its own heat anomaly.

Within this overarching factor that distinguished northern from southern Pangea, plate-tectonic forces modulated by the growth of the Pangean heat anomaly brought about a sedimentary/tectonic evolution that reflects the repetition of couplets of shortening and extension. Initial Variscan/Appalachian (325 to 290 Ma) and Kanimblan/Alice Springs (350 to 325 Ma) collisional shortening and uplift were followed at 290 Ma by Extension I. The lithosphere underwent thermal subsidence in modes that depended on basement structure: Hot, newly formed orogenic basement subsided in volcanic rifts, whereas cratonic basement types were nonvolcanic; the cratonic Proterozoic foldbelts of the Zambezian terrain subsided in linear fault-bounded zones or rifts; cratonic nuclei of the Karoo terrain subsided in oval-shaped basins or sags. Subsequent Gondwanide/Indosinian (255 to 230 Ma) shortening and uplift were followed at 230 Ma by Extension II, mainly by rifting. Final dispersal started when continental rifting was superseded by seafloor spreading.

Glaciation in the Gondwanaland province during the Pennsylvanian-Permian and coal-forming conditions during the Pennsylvanian in Euramerica and Permian in the Gondwanaland province and Asia were terminated by global warming that accompanied excessive venting of CO_2 into the atmosphere during the eruption of the Permian/Triassic (~250 Ma) Siberian Traps and other volcanics. The resulting gap in coal deposition lasted through the Early and Middle Triassic until the excessive CO_2 was finally resorbed by the crust, at which time coal deposition resumed during the Late Triassic.

Veevers, J. J., 1994, Pangea: Evolution of a supercontinent and its consequences for Earth's paleoclimate and sedimentary environments, *in* Klein, G. D., ed., Pangea: Paleoclimate, Tectonics, and Sedimentation During Accretion, Zenith, and Breakup of a Supercontinent: Boulder, Colorado, Geological Society of America Special Paper 288.

INTRODUCTION

Here I explore some sedimentary/tectonic manifestations of the Pangean world through the following arguments. Pangea comprised two contrasting morphotectonic provinces: emergent or nonmarine in the south (Gondwanaland), submergent or marine in the north (Laurasia). The pulsed release of heat from the Pangean-induced heat anomaly generated tectono-sedimentary stages of subsidence connected with two couplets of crustal shortening and extension and a final stage of seafloor spreading, described below.

Tectono-sedimentary stages of subsidence

Pangean stages X (encircled numerals) and XI (sequences on the Gondwanaland platform), shown in Figure 1, are as follows (based on Veevers, 1990a). *Stage 1 (320–290 Ma)*, represented on the platform by a stratigraphic gap or lacuna, reflects the initial accumulation of heat beneath the Pangean insulator and thermal uplift. *Stage 2 (290–230 Ma)*, represented by the epi-Carboniferous to mid-Triassic early Gondwana sequence and equivalents, marks the local thinning of the Pangean crust to form broad basins or sags and locally (on

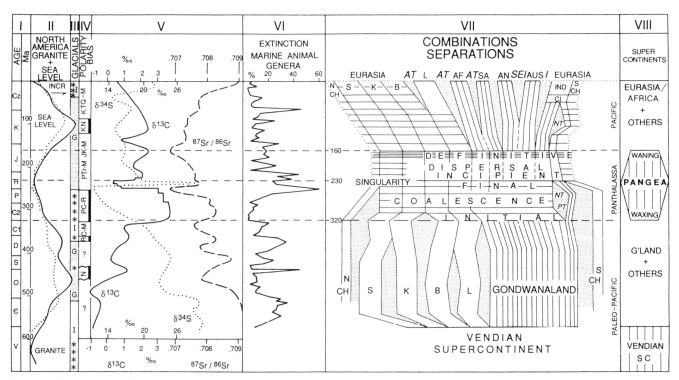

Figure 1. Phanerozoic sedimentary and tectonic indices, combinations and separations of the continents and oceans, supercontinents, flood lava, the Pangean heat anomaly, platform sequences, flooded area, and extension/shortening events, from a modified and augmented Figure 3 of Veevers (1990a). Values increase to the right. I and XV: Timescale (Palmer, 1983), with the Permian/Triassic (P/Tr) boundary changed from 245 Ma to 250 Ma (Veevers, Conaghan, and Shaw, this volume). II. Solid line = ages of North American granites; dotted line = sea level (Fischer, 1984). III: Glacial occurrences (asterisks) with alternating icehouse (I) and greenhouse (G) states from Fischer (1984), with icehouse/greenhouse boundary changed to the P/Tr boundary. IV: Magnetic polarity bias (N normal, R reversed, both with heavy bar; M mixed) (Harland et al., 1990). C—Carboniferous; PC—Permo-Carboniferous; PTr—Permo-Triassic; JK—Jurassic-Cretaceous; K—Cretaceous; T—Tertiary; Q—Quaternary. V: $\delta^{13}C$ in carbonate = solid line and $\delta^{34}S$ = dotted line (Holser et al., 1988); $^{87}Sr/^{86}Sr$ = broken line (Koepnick et al., 1988). VI: Percentage extinction for marine animal genera: <260 Ma from Raup and Sepkoski (1986); >260 Ma from Sepkoski (1992). VII: Continental and oceanic combinations and separations, after Briden et al. (1974), Ziegler et al. (1979), Bond et al. (1984), and Sengor (1984). Gondwanaland and subsequent fragments marked with longitudinal lines, Pangea and Eurasia with transverse lines, and rift oceans with stipple; dotted lines alongside Eurasia join on either side. Continents: AF—Africa, AN—Antarctica, AUS—Australia, B—Baltica, CI—Cimmeria, IND—India, K—Kazakhstania, L—Laurentia, N CH—north China, S—Siberia, SA—South America, S CH—south China; oceans (oblique letters): AT—Atlantic (north, central, south), I—Indian, NT—NeoTethys, PT—PaleoTethys, SEI—Southeast Indian. VIII: Supercontinents (vertical lines), large continents, and others. IX: Late Paleozoic and Mesozoic flood lavas: A—European (Wopfner, 1984; Ziegler, 1988) and eastern Australian (Veevers, 1984); B—Siberian Traps (Renne and Basu, 1991); C—Amazon (Mosmann et al., 1986); D—Karoo (Bristow and Saggerson, 1983); E—Transantarctic and Tasmanian (Kyle et al., 1981; Schmidt and McDougall, 1977); F—Serra Geral (Schobbenhaus, 1984); G—Pacific ridge-crest (Watts et al., 1980); H—Rajmahal (Baksi, 1988); J—Pacific mid-plate (Schlanger et al., 1981); K—Deccan (Jaeger et al., 1989). X: 320 to 0 Ma accumulation and dissipation of Pangean heat anomaly in stages 1 through 5; rate of loss of heat (dotted line) that drives plate tectonics, emplaces volcanics, and initiates basin structure; residual heat or balance (solid line). 650 to 320 Ma accumulation and dissipation of Vendian super-

orogens) bimodal volcanic rifts, generated by the initial withdrawal of heat from beneath Pangea. *Stage 3 (230–160 Ma)*, represented by the mid-Triassic (Carnian) to mid-Jurassic rift sequence, reflects a faster withdrawal of heat and concomitant crustal thinning along the incipient rifted margins of Pangea. *Stage 4 (160–85 Ma)*, represented by the mid-Jurassic to mid-Cretaceous drift sequence, reflects the wholesale loss of Pangean heat by fast seafloor spreading. *Stage 5 (85 Ma to present)*, represented by the Late Cretaceous and younger drift sequence, reflects a slower loss of heat from the depleted Pangean heat store.

Pangean model derived from the stratigraphic sequences

The model shown in Figure 2 includes the following five stages. *Stage 1—platform lacuna.* Following the elimination of the rift oceans, the clustered parts of the Earth compose the single supercontinent Pangea and the single superocean Panthalassa. The total length of the mid-ocean (Panthalassan) ridge and the total amount of spreading/subduction are minimal. The corresponding minimal turnover of mantle material at the surface leads to a minimal venting of CO_2 and a resulting icehouse climatic state by maximal long-wave radiation of

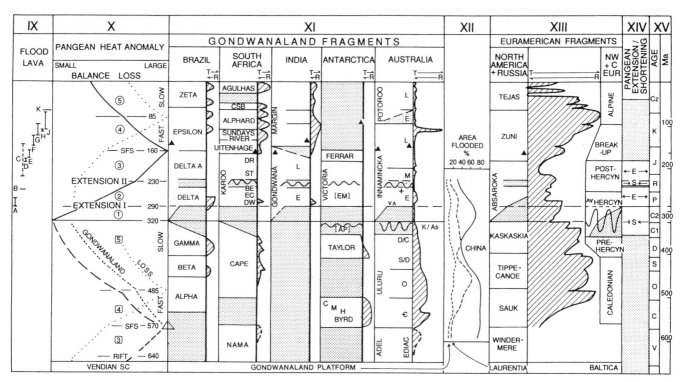

continental heat anomaly (broken line); rate of loss of heat (dotted line); accumulation of Gondwanaland heat anomaly (double dotted line); stages 3 to 5 predicted from Pangean model. XI: Sequences of the 570 to 320 Ma Gondwanaland platform and of the <320 Ma Gondwanaland fragments, with transgressive (T)-regressive (R) curves (oblique ruled pattern); lacunas shown by stipple, onset of drift by triangle, tectonic shortening by wavy lines, Early Permian extensional volcanics by V's. Brazil (Soares et al., 1978). South Africa (Dingle et al., 1983): BE—Beaufort; CSB—Cape St. Blaize; DR—Drakensberg; DW—Dwyka; EC—Ecca; ST—Stormberg. India: the Gondwana sequence, divided by the mid-Triassic lacuna into two parts, E—Early and L—Late, and the overlying sequence of the eastern margin. Antarctica: H—Heritage; M—Minaret; C—Crashsite (J. W. Collinson, personal communication, 1992). The Gondwanide shortening is confined to the Ellsworth Mountains [EM] (Grunow et al., 1991) and the mid-Carboniferous shortening to the Antarctic Peninsula [AP] (Milne and Millar, 1989). Australia (Veevers, 1984): Onset of deposition on the Pangean platform is dated at 290 Ma (epi-Carboniferous or Gzelian, East Australian palynological stage 2) and is accompanied by thick transtensional volcanics; the cross at the P/Tr boundary signifies the peak eruption of calc-alkaline ignimbrite in Eastern Australia. ADEL—Adelaidean; ∈—Cambrian; D/C—Late

Devonian/Early Carboniferous; E—Early; EDIAC—Ediacarian; L—Late; M—Middle; O—Ordovician; S/D—Silurian/Middle Devonian. K/AS—Kanimblan/Alice Springs. XII: percentage area of continents flooded by the sea (Algeo and Wilkinson, 1991). XIII: Sequences of the 570 to 320 Ma Laurentia and Baltica, of the 320 to 160 Ma Pangean platform, and of the <160 Ma Euramerican fragments, with transgressive (T)-regressive (R) curves (Vail et al., 1977); note that the North American sequences are paralleled by those of Russia (Sloss, 1976). North America: sequences from Sloss (1988); in the Permian Basin of Texas and New Mexico, the earliest Permian (286 Ma) Wolfcamp Series overlaps the Central Basin Platform (Sloss, 1988, p. 265); the base of the Absaroka II subsequence (268 Ma) is marked by greatly accelerated rates of subsidence (Sloss, 1988, p. 39). Northwest and Central Europe: main phases of plate boundary reorganization, from Ziegler (1988); in the Permian basins of Europe, subsidence was initiated in the Oslo (volcanic) Graben and renewed in the half grabens between Norway and Greenland at the same time (290 Ma, Stephanian B or Gzelian) as sagging in the south was accompanied by the eruption of flood lavas and the deposition of the Rotliegend and later successions (Ziegler, 1988). HERCYN—Hercynian. XIV: Pangean extension (E)/shortening (S) couplets.

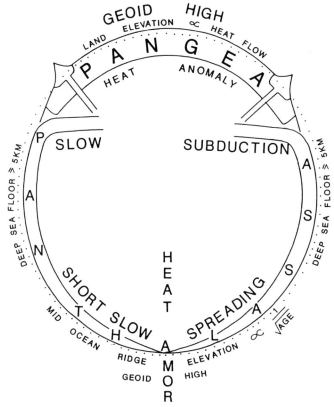

Figure 2. Model of Pangea/Panthalassa (from Fig. 4 of Veevers, 1990a), showing the three first-order modes of elevation: the land of the Pangean continental platform, the antipodal mid-ocean ridge (MOR) of Panthalassa, and the platform of the deep ocean floor.

solar energy. Three effects lead to a maximal continental freeboard above sea level: (1) the short and narrow mid-ocean ridge of Panthalassa displaces less water than did the subsequent ridge, (2) the continental crust of Pangea has a maximal mean thickness because its ocean frontage of thin (rifted) crust is minimal, and (3) the self-induced Pangean heat store and accelerated mantle plumes generate a geoid high across Pangea. The earth is geocratic: dominated by dry land. The heat impounded beneath Pangea soon leads to localized thinning of the Pangean crust and lithosphere, initially by *Stage 2—extension I by sagging of cratonic basement and rifting of orogenic basement* and subsequently by *Stage 3—extension II by rifting* between the incipient continents. Pangea breaks up by *Stage 4—spreading of intra-Pangean rift oceans* to effect a change of state from clustered to dispersed continents and oceans. The total length of the mid-ocean ridge in the rift oceans as well as in the Panthalassan relict of the Pacific Ocean and the total amount of spreading/subduction are at a maximum. The corresponding maximal turnover of mantle material at the surface leads to a maximal venting of CO_2 and a resulting greenhouse climatic state by minimal long-wave radiation of solar energy.

Three effects lead to minimal continental freeboard above sea level: (1) the long and wide mid-ocean ridge displaces more water, (2) the crust of the continents has a minimal mean thickness because its ocean frontage of thin (rifted) crust is maximal, and (3) the rapidly depleting Pangean heat store and decelerated mantle plumes support a lower geoid high. The earth is thalassocratic: dominated by ocean water. The wholesale running down of the heat store by fast spreading leads to *Stage 5—slower spreading/subduction* and preferential closing of the rift oceans so that eventually the continents form a Pangea and the oceans a Panthalassa in a return to Stage 1.

The long-term changes in atmospheric pCO_2 of the model were punctuated by the short-term increase of pCO_2 at the Permian/Triassic (P/Tr) boundary (~250 Ma), provided by the Siberian Traps, which produced an instant greenhouse climate.

SEA LEVEL AND THE FIRST-ORDER HYPSOMETRY OF THE SOLID EARTH

A prerequisite to interpreting the shifting shorelines of the Phanerozoic is an understanding of the tectonic factors that influence changing levels of the sea and land. Land level, the absolute elevation of the continental platform, is no less variable than absolute sea level, which—measurable only against the land—is better called "sea/land level" ("sea level measured against land level") than the familiar "relative sea level." The land platform itself is of utmost importance in Earth history because it is the depository of the bulk of preservable sediment.

The elevation of the surface of the solid Earth, exemplified in Figure 2 by Pangea/Panthalassa, has three first-order modes: (1) the land of the continental platform, (2) the mid-ocean ridge (MOR), and (3) the platform of the deep ocean floor. The boundary between the land and the surface of the sea—the shoreline—is a function of the variables of the volume of seawater (assumed here to be constant) and the three model elevations of the solid Earth. The only directly observable quantity in Earth history is the shifting shoreline, expressed in the transgressive-regressive (or flooding) curve. The mean level of the Panthalassan ocean floor is the sum of the depth of the deep ocean floor (>5 km) and the MOR, which is inversely proportional to age½ (Sclater et al., 1971). The short (and what I presume to have been slow-spreading) Panthalassan ridge had a smaller displacing volume (and a presumably lower mean elevation) than the long (and presumably fast-spreading) MOR after 160 Ma. Changes in the long-wavelength elevation of the Pangean continental platform and of the sea level surface (the geoid) are a function of Pangean heat flow (Anderson, 1981, 1982; Worsley et al., 1984; Veevers, 1990a, Fig. 2). The elevation of different parts of the Pangean platform is related directly to the thickness of the crust. The flooding curves of Pangea and the large and small continents are now interpreted according to these principles.

SOUTHERN AND NORTHERN HYPSOMETRIC PROVINCES

States of emergence/submergence and the unequal size of the large and small dispersed continents

During its life span from mid-Carboniferous (320 Ma) merger to mid-Jurassic (160 Ma) breakup (Fig. 1, VII), Pangea comprised two contrasting sedimentary provinces (Table 1): (1) an emergent southern (Gondwanaland) province, with no more than 15% of the landmass covered by the sea (Fig. 1, XII) and dominated by nonmarine facies; and (2) a submergent northern (Laurasian) province, at least during the Permian, 25% or more covered by the sea and dominated by marine facies.

I interpret the contrast as arising from the unequal size of Pangea's original components. Pangea was preceded by a Vendian supercontinent or ProtoPangea (Fig. 1, VII and VIII). Near the end of the Proterozoic (~600 Ma), this supercontinent broke into a large emergent continent, Gondwanaland, and several small submergent continents (Fig. 3) by the growth of seafloor in rift oceans. The merger of Gondwanaland and the small continents produced the emergent southern province and the initially submergent northern province of Pangea (Fig. 4), which became a uniformly emergent Pangea in the Triassic (Fig. 5). Starting at 160 Ma, Pangea broke up into the fragments of the emergent Gondwanaland province and submergent Laurasia province. I believe the Gondwanaland fragments, though small, remained emergent because of their residual Pangean heat anomaly and thick cratonic crust. The submergent Laurasian fragments were the small continent of Laurentia and the large continent of Eurasia. The 100-million-km^2 area of emergent

TABLE 1. EMERGENT STATE OF GONDWANALAND AND ITS DESCENDANTS VERSUS SUBMERGENT LAURASIA

Ma	Gondwanaland		Laurasia
0		**Fragments**	*Eurasia*
	Emergent		Submergent
160	---------------- **Breakup** --------------------		
			Emergent (Triassic)
	Emergent	Pangea	
			Submergent (Permian)
320	---------------- **Merger** --------------------		
	Gondwanaland		**Fragments**
	Emergent		Submergent
600	---------------- **Breakup** --------------------		
	?Emergent	Vendian Supercontinent	Emergent?

Paleozoic Gondwanaland dwarfed the 30-million-km^2 area of submergent Laurentia and was 10 times the size of the submergent Chinese and other microplates (Fig. 3). Today (Fig. 6), again despite its size, the very large continent of North America–Eurasia remains submergent because of its smaller content of cratonic crust, and the small continental descendants of Gondwanaland are emergent, except for the submergent microcontinental New Zealand–New Caledonia.

Role of supercontinental and large continental heat anomalies

Following Anderson (1981, 1982), Worsley et al. (1984) argued that the self-induced heat anomaly beneath Pangea, reflected in the Pangean elevation (geoid) anomaly, played a part in raising most of the Pangean platform above the level of the sea. I reiterated the idea in terms of depositional supersequences (Veevers, 1989, 1990a). Here I extend the idea to suggest that the large continent of Gondwanaland acted as an insulator of heat from the interior (less effective than Pangea but more effective than the small continents) to generate its own heat anomaly and that this was added to the presumed heat anomaly inherited from the Vendian supercontinent (Fig. 1, X). In turn, the Gondwanaland province of Pangea inherited what remained of the heat anomaly and augmented it greatly. Finally, the fragments of the Gondwanaland province inherited the residual heat anomaly to remain largely emergent today. This is despite the fact that the smallest continental fragment, Australia, has a land area of only 8 million km^2.

The emergent (lukewarm) state of Phanerozoic Australia is indicated by two factors. The first is the small amplitude of the transgressive-regressive curve (Fig. 1, XI). Interior Australia was crossed by the sea only twice, in the Cambrian-Ordovician (Fig. 3) and Early Cretaceous (Fig. 1, XI). Compared with the transgressive-regressive curve of Euramerica (Fig. 1, XIII), the Australian curve, though not strictly quantitative, has a small amplitude, and its Early Cretaceous (Aptian-Albian) transgression is an isolated spike set against the very broad peak in Euramerica. Moreover, against the trend of the rest of the world, the Australian land level overtook the presumed rising sea level of the Late Cretaceous (Veevers, 1984, p. 212–213) to produce a platform-wide lacuna. In contrast, the mid-continent of the United States has a fairly complete marine (carbonate) Paleozoic record and a fully marine Cretaceous one. The second factor is that according to Andrew Gleadow (personal communication, 1992), Australia, in company with other Gondwanaland fragments, contains no known apatite fission-track (f-t) ages >500 Ma, whereas parts of Laurasia have apatite f-t ages >2,000 Ma. This is direct evidence of a Gondwanaland-wide event of cooling through 100°C by surface stripping at the 500-Ma end of the Pan-African event, attributable to the maximum rate of loss of heat anomaly induced beneath the Vendian superconti-

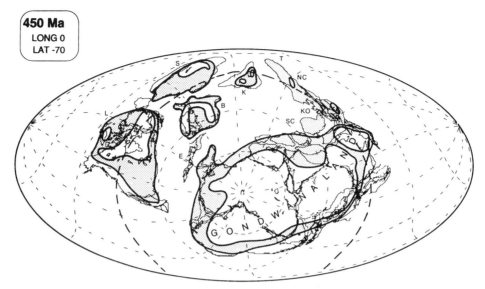

Figure 3. Configuration 450 Ma, toward the end of the Ordovician, of the supercontinent of Gondwanaland and the continents of Laurentia (L); Siberia (S); Baltica (B); England and others (E); Kazakhstania (K); North China (NC), including Tarim (T) and Korea (KO); and South China (SC). Within the continents, the shallow sea is shown by light stipple. Base map and paleolatitude drawn by computer from the Terra Mobilis program (Scotese and Denham, 1988), with a center of projection (printed below the age) chosen to concentrate the continents in the middle. Projection: Lambert equal-area full globe. Paleogeography from Scotese et al. (1979, Figs. 8–13), with the addition of a seaway across Australia (Veevers, 1984).

South pole is located in central Africa, in a region affected by glaciation at the end of the Ordovician (438 Ma), at a time of widely dispersed, flooded continents during a greenhouse state. This glaciation was a forerunner of the Quaternary intragreenhouse ice age (Fig. 6) (Worsley et al., 1986, p. 247–248, Fig. 7).

nent and early Paleozoic Gondwanaland (Fig. 1, X). Inheriting what was left of this large heat anomaly, the Gondwanaland province of Pangea remained wholly emergent, except during the postglacial Sakmarian (280 Ma) transgression/regression, to accumulate the nonmarine Gondwanan sequence of India and equivalents elsewhere (Fig. 1, XI; Figs. 4 and 5). After breakup, the newly rifted margins were covered by the sea but the interiors remained dry.

The transgressive-regressive curve registered against the Euramerican land platform is not eustatic though it is generally taken to be so. It can directly reflect eustatic changes in sea level only in the unlikely event that Euramerica had a zero vertical motion. The Euramerican curve is therefore local, not global or eustatic, and represents the transgressive-regressive behavior proper to small continents.

TECTONO-SEDIMENTARY STAGES OF PANGEAN HEAT ANOMALY RELEASE AND COUPLETS OF SHORTENING AND EXTENSION

Plate-tectonic processes modulated by the growth and later decay of the Pangean heat anomaly brought about the five tectono-sedimentary stages (Veevers, 1990a) outlined in the Introduction (Figs. 1 and 2). The first three stages involve two couplets of shortening and extension (Dewey, 1988; Menard and Molnar, 1988).

Couplet 1

Carboniferous shortening and uplift. Carboniferous shortening and uplift events in eastern Australia (Kanimblan/early New England, K in Fig. 1, XI) and Europe (Variscan or Hercynian) were effected by right-lateral transpression, and together with compressive events in North America (Marathon-Ouachita-Appalachian) (Fig. 1, XIII; Fig. 4) and central Australia (Alice Springs, AS in Fig. 1, XI) marked the initial coalescence of Pangea. Metamorphism in the Antarctic Peninsula (AP) (Fig. 1, XI) at 325 Ma (Milne and Millar, 1989) probably reflected this event. From the distribution of the Gondwana sequence and equivalents and their paleocurrents in a system of radial drainage, Tewari and Veevers (1993) infer Tibetan-scale uplift in the vicinity of the Gamburtsev Sub-glacial Mountains in East Antarctica (Fig. 4) by intense crustal shortening in the mid-Carboniferous.

Stage 1 of the Pangean heat anomaly accumulated during the initial coalescence of Pangea. The stage is represented by a platform-wide lacuna of nondeposition on the craton and erosion of the thermally uplifted platform and shortened foldbelts (Fig. 1 X).

280 Ma

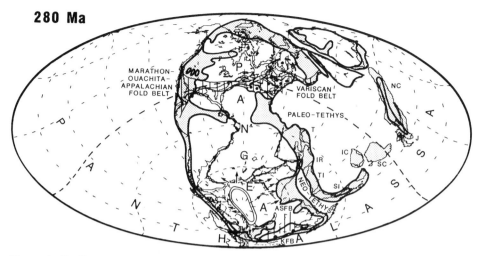

Figure 4. Configuration 280 Ma, Early Permian, soon after the merger of Gondwanaland and Laurussia in Pangea and just before the merger of Kazakhstania and Siberia. Independent continents are Indochina (IC), South China (SC), and North China (NC), including Japan (J). The narrow Cimmerian continent, comprising Turkey (T), Iran (IR), Tibet (TI), and Sibumasu (China-Burma-Malaya-Sumatra) (SI), was drifting northward from Gondwanaland by generation of the ocean floor of the Neo-Tethys and subduction of Paleo-Tethys. Inferred upland of central Antarctica (oval in double line) and radial drainage in Gondwana facies from Tewari and Veevers (1993) for comparison with present central Asian upland (Fig. 6). Base map from Scotese and Denham (1988). Pennsylvanian paleogeography from Scotese et al. (1979, Figs. 32–37). Stephanian-Autunian (Permo-Carboniferous) of Europe from Ziegler (1990), of Australia from Veevers (1984), and of Southeast Asia from Metcalfe (1988). The Hercynian mega-suture (Marathon-Ouachita-Appalachian foldbelt on west, Variscan foldbelt on east) marked the Pennsylvanian collision of Gondwanaland and Laurussia (Ziegler, 1989, Plate 2, Westphalian). Transtension of the Variscan foldbelt and the craton to the north, including the Oslo area, was accompanied by the emplacement of S-type granitoids (solid circle) and extrusives. Eastern Australia had a parallel development with a couplet of a Carboniferous deformation (Kanimblan/Coffs Harbour or Proto–New England foldbelt) (KFB), including oroclinal bending, followed in the Early Permian by transtensional emplacement of S-type granites and extrusives and tuff. Central Australia was deformed in the mid-Carboniferous Alice Springs foldbelt (ASFB).

Permian extension I. Stage 2 of the Pangean heat anomaly in the latest Carboniferous/earliest Permian (290 Ma) is caused by thermal subsidence and is expressed by platform-wide extension that accumulated the Pangean supersequence (Fig. 4). The modes of subsidence depended on basement structure. The hot, newly formed orogenic basement of the Variscides of Europe and to the east (Sengor et al., 1991) and the Kanimblides/proto–New England Foldbelt of Eastern Australia collapsed in intramontane rifts that accumulated volcanics and volcanic sediment intruded by plutons. The basement of the Karoo tectono-sedimentary terrain of Africa (Rust, 1975) and of Australia east of the (present) western margin (116°E) (Tewari and Veevers, 1993) subsided in oval-shaped basins or sags and accumulated nonvolcanic sediment. Examples are the Karoo Basin itself in South Africa and the Cooper Basin in central-eastern Australia. The anisotropic Late Proterozoic foldbelt basement of the Zambezian tectono-sedimentary terrain of East Africa (Rust, 1975) extended across Madagascar and peninsular India to the western margin of Australia (116°E) (Tewari and Veevers, 1993), subsided between faults guided by basement weakness to

form elongate basins or rifts, and accumulated nonvolcanic sediment. Examples are the Zambezian rifts of East Africa, the Gondwana basins of peninsular India, and the Perth Basin of Western Australia.

Couplet 2

Late Permian–Early and Middle Triassic shortening and uplift. Gondwanide, Indosinian, and Cimmeride shortening and uplift followed in the Late Permian–Early and Middle Triassic (255 to 230 Ma) (Fig. 5). Research currently underway by J. J. Veevers and others indicates that the Gondwanide shortening, presumably caused by shallow subduction beneath the 10,000-km-long Panthalassan margin of the Gondwanaland province as well as by local collision with terranes, involved the Sierra de la Ventana Foldbelt of Argentina, the Cape Foldbelt of South Africa, and the New England Foldbelt of Eastern Australia and probably the intervening orogen of the Ellsworth and Pensacola mountains of Antarctica (Grunow et al., 1991). North China collided with Asia ahead of the Cimmerian conti-

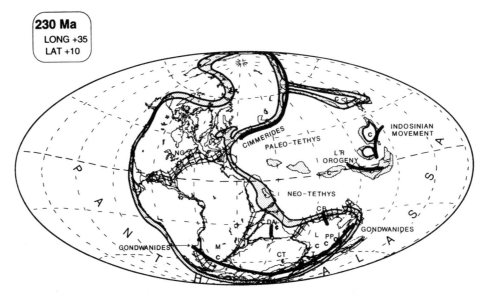

Figure 5. Configuration 230 Ma, Carnian or Late Triassic, immediately after the widespread deformation (heavy lines) of the Gondwanides, Cimmerides, the Indosinian Movement, and the Malayan
orogeny and the less intense folding and faulting in the Dadomar River area (DA) of India and the
Canning Basin (CB) of northwest Australia (short heavy lines) and at the start of the continental
rifting that prefigured the rift oceans of the Atlantic and Indian Oceans (Veevers, 1989). After the
Early and Middle Triassic coal gap (250 to 230 Ma) (Veevers, Conaghan, and Shaw, this volume),
deposition of coal (C) resumed in newly created rift basins in the eastern United States (Newark
Group [NG]; Olsen, 1989) and Australia (Ipswich Coal Measures, Peera Peera Formation [PP],
Leigh Creek Coal Measures [L], and coal measures in Tasmania [T]; Veevers, 1990b). The
Molteno Coal Measures (M) of South Africa (Dingle et al., 1983) followed the terminal (Gondwanide) deformation of the Cape Fold Belt. Carbonaceous sediment(¢) was deposited conformably
on Early and Middle Triassic noncarbonaceous sediment in the central Transantarctic (CT) Mountains (J. W. Collinson, personal communication, 1991), and in the Chinas and Tibet coal succeeded
red beds (Zunyi et al., 1986).
          Base map from Scotese and Denham (1988). Paleogeography from Ziegler et al. (1983, Fig. 2,
Early Jurassic), except Keuper of Europe (Ziegler, 1988, Plate 10).

nent, which had broken into several parts strung along the
equator. These parts finally collided with Asia during the
Jurassic (Sengor, 1984), so that the earliest (Carnian) phase of
Cimmeride deformation must have been driven by shallow
subduction along the southern margin of Asia.

    Late Triassic extension. Mid-Triassic compression was
followed immediately by the stage 3 release of the Pangean
heat anomaly, during which Late Triassic (230 Ma) and later
extensional deformation in the form of the continental rifting
prefigured the Atlantic and Indian rift oceans (Fig. 5). The
second couplet is seen in stratigraphic superposition in northwestern Australia, with latest Middle Triassic transpression-
ally deformed sediment unconformably overlain by Carnian
rift deposits (Veevers, 1990b, Fig. 9). Elsewhere in Australia,
the intramontane Ipswich Coal Measures and volcanics were
deposited in extended parts of the northern (in present coordi-
nates) Gondwanide foldbelt, and on the platform the carbonaceous Peera Peera Formation was deposited in the broad sag
of the Great Artesian Basin, in the Leigh Creek Coal Measures
in grabens, and in the Tasmanian coal measures in sags.

Seafloor spreading (Stages 4 and 5)

    Definitive dispersal started when continental rifting was
superseded by seafloor spreading.

CHANGES IN ATMOSPHERIC CO₂

    A by-product of the release of Pangean heat in the Early
Permian volcanics of Europe and eastern Australia was an accompanying release of mantle carbon and an increase in atmospheric pCO_2. This condition led to the melting of most of
the Gondwanan ice sheets by 275 Ma, with a resulting rise of
sea level over the glaciated parts of the Gondwanaland province ahead of the slower isostatic recovery of the deglaciated
land. Marine dropstones in eastern Australia persisted almost
to the end of the Permian, when the icehouse state was abruptly replaced by the greenhouse state.

PERMIAN/TRIASSIC (P/Tr) EVENT

    As described by Veevers, Conaghan, and Shaw (this vol-
ume), a catastrophic discharge of CO_2 into the atmosphere at

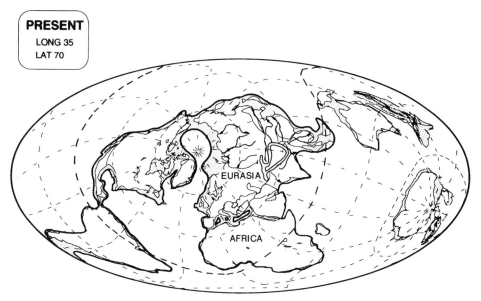

Figure 6. Configuration now, in the Quaternary, showing the large continent of Eurasia-Africa, separated from the Americas (except at their touching point in Bering Strait) by the Arctic and Atlantic oceans and from Australasia by the narrow Banda Arcs (not shown), as Antarctica is separated from South America by the Scotia Arc (not shown). For all their near contiguity the present land-masses are nevertheless widely dispersed by wide rift oceans (the Atlantic and Indian oceans), and the next Pangea will appear only after the demise of the rift oceans. The dominant Central Asian upland today (double line encloses ground higher than 4 km) and its radial drainage are matched by the Permian-Triassic central Antarctic upland (Tewari and Veevers, 1993), shown in Figure 4. Base map from Scotese and Denham (1988).

the P/Tr boundary (250 Ma) from the eruption of the widespread Siberian Traps (Renne and Basu, 1991), augmented by ignimbrites along the convergent Panthalassan margin of the Gondwanaland province, marked the onset of biotal extinctions and the change from an icehouse to a greenhouse, reflected in Gondwanaland by a change in deposition from coal measures to redbeds. We envisage the succession of events as: (1) Siberian Traps and subsidiary volcanics along the Panthalassan margin vent excessive CO_2 into atmosphere; (2) greenhouse effect causes instant heating; (3) surface sediment, including progenitors of coal, oxidized; (4) warm surface water at high latitudes slows or stops bottom ocean-water circulation and the ocean floor becomes anoxic.

STABLE ISOTOPES

Other notable changes at this time were registered by the isotopes of carbon, sulfur, and strontium in seawater (Fig. 1, V). Veevers, Conaghan, and Shaw (this volume) interpreted the minimum in the $\delta^{13}C$ curve as due to the extinction of the *Glossopteris* flora and the low preserved floral biomass in the warm, oxidized Early and Middle Triassic coal gap, and the maximum in $\delta^{34}S$ as due to anoxic oceanic conditions. Both isotopes indicate a shift at the surface from the reduced to the oxidized state. The minimum in the $^{87}Sr/^{86}Sr$ ratio is interpreted as reflecting the leaching of the Siberian Traps, which

have a low $^{87}Sr/^{86}Sr$ ratio, and possible mid-plate equivalents in the ocean.

The initial coalescence of Pangea, at 320 Ma, is marked by an upward step in the $\delta^{13}C$ curve at the start of the Pennsylvanian-Permian epoch of coal deposition. As shown above, the curve steps down at the P/Tr boundary, remains low during the coal gap, steps up at the Middle/Late Triassic boundary, recovers during the Late Triassic and Early/Middle Jurassic, and starts to drop again after the definitive breakup of Pangea at 160 Ma.

The $\delta^{34}S$ curve is a mirror image of the $\delta^{13}C$ curve. The long decline from the Devonian reverses to an Early/Middle Triassic spike during the coal gap and then declines to the Cretaceous. The Triassic spike is taken to indicate oceanic anoxia and surface oxidation.

The seawater $^{87}Sr/^{86}Sr$ curve indicates two episodes of alternating crust- and mantle-derived strontium. The high values from 330 to 270 Ma derive from the intense crustal erosion that accompanied the orogenic uplift that followed the Marathon/Ouachita/Appalachian/Variscan and Kanimblan/Alice Springs/?Gamburtsev compressive events (shown on Fig. 4) during the initial coalescence of Pangea. The short maximum from 240 to 230 Ma represents the uplift and erosion that accompanied the Gondwanide, Cimmerian, Malayan, and Indosinian movements (Fig. 5) that preceded rifting. This interpretation follows that of Richter et al. (1992), who found that the total amount of erosion of the Himalaya-Tibet region since collision accounts for the sharp rise in $^{87}Sr/^{86}Sr$ since 40 Ma. The first depression of the Sr curve within the Pangean epoch is the already-mentioned minimum at the P/Tr boundary, which we attribute to exposure of the Siberian Traps and possible mid-plate oceanic counterparts. The second depression of the curve is at 160 Ma, at the start of definitive breakup of Pangea by seafloor spreading of the Atlantic and Indian rift oceans. The consequently increased length of the mid-ocean ridge system contributed the light isotope from the mantle. The subsequent rise in the curve is attributable to the greater exposure of continental crust during the Andean/Cordilleran/Alpine/Himalayan compressive events.

MAGNETIC SUPERCHRONS

As outlined by Veevers, Conaghan, and Shaw (this volume), the change of magnetic polarity from the Permo-Carboniferous Reversed Chron to the Permo-Triassic Mixed Chron is consistent with the idea that changes at the core/mantle boundary that initiated a new magnetic chron also induced the magmatic release of CO_2 that triggered the environmental changes.

THE NEXT PANGEA

Today, the continents are continuous from Africa through Eurasia and the Americas and, past the 600-km-wide gap of the Drake Passage, to Antarctica. Australasia is on the point of merging in Southeast Eurasia. Yet, in an effective tectonic sense, the continents remain dispersed by the wide Atlantic and Indian rift oceans (Fig. 6). Another Pangea will arise only after the rift oceans are removed by subduction (Veevers, 1990a). According to this view, the current Quaternary glaciation is a repetition of the Ordovician/Silurian intragreenhouse glaciation (Worsley et al., 1986) but is intensified by the extraordinary orogenic uplift of Tibet occasioned by the collision of India with Asia (Raymo, 1991).

ACKNOWLEDGMENTS

I thank my colleagues in the Panthalassan margin project—Doug Cole, Jim Collinson, Pat Conaghan, Oscar Lopez Gamundi, and Chris Powell—for sharing their geological insights of Gondwanaland; John Hayes, Ric Morante, and Ian Percival for discussion; and Tom Worsley and an anonymous reviewer for helpful reviews. Judy Davis made the line drawings, and Andrew Roach the computer drawings from Scotese and Denham's (1988) Terra Mobilis program. This work was supported by the Australian Research Council. My attendance at the workshop was facilitated by a travel grant from the workshop funds of the Global Sedimentary Geology Program.

REFERENCES CITED

Algeo, T. J., and Wilkinson, B. H., 1991, Modern and ancient continental hypsometries: Journal of the Geological Society, London, v. 148, p. 643–653.

Anderson, D. L., 1981, Hotspots, basalts, and the evolution of the mantle: Science, v. 213, p. 83–89.

Anderson, D. L., 1982, Hotspots, polar wander, Mesozoic convection and the geoid: Nature, v. 297, p. 391–393.

Baksi, A. K., 1988, Reply to Comment on 'Critical evaluation of the age of the Deccan Traps, India: Implications for flood-basalt volcanism and faunal extinctions': Geology, v. 16, p. 758–759.

Bond, G. C., Nickerson, P. A., and Kominz, M. A., 1984, Breakup of a supercontinent between 625 Ma and 555 Ma: New evidence and implications for continental histories: Earth and Planetary Science Letters, v. 70, p. 325–345.

Briden, J. C., Drewry, G. E., and Smith, A. G., 1974, Phanerozoic equal-area world maps: Journal of Geology, v. 82, p. 555–574.

Bristow, W., and Saggerson, E. P., 1983, A general account of Karoo vulcanicity in southern Africa: Geologische Rundschau, v. 72, p. 1015–1059.

Dewey, J. F., 1988, Extensional collapse of orogens: Tectonics, v. 7, p. 1123–1139.

Dingle, R. V., Siesser, W. G., and Newton, A. R., 1983, Mesozoic and Tertiary geology of Southern Africa: Rotterdam, A. A. Balkema, 375 p.

Fischer, A. G., 1984, The two Phanerozoic supercycles, in Berggren, W. A., and van Couvering, J. A., eds., Catastrophes and Earth history: Princeton, New Jersey, Princeton University Press, p. 129–150.

Grunow, A. M., Kent, D. V., and Dalziel, I.W.D., 1991, New paleomagnetic data from Thurston Island: Implications for the tectonics of West Antarctica and Weddell Sea opening: Journal of Geophysical Research, v. 96, p. 17935–17954.

Harland, W. B., Armstrong, R. L., Cox, A. V., Craig, L. E., Smith, A. G., and Smith, D. G., 1990, A geological time scale 1989: Cambridge, Cambridge University Press, 263 p.

Holser, W. T., Schidlowski, M., Mackenzie, F. T., and Maynard, J. B., 1988, Biogeochemical cycles of carbon and sulfur, in Gregor, C. B., Garrels, R. M., Mackenzie, F. T., and Maynard, J. B., eds., Chemical cycles in the evolution of the Earth: New York, John Wiley and Sons, p. 105–173.

Jaeger, J.-J., Courtillot, V., and Tapponnier, P., 1989, Paleontological view of the ages of the Deccan Traps, the Cretaceous/Tertiary boundary, and the India-Asia collision: Geology, v. 17, p. 316–319.

Koepnick, R. B., Denison, R. E., and Dahl, D. A., 1988, The Cenozoic seawater $^{87}Sr/^{86}Sr$ curve: Data review and implications for correlation of marine strata: Paleoceanography, v. 3, p. 743–756.

Kyle, P. R., Elliot, D. H., and Sutter, J. F., 1981, Jurassic Ferrar Supergroup tholeiites from the Transantarctic Mountains, Antarctica, and their relationship to the initial fragmentation of Gondwana, in Cresswell, M. M., and Vella, P., eds., Gondwana five: Rotterdam, A. A. Balkema, p. 283–287.

Menard, G., and Molnar, P., 1988, Collapse of a Hercynian Tibetan plateau into a late Palaeozoic European Basin and Range province: Nature, v. 334, p. 235–237.

Metcalfe, I., 1988, Origin and assembly of south-east Asian continental terranes, in Audley-Charles, M. G., and Hallam, A., eds., Gondwana and Tethys: Geological Society of London, Special Publication, v. 37, p. 101–118.

Milne, A. J., and Millar, I. L., 1989, The significance of mid-Palaeozoic basement in Graham Land, Antarctic Peninsula: Journal of the Geological Society, London, v. 146, p. 207–210.

Mosmann, R., Falkenhein, F.U.H., Goncalves, A., and Nepomuceno, F., 1986, Oil and gas potential of the Amazon Paleozoic basins, in Halbouty, M. T., ed., Future petroleum provinces of the world: American Association of Petroleum Geologists Memoir 40, p. 207–241.

Olsen, P. E., 1989, Stratigraphy, facies, depositional environments and paleontology of the Newark supergroup, in Hatcher, R. D., Thomas, W. A., and Viele, G. W., eds., The Appalachian-Ouachita orogen in the United States: The Geology of North America, v. F-2: Boulder, Colorado, Geological Society of America, p. 743–750.

Palmer, A. R., 1983, The Decade of North American Geology 1983 geologic time scale: Geology, v. 11, p. 503–504.

Raup, D. M., and Sepkoski, J. J., 1986, Periodic extinction of families and genera: Science, v. 231, p. 833–836.

Raymo, M. E., 1991, Geochemical evidence supporting T. C. Chamberlin's theory of glaciation: Geology, v. 19, p. 344–347.

Renne, P. R., and Basu, A. R., 1991, Rapid eruption of the Siberian Traps flood basalts at the Permo-Triassic boundary: Science, v. 253, p. 176–179.

Richter, F. M., Rowley, D. B., and DePaolo, D. J., 1992, Sr isotope evolution of seawater: The role of tectonics: Earth and Planetary Science Letters, v. 109, p. 11–23.

Rust, I. C., 1975, Tectonic and sedimentary framework of Gondwana Basins in Southern Africa, *in* Campbell, K.S.W., ed., Gondwana geology: Canberra, Australian National University Press, p. 537–564.

Schlanger, S. O., Jenkyns, H. C., and Premoli-Silva, I., 1981, Volcanism and vertical tectonics in the Pacific Basin related to global Cretaceous transgressions: Earth and Planetary Science Letters, v. 52, p. 435–449.

Schmidt, P. W., and McDougall, I., 1977, Palaeomagnetic and potassium-argon studies of the Tasmanian Dolerites: Geological Society of Australia Journal, v. 24, p. 321–328.

Schobbenhaus, C., ed., 1984, Geologia do Brasil: Brasilia, Departamento Nacional da Productaçao Mineral, 501 p.

Sclater, J. G., Anderson, R. N., and Bell, M. L., 1971, Elevation of ridges and evolution of the central eastern Pacific: Journal of Geophysical Research, v. 76, p. 7888–7915.

Scotese, C. R., and Denham, C. R., 1988, Terra Mobilis: Plate tectonics for the Macintosh: Austin, Texas, Earth in Motion Technologies, 2 disks.

Scotese, C. R., Bambach, R. K., Barton, C., Van der Voo, R., and Ziegler, A. M., 1979, Paleozoic base maps: Journal of Geology, v. 87, p. 217–277.

Sengor, A.M.C., 1984, The Cimmeride orogenic system and the tectonics of Eurasia: Geological Society of America Special Paper 195, 82 p.

Sengor, A.M.C., Cin, A., Rowley, D. B., and Shangyou, N., 1991, Magmatic evolution of the Tethysides: A guide to reconstruction of collage history: Palaeogeography, Palaeoclimatology, Palaeoecology, v. 87, p. 411–440.

Sepkoski, J. J., 1992, Major bioevents during the Paleozoic Era: A view from global taxonomic data bases: International Geological Correlation Programme, Project 303, Late Precambrian and Cambrian event stratigraphy, Newsletter 5, p. 25–26.

Sloss, L. L., 1976, Areas and volumes of cratonic sediments, western North America and eastern Europe: Geology, v. 4, p. 272–276.

Sloss, L. L., ed., 1988, Sedimentary cover—North American Craton, *in* The geology of North America, v. D-2: Boulder, Colorado, Geological Society of America, 506 p.

Soares, C. S., Landim, P.M.B., and Fulfaro, V. J., 1978, Tectonic cycles and sedimentary sequences in the Brazilian intracratonic basins: Geological Society of America Bulletin, v. 89, p. 181–191.

Tewari, R. C., and Veevers, J. J., 1993, Gondwana basins of India occupy the middle of a 7,500-km sector of radial valleys and lobes in central-eastern Gondwanaland, *in* Findlay, R. H., ed., Gondwana Eight: Proceedings, Eighth Gondwana Symposium, Hobart: Rotterdam, A. A. Balkema, p. 507–512.

Vail, P. R., Mitchum, R. M., and Thompson, S., 1977, Seismic stratigraphy and global changes of sea level. Part 4: Global cycles of relative changes of sea level: American Association of Petroleum Geologists Memoir 26, p. 83–97.

Veevers, J. J., ed., 1984, Phanerozoic earth history of Australia: Oxford, Clarendon Press, 418 p.

Veevers, J. J., 1989, Middle/Late Triassic (230±5 Ma) singularity in the stratigraphic and magmatic history of the Pangean heat anomaly: Geology, v. 17, p. 784–787.

Veevers, J. J., 1990a, Tectonic-climatic supercycle in the billion-year plate-tectonic eon: Permian Pangean icehouse alternates with Cretaceous dispersed-continents greenhouse: Sedimentary Geology, v. 68, p. 1–16.

Veevers, J. J., 1990b, Development of Australia's post-Carboniferous sedimentary basins: Petroleum Exploration Society of Australia Journal, v. 16, p. 25–32.

Watts, A. B., Bodine, J. H., and Ribe, N. M., 1980, Observations of flexure and the geological evolution of the Pacific Ocean basin: Nature, v. 283, p. 532–537.

Wopfner, H., 1984, Permian deposits of the Southern Alps as product of initial alpidic taphrogenesis: Geologische Rundschau, v. 73, p. 259–277.

Worsley, T. R., Nance, R. D., and Moody, J. B., 1984, Global tectonics and eustasy for the past 2 billion years: Marine Geology, v. 58, p. 373–400.

Worsley, T. R., Nance, R. D., and Moody, J. B., 1986, Tectonic cycles and the history of the earth's biogeochemical and paleoceanographic record: Paleoceanography, v. 1, p. 233–263.

Ziegler, A. M., Scotese, C. R., McKerrow, W. S., Johnson, M. E., and Bambach, R. K., 1979, Paleozoic paleogeography: Annual Review of Earth and Planetary Science, v. 7, p. 473–502.

Ziegler, A. M., Scotese, C. R., and Barrett, S. F., 1983, Mesozoic and Cenozoic paleogeographic maps, *in* Brosche, P., and Sundermann, J., eds., Tidal friction and the earth's rotation II: Berlin, Springer-Verlag, p. 240–252.

Ziegler, P. A., 1988, Evolution of the Arctic–North Atlantic and the Western Tethys: American Association of Petroleum Geologists Memoir, v. 43, 198 p., 30 plates.

Ziegler, P. A., 1989, Evolution of Laurussia: a study in Late Palaeozoic plate tectonics: Dordrecht, Kluwer, 102 p.

Ziegler, P. A., 1990, Geological atlas of Western and Central Europe, 2d ed.: The Hague, Shell Internationale Petroleum Maatschappij B.V., 239 p., 56 enclosures.

Zunyi, Y., Yuqi, C., and Hongzhen, W., 1986, The geology of China: Oxford, Clarendon Press, 303 p.

MANUSCRIPT ACCEPTED BY THE SOCIETY MAY 14, 1993

Geological Society of America
Special Paper 288
1994

Pangean climates

Thomas J. Crowley*

Applied Research Corporation, 305 Arguello Drive, College Station, Texas 77840

ABSTRACT

The climates of Pangea are reviewed, with an emphasis on results from modeling studies. A moderate amount of progress has been made in modeling Pangean climates since the first studies were conducted in 1989. One of the most dominant features of the modeled supercontinent involves the very large annual cycles, which are directly related to low heat capacities of large land areas. Sensitivity experiments suggest that changes in CO_2 and orbital insolation forcing can sometimes shift the winter freezing line to 50 to 60° paleolatitude; however, significant subfreezing winter temperatures still occur in higher latitudes. These results are not easily reconcilable with some geologic data and represent a significant impediment to confident application of modeling results to Pangean climate. Additional simulations suggest that the large landmass considerably amplifies system sensitivity to Milankovitch forcing in both hemispheres. Unusually high temperatures during 10,000-year precession half cycles could complicate interpretations of geologic deposits from high latitudes. Preliminary work coupling geography, CO_2, and orbital insolation changes provides insight into onset and retreat of Permo-Carboniferous glaciers, along with cyclical sea-level fluctuations during that time. Modeled precipitation-minus-evaporation for Pangean land areas is about 50 to 60% that of present; this result supports the concept of dry Mesozoic climates. Combined temperature and precipitation changes during Pangean time may have significantly influenced the distribution of terrestrial biota. Several suggestions are made for improving validation of Pangean climate simulations.

INTRODUCTION

The "discovery" of Pangea represents one of the most intriguing scientific contributions from the geologic record. Although observational studies of Pangean climates span many decades, the first climate modeling studies were not done until 1989 (Crowley et al., 1989; Kutzbach and Gallimore, 1989). Since then there has been increased interest in Pangean climates. It is the purpose of this chapter to review the present level of understanding of Pangean climates, with primary emphasis on modeling studies.

TRENDS IN PANGEAN CLIMATES

Perhaps the two most significant features of Pangean climates involve the late Paleozoic glaciation and subsequent transition to arid and nearly ice-free supercontinents of the Triassic and Jurassic. The first evidence for pre-Pleistocene glaciation was from the Permo-Carboniferous on Gondwana (~330 to 230 Ma), at the initial time of Pangean assembly (Fig. 1). For the remaining 80 million years of its existence the landmass was free of large ice sheets. However, some (limited) evidence exists for perhaps seasonal ice (Frakes and Francis, 1988), and the presence of small undiscovered ice caps cannot be excluded.

Geologic studies indicate that during the Triassic and Jurassic, aridity was extensive over much of Pangea (e.g.,

---

*Present address: Department of Oceanography, Texas A&M University, College Station, Texas 77843.

Crowley, T. J., 1994, Pangean climates, *in* Klein, G. D., ed., Pangea: Paleoclimate, Tectonics, and Sedimentation During Accretion, Zenith, and Breakup of a Supercontinent: Boulder, Colorado, Geological Society of America Special Paper 288.

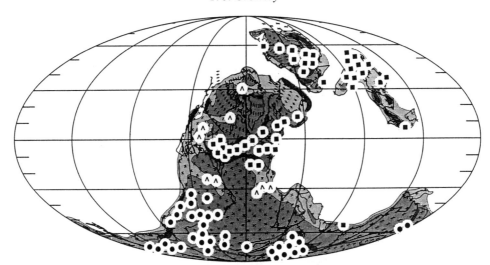

Figure 1. Evidence for extensive Carboniferous glaciation on Gondwana. Figure illustrates Westphalian (Late Carboniferous; ~360 Ma) paleogeography and distribution of climatically controlled sediments. Key: circles, tillites; squares, coals; inverted *v*, evaporites; dark shading, highland; medium shading, lowland; light shading, continental shelf. After Parrish et al., 1986; published in Crowley and Baum, 1992.

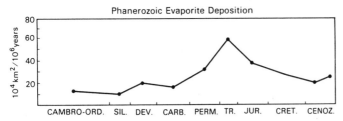

Figure 2. Areas covered by evaporite deposits throughout the Phanerozoic. Evaporite deposits form in arid environments, and the Triassic peak in the formation rate may be due to extreme aridity on a very large landmass. After Gordon, 1975.

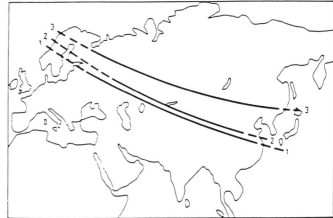

Figure 3. Evidence for a warming trend in the Jurassic as illustrated by the northward shift in the Indo-European and Siberian floral province boundary in Eurasia during the Early (1) and Mid (2) to Late (3) Jurassic. From Hallam, 1982; adapted from Vakhrameev, 1964.

Robinson, 1973). An example involves an inferred peak in global evaporite formation at this time (Fig. 2). Clay mineralogy also suggests increasing aridity during the Late Triassic (Tucker and Benton, 1982; Hallam et al., 1991). High aridity may have removed at least 10% of salt from the world ocean (Stevens, 1977; Railsback and Anderson, 1987), thereby significantly changing its composition and perhaps even response to temperature variations. Other biotic and sedimentologic evidence, such as vegetation shifts (Fig. 3), point to warming and drying in the Late Jurassic. Some of these changes may be associated with a rise in sea level accompanying the breakup of Pangea. Organic carbon–rich layers are coincident with peaks in sea-level highs during these times (Jenkyns, 1988).

Evidence exists for higher-frequency Milankovitch-scale fluctuations on Pangea. Cyclothem records from the Permo-Carboniferous possess a time scale of Milankovitch fluctuations (Heckel, 1986), as do lake deposits from Triassic rift system of eastern North America (Olsen, 1986).

"Equable" climates have been inferred for the Late Triassic and the Jurassic (Hallam, 1985), based on fairly cosmopolitan distributions of biota (Hallam, 1985; Shubin et al., 1991). Other significant biotic events during Pangean time include the appearance of "gymnosperms" during the Carboniferous, a Late Permian transition from amphibian-dominated vertebrates to reptile-dominated vertebrates (Benton, 1987), the end-Permian extinction (the greatest in the fossil record), and two late Triassic extinctions that ultimately gave rise to the dinosaurs (Tucker and Benton, 1982; Olsen et al., 1987).

In addition to climate and biotic changes, there were significant variations in the carbon cycle during Pangean times. The largest carbon sequestration "event" in the Phanerozoic (Berner, 1987) reflects the major time of coal formation in the

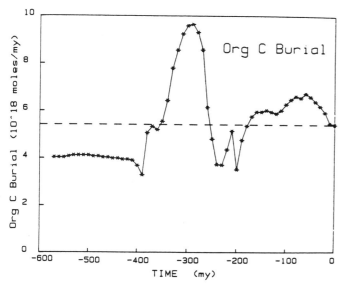

Figure 4. Estimated organic carbon burial rates through the Phanerozoic. After Berner, 1987. Dashed line indicates present value.

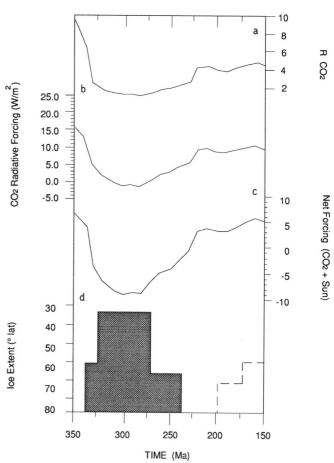

CO₂-GLACIATION COMPARISON

Figure 5. a, CO_2 variations (150 to 350 Ma) as calculated by a geochemical model (after Berner, 1991); R refers to ratio of past CO_2 values to present levels. b, radiative departures from present, based on CO_2 concentration/radiative forcing relationship discussed in Kiehl and Dickinson (1987); c, combined effect of radiative forcing and solar luminosity variations (cf. Fig. 6) versus time; d, area of glaciation versus time as estimated by Frakes and Francis (1988). Dashed areas represent evidence for ice but not necessarily continental glaciation; shaded areas represent times of continental glaciation.

Permo-Carboniferous (Fig. 4). The high carbon burial rates may reflect absence of lignin-degrading organisms during the first extensive phase of terrestrial land plant occupation (Robinson, 1990). The carbon changes contributed to the estimated low atmospheric CO_2 levels at that time (Fig. 5). Estimated levels were comparable to the present during the Carboniferous glaciations (Berner, 1991) and increased to levels perhaps five times the present during the Late Jurassic. In addition to the CO_2 changes, increases of solar luminosity over Pangean time are approximately equivalent to a 75% increase in atmospheric CO_2 levels above present levels (cf. Fig. 6). For reference, these luminosity changes are 50% larger than the much-discussed ice-age atmospheric CO_2 changes that have been linked to so many Pleistocene climate phenomena.

CLIMATE MODELS

Although it is beyond the scope of this chapter to discuss in depth the climate models used in the reviewed simulations (see Crowley and North, 1991, for a general review of the subject), some general comments are appropriate. Results involve two main classes of climate models: energy balance models (EBMs) and general circulation models (GCMs). The former are thermodynamic models that resolve the land-sea distribution and provide information on the seasonal cycle of surface temperature (North et al., 1983; Hyde et al., 1990). Numerous comparisons indicate that EBMs have approximately the same sensitivity to seasonal cycle variations as GCMs and observations (e.g., Hyde et al., 1990; Crowley et al., 1991; Kim and North, 1991).

GCMs explicitly compute physical fields such as winds and moisture based on the standard equations of motion and thermodynamics. Although these models do not perfectly cap-

ture the true nature of these fluctuations in the real world, their performance is more than acceptable for exploring their response to paleoclimate variations. As a rule of thumb the reader might bear in mind that uncertainties in climate model products are probably of the same magnitude as uncertainties in some of the geologic data used to infer climate variations.

MODELING CLIMATE VARIATIONS ON PANGEA

General trends in temperature

The first two modeling studies for Pangea identified its most basic response. For both idealized geography and a Late Permian (Kazanian) configuration, seasonal cycle variations

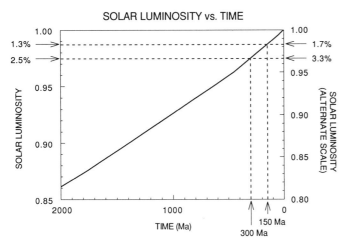

SOLAR LUMINOSITY vs. TIME

Figure 6. Evolution of solar luminosity versus time as computed from a model of solar evolution (after Endal and Sofia, 1981), with changes over Pangean time bracketed by arrows. Two different scales are used, representing uncertainties in the initial luminosity, which in turn are dependent on estimates of the original composition of the Sun's core (see discussion in Crowley et al., 1991).

were comparable to, if not larger than, those occurring on the present Eurasian landmass (e.g., Fig. 7; Crowley et al., 1989; Kutzbach and Gallimore, 1989). A large seasonal cycle reflects both high summer temperatures and low winter temperatures (Fig. 8). Subsequent GCM studies also found large seasonal cycles and significant winter cooling for Carboniferous and Jurassic reconstructions (Chandler et al., 1992; Moore et al., 1992a, b; Crowley et al., 1993; Crowley and Baum, 1993). Problems with these results will be discussed in a subsequent section.

Sensitivity to Milankovitch fluctuations

Further studies (Crowley et al., 1992a) indicate that Milankovitch variations could be quite large on a supercontinent. Early Jurassic EBM simulations result in maximum summer temperatures differing by 14 to 16°C (Fig. 9), with the magnitude depending on whether high or low summer insolation values are chosen. For orbital configurations yielding maximum summer insolation in high latitudes, Early Jurassic summer temperatures of 25°C extend as far poleward as 65° paleolatitude (Fig. 10). These results indicate that some caution is needed when interpreting evidence for high-latitude warmth in the Jurassic, because some geologic deposits may have formed during a 10,000-year precession half cycle, thus yielding a bias to interpretation of supercontinent climates. In an extreme illustration of this effect, Crowley et al. (1993) calculated that, even with luminosity reduced 3% in the Carboniferous, orbital configurations favorable for peak interglacials result in January (summer) temperatures at the South Pole of 27°C. The entire Gondwanan landmass is snow free for such conditions (winter temperatures were significantly below 0°C, however). It would be useful if geologists provided information to climate modelers about the estimated length of time their records represent, for such information may help separate mean-conditions from those occurring during "short" insolation peaks of 10,000 years' duration.

Supercontinents also exhibit significant response to Milankovitch fluctuations in tropical regions (Olsen, 1986). EBM simulations suggest that the large landmass amplifies fluctuations at the 100,000-year eccentricity period. During the Pleistocene this period is usually associated with ice volume fluctuations (Imbrie et al., 1984). However, climate modeling study (Crowley et al., 1992b) suggested that a significant

KAZANIAN 255 MA (ANNUAL CYCLE)

Figure 7. Simulated annual range of temperatures (°C) for the Late Permian (Kazanian). Base map, with shaded topography for reference (>1,000 m elevation), is from Scotese (1986). From Crowley et al., 1989.

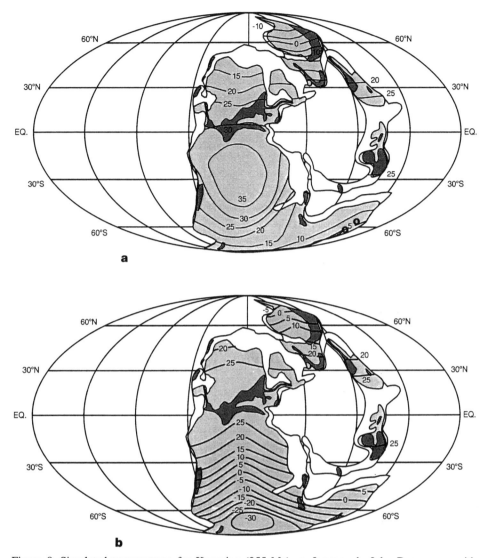

Figure 8. Simulated temperatures for Kazanian (255 Ma). a, January; b, July. Base maps, with shaded topography for reference (>1,000 m elevation), are from Scotese (1986). Open circles refer to evidence for ice cover (the latter from Parrish et al., 1986).

100,000-year response can occur in equatorial land areas subject to the twice-yearly passage of the sun across the equator. Good agreement exists between simulated and observed variations of Triassic lake levels in the tropics (Fig. 11).

Precipitation variations

Model results indicate that a supercontinent has a significant effect on precipitation. Simulations for an idealized supercontinent (Kutzbach and Gallimore, 1989; Hay et al., 1990) indicate that precipitation-minus-evaporation (P–E) is about one-half that of the control run (Fig. 12). P–E is reduced because moisture is limited to coastal regions and temperatures are higher. These results are consistent with abundant geologic

evidence for arid conditions on the Pangean supercontinent for much of Pangean time.

An exception to a dry interior Pangea has been found for simulations with altered Milankovitch forcing (Crowley and Baum, 1993). GCM simulations (Fig. 13) for the Westphalian (306 Ma) indicate that extreme summer insolation forcing leads to development of a monsoon that produces a wet pulse penetrating to 50 to 60° paleolatitude. In equatorial belts much of the precipitation in the Intertropical Convergence Zone is over the ocean, with generally dry conditions in the lee of the Appalachian-Hercynian chain. However, there is some focusing of precipitation on the windward side of the mountains, with the locus of maximum precipitation varying with orbital configuration (Crowley et al., unpublished results, 1993; cf.

PRESENT JULY ΔT − HSO−CSO

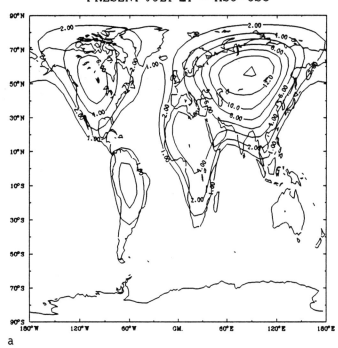

a

JURASSIC JULY ΔT − 1X CO₂, HSO−CSO

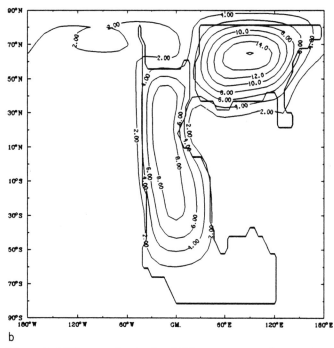

b

Figure 9. Differences in simulated July temperatures between two different orbital configurations for two different geographies. Plots illustrate peak summer insolation (hot summer orbit, HSO) minus minimum summer insolation (cold summer orbit, CSO). a, present; b, Early Jurassic. From Crowley et al., 1992a.

COMPARISON OF SUMMER WARMING

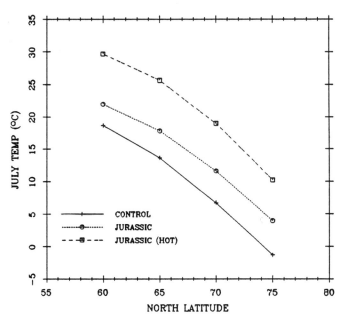

Figure 10. Simulated summer temperature trends along 90°E paleolongitude (central Eurasia; cf. Fig. 9) for present geography and Early Jurassic values with present and hot summer orbits. In the Jurassic case (cf. Fig. 9), runs were made with 4× CO_2 levels and −2.25% solar luminosity. From Crowley et al., 1992a.

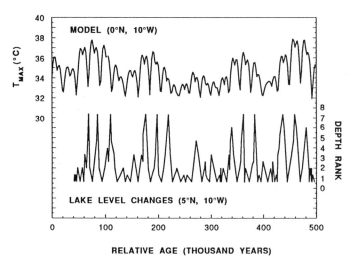

Figure 11. Comparison of modeled and observed time series for the late Triassic. Modeled fluctuations on the equator are for maximum summer temperatures as they vary due to Milankovitch insolation forcing. These changes should affect strength of the monsoon, with peak temperatures postulated as causing maximum precipitation. The observed time series is a modified version (Kominz and Bond, 1990) of a Triassic lake-level time series (Olsen, 1986). From Crowley et al., 1992b.

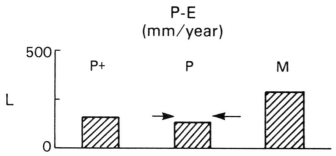

Figure 12. Comparison of net precipitation-minus-evaporation (P-E) for all land areas (L) as calculated for present geography (M), an idealized Pangea (P), an idealized Pangea with higher CO_2 forcing (P+), and an idealized Pangea with topography elevated 1 km (arrows on "P" bar). From Kutzbach and Gallimore, 1989.

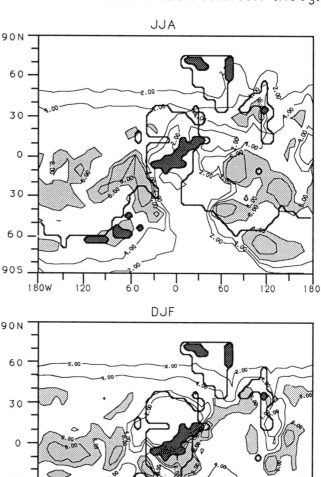

Figure 13. Precipitation (mm/day) for Westphalian simulation with orbital configuration favorable to hot summers in the Southern Hemisphere (HSOs). Heavy shading indicates topography (from Scotese, 1986). Light shading indicates peak precipitation areas (>6 mm/day). No icecaps are assumed for this interglacial simulation. Top, June-July-August; bottom, December-January-February. Based on results in Crowley and Baum (1993).

Hay et al., 1982). For peak summer insolation in the Northern Hemisphere, a low-level heat source develops in the lee of the Appalachians, drawing in moisture from the paleo-Pacific. Some "lee-side" precipitation occurs in the Appalachians. This response could help explain the coal deposits of the U.S. Midwest, which formed in the lee of the mountain chain.

GONDWANAN GLACIATIONS

Ice cover on Gondwana presents some intriguing challenges to climate modelers. Although the areal extent of the Carboniferous ice sheets was comparable to that of the Pleistocene (e.g., Crowley and Baum, 1991), the presence of the ice sheet on a supercontinent creates a dilemma, for summer warming over the Gondwanan ice sheet should be as much as 15°C greater than over the Laurentide Ice Sheet of the Pleistocene (Fig. 14a). However, since solar luminosity may have been 3% less than present during the Carboniferous (Crowley et al., 1991), temperatures would have been significantly less than illustrated in Figure 14a. Combining the effects of decreased luminosity with altered Milankovitch forcing favorable to cool summers results in seasonal warming patterns over the Gondwanan ice sheet comparable to those modeled for the Laurentide Ice Sheet (Fig. 14b). The decreased luminosity results in temperatures in the tropics 4°C less than present, a result that may be detectable with geochemical methods. Thus, luminosity and Milankovitch help resolve what on the surface appears to be a significant climate problem.

Since there were changes in geography, luminosity, and CO_2 levels during the late Paleozoic, it is necessary to assess the relative importance of these factors for Permo-Carboniferous glaciation. Crowley and Baum (1992) conducted a number of sensitivity tests for the effects of each of these variables (Fig. 15) and found that, although geographic changes had a significant effect on modeled snow cover, changes in luminosity and, more importantly, CO_2 seem to be required for explaining onset and demise of Permo-Carboniferous glaciers.

Even though "hot" summer orbit configurations resulted in snow-free conditions in the above simulations, model-generated summer snow cover during "cold" summer orbital configurations resulted in snow cover 50% larger than the Laurentide Ice Sheet of the Pleistocene (Fig. 15). This result may help explain cyclothem fluctuations observed in sea-level variations of the Carboniferous (e.g., Heckel, 1986). Some

SUMMER ΔT THROUGH ICE SHEET CENTER

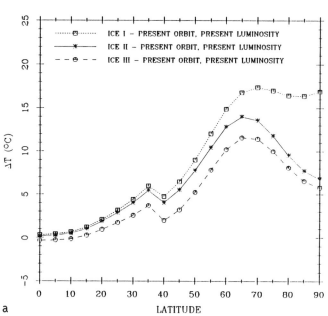

a

SUMMER ΔT THROUGH ICE SHEET CENTER

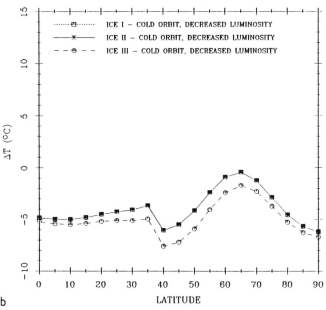

b

Figure 14. Comparison of differences in summer temperatures (Gondwana minus Laurentide) along the longitude of maximum equatorward extent of the Laurentide and Gondwanan ice sheets for three different Gondwanan ice sheet scenarios, with increasing levels of ice cover designated as ICE I, II, and III (see Crowley and Baum, 1991). a, Present levels of luminosity and orbital forcing; b, the combined effect of decreased luminosity and altered (cold) summer orbit. The very large "excess" warming on Gondwana in Fig. 14a reflects the amplification of the seasonal cycle on the large landmass. From Crowley et al., 1991.

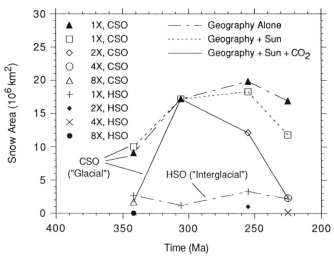

Figure 15. January snow cover (Carboniferous) on Gondwana for different levels of orbital forcing, CO_2, and solar luminosity. X's refer to CO_2 concentration; CSO and HSO refer to cold and hot summer orbits, respectively. Connecting lines indicate effect of geography alone, geography-plus-solar luminosity increases (cf. Fig. 6), and geography-plus-sun-plus-CO_2, The last calculation includes both the effects of solar and CO_2 changes (cf. Fig. 5). From Crowley and Baum, 1992.

modeling results suggest that transitions from a largely snow-free state to one with extensive snow cover may have been abrupt and may reflect an instability in the climate system (Baum and Crowley, 1991; T. J. Crowley and K.Y. J. Yip, unpublished results, 1993). The instability is due to albedo differences between snow and bare land; the discontinuity is translated into a nonlinear response to solar insolation changes (North, 1984; North and Crowley, 1985). An example of modeled Carboniferous snowline variations for different levels of solar forcing is shown in Figure 16. The infinitesimally small luminosity decrease associated with the abrupt transition is approximately 2,000 times smaller than that estimated for the 1991 eruption of Mt. Pinatubo (cf. Hansen et al., 1992).

OCEAN CHANGES

Research is just beginning on modeling the circulation of the Pangean ocean—Panthalassa. Kutzbach et al. (1990) forced an ocean model with atmospheric wind fields generated from their Pangean run (Kutzbach and Gallimore, 1989) to simulate a large-scale surface circulation characterized by strong western boundary currents along the east coasts of Pangea (Fig. 17). These currents may have helped maintain warmth in higher latitudes along the coast of eastern Pangea. A warm paleo-Tethys region should also provide some warmth for continental interiors, in much the same way that the present-day Gulf of Mexico influences moisture and heat transport into the southeastern United States (cf. Oglesby et al., 1989).

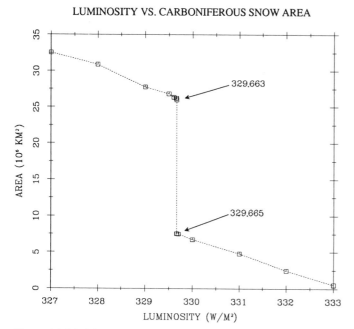

LUMINOSITY VS. CARBONIFEROUS SNOW AREA

329,663

329,665

Figure 16. Modeled summer snow cover on Gondwana (Westphalian) for various levels of solar luminosity forcing. The abrupt transition due to the infinitesimally small changes in solar forcing reflects an instability in the climate model. This response suggests that glacial onset may have been as abrupt in the Carboniferous as it was in the Pleistocene. From Baum and Crowley, 1991.

WINTER COOLING ON SUPERCONTINENTS—A MAJOR MODEL-DATA DISAGREEMENT

Despite some promising progress in modeling Pangean climates, there is a major disagreement between model predictions of significant winter cooling and the observations. Most EBM and GCM studies indicate significant cooling in continental interiors (Crowley et al., 1989; Kutzbach and Gallimore, 1989; Chandler et al., 1992; Moore et al., 1992a). This response is so widespread in climate models because it reflects a fundamental feature of the models—extensive cooling is a direct response to lack of winter insolation and the low heat capacity of land. Given those conditions, cooling results.

Extensive cooling in continental interiors seems to be directly at odds with geologic inferences of equable climates in the Jurassic (Hallam, 1985). Other data from the Late Permian also contradict model predictions (Taylor et al., 1992; Yemane, 1993). These latter conclusions were based on distribution of clay minerals, vertebrates (dicynodonts), and plant remains (lack of evidence for severe freeze damage in macrofossils).

Given that extreme winter cooling seems to be a widespread feature of simulations, it is imperative that the discrepancy with observations be analyzed and understood. As long as it remains, more localized comparisons of models and observations will have limited confidence, for there are many reasons to believe that regional model predictions of, for example, moisture fields can vary greatly between different models. Kellogg and Zhao (1988) have dramatically illustrated these more regional differences by comparing moisture fields for different GCM simulations of a greenhouse warming.

The two main approaches to reconciling model-data discrepancies for large seasonal cycle variations are exploration of any possible way that models can be modified and continued examination of data for alternate, but realistic, interpretations. The first approach should probably focus on mechanisms for increasing heat import from the ocean to continental interiors. Changing cloud cover is also a possibility, but clouds are difficult to simulate and first require a moisture source. Clouds may also influence the diurnal range more than mean monthly temperatures. For these reasons I will focus on increased heat import.

Modeling considerations

Increased ocean heat transport represents one viable mechanism for modifying continental temperatures, but there are limitations in the degree to which oceanic heat transport affects continental interiors. For example, the Gulf Stream, the archetypal example of influence of ocean currents on climate, greatly modifies the climate of northwest Europe, but the effect of this heat source tends to dissipate over a length scale of ~1,500 km. This scale has been found in a number of climate model studies (North, 1984; Manabe and Broccoli, 1985; North et al., 1992) and reflects the scale over which energy is radiated away to space (cf. Schneider et al., 1985). A graphic illustration of this limitation involves comparison of temperatures between London and Berlin or Warsaw. Although almost at the same latitude, winter temperatures of the latter two cities are decidedly colder than that of London. When one considers that these cities are only about one-tenth of the distance into the huge Eurasian landmass, the magnitude of the dilemma for Pangea enlarges in scope. A further complication is that physical considerations require than an oceanic heat source like the Gulf Stream be located east of Pangea, that is, downwind of any major influence on high-latitude climate.

Two other factors that could modify interior temperatures involve Milankovitch insolation variations and carbon dioxide changes. For example, there is some compensation between summer and winter insolation anomalies resulting from orbital insolation variations: Decreased summer insolation is associated with increased winter insolation. Carbon dioxide increases should also increase winter temperatures, for one of the most common responses in models for greenhouse warming involves reduction in winter snow cover (e.g., Schlesinger, 1989).

To demonstrate the potential effect of orbital insolation and CO_2 changes, Figure 18 illustrates results from an energy balance model simulation for the Early Jurassic for a cold summer orbit simulation (i.e., increased winter insolation) and a fourfold increase of CO_2. Winter temperatures are still cold in some regions (–20°C), but these temperatures are about

Currents (25 m) for Idealized Panthalassa Ocean

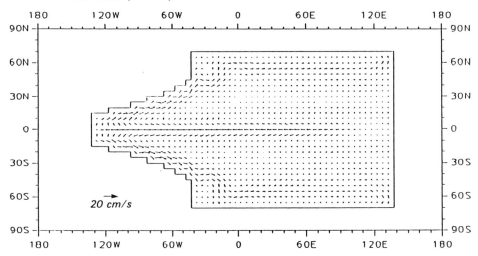

Figure 17. Simulated mean annual surface ocean currents (25 m) for idealized Panthalassa Ocean, utilizing atmospheric boundary conditions from simulation of Kutzbach and Gallimore (1989). From Kutzbach et al., 1990.

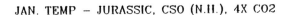

JAN. TEMP – JURASSIC, CSO (N.H.), 4X CO2

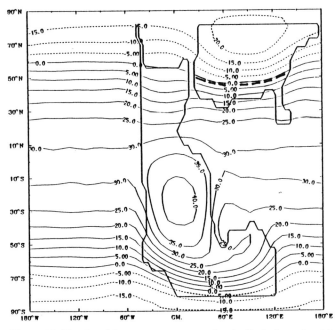

Figure 18. Simulated January temperatures for the Early Jurassic with maximum winter insolation (equals cold summer orbit, CSO), CO_2 levels four times greater than present (cf. Fig. 5), and solar luminosity reduced 2.25%. Dashed line on Eurasia denotes floral boundary from Vakhrameev (1964). From Crowley et al., 1992a.

10°C warmer than winter temperatures for a Late Permian simulation (Fig. 8). These changes occurred despite the fact that a lower solar luminosity (–2.25%) was used for the Early Jurassic simulation.

Despite the still-freezing temperatures in highest latitudes, the 0°C isotherm is about 47 to 48° paleolatitude in the Early Jurassic simulation. The freezing line in Eurasia agrees approximately with a vegetation boundary previously identified by Vakhrameev (1964). The freezing line is also about 12° of latitude farther north than the Late Permian simulation, which used present orbital configuration, present CO_2 levels, and no snow feedback in the EBM (Fig. 8). A similar simulation for the Late Jurassic results in an even greater poleward shift of the freezing line (to almost 60°) at some longitudes (Fig. 19).

One problem with arbitrarily invoking higher and higher CO_2 levels as an explanation for mild winters involves the fact that all climate models also simulate significant summer warming with CO_2 increases. On a supercontinent such a response augments generally high summer temperatures that reflect the land-sea distribution. For example, Moore et al. (1992a) simulate mean seasonal temperatures in excess of 50°C for parts of Gondwana in the Late Jurassic. Given that mean seasonal temperatures can easily be 10°C less than maximum daytime highs, the implications of such results for biota are obvious and should be manifested in the geologic record.

Despite the promising reduction in model-data disagreements due to orbital insolation and CO_2 changes, I am skeptical as to whether such considerations can completely account for model-data disagreements. One additional possibility involves a recent simulation with a different atmospheric GCM (Valdes and Sellwood, 1992). This simulation differed from previous

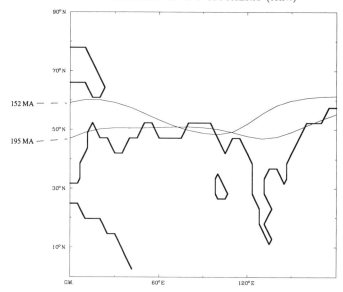

LOCATION OF 0°C ISOTHERM (JAN.)

TABLE 1. EURASIAN AND GONDWANA AREAS*

Area	10^6 km^2
Eurasia (present)	46.1
Eurasia (present, >45°N)	21.5
Gondwana (255 Ma)	71.1
Gondwana (255 Ma, >45°S)	30.0
Gondwana (306 Ma)	71.3
Gondwana (306 Ma, >45°S)	41.1

*Comparison of areas for different Pangean reconstructions of Gondwana with that of present Eurasia, estimated using the same method as for the geologic reconstructions. Paleo-reconstructions are from Scotese and Golonka (1992).

Figure 19. Position of modeled 0°C winter isotherm for the Early and Late Jurassic of part of Eurasia, plotted on Late Jurassic geography. Both simulations used the reconstruction of Scotese (1990) and the energy balance model of Hyde et al. (1990). Calculations used the best estimate of CO_2 and luminosity for these time periods—$4\times CO_2$ and -2.25% luminosity for the Early Jurassic and $5\times CO_2$ and -1.75% luminosity for the Late Jurassic. These boundary conditions are approximately consistent with the CO_2 and luminosity estimates of Figures 5 and 6. Both simulations used orbital configuration favorable for warm winters.

GCMs in being run at $2° \times 2°$ resolution (the Kutzbach and Gallimore [1989] and Chandler et al. [1992] runs were ~$10° \times 10°$, and the Moore et al. [1992a, b] run was ~$5° \times 7°$). The increased horizontal resolution resulted in better model simulation of mid-latitude eddies. These features are important for transporting heat. The net result was that minimum winter temperatures were only about $-15°C$ and restricted primarily to the eastern side of the Jurassic supercontinent (i.e., in the region farthest removed from the effect of westerly wind input).

Before the Valdes and Sellwood (1992) study can be accepted as the reason for model-data discrepancies, two features of their simulation have to be addressed. First, the model specified sea-surface temperatures (SSTs), rather than calculating them as was done in other Pangean simulations. SSTs greatly influence the eventual model product, and it is therefore imperative to determine sensitivity of model results to SST specifications. Another concern is whether the model correctly simulates the present level of winter cooling for the Eurasian landmass when run in a manner similar to the paleoruns. This problem needs to be addressed because the area of Eurasia is less than that of Gondwana (Table 1). Even in the seasonal mean, Eurasia has winter temperatures less than $-15°C$ (Fig. 20). Synoptic-scale cooling events cause temperature reductions significantly below these mean values, especially at night. Given these temperatures it is therefore necessary to inquire whether the Valdes and Sellwood (1992)

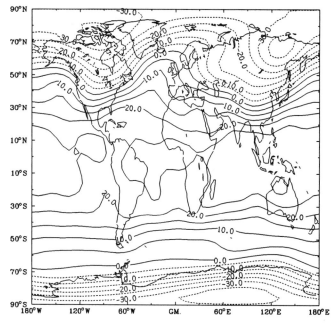

OBSERVED TEMPERATURES (DJF)

Figure 20. Observed December-January-February temperatures (in degrees Celsius after Crutcher and Meserve, 1970). These are climatological means for the meteorological winter and are daytime-nighttime averages. Note the magnitude of cooling on North America and Eurasia and that the cooling in Eurasia is shifted toward the easternmost edge of the continent (see text discussion).

model accurately simulates them. If so, then some explanation is required for why it does not simulate temperatures that low on Pangea. However, if the Valdes and Sellwood (1992) results can be clarified and confirmed, then increased eddy transport may be a significant factor in reconciling models and observations for Pangean climates.

Data considerations

Another factor to consider involves possibilities for alternate interpretations of data. This concept may seem anathema to some, but in fact there are many examples in geology where more than one interpretation of data is possible and also where new measurements have required reassessment of conclusions. Originally, Crowley et al. (1989) suggested that dicynodont populations in South Africa may reflect seasonal migration into the region, thereby alleviating disagreements with winter simulations. Although the functional morphology of this group does not seem to permit that type of long-range migration (Ziegler, 1993), the example nevertheless applies. But other questions arise. For example, the potential biasing effect of sampling at Milankovitch cycles has to be addressed (see previous discussion). It may also be prudent to reexamine whether paleopoles for southern Gondwana in the late Paleozoic are in lower latitudes than usually specified. This suggestion may not be as farfetched as it seems, for Van Fossen and Kent (1992) have recently questioned the standard Jurassic polar wander path for North America. A comparison of mid-Carboniferous reconstructions of Scotese (1986) and Scotese and Golonka (1992) indicates that the South Pole is much more toward the interior of the continent in the earlier reconstruction. If future reconstructions place other high latitude sites in coastal regions, I would expect significantly milder winter temperatures to be simulated *for those sites*. However, cooling may still be large in the interiors.

Another subject that requires more investigation involves the climate effect of extensive lakes in southern Gondwana (Yemane, 1993). Such deposits have been found for the Late Permian (Yemane, 1993). This evidence has been used to criticize modelers for not incorporating realistic geologic boundary conditions into their simulations. This criticism is not quite fair, since modelers used boundary conditions supplied by geologists. Since the lake "discoveries" postdate the time of actual publication of the modeling studies, a posteriori criticism seems inappropriate. Nevertheless, inclusion of extensive lakes should certainly make a difference in model results. But the magnitude of the difference is still uncertain. Yemane (1993) suggested that there may have been several million square kilometers of lakes in the Late Permian. This number is impressive, but it is still only about one-tenth the total area of Gondwana (Table 1). There still might be extensive cooling in interpaludal regions.

A further question arising from Gondwanan lake studies involves the duration over which they were present; that is, why were they there at all? Lakes are transient features of the landscape. They mainly occur either in geologically young terrain or in glaciated regions. As Gondwana was a unit for 300 million years prior to the Late Permian, the first explanation seems implausible. The lakes could reflect postglacial infilling of hummocky terrain following Permo-Carboniferous glaciation. If so, inference of extensive lake cover for all Pangean time may not be justifiable. Large seasonal cycles should still occur during non-lake intervals.

This discussion prompts me to propose an explanation that may reconcile models and observations. Including lakes, altered orbital insolation forcing, higher CO_2 levels, and increased horizontal resolution should significantly increase winter temperatures, especially in regions adjacent to lakes. Winter cooling in intervening regions should still be quite large, however. The latter result may not be at variance with biologic data, for organisms might reasonably cluster around lakes as refugia. Preservation of these and other indicators of mild climate might reflect preferential biasing of sites of active sedimentation.

Although plausible, the above explanation is difficult to test because it suggests that many of the high-latitude sampling sites are not yielding a fully representative picture of high-latitude climates; that is, they are biased. I can think of one test that is still possible, however. Both observations and general circulation model results indicate maximum winter cooling occurs on the easternmost edge of a landmass (this feature does not occur in EBMs [Fig. 8] because there is no wind field to displace patterns longitudinally). Siberia and the Sea of Okhotsk are two classic examples from the present climate (Fig. 20). Thus the best place to look for extreme cooling in the geologic record might be along the easternmost margins of supercontinents, poleward of regions affected by paleo–warm currents (i.e., poleward of ~45° latitude). Nearshore marine deposits adjacent to such regions may also record winter cooling. It would be helpful if investigators developed additional tests of model predictions for Pangean seasonality.

EFFECT OF CLIMATE CHANGE ON BIOTA

Although the Cretaceous-Tertiary asteroid impact hypothesis has received a great deal of attention during the last decade, evidence is more debatable as to importance of impacts for extinctions at other boundaries. An abrupt extinction is known at the Triassic-Jurassic boundary (Olsen et al., 1987) but the Manicouagan (Canada) impact structure with which it was tentatively linked has now been dated as occurring 12 million years prior to the boundary (Hodych and Dunning, 1992), near the Carnian-Norian boundary. Because the terrestrial tetrapod record indicates that the late Carnian event was more important than the end-Triassic event (Benton, 1991; Weems, 1992), an extraterrestrial influence is still plausible. For the Triassic-Jurassic boundary, shocked quartz from Italian deposits supports an interpretation of three closely spaced impacts at the end of the Triassic (Bice et al., 1992), but $\delta^{18}O$ evidence from nearby Austria indicates no significant cooling associated with the Triassic extinctions (Hallam and Goodfellow, 1990).

Given that there were several major changes in biota during the 150-million-year life span of Pangea, it is interesting to inquire as to whether any of the discussed model results might provide insight into these changes. Because changes in CO_2 seem to be important for ending the Permo-Carboniferous glaciations (Fig. 15), and an ice-free supercontinent is subject to considerable drying, Crowley et al. (1989) suggested that the onset of warm and dry conditions may have contributed to the major vertebrate turnover in the Early Permian (265 Ma) that was associated with the replacement of an amphibian-dominated fauna by more drought-tolerant reptiles—the largest extinction event in the vertebrate fossil record (Olson, 1982; Benton, 1987).

In addition to the arid conditions of the Triassic and Jurassic, temperature variations may also have influenced terrestrial biota. If my conjecture is correct that Gondwanan lakes are primarily postglacial transient features, large seasonal cycles should still occur for the Triassic and Jurassic. However, significant winter cooling is not necessarily in conflict with a vertebrate population dominated by reptilians. For example, Bakker (1980) has suggested that dinosaurs may have been warm-blooded. Such an adaptation would have been ideal for the large seasonal cycles simulated by climate models (Crowley and North, 1991, p. 234–236). In addition, higher metabolic rates would enable faster seasonal migrations to lower latitudes.

On a final note I suggest that high seasonality, which may have dominated the entire landmass during the Triassic and Jurassic, may allow for an alternate interpretation of environments during that time. Hallam (1985) cited the near-cosmopolitan distribution of biotas as evidence for an equable climate. But ecological and paleontological studies also indicate that biota with cosmopolitan distributions are often adapted to a broad range of environmental conditions. Thus, the Jurassic distribution of biota may represent the opposite of what is normally inferred. Viewed from this vantage point, some of the paleontologic data may be more reconcilable with model results discussed above.

SUMMARY AND DISCUSSION

Significant progress has been made in delineating some of the important processes responsible for climates of Pangea. Changes in climate over that time interval may possibly have influenced biotic trends. Despite this progress, and other agreements between models and data (Chandler et al., 1992; Moore et al., 1992a, b), a need exists for more precise validation of model results with respect to several first-order features of the climate system.

1. Can models and data be reconciled for interior temperatures in Pangea? Additional simulations need to examine the effect of CO_2, altered Milankovitch forcing, and higher resolution in models. More accurate stipulations of paleogeographic boundary conditions (lakes, seaways) are also required. It may also be prudent to reexamine paleogeographic reconstructions for southern Gondwana. Finally, it would be helpful if geologists specified the duration of time over which their deposits

formed, so that modelers could assess whether some model-data discrepancies might reflect Milankovitch-scale processes.

2. Can Triassic-Jurassic atmospheric CO_2 levels four to five times present levels be validated (Fig. 5)? Initial proxy attempts at validating geochemical models have been encouraging (Cerling, 1991), but much more work is needed.

3. Was solar luminosity 3% lower in the Carboniferous? This reduction is needed for model simulations of high-latitude Gondwanan glaciation, but such a decrease also results in a 4°C cooling in the tropics. Such changes should be detectable with $\delta^{18}O$ records.

Many other regional features of climate model predictions are also worth testing, but if the above first-order controls cannot be properly evaluated, then model-data comparisons for Pangean climates will remain at a somewhat unsatisfactory level.

ACKNOWLEDGMENTS

I thank George D. Klein for the invitation to write this chapter, and S. Baum for assistance. I have benefited from comments by G. D. Klein and two anonymous reviewers. This work was supported by NSF grant ATM90-02808.

REFERENCES CITED

Bakker, R. T., 1980, Dinosaur heresy—dinosaur renaissance: Why we need endothermic archosaurs for a comprehensive theory of bioenergetic evolution, *in* Thomas, R.D.K., and Olson, E. C., eds., A cold look at the warm-blooded dinosaurs: American Association for the Advancement of Science Symposium, v. 28, p. 351–462.

Baum, S. K., and Crowley, T. J., 1991, Seasonal snowline instability in a climate model with realistic geography: Application to Carboniferous (~300 Ma) glaciation: Geophysical Research Letters, v. 18, p. 1719–1722.

Benton, M. J., 1987, Mass extinctions among families of nonmarine tetrapods: The data: Mémoires de la Société Géologique de France, Mémoire 150, p. 21–32.

Benton, M. J., 1991, What really happened in the Late Triassic?: Historical Biology, v. 5, p. 263–278.

Berner, R. A., 1987, Models for carbon and sulfur cycles and atmospheric oxygen: Application to Paleozoic geologic history: American Journal of Science, v. 287, p. 177–196.

Berner, R. A., 1991, A model for atmospheric CO_2 over Phanerozoic time: American Journal of Science, v. 291, p. 339–376.

Bice, D. M., Newton, C. R., McCauley, S., Reiners, P. W., and McRoberts, C. A., 1992, Shocked quartz at the Triassic-Jurassic boundary in Italy: Science, v. 255, p. 443–446.

Cerling, T. E., 1991, Carbon dioxide in the atmosphere: Evidence from Cenozoic and Mesozoic paleosols: American Journal of Science, v. 291, p. 377–400.

Chandler, M., Rind, D., and Ruedy, R., 1992, Pangaean climate during the Early Jurassic: GCM simulations and the sedimentary record of paleoclimate: Geological Society of America Bulletin, v. 104, p. 543–559.

Crowley, T. J., and Baum, S. K., 1991, Estimating Carboniferous sea level fluctuations from Gondwanan ice extent: Geology, v. 19, p. 975–977.

Crowley, T. J., and Baum, S. K., 1992, Modeling late Paleozoic glaciation: Geology, v. 20, p. 507–510.

Crowley, T. J., and Baum, S. K., 1993, General circulation model study of late Carboniferous interglacial climates: Palaeoclimates: Data and Modeling (in press).

Crowley, T. J., and North, G. R., 1991, Paleoclimatology: New York, Oxford

University Press, 339 p.

Crowley, T. J., Hyde, W. T., and Short, D. A., 1989, Seasonal cycle variations on the supercontinent of Pangaea: Geology, v. 17, p. 457–460.

Crowley, T. J., Baum, S. K., and Hyde, W. T., 1991, Climate model comparison of Gondwanan and Laurentide glaciations: Journal of Geophysical Research, v. 96, p. 9217–9226.

Crowley, T. J., Baum, S. K., and Hyde, W. T., 1992a, Milankovitch fluctuations on supercontinents: Geophysical Research Letters, v. 19, p. 793–796.

Crowley, T. J., Kim, K.-Y., Mengel, J. G., and Short, D. A., 1992b, Modeling 100,000 year climate fluctuations in pre-Pleistocene time series: Science, v. 255, p. 705–707.

Crowley, T. J., Baum, S. K., and Kim, K.-Y., 1993, GCM sensitivity experiments with pole-centered supercontinents: Journal of Geophysical Research, v. 98, p. 8793–8800.

Crutcher, H. L., and Meserve, J. M., 1970, Selected level heights, temperatures, and dew points for the northern hemisphere: Rep NAV AIR 50-1C-52 (revised), Chief of Naval Operations, Washington, D.C.

Endal, A. S., and Sofia, S., 1981, Rotation in solar-type stars: I: Evolutionary models for the spin-down of the sun: Astrophysical Journal, v. 243, p. 625–6540.

Frakes, L. A., and Francis, J. E., 1988, A guide to Phanerozoic cold polar climates from high-latitude ice-rafting in the Cretaceous: Nature, v. 333, p. 547–549.

Gordon, W. A., 1975, Distribution by latitude of Phanerozoic evaporite deposits: Journal of Geology, v. 83, p. 671–684.

Hallam, A., 1982, The Jurassic climate, in Berger, W. H., and Crowell, J. C., eds., Climate in earth history: Washington, D.C., National Academy Press, p. 159–163.

Hallam, A., 1985, A review of Mesozoic climates: Journal of the Geological Society (London), v. 142, p. 433–445.

Hallam, A., and Goodfellow, W. D., 1990, Facies and geochemical evidence bearing on the end-Triassic disappearance of the Alpine reef ecosystem: Historical Biology, v. 4, p. 131–138.

Hallam, A., Grose, J. A., and Ruffell, A. H., 1991, Palaeoclimatic significance of changes in clay mineralogy across the Jurassic-Cretaceous boundary in England and France: Palaeogeography, Palaeoclimatology, Palaeoecology, v. 81, p. 173–187.

Hansen, J., Lacis, A., Ruedy, R., and Sato, M., 1992, Potential climate impact of Mount Pinatubo eruption: Geophysical Research Letters, v. 19, p. 215–218.

Hay, W. W., Behensky, J. F., Jr., Barron, E. J., and Sloan, J. L. II, 1982, Late Triassic-Liassic paleoclimatology of the proto–central North Atlantic rift system: Palaeogeography, Palaeoclimatology, Palaeoecology, v. 40, p. 13–30.

Hay, W. W., Barron, E. J., and Thompson, S. L., 1990, Results of global atmospheric circulation experiments on an Earth with a meridional pole-to-pole continent: Journal of the Geological Society (London), v. 147, p. 385–392.

Heckel, P. H., 1986, Sea-level curve for Pennsylvanian eustatic marine transgressive-regressive depositional cycles along midcontinent outcrop belt, North America: Geology, v. 14, p. 330–334.

Hodych, J. P., and Dunning, G. R., 1992, Did the Manicouagan impact trigger end-of-Triassic mass extinction?: Geology, v. 20, p. 51–54.

Hyde, W. T., Kim, K.-Y., Crowley, T. J., and North, G. R., 1990, On the relation between polar continentality and climate: Studies with a nonlinear energy balance model: Journal of Geophysical Research, v. 95, p. 18653–18668.

Imbrie, J., and eight others, 1984, The orbital theory of Pleistocene climate: Support from a revised chronology of the marine $\delta^{18}O$ record, in Berger, A., Imbrie, J., Hays, J., Kukla, G., and Saltzman, B., eds., Milankovitch and climate: Dordrecht, Riedel, p. 269–305.

Jenkyns, H. C., 1988, The early Toarcian (Jurassic) anoxic event: Stratigraphic, sedimentary, and geochemical evidence: American Journal of Science, v. 288, p. 101–151.

Kellogg, W. W., and Zhao, Z-C., 1988, Sensitivity of soil moisture to doubling of carbon dioxide in climate model experiments. Part I: North America: Journal of Climate, v. 1, p. 348–378.

Kiehl, J. T., and Dickinson, R. E., 1987, A study of the radiative effects of enhanced atmospheric CO_2 and CH_4 on early earth surface temperatures: Journal of Geophysical Research, v. 92, p. 2991–2998.

Kim, K.-Y., and North, G. R., 1991, Surface temperature fluctuations in a stochastic climate model: Journal of Geophysical Research, v. 96, p. 18573–18580.

Kominz, M. A., and Bond, G. C., 1990, A new method of testing periodicity in cyclic sediments: Application to the Newark supergroup: Earth and Planetary Science Letters, v. 98, p. 233–244.

Kutzbach, J. E., and Gallimore, R. G., 1989, Pangean climates: Megamonsoons of the megacontinent: Journal of Geophysical Research, v. 94, p. 3341–3357.

Kutzbach, J. E., Guetter, P. J., and Washington, W. M., 1990, Simulated circulation of an idealized ocean for Pangaean time: Paleoceanography, v. 5, p. 299–317.

Manabe, S., and Broccoli, A. J., 1985, The influence of continental ice sheets on the climate of an ice age: Journal of Geophysical Research, v. 90, p. 2167–2190.

Moore, G. T., Haysahida, D. N., Ross, C. A., and Jacobson, S. R., 1992a, Paleoclimate of the Kimmeridgian/Tithonian (Late Jurassic) world. I: Results using a general circulation model: Palaeogeography, Palaeoclimatology, Palaeoecology, v. 93, p. 113–150.

Moore, G. T., Sloan, L. C., Hayashida, D. N., and Umrigar, N. P., 1992b, Paleoclimate of the Kimmeridgian/Tithonian (Late Jurassic) world. II: Sensitivity tests comparing three different paleotopographic settings: Palaeogeography, Palaeoclimatology, Palaeoecology, v. 95, p. 229–252.

North, G. R., 1984, The small ice cap instability in diffusive climate models: Journal of Atmospheric Science, v. 41, p. 3390–3395.

North, G. R., and Crowley, T. J., 1985, Application of a seasonal climate model to Cenozoic glaciation: Journal of the Geological Society, London, v. 142, p. 475–482.

North, G. R., Mengel, J. G., and Short, D. A., 1983, Simple energy balance model resolving the seasons and the continents: Application to the astronomical theory of the ice ages: Journal of Geophysical Research, v. 88, p. 6576–6586.

North, G. R., Yip, K.-J., Leung, L.-Y., and Chervin, R. M., 1992, Forced and free variations of the surface temperature field: Journal of Climate, v. 5, p. 227–239.

Oglesby, R. J., Maasch, K. A., and Saltzman, B., 1989, Glacial meltwater cooling of the Gulf of Mexico: GCM implications for Holocene and present-day climates: Climate Dynamics, v. 3, p. 115–133.

Olsen, P. E., 1986, A 40-million-year lake record of Early Mesozoic orbital climatic forcing: Science, v. 234, p. 842–848.

Olsen, P. E., Shubin, N. H., and Anders, M. H., 1987, New Early Jurassic tetrapod assemblages constrain Triassic-Jurassic tetrapod extinction event: Science, v. 237, p. 1025–1029.

Olson, E. C., 1982, Extinctions of Permian and Triassic nonmarine vertebrates: Geological Society of American Special Paper 190, p. 501–511.

Parrish, J. M., Parrish, J. T., and Ziegler, A. M., 1986, Permian-Triassic paleogeography and paleoclimatology and implications for therapsid distribution, in Hotton, N. II, MacLean, P. D., Roth, E. C., eds., The ecology and biology of mammal-like reptiles: Washington, D.C., Smithsonian Institution Press, p. 109–131.

Railsback, L. B., and Anderson, T. F., 1987, Control of Triassic seawater chemistry and temperature on the evolution of post-Paleozoic aragonite-secreting faunas: Geology, v. 15, p. 1002–1005.

Robinson, J. M., 1990, Lignin, land plants, and fungi: Biological evolution affecting Phanerozoic oxygen balance: Geology, v. 15, p. 607–610.

Robinson, P. L., 1973, Palaeoclimatology and continental drift, in Tarling, D. H., and Runcorn, S. K., eds., Implications of continental drift to earth sciences, Vol. 1): New York, Academic Press, p. 451–476.

Schlesinger, M. E., 1989, Model projections of the climatic changes induced by increased atmospheric CO_2, *in* Berger, A., Schneider, S. H., and Duplessy, J.-C., eds., Climate and geo-sciences: Dordrecht, Kluwer, p. 375–415.

Schneider, S. H., Thompson, S. L., and Barron, E. J., 1985, Mid-Cretaceous continental surface temperatures: Are high CO_2 concentrations needed to simulate above freezing winter conditions? *in* Sundquist, E. T., and Broecker, W. S., eds., The carbon cycle and atmospheric CO_2: Natural variations Archean to Present: Washington, D.C., AGU Geophysical Monograph, v. 32, p. 554–560.

Scotese, C. R., 1986, Phanerozoic reconstructions: A new look at the assembly of Asia: University of Texas Institute for Geophysics Technical Report, v. 66, 54 p.

Scotese, C. R., 1990, Atlas of Phanerozoic plate tectonic reconstructions International Lithosphere Program (IUGG-IUGS): Arlington, University of Texas–Arlington, Paleomap Project Technical Report No. 10-90-1, 54 p.

Scotese, C. R., and Golonka, J., 1992, Paleogeographic atlas: Arlington, University of Texas–Arlington, Paleomap Project.

Shubin, N. J., Crompton, A. W., Sues, H.-D., and Olsen, P. E., 1991, New fossil evidence on the sister-group of mammals and early Mesozoic faunal distributions: Science, v. 251, p. 1063–1065.

Stevens, C. H., 1977, Was development of brackish oceans a factor in Permian extinctions?: Geological Society of America Bulletin, v. 88, p. 133–138.

Taylor, E. L., Taylor, T. N., and Cúneo, R., 1992, The present is not the key to the past: A polar forest from the Permian of Antarctica: Science, v. 257, p. 1675–1677.

Tucker, M. E., and Benton, M. J., 1982, Triassic environments, climates and reptile evolution: Palaeogeography, Palaeoclimatology, Palaeoecology, v. 40, p. 361–379.

Vakhrameev, V. A., 1964, Jurassic and Early Cretaceous floras of Eurasia and the paleofloristic provinces of this period: Transactions of the Geological Institute of Moscow, v. 102, p. 1–263 (in Russian).

Valdes, P. J., and Sellwood, B. W., 1992, A palaeoclimate model for the Kimmeridgian: Palaeogeography, Palaeoclimatology, Palaeoecology, v. 95, p. 47–72.

Van Fossen, M. C., and Kent, D. V., 1992, Paleomagnetism of the Front Range (Colorado) Morrison Formation and an alternative model of Late Jurassic North American apparent polar wander: Geology, v. 20, p. 223–226.

Weems, R. E., 1992, The "terminal Triassic catastrophic extinction event" in perspective: A review of Carboniferous through Early Jurassic terrestrial vertebrate extinction patterns: Palaeogeography, Palaeoclimatology, Palaeoecology, v. 94, p. 1–29.

Yemane, K., 1993, Contribution of Late Permian palaeogeography in maintaining a temperate climate in Gondwana: Nature, v. 361, p. 51–54.

Ziegler, A. M., 1993, Models come in from the cold: Nature, v. 361, p. 16–17.

MANUSCRIPT ACCEPTED BY THE SOCIETY MAY 14, 1993

Geological Society of America
Special Paper 288
1994

Idealized Pangean climates: Sensitivity to orbital change

John E. Kutzbach
Center for Climatic Research, University of Wisconsin, Madison, Wisconsin 53706

ABSTRACT

A climate model is used to simulate, for an idealized Pangean continent, the changes of temperature, wind, and precipitation produced by changes in earth's orbital parameters. The calculation uses an orbit of moderate eccentricity (0.025). Enhanced summer and winter monsoon circulations and increased summer rainfall and runoff are simulated for the hemisphere where perihelion occurs in summer and aphelion in winter. The increases in rainfall and runoff are about 25% or more, relative to the average climate. These increases occur in the tropical and subtropical belt extending from the equator to about 40° latitude in some regions. These same regions would experience 25% or more reductions in rainfall and runoff in the opposite phase of the precession cycle. These model results suggest that rainfall and runoff would undergo cyclic changes of ± 25% or more with periods of 23,000 years over a substantial fraction of the Pangean tropics and subtropics.

INTRODUCTION

Earth's climate changes as earth's orbit changes. This cause-and-effect relationship was proposed more than a century ago by Croll and developed extensively by Milankovitch and others (Imbrie and Imbrie, 1979). Quasi-cyclic variations of climate at the periods of known orbital cycles around 23,000, 41,000 and 100,000 years are found in many different periods of earth history. Studies of ocean sediment cores covering the past several hundred thousand years have focused on the effects of orbital cycles on glacial-interglacial cycles (Hays and others, 1976; Imbrie and others, 1992) or on cycles of enhanced or diminished monsoons (Rossignol-Strick, 1983; Prell, 1984; Prell and others, 1993). Sediments from much earlier times in the Paleozoic and Mesozoic also display cyclic depositional patterns (Gilbert, 1895; Fischer and Schwarzacher, 1984; Arthur, 1984; Olsen, 1986; Anderson, 1986). These cyclic patterns may be caused by various combinations of episodic tectonic processes and orbital cycles affecting glacially induced eustatic sea-level changes (Klein and Willard, 1989).

Experiments with climate models have helped explain some of the basic physical mechanisms that link orbital changes and climatic changes. Changes in the season of peri-

helion, associated with the 23,000-year precession cycle, cause changes in the amplitude of the seasonal cycle of solar radiation that are large enough to modify monsoon circulations significantly (Kutzbach, 1981; Kutzbach and Otto-Bliesner, 1982; Kutzbach and Guetter, 1986; Kutzbach and Gallimore, 1989). When perihelion occurs in the summer hemisphere, the summers are warmer and the winters colder relative to the situation with perihelion in the winter hemisphere (Fig. 1a). Moreover, because the seasonal range of temperature over land greatly exceeds the range over ocean (Fig 1b), this type of orbital forcing produces changes in land-sea temperature contrasts that drive changes in monsoon circulations (Fig. 1c). Climate models incorporating these orbital changes have simulated monsoon circulations and precipitation patterns that agree reasonably well with observational evidence from the past 150,000 years (Kutzbach and Street-Perrott, 1985; Prell and Kutzbach, 1987). The role of orbital cycles in causing glacial/interglacial cycles and implied changes in sea level of about 100 m is also being simulated with climate models (Berger and others, 1990).

Climate models have been used to simulate possible effects of orbital parameter changes on climate during earlier geologic periods. For example, Barron and others (1985) and

Kutzbach, J. E., 1994, Idealized Pangean climates: Sensitivity to orbital change, *in* Klein, G. D., ed., Pangea: Paleoclimate, Tectonics, and Sedimentation During Accretion, Zenith, and Breakup of a Supercontinent: Boulder, Colorado, Geological Society of America Special Paper 288.

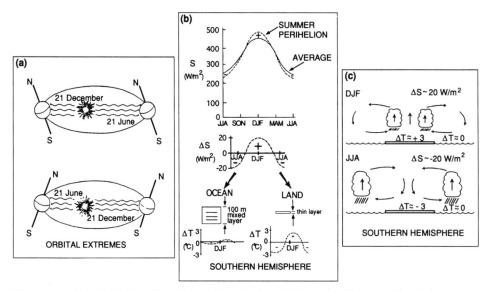

Figure 1. a, Top: Orbital configurations with perihelion in December (Southern Hemisphere summer); bottom: orbital configuration halfway through a precession cycle with perihelion in June (Northern Hemisphere summer). b, Top: Solid curve is the Southern Hemisphere average seasonal cycle of solar radiation (S) for an orbit with zero eccentricity; dashed curve is the same variable (S) for an orbit with eccentricity 0.025 and with perihelion in southern summer; middle: the change in solar radiation (ΔS) between the two curves above; bottom: schematic change in ocean and land temperature (ΔT) for the Southern Hemisphere caused by the change in solar radiation (ΔS). The response (ΔT) of the land temperature greatly exceeds that of the ocean temperature because of the smaller heat capacity of the earth's thin insulative surface layer compared with the deep layer of ocean water that is involved in seasonal heat exchange with the atmosphere. c, Schematic changes of land-ocean monsoon circulations caused by the different thermal response of land and ocean to orbital (precessional) forcing. Illustrations are for the Southern Hemisphere. With perihelion in southern summer (December-January-February [DJF]) the enhanced solar radiation warms the land by several degrees Celsius while the ocean temperature remains almost unchanged. This causes increased upward motion over land and increased inflow of moist air along the coasts and increased precipitation. The opposite kind of circulation change occurs in southern winter (JJA) when the land is cooler than average.

Glancy and others (1986) used climate models to investigate the part that changes in both the season of perihelion and the axial tilt (obliquity) play in Cretaceous climates. They found that the climate of the northern margin of the Tethys Ocean was quite sensitive to orbital changes, particularly in northern winter. Crowley and others (1987) used an energy budget climate model to estimate that summer temperatures in the Paleozoic might have changed by as much as ±10°C depending upon the values of the orbital parameters and the continent/ocean configurations. Oglesby and Park (1989) used a climate model for Cretaceous geography to demonstrate large changes in monsoonal circulations and hydrologic budgets in response to precessional cycles; they explored how these changes might result in the cyclical beddings found in Cretaceous marine sediments.

This chapter will focus on the sensitivity of the climate of

an idealized Pangean continent to orbital changes associated with the precession cycle. The experiment uses an orbit with moderate eccentricity (0.025), with perihelion occurring in southern summer, and with present-day axial tilt (23½°). The idealized form of the Pangean continent (Fig. 2) presents both advantages and disadvantages for studying the climatic response to orbital changes. The large size and hemispheric symmetry of the supercontinent ensures that strong monsoon circulations will occur in both hemispheres. These strong monsoons are then modified as earth's orbital parameters are changed. Moreover, the effects of the orbital change on monsoons are not complicated by details of geography, such as the shape of coastlines, the location and height of mountains, and the location and size of inland lakes and seas. Instead, very simple patterns of climatic response to orbital changes emerge. The idealized form of the supercontinent also avoids the issue

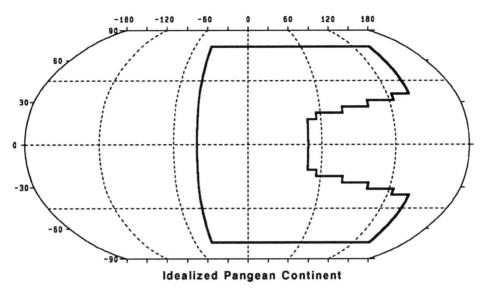

Figure 2. Idealized Pangean continent.

of specifying the precise geologic time period being simulated. The supercontinent existed from about 300 to 200 million years ago, and many of the climatic features simulated by the model should be generally applicable to this long period of time. A disadvantage of the idealized geography is that the results cannot be associated directly with any particular geologic time and region.

MODEL DESCRIPTION

The simulation experiments were made with the Community Climate Model (CCM) of the National Center for Atmospheric Research (NCAR); see Randel and Williamson (1990) for a description of the model. The model incorporates atmospheric dynamics based upon the equations of fluid motion; it includes radiative and convective processes, condensation, precipitation, and evaporation. Surface energy and hydrologic budget equations permit the calculation of surface temperature, soil moisture, snow melt, and runoff. The version of the CCM used here was modified by Covey and Thompson (1989) to include a 50-m-thick mixed-layer ocean for calculating ocean temperature and sea-ice thickness and location. The ocean has no explicit currents but include, as a prescribed flux, a poleward transport of heat by the modern-day oceans. The magnitude of this heat flux was set at about 2×10^{15}W at 30° latitude. The model has twelve vertical levels in the atmosphere and one ocean level and uses a spectral waveform representation, to wavenumber 15, of the horizontal fields of wind, temperature, pressure, and moisture. When needed for certain calculations, the spectral representation is converted to

a grid of 4.4° latitude by 7.5° longitude. The model simulates the entire seasonal cycle, January through December, with a time step of 30 minutes. The model was run for 20 years with the last five years being used for this analysis. The 20 years of calculation allowed the mixed-layer ocean and sea-ice distributions to reach quasi-equilibrium values in response to the imposed seasonal cycle of solar radiation.

The control case simulations of the CCM have known shortcomings in comparison to observations (Randel and Williamson, 1990), and these deficiencies may also have an effect on the model's sensitivity to orbital change. For example, the model's troposphere is colder, by several degrees Celsius, than the observed atmosphere and has weaker mid-latitude westerlies and weaker subtropical easterlies than the observed atmosphere. The simulated transient disturbances, such as mid-latitude storms, are weaker than observed. On the other hand, the general patterns of large-scale circulation, temperature, and precipitation are similar to observations (Pitcher and others, 1983). Because of the coarse spatial resolution of the model, the simulated boundaries separating warm/cold and wet/dry regions are not as sharply defined as the observed boundaries.

This model has several important differences compared to the model used in previous Pangean climate experiments (Kutzbach and Gallimore, 1989): (1) the horizontal and vertical resolution of the model is significantly increased, and (2) the parameterizations for radiation, clouds, snow cover, and vertical diffusion—processes that are important for the surface energy balance—are greatly improved. An important limitation that remains in the model is the greatly oversimplified treatment of the ocean.

EXPERIMENTAL DESIGN

A number of internal and external boundary conditions are prescribed, including land/ocean distribution, orography, land surface albedo, ocean heat flux, solar irradiance, atmospheric CO_2 concentration, and orbital parameters—eccentricity, tilt, date of perihelion.

The land/ocean distribution is generally the same as in Kutzbach and Gallimore (1989). The idealized Pangean continent is exactly symmetric about the equator, extends from 72N to 72S, and spans 180° of longitude at high latitudes and 90° of longitude at the equator (Fig. 2). The north and south halves of Pangea correspond roughly to Laurasia and Gondwana. The west coast is oriented exactly north-south. The Tethys Sea forms the major wedge-shaped feature on the east. Overall, the idealized Pangea covers 36% of the globe compared to the modern land, which covers 31% of the globe.

The surface of the continent is elevated about 500 m relative to the ocean. A region of sloping terrain rises from sea level at the coast to 500 m in the interior over a distance of about 1,000 km. This idealized specification of orography provides a land/ocean height differential of about the same magnitude as in the modern climate while omitting the details of mountains and plateaus. The land surface albedo is prescribed at values ranging from about 0.13 to about 0.24. The high albedos (0.18 to 0.24) are prescribed for those areas of the tropics and subtropics where a previous experiment simulated arid or semiarid conditions with annual soil moisture levels between about 1 and 6 cm (Kutzbach and Gallimore, 1989, Fig. 6). The low albedos (0.13 to 0.16) are prescribed for those areas where a previous experiment indicated soil moisture levels between about 8 and 15 cm. The maximum soil moisture allowed in the model was 15 cm.

The poleward heat transport by ocean currents is prescribed to be consistent with the results of a dynamical ocean simulation for a Pangean-type ocean basin (Kutzbach and others, 1990, Fig. 9); this transport is also similar to that prescribed for the present-day ocean.

Atmospheric carbon dioxide concentration is set at five times modern value: 1,650 ppm as compared to 330 ppm (the modern control for CCM1). This level of carbon dioxide is consistent with the enhanced greenhouse conditions that were simulated in a previous experiment for an idealized Pangea (Kutzbach and Gallimore, 1989). There is great uncertainty about the concentration of carbon dioxide during the time of existence of Pangea, the period from approximately 300 to 200 million years ago. Berner (1990) has estimated carbon dioxide concentrations as high as five times the present value and as low as the present value at various times during this 100-million-year interval. The range of uncertainty, based only on Berner's model sensitivity studies, indicates that the concentration could have been even higher (six to seven times present) or lower (slightly less than present). If the value of

five times present, used in this experiment, is too high, then the simulation will be biased toward warm conditions, especially in the polar regions. Solar irradiance is reduced 1% from present values, from 1,370 W/m^2 to 1,356W/m^2, consistent with a previous experiment (Kutzbach and Gallimore, 1989).

The key feature of this experiment, compared to the earlier experiments for an idealized Pangean continent, is that the earth's orbit about the sun is eccentric rather than circular. The eccentricity of the orbit is set at 0.025, about halfway between the extremes of about 0 and 0.06 as calculated for the past 10 million years (Berger and Loutre, 1991). Perihelion is set at the modern-day value of 3 January. This choice of the season of perihelion causes the seasonality of climate to be larger on the southern continent than on the northern continent. The axial tilt is 23½°, the same as the modern tilt.

THE CONTROL CLIMATE

Before describing the climatic extremes of increased and decreased seasonality produced by the orbital change, we describe the "control" climate. This control climate was obtained by averaging the climate of the southern continent (increased seasonality) with that of the northern continent (decreased seasonality) and then displaying this average climate for both hemispheres. This averaging technique ensures that the annual control climate is symmetric about the equator and that the summer (winter, etc.) climate of the southern continent is identical to the summer (winter, etc.) climate of the northern continent. This control climate is not necessarily identical to a standard control climate that would be calculated for an orbit with eccentricity equal to zero. The approximate control climate, used here, would be identical to the more standard control climate (ignoring the effects of model variability) only if the model's response to the orbital change is linear, and such a linear response is unlikely in a model incorporating the many dynamical and hydrological feedbacks of the CCM. Nevertheless, the use of this approximate control climate provides a convenient point of reference and avoids the computational expense of an additional numerical experiment with the orbital eccentricity set to zero.

Temperature

The temperature distributions for December-January-February (DJF) (southern summer, northern winter), June-July-August (JJA) (northern summer, southern winter), and the annual average are shown in Figure 3. Summer tempera-

---

Figure 3. Surface temperature (°C) for December-January-February (DJF), June-July-August (JJA), and the full year (Annual) for the control climate. The control climate was calculated by averaging the seasonal simulations for the high-seasonality (Southern) and low-seasonality (Northern) Hemispheres.

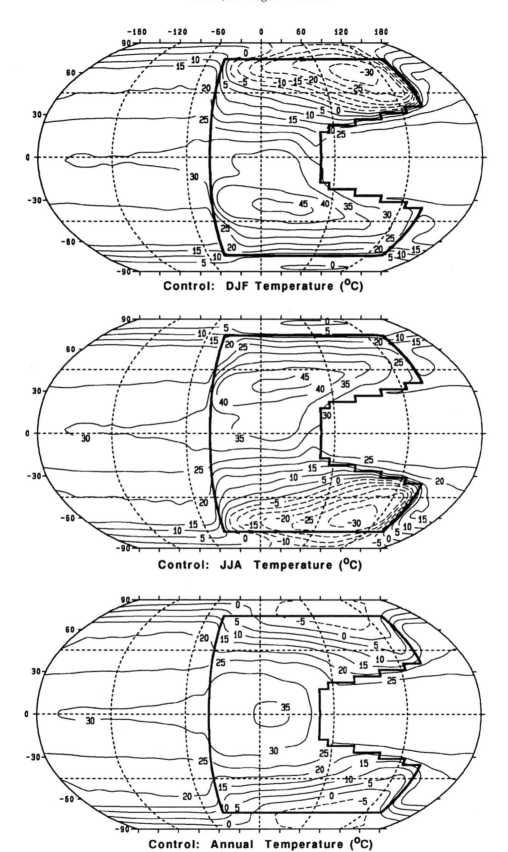

Control: DJF Temperature (°C)

Control: JJA Temperature (°C)

Control: Annual Temperature (°C)

tures exceed 45°C, and winter temperatures drop below –30°C in the continental interiors. The annual average temperature exceeds 35°C at the equator and is slightly below 0°C at the poleward and eastward margins of the continent. These results are similar to those reported in Kutzbach and Gallimore (1989, Fig. 8), except that the high-latitude winter temperatures are not as low as in the previous sensitivity experiments, only one of which prescribed radiative fluxes appropriate for enhanced greenhouse gases.

Sea-level pressure and surface winds

The strong seasonal monsoon circulations (Fig. 4) show summer monsoon low-pressure centers (990 mb) and winter monsoon high-pressure centers (1,035 mb) with strong cross-equatorial flow from the winter to the summer hemisphere.

Precipitation, soil moisture, and snow cover

Summer monsoon precipitation exceeds 8 mm/day along the Tethys coast (Fig. 5). The heaviest precipitation is concentrated along the coastline, where the sloping terrain causes upslope flow. In the winter hemisphere, precipitation associated with mid-latitude storms is 4 to 6 mm/day along the west coast and 2 to 4 mm/day along parts of the east coast. The annual average precipitation (Fig. 5) exceeds 4 mm/day (1,500 mm/yr) along the Tethys coasts and the west coasts in mid latitudes. In west equatorial Pangea precipitation exceeds 2 mm/day year-round. The precipitation in large areas of the interior is less than 1 to 2 mm/day (350 to 700 mm/year) (Fig. 5). The distribution of precipitation is reflected in the seasonal and annual average distributions of soil moisture (Fig. 6). Soil moisture exceeds 10 cm in regions of summer monsoon rains and in regions of winter storms. For comparison, the maximum soil moisture capacity allowed in the model is 15 cm. The annual average soil moisture is low in the arid interior and relatively high in the moist coastal regions. Extensive snow cover exists in winter (Fig. 7), but the snow melts completely in spring and summer and no net buildup of snow occurs from year to year.

Global and regional averages

The simulated annual-average temperatures of the land, ocean, and globe (land plus ocean) for the idealized continent and ocean are considerably elevated compared with the modern climate, owing to the enhanced level of atmospheric carbon dioxide concentration, five times present, and to the lowered surface albedo caused by the absence of permanent snow cover and sea ice (Table 1). The global average temperature is 21.6°C compared to 14.8°C for the simulation with mod-

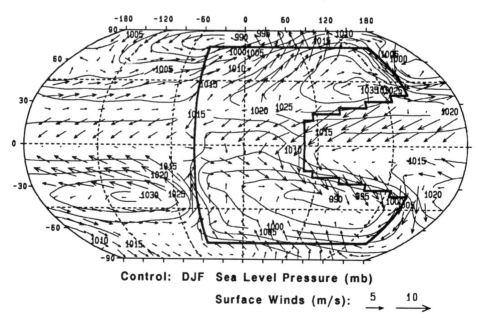

Control: DJF Sea Level Pressure (mb)

Surface Winds (m/s): 5 → 10 →

Figure 4. Sea-level pressure (millibars) and surface layer winds (m/s) for December-January-February (DJF) for the control climate. Speed (m/s) is calibrated for the wind arrows at lower right.

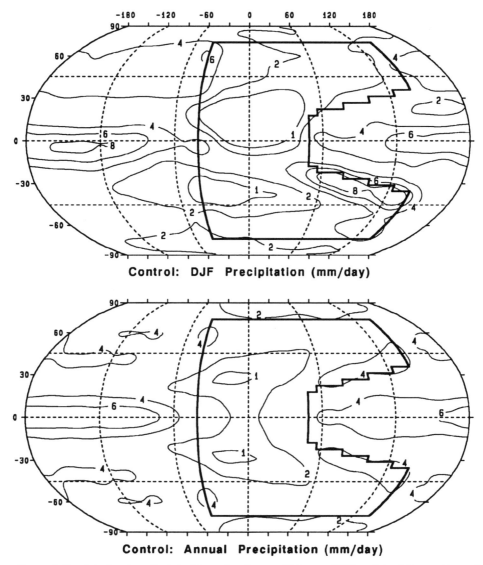

Figure 5. Precipitation (mm/day) for December-January-February (DJF) and the full year (Annual) for the control climate. Precipitation values are smoothed with a nine-point binomial filter.

ern geography and modern CO_2 levels, an increase of 6.8°C. This amount of greenhouse-related warming is similar to that reported by Manabe and Bryan (1985) in experiments with a different pattern of highly idealized geography. They found a temperature increase of 5.4°C, from 14.4°C (modern CO_2 level) to 19.8°C (4 × present CO_2 level). The average land temperature for the idealized Pangean continent is 19.1°C, compared to 6.3°C for the simulation with modern geography.

Global precipitation rates for the calculated Pangean control simulation and the modern simulation are equal (Table 1). This result, similar to that in a previous experiment with enhanced greenhouse forcing (Kutzbach and Gallimore, 1989), is

explained as the consequence of cancellation by two competing factors. Increasing the level of CO_2 tends to increase the intensity of the hydrologic cycle; for example, Manabe and Bryan (1985) found a 15% increase of precipitation with the CO_2 increase from one to four times that at present. A similar increase of precipitation (11%) occurs in this experiment over the oceans (Table 1). On the other hand, the huge Pangean continent has a large and relatively dry interior because of the great distance of the interior from the ocean (Kutzbach and Gallimore, 1989). As a result, the precipitation over land and the runoff from land are considerably less than in the modern simulation by about 22% and 46%, respectively (Table 1).

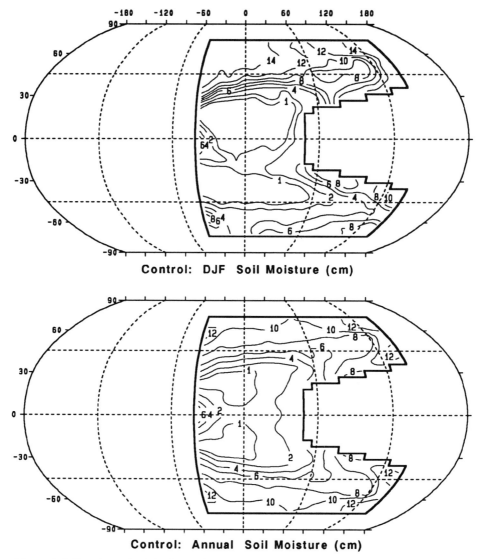

Figure 6. Soil moisture (cm) for December-January-February (DJF) and the full year (Annual) for the control climate.

INCREASED AND DECREASED SEASONALITY DUE TO PRECESSION CYCLE

This section describes the results of the simulation with increased seasonality of insolation in the southern hemisphere and decreased seasonality of insolation in the Northern Hemisphere, as prescribed by perihelion in January, and compares these results of increased and decreased seasonality to the calculated control climate of average seasonality that was described in the previous section. The magnitude of the difference in seasonal solar radiation produced by the eccentric orbit is large. Averaged over the entire hemisphere, solar radiation is 470 W/m² in the southern summer (DJF) compared to 430 W/m² in the northern summer (JJA) and 215 W/m² in southern winter (JJA) compared to 240 W/m² in northern winter (DJF).

The calculated control values are 450 W/m² (summer) and 227.5W/m² (winter). The largest differences occur in the summer hemisphere at about 30° latitude. At this latitude the solar radiation is increased by more than 20 W/m², compared to the control, when perihelion is in summer and is decreased by more than 20 W/m² when aphelion is in summer.

Changes in circulation, precipitation, runoff, snowcover, and temperature

The increased intensity of the summer monsoon on the southern continents is apparent in the larger area covered by low pressure (990 mb) and the stronger winds blowing toward this area (compare Fig. 8 with Fig. 4). With the stronger mon-

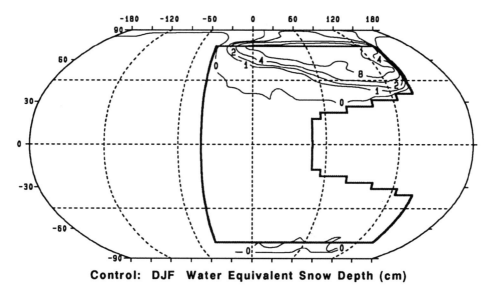

Control: DJF Water Equivalent Snow Depth (cm)

Figure 7. Water equivalent snow depth (cm) for December-January-February (DJF) for the control climate. If 10 cm of snow correspond to 1 cm of water, then these water equivalent depths can be multiplied by 10 to approximate actual snow depth. The snow over polar oceans indicates the presence of sea ice.

soon circulation, rainfall increases along the Tethys coast and into the interior (compare Fig. 9a with Fig. 5a). This increase is illustrated by calculating the difference between the strengthened summer monsoon (Fig. 9a) and the average monsoon (Fig. 5a). The increases range from 25 to 50%, compared to the control climate, over much of the southern tropics and subtropics (Fig. 9b). Parts of the middle-latitude continental interior are slightly drier (Fig. 9b).

The northern hemisphere winter climate has slightly increased precipitation along the northern Tethys coast (Fig. 9b). This appears to be related to the slightly decreased intensity of the northern winter monsoon that allows a somewhat more active winter storm track along the Tethys coast (Fig. 9b). The climatic departures for the southern winter of increased seasonality (JJA), not shown, have the same pattern and magnitude as shown for the northern winter of decreased seasonality (DJF) in Fig. 9b, but with reversed sign, that is, decreased winter rainfall along the Tethys coast. Seasonal snow cover increases by a small amount (about 2%) in the northern winter (DJF) that is, in the hemisphere with reduced seasonality of solar radiation. Seasonal snow cover decreases by the same small amount in the southern winter (JJA), the hemisphere with increased seasonality of solar radiation.

Annual-average changes in precipitation (Fig. 10a) and soil moisture (Fig. 10b) reflect the seasonal changes of summer and winter in most locations. The annual precipitation and runoff increases (decreases) by 25% or more in the subtropics of the Southern (Northern) Hemisphere.

Changes in surface temperature (not shown) are in the expected sense of increased seasonal extremes (warmer summer, cooler winters) in the southern continent and decreased sea-

sonal extremes in the northern continent (cooler summers, warmer winters). However, these changes are relatively small (several degrees Celsius) compared to the large seasonal range of temperature in the control climate (Fig. 3). Moreover, the largest changes in temperature tend to occur in summer when the continental climates are most influenced by radiative rather than advective effects. In some areas, such as the region of increased summer monsoon rainfall, the increased cloudiness and evaporation lead to slightly lower temperatures rather

TABLE 1. ANNUAL AVERAGE TEMPERATURE, PRECIPITATION, AND RUNOFF FOR THE CALCULATED PANGEAN CONTROL AND FOR A SIMULATION WITH MODERN GEOGRAPHY*

Variable	Area	Idealized Pangea	Modern Geography
		(°C)	(°C)
Temperature	L + O	21.6	14.8
	L	19.1	6.3
	O	23.0	18.2
		(mm)	(mm)
Precipitation	L + O	1,200	1,200
	L	925	1,190
	O	1,360	1,220
		(mm)	(mm)
Runoff	L	240	450

*Values are for the global average (L + O = land plus ocean; L = land, and O = ocean).

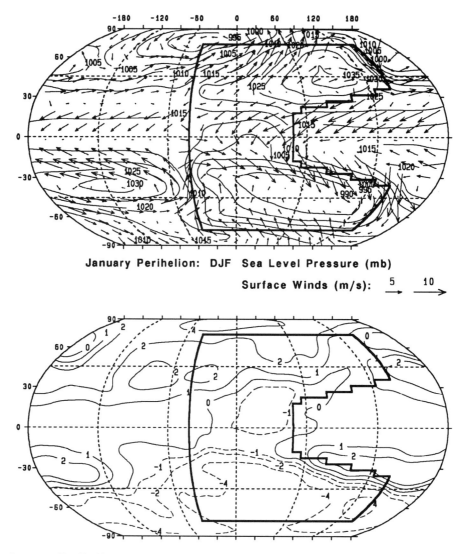

January Perihelion: DJF Sea Level Pressure (mb)

Surface Winds (m/s): 5 10

January Perihelion minus Control: DJF Sea Level Pressure difference (mb)

Figure 8. Top, Sea-level pressure (millibars) and surface layer winds (m/s) for December-January-February (DJF) for the simulation with perihelion in January (southern summer). Speed (m/s) is calibrated for the wind arrows at lower right. Bottom, Sea-level pressure difference (millibars) for DJF between the simulation with perihelion in January (southern summer) and the calculated control.

than the higher temperatures that would be predicted based on increased insolation alone.

Changes in Koeppen climate classification

The Koeppen climate classification (Guetter and Kutzbach, 1990) provides another means of summarizing the climate of the idealized continent and the effects of increased and decreased seasonality (Fig. 11). This classification incorporates information on the seasonal cycle of both temperature and precipitation. The striking aridity of the continental interior is shown in both hemispheres by the large areas of dry climates (BW, desert, and BS, steppe). The occurrence of seasonally extreme climates (D climates) in high latitudes is associated with the large range of temperature (hot summers, cold winters) in both hemispheres. The D climates probably extend farther equatorward than would otherwise be expected because of the relatively high elevation of the continent (500 m).

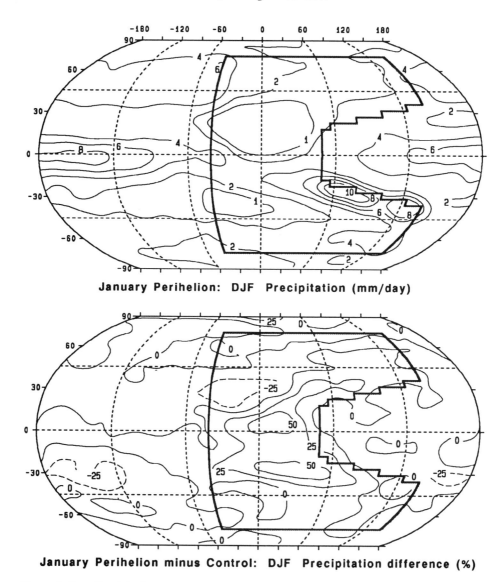

Figure 9. Top, Precipitation (mm/day) for December-January-February (DJF) for the simulation with perihelion in January (southern summer). Bottom, Change in precipitation (%) for DJF for the simulation with perihelion in January (southern summer), relative to the control. Precipitation values are smoothed with a nine-point binomial filter.

Superimposed on these basic climatic zones, the hemisphere with increased seasonality (in this experiment, the southern continent) has tropical monsoon climates (A climates) along the Tethys coast and south of the equator, compared to steppe climates to the north in the hemisphere of decreased seasonality. Similarly, the region of desert climate (BW) in the continental interior is considerably smaller in the southern continent (enhanced seasonality) that in the northern continent (decreased seasonality). Finally, temperate wet and temperate summer-wet climates (Cf and Cw) are more extensive in the regions of intensified summer monsoons of the southern continent. The climate classification map illustrates where changes might occur between major climate zones but obscures changes within zones. One needs to consider both the direct hydrologic indicators (precipitation and soil moisture, Figs. 9b, 10a and b) as well as the climate zonation (Fig. 11) to assess the regional changes that might be produced by this orbital change.

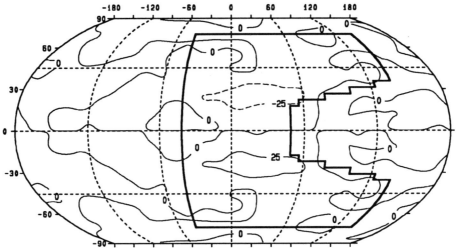

January Perihelion minus Control: Annual Precipitation difference (%)

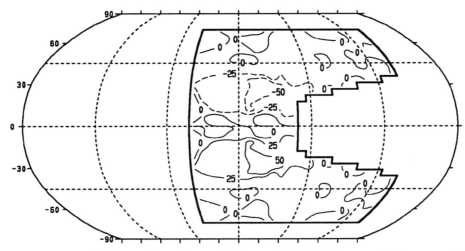

January Perihelion minus Control: Annual Soil Moisture difference (%)

Figure 10. Change in annual precipitation (%) and soil moisture (%), for the simulation with perihelion in January (southern summer), relative to the control.

Time-dependent changes

The changes in climate due to orbital changes are depicted in Figures 8 through 11 as spatial patterns. However, if these simulations are indications of actual climate shift due to orbital change, then the geologic data should display changes in the sedimentary record in time (depth). Figure 12 and Table 2 show the model-simulated changes in temperature, precipitation, and runoff for three locations on the southern continent for an idealized 23,000-year precession cycle. Areas in the tropical and subtropical continental interior might shift from "steppe" to "desert" and back with periods of the precession

cycle and might experience rainfall and runoff changes of ± 25% or more. Similar large changes of rainfall and runoff are to be expected along the coast of the Tethys Sea where the climate shifts between "rain forest" and "steppe". By way of contrast, the middle-latitude interior might have only very small changes of precipitation and runoff (in some areas out of phase with the tropical changes) but large changes in temperature. Summers could be 6°C warmer when perihelion is in summer than when it is in winter. The corresponding climatic changes in the Northern Hemisphere would be 180° (about 11,500 years) out of phase with the changes in the Southern Hemisphere.

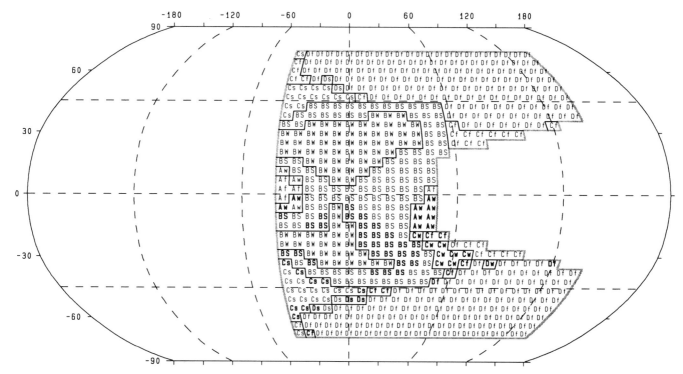

Figure 11. Koeppen climate classes for the simulation with perihelion in January (southern summer). The model grid squares where the Southern Hemisphere class differs from the northern hemisphere class are in bold print. The major Koeppen classes are moist tropical (A), dry (BW, BS), warm moist temperate (C), "boreal" (D), and polar (E). The subdivisions f, w, s refer to year-round rain, summer rain, and summer dry, respectively. See Guetter and Kutzbach (1990) for details of class subdivisions.

CONCLUSIONS

Climate model experiments with idealized Pangean geography are used to illustrate the effect of orbital changes on Pangean climate. With moderate eccentricity of the earth's orbit (0.025), the enhanced seasonality of insolation in the hemisphere with summertime perihelion (wintertime aphelion) produces increases of rainfall and runoff along tropical coastlines and tropical or subtropical continental interiors of about 25% or more—and comparable percentage decreases in the hemisphere with reduced seasonality. These changes should be large enough to significantly alter the patterns of vegetation, drainage, and sedimentation. However, it is beyond the scope of this chapter to examine in detail how these changes might contribute to the formation of the various kinds of cyclic sequences of sediments that are found in the geologic record. This topic is addressed by Oglesby and Park (1989) and others.

These specific results could be modified depending upon the choice of geography, topography, and CO_2 level for Pangean time. For example, the use of high levels of atmospheric CO_2 (five times present) in this simulation effectively eliminated the possibility of large orbitally induced modifications of snow cover that might, in turn, allow inferences about possible glacial-type responses.

The model used here has significant limitations in its ability to simulate the present climate, and therefore the estimates of past climate are also subject to error. The lack of a coupled dynamical ocean as part of the climate model is a very significant limitation. These kinds of experiments should be repeated when calculations with coupled dynamical atmosphere/ocean models are feasible. The lack of interactive vegetation limits the interpretation of the sensitivity of land climate to orbital change because vegetation feedbacks (such as those produced by the changing albedo of the vegetated land surface) are excluded here. Finally, this study ignores the role of changes in axial tilt in causing climate change. Future experiments should include studies of the climate's sensitivity to changes in axial tilt.

J. E. Kutzbach

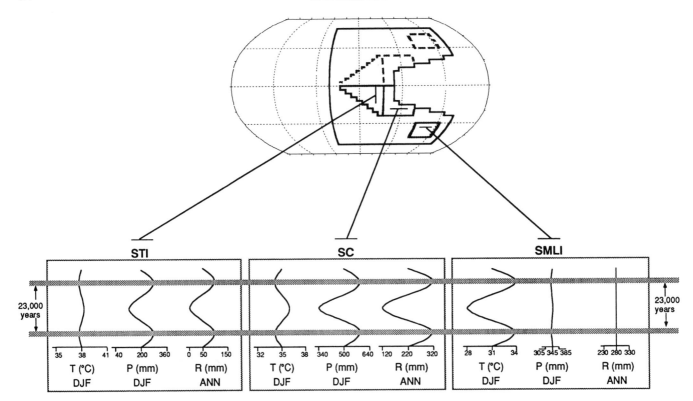

Figure 12. Schematic time series through a 23,000-year precession cycle of summer (December-January-February: DJF) temperature, T(°C); summer precipitation, P (mm); and annual runoff, R (mm) for three regions in the Southern Hemisphere of the idealized Pangean continent. The regions (shown with solid boundaries) are the southern tropical interior (STI), the southern coast (SC), and the southern middle-latitude interior (SMLI). The extreme values of the time series are taken from the model simulations of maximum seasonality (Southern Hemisphere) and minimum seasonality (Southern Hemisphere) and displayed here with the appropriate magnitude and phase for the Southern Hemisphere locations. The schematic time series for the corresponding regions in the Northern Hemisphere (dashed boundaries) would be phase-shifted by 180°, i.e., by half the precession cycle or 11,500 years. The schematic curves display in time (depth) perspective the same information contained in the spatial patterns of Figures 8 through 11. It is the climatic changes in this time (depth) perspective that might be recorded in sediments. The scale for each individual variable (T, P, and R) is the same for the three regions so that the relative amplitude of the precession-forced changes can be compared. The middle number on each scale is the control value.

TABLE 2. CHANGES OF SUMMER (DJF) TEMPERATURE, SUMMER (DJF) PRECIPITATION, AND ANNUAL RUNOFF FOR EXTREMES OF THE PRECESSION CYCLE, AND FOR THE THREE AREAS SHOWN IN FIGURE 12

Cycle	Southern Tropical Interior			Southern Coast			Southern Middle Latitude Interior		
	Temperature (°C)	Precipitation (mm)* (%)	Runoff (mm)[†] (%)	Temperature (°C)	Precipitation (mm)* (%)	Runoff (mm)[†] (%)	Temperature (°C)	Precipitation (mm)* (%)	Runoff (mm)[†] (%)
P_S[§]	37.7	280 +40%	60 +20%	34	660 +33%	320 +40%	34	340 0%	280
A_S**	38.3	120 -40%	40 -20%	36	340 -33%	120 -40%	28	350 0%	280
P_S[§]	37.7	280 +40%	60 +20%	34	660 +33%	320 +40%	34	340 0%	280

*per season
[†]per year
[§]Perihelion in southern summer.
**Aphelion in southern summer.

ACKNOWLEDGMENTS

A research grant to the University of Wisconsin–Madison from the National Science Foundation, Climate Dynamics program, supported this work; the grant number is ATM 89-02849. The climate model computations were made at the National Center for Atmospheric Research (NCAR), which is sponsored by the National Science Foundation, with computing grant 35381017 from the NCAR computing facility. The author thanks Peter Guetter for running the climate model experiments and calculating the Koeppen climates, Pat Behling and Rich Selin for statistical summaries and graphics, Mary Kennedy for manuscript preparation, and T. J. Crowley and R. Oglesby for comments and suggestions.

REFERENCES CITED

Anderson, R. Y., 1986, The varve microcosm: Propagator of cyclic bedding: Paleoceanography, v. 1, p. 373–382.

Arthur, M. A., 1984, Rhythmic bedding in Mesozoic-Cenozoic pelagic carbonate sequences: The primary and diagenetic origin of Milankovitch-like cycles, *in* Berger, A., Imbrie, J., Hays, J., Kukla, G., and Saltzman, B., eds., Milankovitch and climate: Dordrecht, D. Riedel Publishing Company, p. 191–222.

Barron, E. J., Arthur, M. A., and Kauffman, E. G., 1985, Cretaceous rhythmic bedding sequences: A plausible link between orbital variations and climate: Earth and Planetary Science Letters, v. 72, p. 327–340.

Berger, A., and Loutre, M. F., 1991, Insolation values for the climate of the last 10 million years: Quaternary Science Reviews, v. 10, p. 297–317.

Berger, A., Fichefet, T., Gallée, H., Marsiat, I., Tricot, C., and van Ypersele, J. P., 1990, Physical interactions within a coupled climate model over the last glacial-interglacial cycle: Transactions of the Royal Society of Edinburgh: Earth Sciences, v. 81, p. 357–370.

Berner, R. A., 1990, Atmospheric carbon dioxide levels over Phanerozoic time: Science, v. 249, p. 1382–1392.

Covey, C., and Thompson, S. L., 1989, Testing the effects of ocean heat transport on climate: Paleogeography, Paleoclimatology, Paleoecology, v. 75, p. 331–334.

Crowley, T. J., Mengel, J. G., and Short, D. A., 1987, Gondwanaland's seasonal cycle: Nature, v. 329, p. 803–807.

Fischer, A. G., and Schwarzacher, W., 1984, Cretaceous bedding rhythms under orbital control? *in* Berger, A., Imbrie, J., Hays, J., Kukla, G., and Saltzman, B., eds., Milankovitch and climate: Dordrecht, D. Riedel Publishing Company, p. 163–175.

Gilbert, G. K., 1895, Sedimentary measurement of geologic time: Journal of Geology, v. 3, p. 121–127.

Glancy, T. J., Jr., Barron, E. J., and Arthur, M. A., 1986, An initial study of the sensitivity of modeled Cretaceous climate to cyclical insolation forcing: Paleoceanography, v. 1, p. 523–537.

Guetter, P. J., and Kutzbach, J. E., 1990, A modified Köppen classification applied to model simulations of glacial and interglacial climates: Climatic Change, v. 16, p. 193–215.

Hays, J. D., Imbrie, J., and Shackleton, N. J., 1976, Variations in the Earth's orbit: Pacemaker of the ice ages: Science, v. 194, p. 1121–1132.

Imbrie, J., and Imbrie, K. P., 1979, Ice ages: Solving the mystery: Hillside, New Jersey, Enslow Publishers, 224 p.

Imbrie, J., and 17 others, 1992, On the structure and origin of major glaciation cycles: 1: Linear responses to Milankovitch forcing: Paleoceanography, v. 7, p. 701–738.

Klein, G. deV., and Willard, D. A., 1989, Origin of the Pennsylvanian coal-bearing cyclothems of North America: Geology, v. 17, p. 152–155.

Kutzbach, J. E., 1981, Monsoon climate of the early Holocene: Climatic experiment using the Earth's orbital parameters for 9000 years ago: Science, v. 214, p. 59–61.

Kutzbach, J. E., and Gallimore, R. G., 1989, Pangaean climates: Megamonsoons of the megacontinent: Journal of Geophysical Research, v. 94, p. 3341–3358.

Kutzbach, J. E., and Guetter, P. J., 1986, The influence of changing orbital parameters and surface boundary conditions on climate simulations for the past 18,000 years: Journal of Atmospheric Research, v. 43, p. 1726–1759.

Kutzbach, J. E., and Otto-Bliesner, B. L., 1982, The sensitivity of the African-Asian monsoonal climate to orbital parameter changes for 9000 yr BP in a low-resolution general circulation model: Journal of the Atmospheric Sciences, v. 39, p. 1177–1188.

Kutzbach, J. E., and Street-Perrott, F. A., 1985, Milankovitch forcing of fluctuations in the level of tropical lakes from 18 to 0 kyr BP: Nature, v. 317, p. 130–134.

Kutzbach, J. E., Guetter, P. J., and Washington, W. M., 1990, Simulated circulation of an idealized ocean for Pangaean time: Paleoceanography, v. 5, p. 299–317.

Manabe, S., and Bryan, K., 1985, CO_2-induced change in a coupled ocean-atmosphere model and its paleoclimatic implications: Journal of Geophysical Research, v. 90, p. 11689–11708.

Oglesby, R., and Park, J., 1989, The effect of precessional insolation changes on Cretaceous climate and cyclic sedimentation: Journal of Geophysical Research, v. 94, p. 14793–14816.

Olsen, P. E., 1986, A 40-million-year lake record of early Mesozoic orbital climatic forcing: Science, v. 234, p. 842–848.

Pitcher, E. J., Malone, R. C., Ramanathan, V., Blackmon, M. L., Puri, K., and Bourke, W., 1983, January and July simulations with a spectral general circulation model: Journal of the Atmospheric Sciences, v. 40, p. 580–604.

Prell, W. L., 1984, Monsoonal climate of the Arabian Sea during the late Quaternary: A response to changing solar radiation, in Berger, A., Imbrie, J., Hays, J., Kukla, G., and Saltzman, B., eds., Milankovitch and climate: Dordrecht, D. Reidel, p. 349–366.

Prell, W. L., and Kutzbach, J. E., 1987, Monsoon variability over the past 150,000 years: Journal of Geophysical Research, v. 92, p. 8411–8425.

Prell, W. L., Murray, D. W., Clemens, S. C., and Anderson, D. M., 1993, Evolution and variability in the Indian Ocean: A synthesis of results from the ocean drilling program: Washington, D.C., America Geophysical Union, Geophysical Monograph, v. 70, (in press).

Randel, W. J., and Williamson, D. L., 1990, A comparison of the climate simulated by the NCAR Community Climate Model (CCM1:R15) with ECMWF analyses: Journal of Climate, v. 3, p. 608–633.

Rossignol-Strick, M., 1983, African monsoons, an immediate climate response to orbital insolation: Nature, v. 304, p. 46–49.

MANUSCRIPT ACCEPTED BY THE SOCIETY MAY 14, 1993

Geological Society of America
Special Paper 288
1994

Phanerozoic CO$_2$ levels and global temperatures inferred from changing paleogeography

Thomas R. Worsley
Department of Geological Sciences, Ohio University, Athens, Ohio 45701-2979
Thomas L. Moore
Department of Geosciences, University of Arizona, Tucson, Arizona 85721
Carmen M. Fraticelli and Christopher R. Scotese
Department of Geology, University of Texas at Arlington, Arlington, Texas 76019

ABSTRACT

A simple model that tracks global land area and its average latitude to specify CO$_2$ levels and consequent surface temperatures has been used to infer paleotemperatures of 20 Phanerozoic global paleogeographic reconstructions. The model is based on the premise that global CO$_2$ levels and temperature are directly proportional to the average latitude of the world landmass and inversely proportional to total land area. In all 20 cases, inferred CO$_2$ and paleotemperature values are plausible and generally compatible with previous estimates. However, raw model output must be refined to take into account changes in rates of other climate modifiers such as orogeny, organic carbon burial, and precipitation that can be inferred from additional evidence.

Results show a warm (19°C) ice-free Cambrian world of small land area (75% emergent) at mid-latitudes (35°). Rapid equatorward migration of world landmass to 25° latitude then led to a cool (13°C) ice-capped late Ordovician world that was 70% emergent. Equally rapid migration back to higher latitudes (39°) by the Silurian coupled with decreased emergence (64%) produced the warmest temperatures of the Phanerozoic (22°). Return of the landmass to mid-latitudes (32°) coupled with reemergence (71%) by early Devonian reestablished cooler (18°) temperatures. As Pangea coalesced from early Devonian to late Carboniferous, percent emergence continually increased to virtually 100% as average latitude continually increased to 38°, resulting in an ice-capped world of 16°C. High organic carbon burial rates and orogeny at that time would suggest that our temperature estimates are slightly too high for this interval. By early Triassic, our results indicate continual ice-enhanced emergence at virtually 100% and equatorward migration of land to 33° latitude, yielding a global temperature of 16°C. Other lines of evidence (absence of ice, low organic carbon burial, weak orogeny, aridity) suggest a slightly warmer world, or at least one with a lower pole-equator thermal gradient. From Triassic to mid Cretaceous, average latitude again increased to 38° and emergence decreased to 75%, producing a warming of global temperature to 20°C. Cretaceous to Recent results indicate that average latitude of the landmass decreases to 30° as India and Australia move equatorward and that there is an increase to as much as 100% emergence during maximum late Cenozoic ice-sheet growth. Corresponding global temperatures decline to as low as 13°C.

Worsley, T. R., Moore, T. L., Fraticelli, C. M., and Scotese, C. R., 1994, Phanerozoic CO$_2$ levels and global temperatures inferred from changing paleogeography, *in* Klein, G. D., ed., Pangea: Paleoclimate, Tectonics, and Sedimentation During Accretion, Zenith, and Breakup of a Supercontinent: Boulder, Colorado, Geological Society of America Special Paper 288.

INTRODUCTION

The notion that atmospheric concentration of CO_2 dominates all other climate control variables on time scales $>10^5$ years has been slow to influence the Earth sciences. Chamberlin (1899) first espoused the principle that because CO_2 is the main greenhouse control gas of the Earth's atmosphere, climate maintenance can be viewed in terms of the rates of addition of CO_2 to and removal of CO_2 from the atmosphere. Urey (1952) elegantly summarized the maintenance process in the form of simple chemical equations commonly known as the Urey reactions (Berner, 1990).

Walker et al. (1981) reported that the Urey reactions provide a negative feedback loop (Fig. 1) that automatically adjusts the atmospheric CO_2 throughput rate to keep global surface temperatures within narrow limits in the liquid water range. Such stabilization occurs because chemical reaction rates increase exponentially with temperature. For example, any process that serves to increase CO_2 input to the atmosphere would also initially serve to increase surface temperatures via the greenhouse effect. Increased surface temperatures would result in higher H_2O saturation vapor pressure (and presumably precipitation rate). The combination of higher temperature, precipitation rate, and carbonic acid content of the precipitation would accelerate the weathering of silicates and hence remove CO_2 and lower the greenhouse warming until equilibrium was restored. A lowered CO_2 input would reverse the process. Berner et al. (1983) and Lasaga et al. (1985) constructed a detailed computer-based geochemical model of these effects that calculates surface temperatures when a host of other mass and rate data are specified.

Berner et al. (1983) and Lasaga et al. (1985) observed that silicate weathering rates are actually a complex function

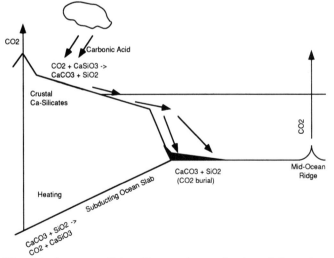

Figure 1. Summary of the silicate-carbonate fraction of the carbon cycle. Surface temperature is controlled by the balance between the release rate of CO_2 and its burial rate as carbonates. (Note that $CaSiO_3$ and $CaCO_3$ can proxy for any Ca- or Mg-containing silicate or carbonate.)

of biotic enhancement of inorganic reaction rates. Brady (1991) summarized current knowledge of the activation energies of common Ca- and Mg- containing silicates under sterile conditions. He found most activation energies to be between 10 and 20 kcal/mole. The Berner et al. (1983) and Lasaga et al. (1985) model yields a nominal value of ~8 kcal/mole. Basically, the higher the activation energy of a mineral, the faster its weathering rates. Brady (1991) found that silicate weathering rate would increase by a factor of ~1.75 for an activation energy of 10 and by a factor of ~3.25 for one of 20 as temperatures increase from 15°C to 25°C, if activation energies were the only controlling factor of aqueous chemical weathering. (Corresponding values are ~1.5 for the Berner et al. (1983) and Lasaga et al. (1985) model that uses an activation energy of 8.) As Brady (1991) pointed out, however, activation energies are *not* the sole controlling factor. Biotic activity, via its tendency to form soils rich in organic acids, traps the aqueous CO_2 released from organic matter as it oxidizes and also increases fluid-rock ratios (i.e., pulverizes rock). Both processes serve to appreciably increase the silicate weathering rate at any given temperature. The result is a lowering of the apparent value of silicate activation energies compared with the sterile values quoted above. Such biotic enhancement of silicate weathering rates would serve to make surface temperatures colder than simple inorganic considerations would indicate (Schwartzman and Volk, 1989).

Worsley and Nance (1989) and Worsley et al. (1991) proposed another biotic temperature-lowering mechanism that is independent of changes in silicate weathering rates. They reported that organic productivity does not depend on carbon availability but rather on nutrient supply (most likely phosphorus) from weathering. They showed that any increase in the efficiency of nutrient utilization or of nutrient recycling rates with respect to those of carbon prior to burial as organic matter will result in a greater rate of organic-matter burial for a given amount of the limiting nutrient. The result is a further lowering of atmospheric CO_2 content, making for a yet colder Earth. Although poorly quantified, this mechanism has been proposed as a contributing factor to ice-cap production (see Worsley and Nance [1989] and Worsley et al. [1991] for details). Although we do not directly incorporate the nutrient efficiency mechanism into the model proposed here, we discuss those periods of Earth history during which increases in nutrient utilization efficiency were likely to make the Earth colder than our biotic-independent results specify.

Marshall et al. (1988) reported that the Urey reactions demand warmer global surface temperatures when global landmass is at higher latitudes because the intrinsically colder temperatures at high latitudes would slow silicate weathering. The response would be a slowdown in CO_2 removal rate from the atmosphere. The enhanced CO_2 levels would warm the entire globe until equilibrium was reestablished at a new but higher temperature. Kuhn et al. (1989) and Worsley and Nance (1989) reported that for constant CO_2 degassing rates, the Urey reactions coupled with the above considerations demand that surface temperatures vary inversely with global land area because smaller land areas would require higher temperatures to increase weathering rates enough to balance the carbon cycle.

Worsley and Kidder (1991) fitted the above land area/land latitude relationships into an admittedly simplistic but easy-to-use surface temperature maintenance model (the "2-10" model). The model's main advantage is that it captures the salient climate-determining features of more detailed models without the need for a supercomputer. For simplicity, they assumed constant (1) carbonate/organic burial ratios, (2) solar luminosity, (3) long-term degassing rate, and (4) immersible crustal area of uniform hypsometry that occupies 36% of the Earth's surface. They further assumed that (5) changing paleogeography has no first-order effect on diurnal temperature variation, seasonality, and atmospheric circulation and (6) the mean annual temperature at the average latitude of all land areas is representative of mean global temperatures. They defined average latitude as the latitude that bisects the global landmass into equal poleward and equatorward areas. This definition does not distinguish north from south latitudes, only distance from the equator. They then calibrated their model with a wide suite of published paleotemperature, -geography, and -CO$_2$ estimates. Despite the oversimplifications, generalizations, and approximations used to construct the model, it does yield plausible CO$_2$ levels, global surface temperature, and pole-equator temperature gradients that are compatible with results of more elaborate modeling. Furthermore, it does so for all conceivable paleogeographic situations. Because the 2-10 model and the 20 paleogeographic reconstructions of Scotese and Golonka (1992) are the sole input we will use to infer Phanerozoic climate history, some explanation of the model's workings are in order.

Figure 1 expresses the relationship between the variables required to maintain CO$_2$ flow through the atmosphere. We assume that CO$_2$ degasses at a constant rate. Steady-state mass balance demands that it also be reburied at the same constant rate. Because total silicate weathering is the sink for CO$_2$, its rate must also remain constant. If global land area changes, so too must silicate weathering rate change per unit area. For example, if land area doubles, weathering rate per unit area must halve to maintain balance. Alternatively, if land area were to halve, silicate weathering per unit area must double.

Using this relationship, we can now ask how changing land area actually controls silicate weathering rates. As land area decreases, global CO$_2$ burial would initially slow while its degassing remains unchanged, thereby increasing the CO$_2$ content of the atmosphere. However, because CO$_2$ is a greenhouse gas, as CO$_2$ accumulates the land surface would warm, thereby increasing the silicate weathering rate. A new steady state at some higher temperature would result. The reverse would happen if land area increased. The question then is: How would CO$_2$ level and temperature change? Worsley and

Kidder (1991) suggested that halving land area would yield a tenfold increase in CO$_2$ level and a 10°C increase in temperature (see references in Worsley and Kidder [1991] for details). Solving the Arrhenius equation that relates chemical reaction rates to temperature (see Brady [1991] for a modern geochemical treatment) for such a relationship between land area and temperature requires a nominal average "activation energy" of 12 kcal/mole for all Ca- and Mg-containing silicates. This is a plausible value considering the biotic acceleration of weathering discussed above.

Figure 2 shows the "expected" relationships among land area, silicate weathering per unit area, surface temperature, and CO$_2$ level. We assume that land area was at a maximum at 18 ka during the Last Glacial Maximum when land covered 36% of the Earth's surface (CLIMAP Project Members, 1976). During the Last Glacial Maximum, global CO$_2$ levels were ~180 ppmV and global temperature averaged 12°C (Barnola et al., 1987; CLIMAP Project Members, 1976). If this land-dominated world were drowned so that half the land was covered by sea, then according to the 2-10 model, atmospheric levels of CO$_2$ would be 10 times higher and land temperature would be 10°C. higher.

However, these elevated temperatures and CO$_2$ levels would pertain only if the latitudinal distribution of land did not change. The equilibrium global temperatures and CO$_2$ levels would be slightly lower if more land were near the equator, and conversely, global temperatures and CO$_2$ levels would be slightly higher if more land were closer to the pole. The tem-

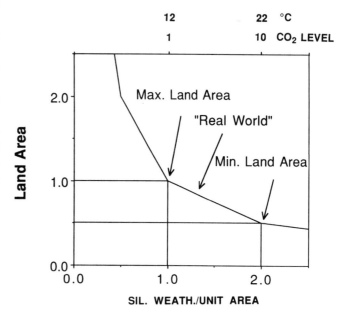

Figure 2. The "2-10" model relationship between land area and silicate weathering per unit area, surface temperature, and CO$_2$ level. Assuming constant CO$_2$ input, halving land area will result in a tenfold increase in CO$_2$ level that in turn results in a 10°C temperature rise. Temperature and CO$_2$ levels are scaled to the 18-ka Pleistocene maximum emergence which in our model represents maximum land area emergence and minimum CO$_2$ levels.

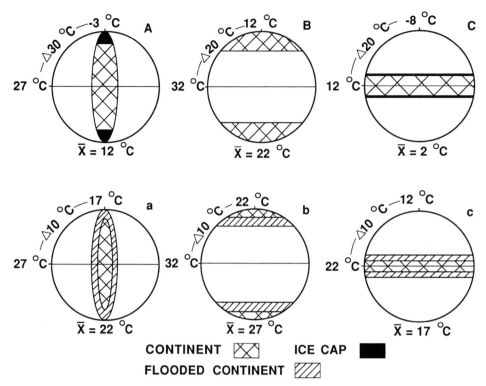

Figure 3. Three hypothetical end-member configurations of emergent (A, B, C) and half-emergent (a, b, c) continents and the surface temperatures that result for each pair using the 2-10 model. X̄ is average global temperature, defined by adding the polar and equatorial temperatures and dividing by two. After Worsley and Kidder, 1991.

peratures shown in Figure 3Aa are an average of values poleward of 60° and within 8° of equator. The actual temperature at the poles will always be colder than shown here, and the temperature at the equator will always be warmer than these average values. This distinction becomes important when deciding where the "ice-line" (Marshall et al., 1988) occurs. The distribution of today's landmass does in fact closely fit the sliceworld configuration of Figure 3Aa.

Figure 3Bb illustrates the end-member scenarios in which all the world's land is near the poles (capworld). Because land area in Figure 3Bb is the same as the land area shown in Figure 3Aa, so, too, must the land temperatures be the same. However, these temperatures occur in polar regions. Therefore, the temperature near the equator must be much warmer, assuming reasonable latitudinal gradient. Ironically, in this capworld, ice caps are precluded because of the warm polar temperatures.

Figure 3C shows a world in which all the land straddles the equator (ringworld). Once again, land temperatures must be the same as those of the capworld and sliceworld in order to maintain the proper level of silicate weathering. Worsley and Kidder (1991) suggested a polar temperature of –18°C for an emergent ringworld (Fig. 3Cc). They chose this figure to preserve a 30°C pole-equator thermal gradient identical to that of 18 ka (Fig. 3Aa). Their resulting global temperature is

–3°C. We feel that both the pole and the globe of the Worsley/Kidder emergent ringworld are too cold and its latitudinal temperature gradient too steep, given the huge expanse of unobstructed mid- and high-latitude ocean available to transport heat. We therefore revise the emergent ringworld polar temperature to –8°C for this study. The new polar temperature produces a 20° pole-equator gradient (identical to that of Fig. 3Bb, which has a similar large expanse of ocean) and a global temperature of 2°C as shown (Fig. 3Cc). Corresponding CO_2 and global temperature increases are now a more reasonable 31.6 times and 15°C respectively. We will use this revision for calculating the paleotemperatures of the paleogeographic reconstructions that follow. We believe that such a ringworld could still grow ice caps at its poleward periphery when emergent.

A final word of caution is required. Because the symmetric cartoons of Figure 3 do not represent the actual positions of land in the northern or southern hemisphere, complications can arise. It is possible to have a unipolar or a bipolar slice-, cap-, or ringworld (i.e., all the land centered at one pole versus the land equally distributed over both poles). Heat balance considerations for these two situations are very different (Ledley, 1988; Crowley et al., 1987; Hyde et al., 1990; all presented differing views). This must be taken into account when applying the model to the "real world." Figure 4 reorganizes

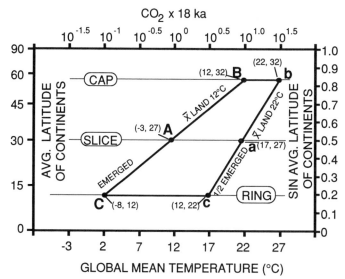

Figure 4. Plot of the information summarized in Figure 3 with corresponding CO₂ levels added (after Worsley and Kidder, 1991). Numbers in parentheses represent polar region and tropical region temperatures (°C). The equatorward margin of an emergent, bipolar capworld would have a latitude of 40°. Its average latitude (halfway point from its periphery to the pole) on an equal-area basis would be 55°. Likewise, the poleward margin of an emergent ringworld would be 21°, and its average latitude would be 10°.

the information outlined in Figure 3 and adds corresponding CO₂ levels.

LAND AREAS AND AVERAGE LATITUDES

Error analysis

The possibility for error occurs in many of the steps we have taken. Some errors are objective, whereas others are more subjective. Objective errors result from the analytic and averaging techniques we used to evaluate the areas shown on the maps. More subjective errors occur when paleomagnetically determining the latitudinal positions of continents and when estimating the proportion of uplands, land, shallow sea, and deep sea. Finally, the presumption that quantitative paleotemperatures can be obtained from an algorithm that uses only land area, its average latitude, and simple geochemical considerations must be simplistic. It ignores such important climatic components as actual areas, positions, and hypsometries of specific landmasses and consequent effects upon atmospheric and oceanic circulation, precipitation, and seasonality.

In the following section, we estimate the nature and magnitude of the likely errors in the increasingly subjective procedures we have used. Finally we offer an opinion as to whether errors are likely to be cancelling or cumulative. We conclude that as large as the errors are, our model represents progress

because it produces an interpretation of paleo–surface temperatures that is consistent with independent evidence and previous interpretations while requiring far fewer complicating factors. Also, even though the absolute values proposed here may be in error, we believe that the pattern of relative change is robust.

Map area measurement error

Figure 5 shows the latitudinal distribution of uplands, platform, and shallow sea areas for the 20 maps (19 reconstructions plus the present-day world) of Scotese and Golonka (1992). The plots were made by dividing each of the maps into 5-degree squares of latitude and longitude and tallying whether land, upland, shallow sea, or deep sea occurred at the lower left-hand corner of each square. As a check on the accuracy of this procedure, we note that the area of land shown in Figure 5 for the present day is 30.5% rather than the accepted value of 29.22%—a difference of <4%. As we see no apparent bias in the tallying procedure that would over- or underestimate specific areas, we assume that the tallying error is a random ±4% with respect to either area or latitude. Similar tallying errors are likely to be present for the remaining maps.

Paleolatitude measurement error

The paleotemperature algorithm we use does not depend on longitude; rather, only the latitude is taken into consideration. Van der Voo (1990) estimated an error of ±5° for Paleozoic pole positions and, hence, an equivalent error in determining the latitudinal positions of crustal blocks. We arbitrarily assume that the error decrease is linear toward the present. Therefore, our Cambrian paleolatitudes may have an error of at least ±5°. Figure 6 plots the average paleolatitudes of world landmass for the 20 maps and shows the minimum range of error back through time.

Land area error

Of all the errors likely to affect our final conclusions, the complex and often subjective interpretations necessary to produce paleogeographic maps are the least quantifiable. Figure 7 shows why. Of today's continental crustal area (42% of Earth's surface area), 28% is flooded. Flooding increases to 38% in the Cretaceous, decreases to 26% during the Permo-Carboniferous, and finally again increases to 55% in the Ordovician. These estimates of platform flooding are somewhat lower than the previous published results of Strakhov (1948), Termier and Termier (1952), and Hallam (1981), who estimated that 50 and 60% of the platform was flooded during the Cretaceous and Ordovician, respectively. In addition, during the same time interval the area of continental crust has apparently decreased from 42% of the Earth's area to 30% of the Earth's area: an internal decrease in its size of 29%. We now

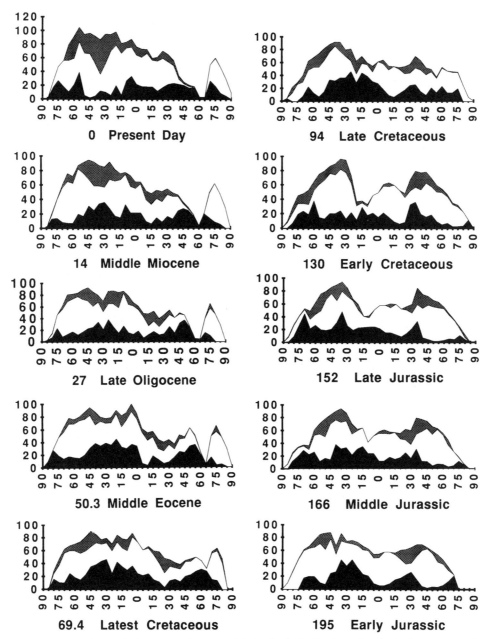

Figure 5 (on this and facing page). Extent and latitudinal distribution of uplands (bottom curve), land (middle curve), and shallow shelf (top curve) for the 20 paleographic reconstructions of Scotese and Golonka (1992). Vertical scale is area in 10^5 km^2. Horizontal scale is latitude with the North Pole at the left.

discuss why we think that this decreasing trend is unrealistic, and how we compensated for it.

If we reasonably assume that the volume of water on Earth has been constant since before the Cambrian, then the volume of continental crust must have remained nearly constant through time, or else unusually large sea-level changes would be predicted. Assuming the volume of the ocean basins is constant, a 12% decrease in continental crust would lower sea level by ~950 m. Alternatively, preserving continental crustal thickness and decreasing its volume would mean a

400-m sea-level fall (see Dockal et al. [1989] for a detailed discussion of both these effects). Sea-level drops of such magnitude would completely emerge the continental crust, whereas Figure 7 shows maximum Phanerozoic drowning (~55%) at 400 to 500 Ma. We therefore believe that the area of continental crust becomes progressively more underestimated back through time. We still think that a small amount of continental volume growth can be accommodated since the Cambrian, but not 12%.

Clearly, the apparent decrease in mapped continental

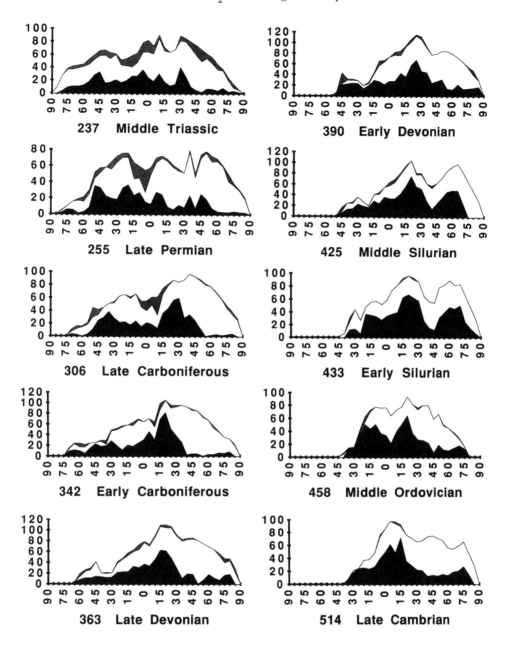

crustal area back through time must be mainly an artifact of an interpretation of the geologic record. Therefore, before we can begin to model paleotemperatures, we must first attempt to take this into account. Many adjustment strategies are possible. We offer two strategies that provide reasonable upper and lower estimates of the amount of change in crustal area during the Phanerozoic.

The first strategy (Fig. 8) preserves continental crustal area by assuming that the measured land/shallow sea ratios are correct and proportionally adds back continental crust. The second strategy (Fig. 9) accepts platform and shallow sea areas as measured, but then preserves today's continental crustal area by adding back only the land component to compensate for the progressive loss of continental crust back

through time. When processed through the 2-10 model, the former method results in an increasingly warmer world, whereas the second method has a bias toward an increasingly colder world back through time.

Obviously, the differences in land area through time produced by the two different strategies to augment continental crust are important because the 2-10 model relies on total land area to produce paleotemperature estimates. Figure 10 shows the progressively diverging percent emergence (18 ka = 100%) back through time that results for each of these methods. By 514 Ma, the internal difference between the two is 37%. We could make further arbitrary adjustments in land area by making yet more assumptions about the nature of the real crustal growth curve. We decline to do so at this point.

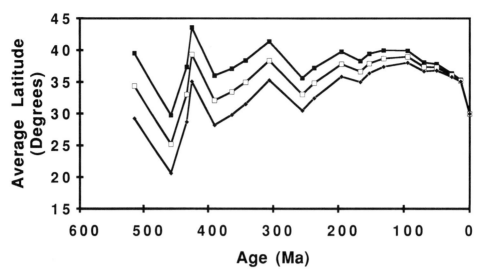

Figure 6. Average continental latitude for the 20 paleogeographic reconstructions. The center line represents the average latitude. The upper and lower lines represent a minimum paleomagnetic error that increases linearly to over ±5° at 514 Ma.

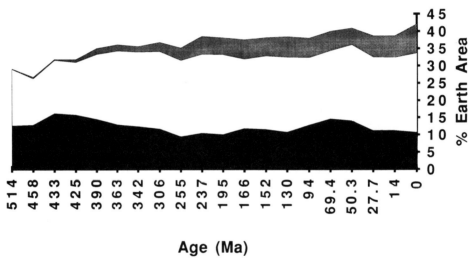

Figure 7. Measured areas of uplands (top curve), land platform (middle curve), and shallow shelf (bottom curve) of the 20 paleogeographic reconstructions as a percentage of the Earth's area.

The extreme disparity of opinion about the shape of the continental growth curve (e.g., Windley, 1984) would only lead us to choose the one that best fit our prejudices, thereby quantifying our prejudices, not the growth curve. Instead, we prefer to reserve further speculation for the discussion section of this work. Therefore, for now, we regard the 37% difference in flooding (or land area) at 514 Ma (Fig. 10) as the maximum in a potential error range that increases uniformly back through time. Likewise, we regard the upper and lower curves of Figure 10 as reasonable upper and lower boundaries of land area through time. We will later "tune" and refine our final estimate of percent land through time using 2-10 postulates and generally agreed upon global temperatures and pole-equator temperature gradients for known icehouses.

Errors associated with the 2-10 model

In constructing the 2-10 model, Worsley and Kidder (1991) made many simplifying generalizations that ignore the known fine structures of Earth's climate (see Crowley and North [1991] for a modern treatment of paleoclimate modeling). Five of these simplifying generalizations significantly affect our interpretation and so require discussion. They are: (1) bipolar averaging, (2) latitudinal gradient averaging, (3) ef-

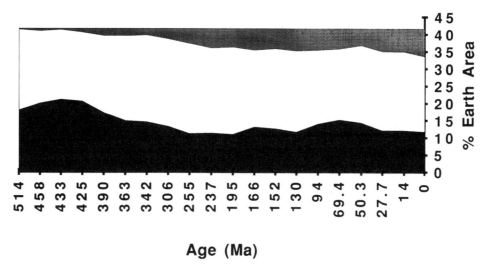

Figure 8. Restored continental crustal areas as a percentage of the Earth's surface assuming that measured ratio of shallow shelf to land is correct and that area of continental crust through time remains approximately constant.

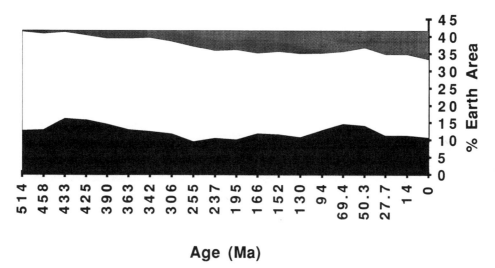

Figure 9. Restored continental crustal areas as a percentage of the Earth's surface assuming that measured shallow shelf area is correct, then increasing the area of land so as to keep continental crustal area constant through time.

fects of large landmasses, (4) hypsometry, and (5) ice-cap feedback effects.

Bipolarity. Not distinguishing between a world that has all its land in a single hemisphere (northern or southern) and one that equally distributes landmass between the two results in polar temperatures and latitudinal temperature gradients that are the average for both hemispheres and not necessarily representative of either. Although this procedure correctly captures "average" global conditions, it does not address the climatic consequences of the potential hemispheric temperature contrast that might result when distribution is not uniformly bipolar (e.g., Crowley et al., 1987; Ledley, 1988). The bipolar-

ity distortion is important because Phanerozoic history shows (Fig. 5) more land in the southern hemisphere during the Paleozoic and the reverse during the Cenozoic. These hemispheric differences have surely produced consequent climatic inequities with respect to polar and hemispheric albedos, temperatures, circulation, precipitation, seasonality, and diurnal temperature ranges that 2-10 does not directly capture. For example, the hemisphere with more land will obviously have the more continental climate. Therefore, we can expect that hemisphere to exhibit the consequences of more pronounced seasonality, as does today's Northern Hemisphere. It is not really possible to assign a percent error to such distortions, but we

T. R. Worsley and Others

will note their likely consequences when we review the chronology of climate change.

   Latitudinal gradient averaging. The 2-10 model assumes that pole-to-equator temperature gradient is linear with respect to the sine of latitude, so that the "average" global temperature occurs at 30° latitude. For today's world, the gradient is nonlinear, and the 15°C world average temperature occurs closer to 40° latitude (e.g., Held et al., 1981). If this difference per-

sists back through time, as is probable, then the 2-10 model estimates of past world temperatures remain reasonable but are likely to be too low for the mid-latitudes and too high for the high latitudes. Such a difference must be taken into account when trying to establish the temperature thresholds required to form ice caps.

   Large landmasses. Large landmasses (Gondwana, Pangea, and Eurasia) have existed throughout the Phanerozoic and have

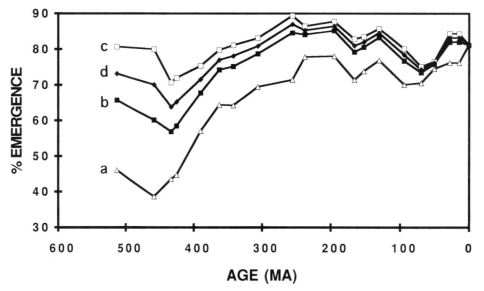

Figure 10. Percent emergence of continental crust through time: a (triangles) uses the values from Figure 7, b (solid squares) uses the values from Figure 8, c (open squares) uses the values from Figure 9, and d (closed diamonds) represents the midpoint between the shaded and open squares and our best estimate of emergence through time. Results are plotted relative to 18 ka when continents are assumed 100% emergent.

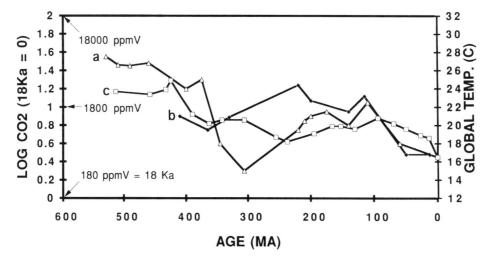

Figure 11. Comparison of a, the Berner (1990, 1991) reconstruction of Phanerozoic CO_2 (open triangle), with b, that of Cerling (1991) and Mora et al. (1991) (solid diamond), and c, the 2-10 model (open square), using the values for average global latitude and land area from Figures 7 and 8. Global paleotemperature results for all three curves are based on the 2-10 model. None of these curves compensates for increasing solar luminosity through time.

strongly influenced climate (see Crowley and North, 1991, for an excellent review). Yet the 2-10 model assigns them no particular importance because their greatest influence is upon seasonality, not average surface temperature (but see Ledley, 1988). Furthermore, although some guidance is provided by the characteristics of today's Eurasia, no simple unidirectional global temperature effects exist that can be universally applied.

Hypsometry. The windward and leeward effect of orography upon precipitation patterns is well known for today's world and certainly influenced previous paleogeographies (Raymo et al., 1988). Although important locally, the effect apparently does not exhibit a first-order influence on global temperature. However, uplift rates alter the exposure rates of silicates to chemical weathering (Raymo et al., 1988; Raymo, 1991) and so must influence CO_2 levels in the atmosphere. Hence, orogenies must indirectly lower global surface temperatures by some unknown factor (Raymo, 1991; Moore and Worsley, this volume). Other than to observe times when continent-continent collision during the Phanerozoic was likely to depress surface temperatures, we assign no quantitative effect to orogeny in this study.

Ice-cap feedback effects. We are of the opinion that the world exists in two mutually exclusive states: icehouse (when an ice cap[s] is in contact with the ocean) and non-icehouse. We also believe that once triggered, ice caps enter a positive feedback loop of rapid growth via increased elevation, albedo, and heat sink effects (Crowley and North, 1991). Furthermore, once established, ice caps are largely self-maintaining, and returning the world to the initial threshold conditions that trigger them will not necessarily destroy them. Alternatively, when conditions finally change sufficiently to destroy ice caps, reestablishment is highly unlikely under those conditions.

In other words, establishment and removal of ice caps exhibit hysteresis. This does not mean that large changes in ice volume are impossible once icehouse conditions are established, for indeed a progressive increase in Cenozoic ice volume that finally led to bipolar icecaps has been documented (e.g., Miller et al., 1987). Nor does it mean that rapid growth and decay of a particular ice sheet is not possible (witness the North American and European ice sheet growth and decay to the Milankovitch frequencies of 10^4 to 10^5 years for the past 3.5 million years; however, the Greenland ice cap always persists to seed new growth). Because ice sheets can grow and decay so rapidly, and hence alter land/sea ratios equally rapidly, it is clear that climate is much more stable in the non-icehouse world. We now consider the effect of rapidly modulating ice volume on the 2-10 model.

Because the 2-10 model is strictly a geochemistry/area driven model, it does not directly consider ice effects upon surface temperatures. Therefore, the main effect of ice volume modulation is in land area, which in turn feeds back into silicate weathering rates. The effect of high-latitude ice cover is ignored because little chemical weathering occurs at high latitude, with or without ice cover. Ice cover at temperate lati-

tudes would act as a negative feedback mechanism, inhibiting further glaciation.

The 2-10 model assumes 100% emergence for the 18-ka ice volume maximum versus 85% emergence today. The silicate-weathering result of the larger 18-ka land area is a 3°C colder world. Alternatively, complete melting of today's ice would decrease land area 6 to 7% and produce a 1°C warming. Thus, a 4° temperature difference results between times of maximum and minimum ice volume. A similar Milankovitch-modulated 20% oscillation in land surface area has likely occurred during past Phanerozoic icehouses and must be taken into account. For these times, we offer both maximum and minimum ice/land area estimates of surface temperatures using a 15% Milankovitch-increased land area for maximum icehouse conditions. We can use climatic analogies with Pleistocene icehouse conditions to tighten paleotemperature estimates for previous icehouses. These adjustments will be discussed along with interpretation of the paleogeographic reconstructions as appropriate.

Interpretation

Figure 11 compares the Phanerozoic CO_2 modeling results of Berner (1990, 1991; open triangles), Cerling (1991; solid diamonds), and Mora et al. (1991; solid diamonds) with those of this study (open squares). All three sets of results were arrived at by independent lines of evidence and are scaled to constant solar luminosity at today's value to facilitate comparison. Berner's results are based on Garrels and Lerman's (1981) geochemical cycling model with modifications using the Ronov (1976) and Barron et al. (1980) paleogeographic maps along with the Berner et al. (1983) CO_2 weathering feedback. The Cerling (1991) and Mora et al. (1991) results are based on carbon isotopic measurements on paleosol carbonate. The results of this study are based on the 2-10 model, the adjusted latitudes of Figure 6, and the unadjusted land areas of Figure 7.

We are fairly confident that the Sun has continually brightened in an approximately linear fashion for the past 4.5 g.y. from an initial value of about 70% of today's luminosity (e.g., Gilliland, 1989). Worsley and Nance (1989) calculate that such a trend would cause the Earth's surface to warm about 3°C/0.4 g.y. Such a tendency toward warming would have to be balanced by a halving of CO_2 levels in the atmosphere on the same time scale to preserve a constant temperature at the Earth's surface. To obtain actual CO_2 levels, one must include the 400-m.y. doubling time of CO_2 back through time. For instance, CO_2 levels would progressively increase back through time and by 400 Ma would be twice the values shown in Figure 11. Berner's and our modeling do not include the solar luminosity trend, but the Cerling (1991) and Mora et al. (1991) results do. Accordingly, we remove the luminosity trend from the paleosol results because it obscures graphic comparison of temperatures between intervals, which is our main concern.

Berner used a different paleogeographic data base (Barron et al., 1980; Ronov, 1976) and very different modeling methods than we do to obtain his CO_2 levels. He did not take into consideration paleolatitude or problems with apparent crustal growth, whereas we have done so. The very detailed model he used to calculate atmospheric CO_2 levels includes changes in CO_2 degassing rates as a function of changing seafloor spreading rates, biotic modification of weathering rates, isotope mass balance, calculations of organic carbon burial, and continental elevation, none of which we used in this study.

The Berner curve, although in qualitative agreement with this preliminary version of our curve (Fig. 11), shows much wider swings in CO_2 and temperature through time, especially in its very high CO_2 levels of the early Paleozoic. Berner himself pointed out the conflict of his results with the record of late Ordovician glaciation. However, we would like to point out the surprisingly small differences in the results given the very different modeling techniques that both authors used. Berner assigned a very wide error envelope (±300%) to his results for the early Paleozoic. Cerling (1991) and Mora et al. (1991) assigned about a ±50% error to their results. Ours are about ±100% for the same interval. Hence, the three sets of results overlap when the admittedly large error of each study is considered. We are encouraged that though we have used a less complex model, we have obtained a result that is qualitatively similar to Berner's much more detailed treatment and one that closely tracks the results from paleosol modeling. Unfortunately, none of these models avoid the dilemma of the very high Paleozoic CO_2 levels coeval with the Late Ordovician glaciation. We will now show that it may be possible to resolve this problem by adjusting the area of continental crust.

In Figure 12 the restored continental crustal areas shown in Figure 10b were used to estimate CO_2 levels and global temperature. Cretaceous and Ordovician temperature peaks are reduced from 22°C and 25°C to 20°C and 22°C, respectively. Likewise, the late Permian/early Triassic and Late Ordovician minima are reduced from about 18°C to 16°C, and 24°C to 16°C, respectively. Taking into account crustal restoration, Cambrian temperatures are now similar to those of the Cretaceous, and temperatures of the mid-Ordovician are similar to today's. Such temperatures are clearly more realistic and permissive of late Ordovician ice sheets.

Figures 13 and 14 show the Phanerozoic history of equatorial and polar surface temperatures generated using the 2-10 model and our best estimates of paleolatitude (Fig. 6b) and continental emergence (Fig. 10b). We cannot show equivalent values for the Berner (1990, 1991) studies as he did not consider the continental paleolatitude information necessary for such temperature reconstruction. The plotted equatorial and polar temperatures represent regions from 0° to 8° and 60° to 90° latitude respectively. We consider the equatorial temperatures (Fig. 13) to be good estimates, because tropical temperatures change little within 8° latitude of the equator. However, the same is not true for the polar temperatures, which appear to be too warm. The "polar" temperatures (Fig. 14) are not the temperatures at the pole, but rather they are an average temperature for the region between 60° and 90° latitude. Because surface temperatures are known to drop rapidly toward the poles (e.g., Held et al., 1981), the poles themselves are likely to be significantly colder. For today's world, the difference is about 10°C (Held et al., 1981). For warm worlds with intrinsically low pole-to-equator temperature gradients (e.g., Cretaceous), the difference will be less. The criteria that define polar temperature are therefore not trivial, because it is the actual temperature at a site, not the average temperature of the

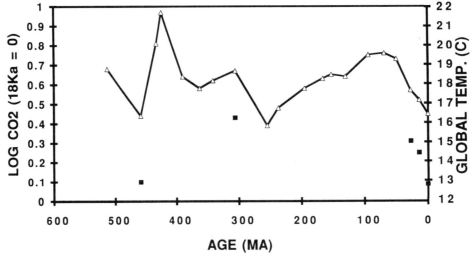

Figure 12. Phanerozoic CO_2 levels and global temperatures (open triangles) calculated using the average global latitudes of Figure 6 and our best estimate of emergence through time (Fig. 10). The black squares are CO_2 and temperature values resulting from a 15% increase in emergence during times of maximum icehouse conditions.

polar region, that determines whether ice caps will form. The question that we must now consider is: What is the maximum average polar area temperature that would permit an ice cap to nucleate?

Comparison of Figure 14 temperatures with the geologic record suggests that ice caps can grow with average polar temperatures below 8°C. Of course, once an ice cap is established, positive feedback effects such as albedo (see Crowley and North, 1991, for a review) result in a further lowering of surface temperatures and the "autocatalytic" growth of the ice cap. We observe here that another geochemical feedback mechanism also operates to further amplify ice-cap growth

once initiated. When ice caps sequester ocean water, continental emergence increases. Increased emergence provides more silicate to weather and therefore operates to consume CO_2, further lowering temperature. Accordingly, we plot ice-cap-lowered values of CO_2 and temperature that would result from a 15% ice-cap-increased land area on Figures 12 through 14.

DISCUSSION OF THE PALEOGEOGRAPHIC RECONSTRUCTIONS

Because the presence of ice is the only indisputable indicator we have for the Earth's surface temperature, we will bias our discussion toward the evidence for ice. Consequently, it is

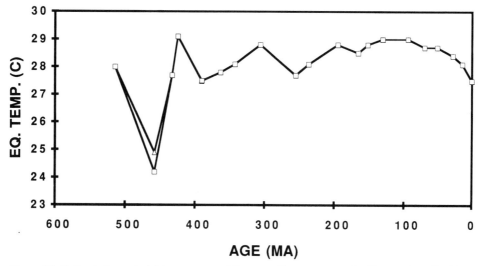

Figure 13. Estimated equatorial temperatures. The upper line represents the "best estimate" of land area and the lower line the best estimate of land area during glacial maximum.

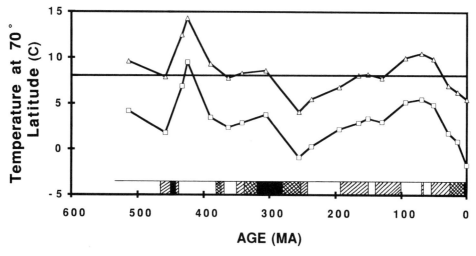

Figure 14. Surface temperatures at 70° latitude. Upper line = non-icehouse world. Lower line = icehouse world. The bar at the bottom summarizes the ice-cap history of Crowell (1983) and the sea-ice history of Frakes and Francis (1988). Solid black represents intervals with evidence for glacioeustatic cycles. The crosshatches indicate intervals with ice caps that seem not to greatly affect eustasy. Right slanting shading indicates sea ice without ice caps.

the history of the sharply fluctuating polar temperatures generated by the 2-10 model (Fig. 14), not the monotonous history of stable equatorial temperatures (Fig. 13), that will be the main focus of discussion. Our main tie points between the 2-10 model and the geologic record will be the study of Frakes and Francis (1988) that plots the Phanerozoic history of ice rafting and the review of Crowell (1983) of the history of Phanerozoic ice caps. Both are summarized on Figure 14. We will also use Figure 5 to determine whether high-latitude land was available to accommodate ice sheets when the 2-10 model indicates polar temperatures were cold enough to nucleate them. We will use other such helpful paleoclimatic indicators as vertebrates and floristic evidence, oxygen isotopes, evaporites, and carbonates to test the prediction of the 2-10 model.

Paleozoic results

We begin our discussion of the surface temperature history of the Phanerozoic with the late Cambrian (514 Ma). Average continental latitudes (35°) were slightly higher than today's, but emergence was much less (73%). Continental configuration, unlike today's, was unipolar, with no land north of 30°N latitude and little north of the equator. However, land was relatively uniformly distributed across latitude, characterizing the reconstruction as a unipolar sliceworld (Figs. 3 and 4). There is no evidence of ice, which is consistent with a high polar temperature of about 10°C owing to the relatively low emergence of the continents.

By middle-late Ordovician (458 Ma), the world landmass remained mainly in the southern hemisphere but rapidly migrated toward the equator. It attained an average latitude of about 25°, the lowest for the entire Phanerozoic, and approached ringworld conditions (Figs. 3 and 4). At the same time, the continents became slightly (70%) less emergent. The strong equatorward movement of the landmass dominated the slight warming effects due to the drowning, to produce colder polar temperatures of 7°C. Evidence for ice rafting (Frakes and Francis, 1988) but not ice caps exists for this time. Although the poles were cold enough to produce ice caps by our reckoning, no polar land was available (Fig. 5) to accommodate them. Interestingly, this reconstruction also represents the coldest equatorial temperature (25°C, Fig. 13) of the entire Phanerozoic.

Figures 5 and 6 show that between the Middle Ordovician and the Early Silurian the world landmass rapidly migrated poleward by about 10° of latitude. By 425 Ma, it moved yet another 5° poleward so that the average of the continents was about 40°—the highest average latitude of the Phanerozoic. During the same time interval, land area shrank another 5% to only 65% emergence (Fig. 10)—the minimum emergence of the entire Phanerozoic. Such dramatic shifts in such a short time interval would be expected to have equally dramatic climatic consequences, and they do. First we observe that the twofold greenhouse enhancement is clearly manifested by polar temperatures that rise from 7°C to 14°C, the warmest of

the entire Phanerozoic. Equatorial temperatures, also the warmest during the Phanerozoic (Fig. 13), show a 4°C shift from 25°C to 29°C.

Evidence for ice rafting exists from about 460 to 430 Ma and an ice cap occurs for a brief—perhaps 5-million-year—interval, centering on 440 Ma (Fig. 14). We adopt the suggestion of Crowley et al. (1987) to explain the ice cap as follows. Figures 5 and 6 show landmass (Gondwana) rapidly migrating toward the South Pole from 458 to 425 Ma. Interpolation suggests that the edge of Gondwana reached the pole about 440 Ma. When Gondwanaland centered on the pole ~425 Ma, average polar temperature peaked. The lack of any polar land at 458 Ma made ice-cap formation improbable. As the edge of the Gondwana landmass reached the South Pole, polar temperatures, although climbing, were still only about 8°C and hence still within the ice-cap threshold.

Having the edge of a landmass at the pole provides an ideal moisture transport versus temperature situation to trigger the growth of an ice cap. Ice-cap formation becomes more difficult as the landmass centers over the pole because of moisture transport difficulties (Crowley et al., 1987). Once initiated, the ice cap entered the positive feedback stage of increasing elevation and albedo (Crowley et al., 1987; Crowley and North, 1991). Figure 14 indicates the lowered polar temperatures that were likely to result from ice-cap formation. However, even these ice-cap enhancing effects were rapidly overcome as the average latitude of the landmass increased, making the poles warmer and warmer. When Gondwana finally centered over the pole by 425 Ma, the edge-effect ice-cap scenario was lost. The result was an ice-free world. In this scenario, we would expect ice to reappear should Gondwanaland's margin again approach the pole.

The temperature changes from the Middle Silurian (425 Ma) to the Late Devonian (363 Ma) are the opposite of the previous interval. The diagrams show decreasing average landmass latitude from 425 Ma to 390 Ma (40° to 32° at 390 Ma, Fig. 7) and increasing emergence (65% to 71% emergence, Fig. 10). Polar temperatures plummeted from a high of 14°C in the Middle Silurian to 8°C during the Late Devonian. However, the ice cap does not appear to have been large enough to have caused major glacioeustatic effects and soon decayed as average landmass latitude (and polar temperature) increased slightly by the end of the Devonian. Ice rafting declined as well but soon reappeared, heralding the appearance of the long-lasting and intense Carboniferous icehouse world.

The interval from Early Devonian to Late Carboniferous shows continuous increase in average landmass latitude from 32°C to 37°C (Fig. 7). The interval from Middle Silurian to Late Permian shows a continuous increase in emergence from 65% to 87% (Fig. 10c). The polar temperature curve clearly shows that the cooling caused by increased emergence dominated the warming caused by increasing landmass latitude to produce declining polar temperatures that finally stabilized at about 8°C by Late Devonian. Thereafter, increasing landmass latitude balanced increasing emergence to keep polar temperatures very near 8°C (the icehouse threshold) until 306 Ma.

With increasing emergence, ice rafting reappears during the Early Carboniferous and persists until Early Triassic (240 Ma). Ice caps appear at about 340 Ma, attain glacio-eustatic proportions at 320 Ma, lose glacioeustatic proportions at 280 Ma, and totally disappear at about 260 Ma. Figure 14 illustrates the cold (4°C) polar temperatures that would characterize an ice-covered world at 306 Ma. We emphasize here that this situation is not exactly analogous to the 18-ka situation of 100% emergence because there was no land at the North Pole until the Triassic. Hence, the Carboniferous ice cap of the southern hemisphere was likely to be colder than the antipodal water-dominated northern hemisphere pole (Crowley and North, 1991). As our "polar temperature" represents the average of the two poles, the Gondwana pole was likely to be colder than shown in Figure 14, and the northern hemisphere pole was likely to be warmer.

Results (Fig. 14) show poles that continue to cool between 306 and 255 Ma while the ice caps simultaneously decayed and disappeared. The Berner results (Fig. 11) show a temperature increase for the same interval, which clearly agrees better with the geologic evidence. Why does the 2-10 model fail here? We suspect that the reason is our neglect of the effect of organic carbon burial and orogeny. The wholesale use of highly refractory cellulose and lignin to build the canopies of the Carboniferous forests surely resulted in a large increase in inorganic carbon burial (Worsley et al., 1986; Worsley and Nance, 1989; Berner, 1990). Such an increase surely enhanced ice-cap potential during the Carboniferous, but the enhancement should have continued to help maintain an ice cap into the Permian and Triassic. Instead, the ice decays within the early Permian. Why? We favor the explanation of Robinson (1990), who reported that because the use of cellulose and lignin was novel to the biota, those compounds would undergo high burial rates until forms that could digest them (e.g., fungi and termites) evolved. Digestion of cellulose and lignin then restored organic carbon burial to the previously lower rates.

Orogenic effects were probably also important. It is no coincidence that the equatorial Alleghenian Orogeny occurred in the Carboniferous and enhanced silicate weathering. The non-equatorial Uralian orogeny that succeeded the Alleghenian in the Permian was probably no match in terms of silicate weathering enhancement (Moore and Worsley, this volume). Orogenic effects also may have modified the climate across the central regions of Pangea. In Europe and North America the climate was much dryer during the Permian and Triassic, resulting in lower rates of organic carbon production and burial.

Mesozoic and Cenozoic results

The surface temperature record from Triassic to Recent is much better constrained and is dominated by the progressive and mainly latitude-parallel breakup of Pangea (except for the latitude-perpendicular motion of India and Australia late in the breakup). Hence, the temperature record is consistent with the progressive submergence of the continents to a minimum land area at about 100 Ma, followed by progressive reemergence to the present. During the same time interval, average landmass latitudes decrease slightly as the small India and Australia landmasses leave high temperate latitudes and move equatorward during the Cenozoic.

The paleogeographic and paleoclimatic record is well understood compared to that of the Paleozoic, for several reasons. First, plate tectonic reconstructions become progressively better with the availability of magnetic anomaly data for the ocean regions. Second, the geologic record becomes progressively more complete and enhanced by the record from deep sea drilling. Finally, ancillary paleotemperature indicators such as land plants and animals, oxygen isotopes, and other marine paleotemperature indicators become increasingly accurate as we approach the present. We do not intend to belabor the predictions of the 2-10 model for this relatively well understood interval because it was the information from this interval that was used to calibrate the 2-10 model in the first place (Worsley and Kidder, 1991). Hence, using 2-10 to "explain" paleoclimate in detail for the interval would be circular. Instead we will note the major highlights.

The Triassic represents transition from a unipolar to a bipolar land distribution (Fig. 5). Average landmass latitude drops to 32° at 255 Ma as Pangea crosses the equator, but then again climbs to 40° by 195 Ma as northern hemisphere landmasses attain high latitudes and the equatorial Tethys seaway develops (Fig. 5). Emergence peaks at 87% at 255 Ma, declines to 85% at 237 Ma, and again increases to 86% at 195 Ma. The landmass latitude and emergence algorithm leads the 2-10 model to specify an ever-increasing polar temperature from 255 until 69 Ma (Fig. 14).

The Triassic remains the only period of the Phanerozoic for which no evidence of ice exists (Frakes and Francis, 1988). Yet the lack of ice is puzzling because so much of the land was situated at intermediate latitudes and at both poles (Figs. 5, 6, and 10). According to the 2-10 model, the world remained colder than the ice threshold (Fig. 14) until about 130 Ma. Dropstones are present throughout the late Permian, disappear in the Triassic, and reappear in the Jurassic and early Cretaceous, indicating at least seasonal ice. But there is no evidence for ice caps. We are forced to conclude that the absence of ice caps during this interval suggests that revisions are needed in the 2-10 model or that the nonglacial climate has a cause that is not accounted for in the 2-10 model. Biotic innovations that would lead to increased organic carbon burial were few during the interval (Worsley and Nance, 1989), whereas those that would slow it were being developed (Robinson, 1990). Monsoons, seasonality, and diurnal temperature range were at an extreme on the large pole-to-pole Pangean landmass (Crowley and North, 1991), and aridity would have been high because a large fraction of the supercontinent was situated in the desert belts. The early Triassic "coal gap" (Veevers, this volume) lends support to the notion of aridity during the early and middle Triassic. Increased mantle degassing during the breakup of Pangea (Larson, 1991, a, b) is possible, but the warming trend seems to precede breakup. Given the above, the Triassic is a fine choice for the forthcoming detailed climatic studies of Project Pangea.

The mainly latitude-parallel breakup of Pangea begins in earnest with the opening of the North Atlantic during the early Jurassic and is followed by a series of rifting events that continue to the present. Passive margin subsidence leads to progressive flooding of the continents that peaks in the late Cretaceous. Because the world landmass hardly changed latitude during the Jurassic and Cretaceous, the polar temperature increase (Fig. 14) was caused by continued submergence of the world landmass. High-latitude dropstones (Frakes and Francis, 1988) appeared in the early Jurassic, persisted into the early Cretaceous, and then ceased at ~100 Ma. The poles were slightly colder than the ice-cap threshold until early Cretaceous, according to the 2-10 model (Fig. 14), then became too warm to harbor ice. Apparently, ice-cap-triggering events were absent during the dropstone interval until it became too warm for even seasonal ice.

The world remained essentially ice free during the late Cretaceous and Paleocene until dropstones reappeared in the early Eocene. Antarctica grew an ice cap during the Oligocene (Miller et al., 1987) that continually expanded during the Late Cenozoic. It was joined by another in Greenland in the Pliocene. The 2-10 model predicts a continued reemergence of the world landmass from the late Cretaceous (Fig. 10) to the present and a 5° equatorward latitudinal shift in its average latitude (Fig. 6). Both serve to make the world colder, again permitting sea ice by the latest Cretaceous and ice caps by the Oligocene. The appearance of northern hemisphere icecaps in the Pliocene again allowed the Milankovitch-mediated cyclical sedimentation. Minimum polar temperatures for maximum ice-cap-induced marine regression are plotted on Figure 14.

CONCLUSIONS AND FUTURE WORK

The application of the 2-10 climatic model to the history of Phanerozoic paleogeography clearly shows that major progress can be made in explaining the surface temperature history of the Earth in terms of the geochemical maintenance of atmospheric CO_2. Using only the area of land and its average latitude as variables that control the intensity of CO_2 mediated weathering, we have outlined a history of Phanerozoic CO_2 levels. Using these model-generated CO_2 levels, we have described a plausible history of global, equatorial, and polar surface temperatures for the Phanerozoic. This model-generated temperature record is in good agreement with geologic evidence for the history of ice on the planet, with the exception of the Triassic. Our modeling results indicate that the Triassic was cold and should contain ice, whereas the geologic record shows the Triassic to be the only ice-free period of the Phanerozoic. In light of our failure to understand Triassic climate, we find it especially fortunate that Project Panjea will address the problems of Triassic climate.

Although we are pleased and pleasantly surprised by our results, we emphasize that changes in paleogeography are not the only cause of climate change. Major progress in the understanding of the other processes that affect the CO_2 content of the atmosphere will surely refine our estimates of CO_2 -mediated surface temperatures through time. Orogeny (see Moore and Worsley, this volume) certainly influences chemical weathering, and it is no coincidence that many Phanerozoic orogenies correspond to times of icehouse conditions. Thus we speculate that lack of orogeny during the Triassic may have influenced its non-icehouse climate. Further modification of the 2-10 climate model must therefore include the effects of orogeny upon chemical weathering.

Organic carbon burial, although never the major sink for CO_2 removal, has been a significant and variable sink for CO_2 through time. The variables that control organic carbon burial must be addressed and incorporated into future versions of the 2-10 model if more accurate climate characterization is to be attained. Mantle degassing changes through time represent a real "wild card" to all paleoclimatic modeling efforts because degassing changes surely represent a major perturbation upon atmospheric CO_2 levels. Unfortunately, mantle degassing rates are not easily extracted from the geologic record. The application of sophisticated general circulation models to pre-Pleistocene times, which is in its infancy, will likely add considerable refinement to our picture of Phanerozoic climate change. We await the results of the application of general circulation models that Project Pangea will use to characterize the climates of a supercontinent. Finally, we can expect continual incremental improvements in data acquisition and in existing analytic and modeling techniques to improve our picture of Phanerozoic climate history.

ACKNOWLEDGMENTS

We are grateful to Tom Algeo and Bob Berner for their thoughtful and highly constructive reviews of a hastily assembled initial manuscript. Likewise, we owe George Klein our deep gratitude for the constant prodding to meet deadlines and for his final editing of the manuscript. The timely appearance of this volume attests to his diligence.

REFERENCES CITED

Barnola, J. M., Raynaud, D., Korotkevich, Y. S., and Loris, C., 1987, Vostok ice core provides 160,000-year record of atmospheric CO$_2$: Nature, v. 329, p. 408–414.

Barron, E. J., Sloan, J. L., and Harrison, C.G.A., 1980, Potential significance of land-sea distributions and surface albedo variations as a climatic forcing factor; 180 million years ago to the present: Palaeogeography, Palaeoclimatology, Palaeoecology, v. 30, p. 17–40.

Berner, R. A., 1990, Atmospheric carbon dioxide levels over Phanerozoic time: Science, v. 249, p. 1382–1386.

Berner, R. A., 1991, A model of atmospheric CO$_2$ over Phanerozoic time: American Journal of Science, v. 291, p. 339–376.

Berner, R. A., Lasaga, A. C., and Garrels, R. M., 1983, The carbonate-silicate geochemical cycle and its effect on atmospheric carbon dioxide over the past 100 million years: American Journal of Science, v. 283, p. 641–683.

Brady, P. V., 1991, The effect of silicate weathering on global temperature and atmospheric CO$_2$: Journal of Geophysical Research, v. 96, p. 18101–18106.

Cerling, T. C., 1991, Carbon dioxide in the atmosphere: Evidence from Cenozoic and Mesozoic paleosols: American Journal of Science, v. 291, p. 377–400.

Chamberlin, T. C., 1899, An attempt to frame a working hypothesis of the cause of glacial periods on an atmospheric basis: Journal of Geology, v. 7, p. 545–584, 667–685, 751–787.

CLIMAP Project Members, 1976, The surface of the ice age Earth: Science, v. 191, p. 1131–1137.

Crowell, J. C., 1983, Ice ages recorded on Gondwanan continents: Transactions of the Geological Society of South Africa, v. 86, p. 237–262.

Crowley, T. J., and North, G. R., 1991, Paleoclimatology: New York, Oxford University Press, 339 p.

Crowley, T. J., Mengel, J. G., and Short, D. A., 1987, Gondwanaland's seasonal cycle: Nature, v. 329, p. 803–807.

Dockal, J. A., Laws, R. A., and Worsley, T. R., 1989, A general mathematical model for balanced global isostasy: Mathematical Geology, v. 21, p. 147–170.

Frakes, L.L A., and Francis, J. E., 1988, A guide to Phanerozoic cold polar climates from high-latitude ice-rafting in the Cretaceous: Nature, v. 333, p. 547–549.

Garrels, R. M., and Lerman, A., 1981, Phanerozoic cycles of sedimentary carbon and sulfur: National Academy of Science Proceedings, v. 78, p. 4652–4656.

Gilliland, R. L., 1989, Solar evolution: Palaeogeography, Palaeoclimatology, Palaeoecology (Global and Planetary change section), v. 75, p. 35–55.

Hallam, A., 1981, Facies interpretation and the stratigraphic record: Oxford, Freeman, 291 p.

Held, I. M., Linder, D. I., and Suarez, M. J., 1981, Albedo feedback, the meridional structure of the effective heat diffusivity and climate sensitivity: Results from dynamic and diffusive models: Journal of Atmospheric Science, v. 38, p. 1911–1927.

Hyde, W. T., Kim, K., Crowley, T. J., and North, G. R., 1990, On the relation between polar continentality and climate: Studies with a nonlinear seasonal energy balance model: Journal of Geophysical Research, v. 95, p. 18635–18668.

Kuhn, W. R., Walker, J.C.G., and Marshall, H. G., 1989, The effect on Earth's surface temperature from variations in rotation rate, continent formation, solar luminosity and carbon dioxide: Journal of Geophysical Research, v. 94, p. 9776–9782.

Larson, R. L., 1991a, Geological consequences of superplumes: Geology, v. 19, p. 963–966.

Larson, R. L., 1991b, Latest pulse of Earth: Evidence of a mid-Cretaceous superplume: Geology, v. 19, p. 547–550.

Lasaga, A. C., Berner, R. A., and Garrels, R. M., 1985, An improved geochemical model of atmospheric CO$_2$ fluctuations over the past 100 million years, *in* Sundquist, E. T., and Broeker, W. S., eds., The carbon cycle and atmospheric CO$_2$: Natural variations Archean to present, Washington, D.C., American Geophysical Union Geophysical Monograph Series, v. 32, p. 397–411.

Ledley, T. S., 1988, A wandering Gondwanaland's impact on summer temperatures: Geophysical Research Letters, v. 15, p. 1397–1400.

Marshall, H. G., Walker, J.C.G., and Kuhn, W. R., 1988, Long-term climate change and the geochemical cycle of oxygen: Journal of Geophysical Research, v. 93, p. 791–801.

Miller, K. G., Fairbanks, R. G., and Mountain, G. S., 1987, Tertiary oxygen isotope synthesis, sea level history, and continental margin erosion: Paleoceanography, v. 1, p. 1–19.

Mora, C. I., Driese, S. G., and Seager, P. G., 1991, Carbon dioxide in the Paleozoic: Evidence from carbon-isotope compositions of pedogenic carbonate: Geology, v. 19, p. 1017–1020.

Raymo, M. E., 1991, Geochemical evidence supporting T. C. Chamberlin's theory of glaciation: Geology, v. 19, p. 344–347.

Raymo, M. E., Ruddiman, W. F., and Froelich, P. N., 1988, Influence of late Cenozoic mountain building on ocean geochemical cycles: Geology, v. 16, p. 649–653.

Robinson, J. M., 1990, Lignin land plants and fungi: Biological evolution affecting Phanerozoic oxygen balance: Geology, v. 15, p. 607–610.

Ronov, A. B., 1976, Global carbon geochemistry, volcanism, carbonate accumulation, and life: Geokhimiya, v. 8, p. 1252–1277.

Schwartzman, D. W., and Volk, T., 1989, Biotic enhancement of weathering and the habitability of the Earth: Nature, v. 340, p. 457–460.

Scotese, C. R., and Golonka, J., 1992, PALEOMAP paleogeographic Atlas: Department of Geology, University of Texas at Arlington, PALEOMAP Progress Report 20, 32 p.

Strakhov, N. M., 1948, Fundamentals of historical geology: Moscow, Gosqeolizdat, Moscow, 632 p.

Termier, H., and Termier, G., 1952, Histoire geologique de la biosphere: Paris, Masson, 721 p.

Urey, H. C., 1952, The planets, their origin and development: New Haven, Yale University Press, 245 p.

Van der Voo, R., 1990, The reliability of paleomagnetic data: Tectonophysics, v. 184, p. 1–9.

Walker, J.G.C., Hays, P. B., and Kasting, J. K., 1981, A negative feedback mechanism for the long-term stabilization of Earth's surface temperature: Journal of Geophysical Research, v. 86, p. 9776–9782.

Windley, B. F., 1984, The evolving continents, 2d ed.: New York, John Wiley, 399 p.

Worsley, T. R., and Kidder, D. L., 1991, First-order coupling of paleogeography and CO$_2$, with global surface temperature and its latitudinal contrast: Geology, v. 19, p. 1161–1164.

Worsley, T. R., and Nance, R. D., 1989, Carbon redox and climate control through earth history: A speculative reconstruction: Palaeogeography, Palaeoclimatology, Palaeoecology, v. 75, p. 259–282.

Worsley, T. R., Nance, R. D., and Moody, J. B., 1986, Tectonic cycles and the history of the Earth's biogeochemical and paleoceanographic record. Paleoceanography, v. 1, p. 233–263.

Worsley, T. R., Nance, R. D., and Moody, J. B., 1991, Tectonics, carbon, life, and climate for the last three billion years: A unified system? *in* Schneider, S. H., and Boston, P. J., eds., Scientists on Gaia: The MIT Press, Cambridge, p. 200–210.

MANUSCRIPT ACCEPTED BY THE SOCIETY MAY 14, 1993

Geological Society of America
Special Paper 288
1994

Orogenic enhancement of weathering and continental ice-sheet initiation

Thomas L. Moore
Department of Geosciences, University of Arizona, Tucson, Arizona 85721-2979
Thomas R. Worsley
Department of Geological Sciences, Ohio University, Athens, Ohio 45701

ABSTRACT

Although geochemical weathering of highlands associated with orogeny can sufficiently remove enough atmospheric CO_2 to cool global climate and possibly initiate glacial epochs, the height of an orogenic belt is not the only major control of geochemical weathering rates. The latitudinal position of an orogenic belt also strongly influences the rate of geochemical weathering. If we assume as a first approximation that precipitation increases with temperature, the silicate weathering rate of an orogenic belt would always be greatest at the warm low latitudes and decrease toward higher latitudes. The actual weathering rate and its weathering gradient with latitude would depend on the specific equatorial and polar temperatures involved. Those temperatures are in turn governed by the geochemical weathering of the global landmass. Equatorial and polar temperatures are coldest when the continents are completely emergent and at the equator. They are warmest for maximally drowned continents situated on the pole. The cooling effect of geochemical weathering of a low-latitude orogenic belt is most intense for a warm world in which a majority of the global landmass is at high latitudes.

The relative silicate weathering enhancement rates for several orogenies that occurred during the Phanerozoic were estimated using initial geochemically modeled climatic conditions, the average latitude of the global landmass, and the average latitude of an orogeny (with orogenic characteristics "standardized" to the modern Himalayas). The only obvious case where an orogeny could have initiated a glacial epoch is during the Carboniferous, when the Alleghany orogen formed at low latitudes. Other cases are equivocal. The Taconic orogeny during the late Ordovician and early Silurian, the Acadian orogeny during the Early Devonian, and the early Himalayan orogeny during the Cenozoic could have contributed to the formation of continental ice sheets, but geochemical conditions for ice formation were already borderline favorable for continental ice, so it is not known whether the orogenies were actual triggers. Orogenies are certainly among the major contributors to global cooling but usually are not the sole cause of glacial epochs.

INTRODUCTION

Earth's climatic history shows a record of global mean surface temperatures that appear not to have deviated from that of the present day by more than ±15°C for the past 3 g.y.

(Kuhn et al., 1989). Fischer (1984) suggested that Earth's Phanerozoic climate fluctuated between icehouse conditions (an ice-containing world characterized by strong latitudinal temperature gradients, low mean ocean temperatures, active oceanic convection, and highly oxygenated oceans) and green-

Moore, T. L., and Worsley, T. R., 1994, Orogenic enhancement of weathering and continental ice-sheet initiation, *in* Klein, G. D., ed., Pangea: Paleoclimate, Tectonics, and Sedimentation During Accretion, Zenith, and Breakup of a Supercontinent: Boulder, Colorado, Geological Society of America Special Paper 288.

house conditions (an ice-free world characterized by low latitudinal temperature gradients, relatively warm polar regions, high mean ocean temperature, weak oceanic convection, and poorly oxygenated oceans). Climatic swings between these extremes have been on the order of ~10°C (e.g., Worsley and Kidder, 1991). For this study, the term *icehouse* will be reserved exclusively for those periods in Earth history in which a continental ice sheet was in contact with the sea.

Causes of icehouse conditions have long been subject to debate; they include astronomical, biotic, and tectonic forcings of circulation and geochemistry. Books by Frakes (1979) and Crowley and North (1991) provide an excellent general review of paleoclimatology, including summaries of the evidence of and theories of climatic change through Earth history. The articles by Walker et al. (1981), Berner et al. (1983), Fischer (1984), Worsley et al. (1984), Worsley et al. (1985), Worsley et al. (1986), Marshall et al. (1988), Bluth and Kump (1991), Raymo (1991), Ruddiman and Kutzbach (1991), Berner (1991), Worsley and Kidder (1991), Raymo and Ruddiman (1992), and Worsley et al. (this volume) emphasize one or more of the astronomical, biotic, tectonic, lithologic, and geochemical aspects of climate forcing. Each of these general causes of climate change could independently, or concurrently, be sufficient to induce ice nucleation if other preconditions are favorable. The effects of orogeny upon the CO_2 content of the atmosphere and its consequent effects on climate form the subject of this study.

OROGENIC CAUSES

Chamberlin (1899) was the first to propose an orogenic theory of glaciation. His model suggested that high chemical weathering rates associated with an orogeny would increase CO_2 consumption, resulting in a reduced CO_2 greenhouse and, hence, a cooler global climate. He therefore proposed that an icehouse would occur only if drawdown of CO_2, owing to silicate weathering, exceeded addition of CO_2 from mantle sources. He further suggested that postorogenic weathering would have to continue long enough to remove three times the present atmospheric CO2 to lower temperature enough for continental ice sheets to form.

Raymo et al. (1988) reviewed Chamberlin's hypothesis by examining possible effects of the Himalayas, Andes, and Tibetan Plateau on global climate. They suggested that relief influences the rate of silicate weathering and, therefore, the flux of dissolved solids to the sea and that it does so in three main ways. First, rapid uplift and the associated high mechanical weathering rates expose silicate minerals to chemical weathering and remove inert coatings that act as chemical weathering inhibitors (Stallard and Edmond, 1983). Second, dissolved river loads, which indicate silicate weathering, would be dominated by the weathering of uplifted sedimentary formations and as a result would be higher than those of well-weathered lowlands (Stallard and Edmond, 1983). Finally,

precipitation and runoff will increase, thereby increasing chemical and mechanical weathering rates (Schmitz, 1987). In support of these three assumptions, Raymo et al. (1988) found a qualitative correlation between the increase in dissolved solids in global water discharge and orogenic uplift for the past 5 m.y. Evidence exists for rapid uplift in the Himalayas and Tibet (Hsu, 1978; Saini et al., 1979; Burbank and Johnson, 1983; West, 1984; Harrison et al., 1992) and in the Andes (Allmendinger, 1986; Benjamin et al., 1987) during this interval. The last 5 m.y. also corresponds to the appearance of continental ice in the Northern Hemisphere (Leg 105 Shipboard Scientific Party, 1986).

Raymo et al. (1988) suggested that the uplift and the associated increase of continental weathering during this 5-m.y. interval would have affected the flux of dissolved carbonates (Ca, Sr) entering the ocean. Calcium carbonate deposition rates and radiogenic (continental crust–derived) Sr fluxes have indeed been increasing during this interval (Davies et al., 1977; Elderfield, 1986; Delaney and Boyle, 1988). The increase in carbonate deposition rates could be attributed to weathering of uplifted carbonates and redeposition in the ocean and, to a lesser extent, to chemical weathering of silicates, which releases calcium to form carbonates from atmospheric CO_2.

The increase of carbonate deposition could be an artifact of carbonate preservation (Moore and Heath, 1977). To evaluate this possibility, Raymo et al. (1988) studied trends in the calcite compensation depth (CCD). The CCD should have deepened as the oceans became more saturated with carbonates due to an increase of the $CaCO_3$-flux. Delaney and Boyle (1988) have shown that the CCD has deepened ~350 m during the last 5 m.y. One can infer that the pelagic $CaCO_3$-flux has increased.

The increase of radiogenic Sr entering the ocean could be attributable to uniformly increased continental weathering. Other explanations include a 40% decrease in hydrothermal fluxes, a 95% decrease in the redissolution flux, or an increase of the proportions of silicate weathering on land by ~16% at the expense of the nonsilicate weathering rate (Palmer and Elderfield, 1985). Raymo et al. (1988) discounted these possibilities because all would require a decrease of the $CaCO_3$-flux, whereas the carbonate sedimentation rates and the deepening of the CCD show the opposite. If the volume of reactants being weathered increased, as shown by Ca and Sr fluxes associated with the recent uplift, then it follows that silicate weathering and associated CO_2 removal from the atmosphere have also increased. This establishes the possibility that the recent uplift could be a contributing cause of the continental ice-sheet formation in the Northern Hemisphere

Raymo (1991) then investigated the possibility that other orogenies caused ice to form throughout Earth's history. Because determination of pre-Mesozoic rates of global carbonate deposition are unreliable, only variations in $\partial^{87}Sr$ were used. $\partial^{87}Sr$ ratios often become more radiogenic (higher in ^{87}Sr due to high silicate weathering rates) when continental ice sheets are present (Crowell, 1983; Koepnick et al., 1988). The presence of ice and high radiogenic Sr values often corresponded with orogenies. This combination occurs during the latest Precambrian (Veizer et al., 1983), during the late Ordovician and early Silurian (Raymo, 1991), during the Carboniferous (Raymo, 1991), and during the Late Cenozoic (Raymo, 1991). Although circumstantial, this relationship between times of known orogeny, icehouses, and high radiogenic Sr flux presents a strong argument for the association of uplift and the development of an icehouse.

This review documents a potential link between orogenic uplift, enhanced silicate weathering, and icehouses. It is important to observe that an orogens effect on silicate weathering and climate is still a second-order perturbation to the major controls of silicate weathering on land (Worsley et al., this volume). As such, orogenically enhanced silicate weathering is more likely to trigger an icehouse when polar temperatures are already near the threshold that would permit continental ice sheets to form. Any enhanced silicate weathering model for orogens must first consider primary nonorogenic controls of silicate weathering to allow world temperatures low enough to permit triggering an icehouse by an orogenic event.

NONOROGENIC FACTORS

For time scales $>10^5$ years, CO_2 levels are controlled by a simple cycle that shows climate as a balance of CO_2 inputs to and outputs from the atmosphere (Walker et al., 1981; see Fig. 1 of Worsley et al., this volume). Mantle degassing, via seafloor spreading and subduction, is the primary source of CO_2. Carbon dioxide thus released into the atmosphere mixes with water vapor to form carbonic acid. Some of this acid will fall onto the land, reacting with calcium-bearing silicate minerals as in the following simplified summary reactions (Walker et al., 1981; Berner et al., 1983; Berner, 1990; Berner, 1991):

$$CO_2 + CaSiO_3 <==> CaCO_3 + SiO_2$$
$$CO_2 + MgSiO_3 <==> MgCO_3 + SiO_2$$

The newly formed minerals then are transported to and buried in the ocean. Hence, changes in the inputs and outputs of the atmospheric carbon cycle can be viewed as the driving variables responsible for maintaining climate. If mantle degassing rates are changed, the content of CO_2 in the atmosphere also changes. An increase in mantle degassing rates raises global temperature, whereas a slowing lowers it. Likewise, if continental paleolatitude and surface area change, the ability of the continental crust to remove CO_2 via chemical weathering will change accordingly.

Marshall et al. (1988) showed that the paleolatitudes of the continents have a major role in climatic change. When continents are near the equator, more CO_2 can be removed from the atmosphere because higher equatorial temperatures

induce higher chemical reaction rates. Thus atmospheric CO_2 content is less and a correspondingly cooler mean global climate results. Alternatively, when continents are more poleward, weathering reaction rates are slowed, allowing CO_2 to increase in the atmosphere until the global climate becomes warm enough to reestablish equilibrium between mantle degassing and silicate weathering.

Kuhn et al. (1989) and Worsley and Nance (1989) showed that changes in land area play an equally important role in climatic change. Emergent continents, with a large surface area, increase the continental crust's ability to remove CO2 from the atmosphere via silicate weathering. When continents are emergent, climate is cool, and vice versa.

Worsley and Kidder (1991) combined both the latitude and emergence controls into a simple unified model that specifies CO_2 levels and consequent global, polar, and equatorial temperatures using only continental paleogeography and land area. The model assumes constant carbonate/organic carbon burial ratios, solar luminosity, long-term CO_2 degassing rates, and continental crustal area of unchanging hypsometry and composition. Furthermore, the Worsley and Kidder (1991) model assumes that changing paleogeography has no first-order effect on diurnal temperature variation, seasonality, and surface circulation and that the average landmass latitude is representative of total global landmass conditions. Doubling the CO_2 content of the atmosphere is also assumed to raise world temperatures 3°C. This 3°C value represents the midpoint of the range of results of the general circulation model experiments reviewed by Ramanathan (1988). Alternatively, a tenfold increase would raise the world temperature 10°C. The 10°C temperature rise is then assumed to double the rate of chemical weathering in accordance with the Arrhenius equation governing inorganic reaction rates (Brady, 1991). Halving world land area, but not changing its average latitude, would allow climate to warm 10°C (Worsley and Kidder, 1991). The 10°C warming would double the rate of chemical reaction on the remaining land and maintain the balance with mantle degassing rates (Worsley and Kidder, 1991). The rate of reaction assumed by Worsley and Kidder (1991) would produce a nominal activation energy of ~12 kcal/mol that is certainly within the range of possible activation energies summarized by Brady (1991) when coupled with the biotic acceleration of chemical weathering rates outlined by Volk (1987). Based on the global land area and global mean temperature of 18 ka (CLIMAP, 1976), Worsley and Kidder (1991) assumed that the average land temperature when land area is at its maximum (36% of the Earth's surface) would be 12°C. When land area is halved (to 18% of the Earth's surface), the mean land temperature would become 10°C warmer, or 22°C.

Worsley and Kidder (1991, Figs. 1 and 2) outlined a range of six possible endpoint global configurations of maximum and minimum land areas and latitudes that could be used to interpolate global, polar, and equatorial temperatures and corresponding CO_2 levels. By knowing the average latitude and relative land area, the Earth's climate can be interpolated. The model accounts for ~50% of the controls on climate. The other 50% is distributed among changes in orogenic intensity that affect atmospheric CO_2. These include orography and its effects on atmospheric and oceanic circulation and consequent changes in precipitation and runoff, albedo, organic carbon burial, mantle degassing rates, and other minor effects (see Crowley and North [1991] for a review).

THE STANDARD OROGEN

To test the main premise that an orogenic uplift affects climate, only continent-continent collisional orogens are considered. All such orogens will have areas and heights considered equivalent to the Himalayas, the modern standard for all continent-continent collisions. Today, the Himalayas cover ~0.6% of the Earth's surface (Berger and Winterer, 1974) as an ~2,500-km-long east-west–trending linear feature (Harrison et al., 1981). For simplicity, the Himalayan and all previous orogens are considered point sources of reactants at the geographic centers of the orogens. The point source assumption, even though simplistic and distortive, is required because the nonlinearities involved for non–point source orogenies complicate the model far beyond the resolution of the paleoclimate record. As an example of the type of distortion introduced by the point-source assumption, silicate weathering rates for a mountain range with a north-south orientation would decrease with temperature toward the pole and increase with temperature toward the equator. However, because weathering rates are a nonlinear function of temperature and the pole-equatorial temperature gradient is not a linear function of latitude, the midpoint of a linear north-south mountain range would yield an average silicate weathering rate lower than a linear average between the endpoint rates. By contrast, no distortion would be produced by a mountain range with an east-west orientation because it would react at the same rate along its entire length; the rate at its midpoint would be representative of the entire orogeny.

The height a mountain range attains is important because the rate of mechanical weathering increases exponentially with altitude (Garrels and MacKenzie, 1971). Mechanical weathering is presumed to be an important part of the silicate weathering process because it exposes new reactants, increases surface area via pulverization, and abrasively removes any reaction inhibitors coating reactants (Stallard and Edmond, 1983; Raymo et al., 1988). However, this presumption must be restricted to specific cases because Garrels and MacKenzie (1971) found no correlation between average elevation and chemical weathering on a global basis. We do this by comparing the active Himalayas and today's remnant Appalachians. The Himalayas, standing ~5 km above sea level, are being rapidly eroded mechanically and generate thick sediment deposits in the Indus and Bengal fans (Curray and Moore, 1974). The ~1-km Appalachians, however, produce relatively little sediment. With respect to dissolved river loads, Raymo and Ruddiman

(1992) concluded that the 4% of the world's drainage area surrounding the Himalayan-Tibetan region yields 25% of the dissolved load of the world's rivers. If the continental crust were of uniform mineralogic composition, we could conclude that the Himalayas have increased the CO_2 drawdown rate by ~25%, whereas today's Appalachians would hardly influence CO_2 drawdown at all.

In reality, the picture is much more complicated. Orogenic cores tend to be richer in igneous rocks (the primary source of unreacted Ca- and Mg-containing silicate minerals) than the average continental surface (Windley, 1984; Edmond, 1992). Early in their histories, erosion takes place on mainly uplifted sediments that contain relatively low quantities of unreacted silicate minerals. As the cores are unroofed, the igneous component of the detritus increases. It is thus likely that an orogen's ability to influence climate increases as its core is progressively unroofed. This would be true because the greater the proportion of igneous rock relative to other rock types, the greater the potential for atmospheric CO_2 drawdown.

Unfortunately, we cannot easily quantify these relationships because the proportions of these rock types and their rates of unroofing would differ from one orogenic belt to the next. At this initial level, simplicity demands that a "standard orogen" be adopted that has the same mineralogic and chemical composition as the "average" granodioritic continental crust (Blatt and Jones, 1975). The main effect to be modeled by this study is the increase in the chemical weathering rate of unreacted silicates in the "average continental crust" resulting from a "standard orogen," rather than the effects of lithologies of individual orogenic systems. It is therefore to be expected that cooling effects of various actual orogens will be greater if the rocks involved contain more unreacted silicates than the average continental crust.

During orogeny, height appears to be controlled mainly by the rate of continental convergence. The greater the convergent "containment," the higher the elevation (Molnar and Tapponnier, 1978). When convergence ceases, lystric faulting will quickly reduce the massif's height (Molnar, 1986) and, therefore, its mechanical weathering rate. Based on estimates in the literature, the average continent-continent collisional orogen would be 3 to 5 km in height and last ~40 to 60 m.y. (Windley, 1984). Four-km-high orogenic belts lasting 50 m.y. are arbitrarily adopted as a "standard orogen" for this study.

The ability of an orogen to cool climate is also limited by another first-order control: the residence time of reactants in conditions favorable to silicate weathering. Two separate types of residence times exist: in-situ and in-transit.

In-situ residence time is the length of time reactants are actually available for chemical weathering at the site of initial exposure. As chemical weathering acts on reactants in situ, a coating of weathering inhibitors (i.e., spent reactants) develops that hinders further weathering (Stallard and Edmond, 1983). As in-situ residence time increases, silicate weathering rates slow, with the end member being laterite. In active orogenic systems, in-situ residence times are reduced in two important ways. First, as an orogen reaches higher altitudes, mechanical weathering increases, removing the weathering inhibitors and increasing the surface area of reactants (Stallard and Edmond, 1983). This effect is somewhat offset (but not removed by) colder temperatures at higher elevations, which inhibit chemical weathering. Second, an active orogen would generate rapid exposure rates of reactants because uplift and denudation continually expose new reactants to silicate weathering. When an orogen becomes inactive and quickly collapses due to faulting (Molnar, 1986), mechanical weathering is greatly reduced, increasing in-situ residence times sufficiently that the inactive orogen contributes relatively little to global silicate weathering.

In-transit residence time is the time reactants are exposed to silicate weathering after being removed from the source and before final burial. During this time, loose material is continually abraded, maintaining high surface areas as weathering inhibitors are removed from reactants. These large, clean surface areas provide a high potential for silicate weathering. Long in-transit residence times allow reactants to be more thoroughly processed. However, the cooler the climate, the longer the in-transit residence time would have to be to fully process reactants.

The distinction between in-situ and in-transit residence times determines where silicate weathering occurs. In-situ residence times for orogenic uplifts are greatly enhanced by ambient temperature. Figure 1 illustrates the relationships between altitude, latitude, and temperature. As shown, the high-altitude temperature of an orogenic highland would be too cool for silicate weathering to be effective, regardless of latitude. Silicate weathering requires moisture with dissolved CO_2 and, hence, temperatures above 0°C. Because of adiabatic cooling, much of the orogenic area will be above the 0°C isotherm and will therefore yield very low silicate weathering rates. Silicate weathering in environments colder than 0°C generates a negligible cooling effect.

In-situ residence time is lessened by mechanical weathering that moves material to lower elevations. Most of the silicate weathering must take place during transport from the peaks to sea level. As reactants move toward lower elevations, temperature-induced reaction rates and grain surface areas increase as the sediments become depleted in reactants.

In-transit residence times for reactants are crucial for silicate weathering, so it is important to consider additional controls of residence times. Potter (1978) proposed that precipitation and relief control the maturity of big river sands. Both precipitation rates and relief enhance in-transit residence times.

High volumes of precipitation, although generally considered beneficial to silicate weathering, can decrease in-transit residence time. High precipitation rates can quickly erode and transport sediment over long distances. Sediments in humid climates would not remain in the transport system very long. Alternatively, reactants in desert conditions would have a relatively long in-transport residence time because of the absence of water, but little chemical weathering would occur.

The relief between an orogen (~4 to 5 km) and sea level plays an important role in in-transit residence time. If the distance between the orogenic belt and the nearest basin is large, stream gradients can quickly decrease and runoff will tend to move slowly, increasing the in-transit residence time of the sediments. In contrast, if the distance between the orogenic belt and the basin is short, stream gradient would be large and the runoff would be fast moving, decreasing in-transit residence times.

Recent studies of sediments derived from the Andes and Himalayas provide evidence of the geographic influence on silicate weathering. Although not directly comparable because the Andes are not the result of a continent-continent collision, the evidence is nonetheless useful. A comparison of the Indus Fan, which contains turbidite sediments eroded from the Himalayas (Jipa and Kidd, 1972), with fluvial Andes-derived sediments in the Orinoco River (Johnsson et al., 1991) in South America shows that low-latitude, long in-transit residence time sediments tend to be depleted in feldspars. To compare these sediments, the ratio of quartz to feldspar can be used to generally establish an estimate of the ratio of unweathered silicate material to that of quartz, the silica end product of silicate weathering. The average igneous rock has a ratio of 0.22, and a pure quartz sandstone has a ratio of 1. The average sandstone has a value of 0.81 (Table 1). However, erosion of uplifted sediments already depleted in feldspar can bias these results. Although quantitative values are used, comparisons between results must be considered qualitatively because of a lack of available information about residence time for systems from different study areas.

The distal turbidites of DSDP sites 221–224 of the Indus Fan (Jipa and Kidd, 1972) contain sands richer in feldspar (ave. $Q/Q+F = 0.74$) (Table 2) than the average sandstone. The Himalayas are clearly not reaching their maximum silicate weathering potential. The in-transit residence times of the sediments would have to be much longer for the silicate

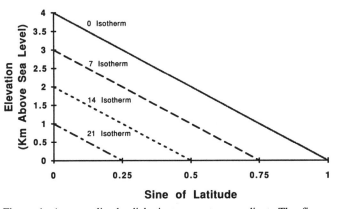

Figure 1. A generalized adiabatic temperature gradient. The figure demonstrates that the adiabatic lapse rate cools quickly enough to place the upper elevations (>4 km) of an orogenic uplift below 0°C regardless of latitude. At lower elevations, material eroding from an uplift will weather much faster at lower latitudes.

TABLE 1. GENERAL ROCK TYPE Q/Q+F RATIOS

Rock Types*	Quartz (%)	Feldspar (%)	Q/Q+F
Mudrocks	30.0	4.0	0.882
Sandstones	65.0	15.0	0.812
Igneous	18.0	62.6	0.223
Surficial mean composition†	32.5	25.2	0.562

*The compositions of the rock types are from Wedepohl (1969) and Blatt (1982).
†An average of 66% sedimentary rocks (a weighted average of sandstones and mudstones) and 34% igneous rocks.

TABLE 2. GEOLOGIC Q/Q+F EXAMPLES

Location	Quartz (%)	Feldspar (%)	Q/Q+F
INDUS FAN			
DSDP 221*	15.2	5.5	0.734
DSDP 222*	26.3	10.9	0.707
DSDP 223*	30.7	9.3	0.768
DSDP 224*	27.1	8.9	0.740
Brahmaputra River†	53.0	24.0	0.668
	48.0	28.0	0.632
ORINOCO RIVER SYSTEM			
Llanos§	72.0	7.0	0.991
	99.0	1.0	0.990
Guayana Shield§	62.0	28.0	0.668
	100.0	0.0	1.000
Mainstem§	95.0	2.0	0.979
Mouth†	93.0	1.0	0.989
	89.0	1.0	0.989

*Jipa and Kidd, 1972.
†Potter, 1978.
§Johnsson et al., 1991.

weathering rate generated by the local mean temperatures to fully weather the feldspars. This observation suggests that global climate would be much cooler if the Himalayas had formed and stayed at lower latitudes or had longer in-transit residence time.

The Orinoco river sediments (Table 2), on the other hand, have feldspar-rich sands near the Andean source terrains (with minimum Q/Q+F values of 0.69), whereas the regions near the mouth of the river tend to be almost completely depleted in feldspar (with maximum Q/Q+F values of 0.98 [Johnsson et al., 1991]). This result suggests that high silicate weathering associated with a low-latitude, long-transport region is manifested in the almost total destruction of feldspars during transport. High temperatures, long in-transit residence time, and

high precipitation make the Orinoco system a highly efficient silicate processor.

These findings suggest that geography and residence time have a great impact on the silicate weathering of sediments being eroded from orogenic terrains. However, the relative impacts of altitude, latitude, and in-situ and in-transit residence times on silicate weathering rates are impossible to quantify from the sparse data. For this initial study, the residence times of all orogenically derived sediments will be considered equal. The equal residence time assumption allows testing of the major premise: The paleogeography of continents and mountains determines the relative silicate weathering rate of sediments eroding from an orogenic terrain.

MODEL

Raymo (1991) relegated ambient air temperature to second-order status compared to the height of an orogen and did not differentiate orographic from latitudinal temperature effects. She reasoned correctly that the higher the mountains, the larger the volume of reactants released by mechanical weathering (Garrels and MacKenzie, 1971) and, hence, the greater the silicate weathering rate, if all other factors are fixed. Raymo (1991) thereby viewed the height of an orogenic belt as the main control on the cooling power. It is self-evident that the higher a mountain range, the greater the potential for global change. It is equally self-evident that a polar mountain range, no matter how large, cannot geochemically alter climate if the polar temperature is already below freezing. Therefore, the size of the range will be held constant so that the relative effects of a "standard orogen" upon differing paleogeographic conditions can be tested. By assuming all orogens have similar sizes, shapes, compositions, and durations, the local surface temperature (and its consequent influence upon precipitation) becomes the primary control on an orogen's ability to cool climate. The question becomes: What controls the ambient air temperature at an orogen? The answer is: altitude and latitude (as shown for today's world in Fig. 2). Results for today's world, however, cannot automatically be considered representative for other paleogeographies.

Marshall et al. (1988) and Worsley and Kidder (1991) demonstrated that global silicate weathering is dependent not only upon volumes of available reactants but also upon the temperature-controlled reaction rates. It is assumed that most chemical reaction rates increase with increasing temperatures. If reactants are located near the equator with a relatively warm temperature, the world would cool. High silicate weathering rates associated with equatorial temperatures would lower CO_2 in the atmosphere until the reaction rate is slowed by cooling to reestablish a balance between silicate weathering and mantle degassing rates (Walker et al., 1981). If reactants are located near the pole, the opposite would be true. Because temperature (and its first-order control on precipitation) at the

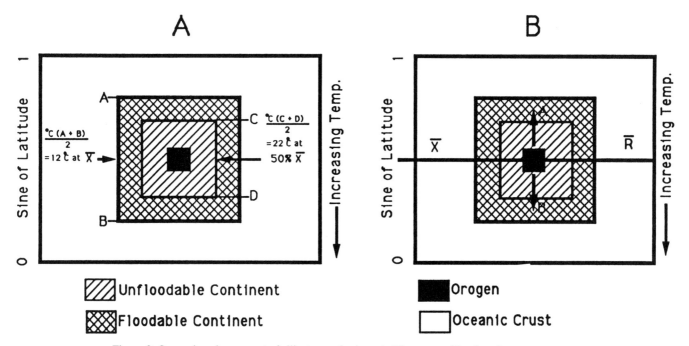

Figure 2. Orogenic enhancement of silicate weathering. A, The range of local surface temperatures for an uplift located at the average latitude of the continents. When a continent is fully emerged (A, B, $\bar{X}$), the local temperature at the average latitude of the continents and the uplift is 12°C (Worsley and Kidder, 1991). When the continents are flooded (C, D, 50% $\bar{X}$), the temperature at the average latitude of the continents and the uplift is 22°C (Worsley and Kidder, 1991). For simplicity, the relative silicate weathering enhancement rate of an uplift at 12°C is given a standard value of 1. B, The changes in relative silicate weathering enhancement rates as the latitude of an uplift deviates from the average latitude of the continents. Similarly, for a given continental area, an uplift at some latitudinal distance (sine) away from the average latitude of the continents will also have the same silicate weathering enhancement rate regardless of the true latitudes. Where an uplift is located at a higher latitude than the average continental latitude (A), the relative silicate weathering rate would be less than $\bar{R}$. Where an uplift is located at a lower latitude than the continental average latitude (B), then the relative silicate weathering enhancement rate would be greater than $\bar{R}$. Hence the continents are fully emerged, the relative silicate weathering enhancement rate for A would be less than 1, whereas for B the rate would be greater than 1.

weathering site is the primary control of silicate weathering, it is also the primary control of an orogen's effect on climate. When the volumes of orogenic reactants are held constant, only air temperature, as determined by the latitude of an orogen, is required for this model. Latitude is very important for determination of silicate weathering rates.

For any given paleogeographic configuration, ambient air temperature is a function of latitude relative to the pole-equator temperature gradient for that paleogeographic configuration. Thus, paleogeography defines the first-order global temperature distribution, which in turn governs the surface temperature at the site of an orogen. That temperature then specifies the amount of enhanced silicate weathering at the site. Worsley and Kidder's (1991) model assumes that the temperature at the average latitude of the continents is the average continental surface temperature. The average temperature must remain constant for a given global land area to maintain the balance of silicate weathering and mantle degassing. The Worsley and Kidder (1991) model specifies that

for a given continental land area, the average latitude of the continents will have a constant temperature (12°C for 36% of the Earth covered by land and 22°C for 18% of the Earth covered by land) regardless of where the land is positioned.

The situation complicates with orogeny. When orogeny occurs at the same average latitude as the world's landmass, the ability of the resultant mountain range to cool world climate will remain constant regardless of whether the range and continents are located at low or high latitudes (Fig. 2A). Changing the amount of global land area will change the relative silicate weathering rate of an orogen located at the average latitude of the continents by changing the temperature at that latitude. For instance, when land area is halved by inundation, the mean global silicate weathering rate must double by raising the mean land temperature 10°C to maintain balance with mantle degassing. The silicate weathering rate of an uplift located at the same latitude as the continental average latitude must initially also double. This relationship may be expressed as

$$R_A = \frac{100\% - A_L}{50\%} \qquad (1)$$

where R_A is the number of doublings of the silicate weathering rate caused by land area control of the temperature at the average continental latitude. A_L is the land area of the Earth expressed as a percentage of the Pleistocene glacial maxima (100% emergence [land area] = 36% of the Earth's surface being land area by definition). The constants limit the range of values for R_A between 0 and 1. Equation (1) assumes that the relative silicate weathering rate for a standard orogen would be a value of 1 when the local surface temperature is 12°C. Therefore, an orogen located at the average latitude of the continents during a period with maximum exposed land area would have a temperature of 12°C and would have zero doublings of the silicate weathering rate. Accordingly, the same orogen occurring during maximum transgression, at a temperature of 22°C, would have its silicate weathering rate doubled once.

From the above, we conclude that silicate weathering enhancement rate of an orogen must be greater or less than the above-determined values if it is equatorward or poleward of the average landmass latitude (Fig. 3B). How much greater or how much less is determined by both the distance from the average latitude of the world landmass and the polar-equatorial temperature gradient for the particular landmass configuration. Fortunately, both parameters can be estimated from the results of Worsley and Kidder (1991, Fig. 1). Periods of maximum land area have a polar-equatorial temperature gradient of 30°C, except during a capworld (all land centered on the poles; average latitude = ~55°), when the gradient is 20°C. Periods of minimum land area have a gradient of 10°C. For a given equatorial-polar temperature contrast, the temperature at the orogenic site relative to that of the mean continental temperature can be calculated. This calculation requires the difference in the sine of latitudes (to linearize interpolation) of the continents and that of the standard orogen (i.e., relative continental-orogenic position) and the slope of the polar-equatorial temperature contrast.

Where average continental and orogenic latitudes are unequal, the difference between the sine of latitude of the continents and that of the orogen defines the possible cooling effect for a given polar-equatorial temperature contrast, regardless of actual paleogeography. The relative positions of the average latitude of the land and orogen (P_{LO}) can be expressed as

$$P_{LO} = \sin(L_L) - \sin(L_o) \qquad (2)$$

where L_L is the average latitude of the land and L_O is the average latitude of the orogen. Equation (2) produces a range of values between ±1. Figure 3 shows the range of possible values for the Worsley and Kidder (1991) slice-, cap-, and ringworld configurations. The actual range of values for P_{LO} does not extend beyond ±0.75. This limit results from the changes in the average latitude of the world landmass during a cap-

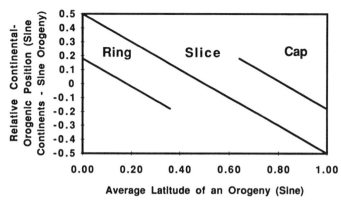

Figure 3. The continental paleogeographic limit of relative continental-orogenic position values. The relative continental-orogenic position may be read by finding the intersection point of the average latitude of an orogeny and the continental configuration curve; ring-, slice-, or capworld (Worsley et al., Fig. 3, this volume). A true ringworld would limit orogenic areas to low latitudes and a narrow range of values (±0.18). Capworlds would have a similar range of available paleolatitudes for orogenic areas and similar range of values (±0.18). The sliceworld allows the greatest range for orogenic paleolatitude, from pole to equator. The relative position values may range to ±0.5.

world or ringworld configuration when an orogen is moved a maximum latitudinal distance away from the continental average latitude. For instance, a capworld (sine of average latitude = 0.82) with an orogen that has no area exactly on the equator would have a P_{LO} value of 0.82 (a ringworld with a polar orogen would have a value of –0.82).

However, because the orogen has mass and area, the orogen cannot have an average latitude of 0° or 90°, values that have no area. To give area to an orogen, area must be removed from the global landmass and given to the orogen. A shift in land area from capworld or ringworld global landmass to an orogen also requires a shift in average latitude of the global landmass. The combination of the orogen requiring an average latitude >0° and <90° and the shift in the average latitude of the global landmass reduces the difference in latitude of the orogen and the global landmass. It is unlikely that the P_{LO} value will attain values beyond ±0.75.

With a known polar-equatorial temperature gradient, the change in temperature from the average latitude of the land to the average latitude of the orogen (D_T) may be found by the following:

$$D_T = \frac{P_{LO} \times T_{EP}}{0.64} \qquad (3)$$

where T_{EP} is the equatorial-polar temperature contrast. The constant 0.64 is the difference between the sines of the average latitude of a capworld (sine 0.18) and ringworld (sine 0.82). The capworld and ringworld average latitudes represent the latitudes of the polar and equatorial temperatures derived from the Worsley and Kidder (1991) model. Because of the exponential nature of silicate weathering's dependence on temperature, the change in temperature is most conveniently represented by multiples of 10°C that result in doubling of weathering rate (D_{T10}), and

$$D_{T10} = \frac{P_{LO} \times T_{EP}}{6.4} \qquad (4)$$

Equation (4) represents the number of doublings of the relative silicate weathering rate for an orogen that would occur as a function of the positional contrast between the orogen and the global landmass. Equation (4) may be combined with equation (1) to find the relative silicate weathering enhancement rate (R):

$$R = 2^{(R_A + D_{T10})} \qquad (5)$$

R_A (global land area enhancement of silicate weathering rates) and D_{T10} (continental and orogenic latitude enhancement of silicate weathering rates) count the number of doublings of the relative silicate weathering rate from the rate of 1 at 12°C. R_A and D_{T10} are used as exponents of 2 to find the relative silicate weathering rate of the orogen. Figure 4 shows possible silicate weathering rates for maximum and minimum land areas.

The large number of uncertainties and assumptions required to produce Equation (5) means that the results are best interpreted in a qualitative fashion only. For this study, the relative silicate enhancement rates of orogenies are arbitrarily di-

vided into three categories: "strongly cooling," "weakly cooling," and "ineffective" (Table 3). Any orogen having a relative silicate enhancement rate ≥2 (the weathering rate of an orogen located at the same average latitude as the global landmass with 50% emergence) will be considered a "strongly cooling" orogen. A "weakly cooling" orogen will have a relative silicate enhancement rate between 2 and 0.43. At relative silicate weathering enhancement rates below 0.43, where the surface temperature is 0°C or colder, an orogen is considered "ineffective" because ice would inhibit silicate weathering.

By using these three general weathering categories, criteria can be established to decide whether an orogen geochemically triggered an icehouse. Two major prerequisites exist for the formation of continental ice sheets. First, global climate must already be cool (i.e., have a low content of CO_2 in the atmosphere). Worsley and Kidder (1991) and Worsley et al. (this volume) define polar area as being the 13% of the Earth's area above 60° latitude. Under this definition, the pole would be <0°C when the average temperature of the entire polar area is below 8°C. Worsley et al. (this volume) have tentatively assumed that the mean polar area temperature (the mean annual temperature at 70° latitude) must be below 8°C to permit a continental ice sheet to form.

Second, land must be present in the polar area. If land area exists within the general temperature parameters, global continental silicate weathering could then be sufficient to produce continental ice. The question of whether an orogen will trigger an icehouse can then be addressed by comparing initial

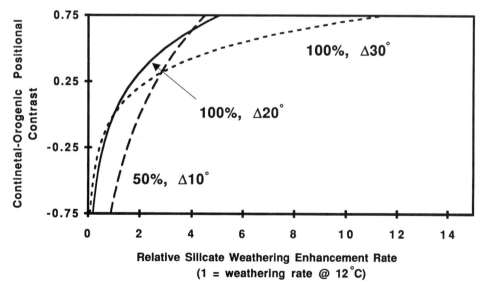

Figure 4. Relative silicate weathering rate type curves generated for three continental configurations. The curves represent the range of possible relative silicate weathering rates when the continents are 50% emerged with a polar-equatorial temperature contrast (Δ) of 10°C, 100% emerged with a 20°C temperature contrast, and 100% emerged with a 30°C temperature contrast. The relative silicate weathering rate for an orogenic area may be read by intersecting the type curve with a relative continental-orogenic position for an orogeny. The relative silicate weathering rates are multiples of the weathering rate at 12°C. Note that the relative silicate weathering rate is at initial conditions, not after orogenically induced cooling occurs.

T. L. Moore and T. R. Worsley

TABLE 3. OROGEN-ICEHOUSE CLASSIFICATION SCHEME

Polar Preconditions	Orogen-Produced Icehouse	Geologic Example	Time Slice Sample Ages (Ma)	Relative Silicate Weathering Enhancement Rate (R)*	Standard Orogen?
	Warm	Possible			
Strongly cooling R>2	Borderline	Likely	Taconic	433, 325	2.7, 3.3	No
			Acadian	390	3.5	No
			E. Alleghenian	342, 306	3.2, 3.8	Yes
			E. Himalayan	50.3, 27.7	3.1, 3.2	No
	Icehouse	N/A	L. Alleghenian	277	4.0	Yes
	Warm	Not likely			
Weakly cooling 2>R>0.43	Borderline	Possible			
	Icehouse	N/A	L. Himalayan	14, 0.018, 0	1.8, 1.0, 1.2	Yes
			Uralian?	277, 255	1.3, 1.3	Yes
	Warm	No			
Ineffective 0.43>R	Borderline	No			
	Icehouse	N/A			

*Data to calculate R from Worsley et al., this volume, and Scotese and Golonka, 1992.

polar temperatures to the 8°C standard for an icehouse. A determination may then be made as to whether an orogen formed during periods that are too warm, borderline, or already in icehouse conditions could have triggered ice nucleation according to the criteria of Table 3.

During periods that are otherwise too warm for ice nucleation, a "strongly cooling" (Table 3) orogen may be able to lower polar temperatures enough to produce an icehouse. The cooling effect of the orogen, however, might not be able to reduce polar temperatures enough for continental ice-sheet formation during exceedingly warm periods. A "strongly cooling" orogen could produce an ice sheet, but the probability of ice nucleation is reduced with higher initial polar temperatures even though the higher global temperatures make the orogen's cooling effects more powerful.

When polar conditions are borderline for continental ice-sheet formation, the likelihood of a "strongly cooling" orogen triggering an icehouse is great. With the cool polar temperatures, a "strongly cooling" orogen will easily reduce polar temperatures well below 8°C. The "strongly cooling" orogen with borderline conditions for continental ice-sheet formation is therefore the most probable condition for the orogenically triggered icehouse.

With high polar temperatures, "weakly cooling" (Table 3) orogens are extremely unlikely to produce an icehouse. However, because warm global temperatures yield intrinsically high silicate weathering rates, even a "weakly cooling" orogen will significantly lower surface temperatures during such times.

As with "strongly cooling" orogens, borderline polar temperatures are also the most likely condition for a "weakly cooling" orogen to trigger an icehouse. Only a minor drop of polar temperatures would be required to trigger ice nucleation.

An "ineffective" (Table 3) orogen, by definition, cannot geochemically trigger an icehouse. It may trigger an icehouse in another way. If polar temperatures are already borderline, the adiabatic cooling of an "ineffective" orogen in a polar area could allow ice to nucleate on the elevated orogenic belt itself. The consequent albedo increase will then allow continental ice sheets to grow (Powell and Veevers, 1987).

If polar climates are already cool enough to produce an icehouse without the aid of an orogen, any orogen's role in continental ice-sheet formation is superfluous. Under these conditions, an orogen cannot be the trigger. However, the orogen can increase the size of the continental ice sheet or allow a unipolar continental ice sheet to become bipolar. Unfortunately, attributing the growth of an existing continental ice sheet to an orogen is difficult using the poorly resolved geologic record.

Before comparing the model-generated results of the relationship of Phanerozoic orogenies to icehouses, a final consideration concerns the already reported (Raymo, 1991) effects of orogens smaller than the "standard orogen." When an orogen can be clearly shown to be smaller than the "standard orogen," its classification must be downgraded in accordance with its intrinsically weaker silicate weathering enhancement rate.

COMPARISON WITH THE GEOLOGIC RECORD

Major Phanerozoic icehouses occurred during the Ordovician-Silurian transition, the Early Devonian, the Carboniferous–Early Permian, and the Cenozoic (Crowell, 1983). They could have been caused, in part, by the Taconian, Acadian, Alleghenian, and Himalayan orogenies respectively (Powell and Veevers, 1987; Raymo et al., 1988; Raymo, 1991). An example of an orogeny that did not produce an icehouse would be the Uralian orogeny during the Permian. The general greenhouse-lowering effects that each of these orogenies is likely to have produced as determined by the model will now be compared to those of Figure 5, the nonorogenic climate results of Worsley et al. (this volume), to evaluate whether these orogenies triggered the ice nucleation.

Three examples exist of a "strongly cooling" orogen generating an icehouse when polar temperatures are already borderline for continental ice-sheet nucleation. The first is the

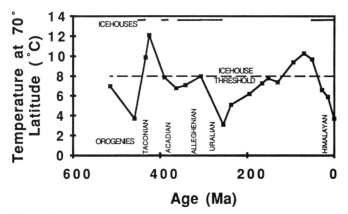

Figure 5. Calculated Phanerozoic polar temperatures (after Worsley et al., Fig. 12, this volume). During periods that are colder than the ice-cap formation temperature threshold, a high probability exists that ice caps were present. Because of other variables (i.e., polar land distribution, polar land orography, and circulation), the threshold can fluctuate as much as ±2°C. Borderline temperature condition for ice-cap formation is 8°C ±2°C. Temperatures above this range are considered too warm for ice-cap formation; temperatures below this range have a high probability of ice-cap formation. (Ice caps from Crowell, 1983.)

Taconic Orogen. The Taconic Orogen records the earliest accretionary phase on the eastern North American continent during the closing of the Iapetus, which resulted in the docking of the Piedmont microcontinent (Williams and Hatcher, 1983) and possibly parts of the Avalon composite terrain (Doig et al., 1990) in the Late Ordovician. The orogenic belt formed at low latitudes with a north-south orientation similar to that of the modern Andes. The Taconic, unlike the Himalaya and Alleghany orogens, probably did not reach the heights of the "standard orogen".

According to the crude model in Raymo et al. (1988), the Taconic Orogen should not have produced ice because of its low elevations. Ice did form during this period when global climate was borderline for continental ice-sheet formation (Crowell, 1983; Worsley et al., this volume). If the Taconic Orogen was the cause of the ice formation during the late Ordovician and early Silurian, then the height hypothesis is clearly not the only first-order control on the effects of an orogen's ability to cool climate. The paleogeographic controls for orogenic silicate weathering suggest that the Taconic Orogen could have been tectonically small but geochemically large and could still have lowered polar temperatures enough to generate continental ice. The possibility also exists that other minor orogens could have been taking place during this period. If so, the net weathering enhancement of these orogens could also have generated an icehouse.

Given the assumption of the "standard orogen", the cooling effect of the Taconic Orogen is classified as a "strongly cooling" orogen (Table 3). Because of its size, the orogen generated a smaller sediment load and less cooling than a "standard orogen". Worsley et al. (this volume) also report that at the time of the Ordovician-Silurian boundary, there were borderline to slightly warmer polar temperatures than the defined precondition for ice nucleation. Hence, the Taconic Orogen could have triggered the formation of continental ice.

An alternate interpretation of the late Ordovician–early Silurian icehouse is that prior to the late Ordovician, the poles lacked land for ice nucleation. As the continents moved poleward, some land edged toward the pole and ice began to nucleate in the Late Ordovician (Crowley et al., 1987). As the continents continued to move poleward, global temperatures would have continually increased in order to maintain balance between silicate weathering and mantle degassing rates. Finally, global temperatures could have become too warm as Gondwana centered at the pole (Worsley et al., this volume). Although plausible, this scenario casts doubt on the adequacy of the Taconic Orogen alone to produce an icehouse. The warming effect generated by the poleward movement of the continents could have been delayed enough by the Taconic Orogen to allow a continental ice sheet to form.

The Acadian orogeny, representing the accretion of another small microcontinent to the North American continent, occurred during the Early Devonian (Hatcher and Odem,

1980; Windley, 1984). Like the Taconic, the Acadian Orogen formed at low latitudes, classifying it as a "strongly cooling" orogen (e.g., Scotese and Golonka, 1992). The polar temperatures (Fig. 5) suggest that this period was borderline for continental ice-sheet nucleation. Again, like the Taconic, the Acadian Orogen did not attain the height of the "standard orogen" nor was the Acadian a true continent-continent collision (Windley, 1984). Both these shortcomings considerably weakened its cooling effects. Nonetheless, under borderline polar conditions, it is certainly possible that the Acadian Orogen triggered the Early Devonian continental ice sheet.

The third example of a "strongly cooling" orogen during a period in which initial polar temperatures are borderline for forming an icehouse is the Alleghany Orogen. The Alleghanian orogeny represents the final orogenic event of the Appalachian Mountain chain (Windley, 1984). The collision of North America and Africa began in the Carboniferous and ended in the Early Permian. Worsley et al. (this volume) calculated that global climate exclusive of orogens would be borderline for ice formation during most of the period (Fig. 5). The additional climatic effects generated by the weathering of the low-latitude Alleghany Orogen (Table 3) classifies the orogen as "strongly cooling." The relative silicate weathering rates for the late Alleghanian are high, ranging from 3.2 to 4. The Alleghany Orogen could have easily provided enough polar cooling to generate and maintain an icehouse. The Early Permian results of Worsley et al. (this volume) are already within the climatic preconditions of polar temperature and high-latitude land that already specify the existence of continental ice. Therefore, a continental ice sheet could have formed, although much later, without the influence of the Alleghany Orogen.

Because "weakly cooling" (Table 3) orogens can only trigger icehouses when conditions are already at the threshold for continental ice-sheet nucleation, the correlation between a "weakly cooling" orogen and icehouse should be poor. An example of a "weakly cooling" orogen occurring with an icehouse is the Himalaya Orogen. The climatic effects caused by the Himalayas may be separated into two distinct phases. Continental ice sheets began forming on Antarctica between ~50 Ma (Frakes, 1979) and ~35 Ma (Miller and Fairbanks, 1983; Harwood et al., 1989). The Worsley et al. (this volume) results, along with isotopic evidence (Savin et al., 1975; Miller et al., 1987; Kennett and Barker, 1990; Raymo and Ruddiman, 1992) for this period, suggest that polar temperatures were borderline for continental ice-sheet formation by ~50 Ma. Coinciding with the formation of the Antarctic ice sheet, the Indian continent came in contact with the Asian continent at ~12° paleolatitude (Scotese and Golonka, 1992), beginning the Himalayan orogeny. The relative silicate weathering enhancement model suggests that the low-latitude early phase of the Himalaya Orogen would be relatively "strong" with rates ~3. The height of the orogen would be much less than that of the "standard orogen" (Mercier et al., 1987). Consequently, the

strength (e.g., Table 3) of the early phase of the Himalayan orogeny must be downgraded from "strongly cooling" to "weakly cooling." It is possible that the initial collision generating the Himalaya Orogen may have induced the formation of the continental ice sheet in Antarctica, but it is equally plausible that the Himalaya Orogen was not needed for the Antarctic continental ice to form. The constraints for the correlation between the Himalayan orogeny and the formation of the Antarctic continental ice are presently not good enough to determine whether or not the Himalayan orogeny played a role (Molnar and England, 1990).

The second phase of the Himalayan orogeny is between ~20 and 0 Ma. The Antarctic ice sheet persisted throughout this period, and a continental ice sheet was initiated in the Northern Hemisphere at ~5 Ma (e.g., Leg 105 Shipboard Scientific Party, 1986). The question then is: Did the Himalayan orogeny trigger the formation of the continental ice sheet in the Northern Hemisphere at ~5 Ma? The orogen model predicts that as the Himalayas moved away from the equator (e.g., Scotese and Golonka, 1992), the orogenic belt would have lost its potential for silicate-weathering–enhanced climatic cooling. Poleward movement of the Himalayas is associated with reduced silicate weathering rates because of the increasingly cooler climates of the higher latitudes. The silicate weathering enhancement rates during the second phase are all less than 2 (Table 3). As the Himalayas moved poleward, they also increased in height. Because the Himalaya Orogen reaches the height of the "standard orogen" during the second phase, the silicate weathering results are not downgraded. The Himalaya Orogen is still considered a "weakly cooling" orogen because of its higher latitude.

The Himalayas experienced a major increase in uplift rates within the last 5 m.y. (Mercier et al., 1987), coinciding with the nucleation of the continental ice sheet in the Northern Hemisphere (Raymo et al., 1988). This correlation between the uplift rates of the Himalayas and the appearance of a continental ice sheet in the Northern Hemisphere suggests that an increase in the silicate weathering associated with the rapid uplift rates could have cooled global climate enough to expand the area with cold polar temperatures, allowing ice to nucleate on lower-latitude land. An equally plausible explanation of the correlation between uplift of the Himalayas and continental ice formation, rather than silicate weathering, could be that the orography of the Himalayas contributed to changes in atmospheric circulation that produced the icehouse (Ruddiman and Kutzbach, 1991). It is still unclear if the enhanced silicate weathering generated by the uplift of the Himalayas caused the nucleation of the continental ice sheet in the Northern Hemisphere (Edmond, 1992).

A striking example of a "weakly cooling" orogen that failed to produce or even maintain continental ice sheets is the Ural Orogen. Following the Alleghenian orogeny, the Urals formed in Asia as a result of the collision of Europe and Siberia during the Permian (Windley, 1984). The transition from the Alleghenian orogeny in the Carboniferous to the Uralian in the Permian appears to correspond to a warming trend. Worsley et al. (this volume) inferred that although polar climate would warm (Fig. 5) during this period, it would still be well within the climatic preconditions for ice formation. Strontium evidence (Koepnick et al., 1988; Raymo, 1991; Edmond, 1992) conflicts with the Worsley et al. (this volume) interpretation, suggesting instead that the Permian could have been warm. The Ural Orogen remained at mid-latitudes throughout its active period in the Permian, yielding a low relative silicate weathering enhancement rate that classifies it as a "weakly cooling" orogen. If the global climate was already cool (Fig. 5), the Carboniferous icehouse should have persisted through the Permian. If the Permian global climate was actually warm, as could be inferred from the strontium data, there would not have been a continental ice sheet if the Ural Orogen was too weak to lower the already warm temperatures. Waning of the Alleghenian orogeny probably resulted in a net drop of silicate weathering, and global climate should have shown an increase in temperature.

Given the failure of the orogenic–silicate weathering model alone to specify continental ice-sheet decay during the Alleghenian-Uralian transition, other nonpaleogeographic/nontectonic mechanisms must be considered to explain the Permian warming trend. Several alternative causes for the formation of the Carboniferous icehouse would violate the simpler assumptions of the Worsley and Kidder (1991) model.

We believe that the one cause that best applies is that biotic innovation increased organic carbon burial rates as the land biota appeared and evolved. Cellulose- and lignin-producing vascular plants appeared in the middle Devonian and were abundant by late Devonian (Retallack, 1990), when presumably no organisms were available to digest their cellulose and lignin. Sparsity of decomposers would have allowed wholesale burial of the organic material. Although fungi appear in the earliest Silurian, and perhaps earlier (Retallack, 1990), they could not have developed the ability to digest lignin. Such inability could have contributed to the massive burial of coals in the Carboniferous (Robinson, 1991, 1990).

The large volumes of organic material buried and formed into coal deposits during this period would have removed large amounts of carbon from the atmosphere (Berner, 1990, 1991). Such a high rate of removal of carbon from the atmosphere could have triggered or enhanced an icehouse. We speculate that a Permian advent of saprophytes and insects that were capable of digesting (not just boring) lignin would have restored lower organic carbon burial rates, thereby rewarming the Earth and destroying the icehouse. Alternatively, the Permo-Triassic boundary extinction of trees could also have stopped coal formation (Robinson, 1991, 1990) and resulted in the early Triassic "coal gap" (Veevers, this volume).

Another admittedly ad hoc cause for the warming during the Permian could be an increase of mantle degassing rates. Such an increase could easily warm the global climate

(Larson, 1991a, b). Although presently there is no supporting data, a possible cause for increased mantle degassing rates might be the reorganization of the Tethys Ocean at the onset of its closure during the Late Permian to Triassic, when the length of its subduction zones increased and new rifts formed (Scotese and Golonka, 1992). Initiation of subduction could have increased mantle degassing rates.

The orogen/silicate weathering model predicts with some accuracy when an icehouse can occur. Using the results as a baseline (Fig. 5 and Table 3), the orogenic model "specifies" the presence of ice during the Ordovician-Silurian boundary, Early Devonian, Carboniferous, and Cenozoic. It does not, however, predict the decay of the ice during the late Permian.

CONCLUSIONS

The controls of silicate weathering associated with orogens are subtle. Orogens with identical sizes, shapes, and compositions can have very different silicate weathering rates depending on paleogeography. In general, high-latitude orogens will have a lower global silicate weathering enhancement rate than low-latitude orogenies. The actual amount of cooling depends upon the latitudinal position of an orogen with respect to the distribution of the global landmass. A high-latitude orogen, when the global landmass is also at high latitude (warm initial global temperature), will generate the same cooling effect as an orogen at low latitudes with a low-latitude global landmass (cool initial temperatures). The cooling effect is strongest when the global landmass is at high latitudes and the orogen is at low latitudes and weakest when the opposite is true.

Three general categories of orogenic effectiveness exist with respect to silicate weathering: "strongly cooling," "weakly cooling," and "ineffective." "Strongly cooling" orogens can trigger an icehouse when global temperatures are too warm to permit one otherwise. "Weakly cooling" orogens can trigger an icehouse only when polar temperatures are already borderline for the nucleation of continental ice sheet. "Ineffective" orogens cannot produce an icehouse via silicate weathering alone.

The results of this orogenic model when tested against the geologic record of icehouses are expectedly mixed. The model appears to explain icehouses during the Ordovician-Silurian boundary, the Early Devonian, and the Carboniferous as corresponding to the Taconic, Acadian, and Alleghenian orogenies, respectively. The Cenozoic Antarctic ice sheet was already present when the Himalayan orogeny initiated and so could not have been caused by the orogenic event. But the Cenozoic icehouse was clearly enhanced by the Himalayan orogeny, which possibly triggered continental ice formation in the Northern Hemisphere.

The model's results become questionable when dealing with the Ural Orogen. The "weakly cooling" Ural Orogen occurred during the Permian. Silicate weathering models alone (Worsley et al., this volume) tend to attribute cool temperatures to the period, whereas other geochemical evidence suggests warmer climates (Koepnick et al., 1988). If the climate was already cool, then the "weakly cooling" Ural Orogen would specify an icehouse. If the climate was warm, however, the model would predict a world without (or with waning) continental ice sheets. The Carboniferous icehouse decayed and disappeared during the Permian to produce the coal-impoverished (Veevers, this volume) and ice-free (Frakes and Francis, 1988) Triassic. The model will allow an icehouse decay only if Permian temperatures were warming from some nonorogenic related mechanism.

We have strongly argued that orogens do influence the occurrence of icehouses. Other factors can also produce or contribute to icehouse formation. Biotic innovations, astronomical variations, high-latitude land, sea-level changes, and changes in global circulation patterns are all plausible contributors to the formation of continental ice sheets. Further improvement toward understanding climate history should therefore be directed toward determining the relative contribution of each of these processes to the generation of an icehouse.

ACKNOWLEDGMENTS

We thank David Kidder, Damian Nance, Judith Parrish, and Kay Havenor for fruitful discussions and for improving an early version of the manuscript (the Master's thesis of T.L.M.). Lee Kump, Greg Retallack, and George Klein reviewed the final version. We are grateful for the clarification and shortening of the final version that resulted from their efforts.

REFERENCES CITED

Allmendinger, R. W., 1986, Tectonic development, southeastern border of the Puna Plateau, northwestern Argentine Andes: Geological Society of America Bulletin, v. 97, p. 1070–1082.

Benjamin, M. T., Johnson, N. M., and Naeser, C. W., 1987, Recent rapid uplift in the Bolivian Andes: Evidence from fission-track dating: Geology, v. 15, p. 680–683.

Berger, W. H., and Winterer, E. L., 1974, Plate stratigraphy and the fluctuating carbonate line, _in_ Hsu, K. J., and Jenkyns, H. C., eds., Pelagic sediments: On land and under the sea: Oxford, Blackwell Scientific Publications, p. 11–48.

Berner, R. A., 1990, Atmospheric carbon dioxide levels over Phanerozoic time: Science, v. 249, p. 1382–1386.

Berner, R. A., 1991, A model for atmospheric CO_2 over Phanerozoic time: American Journal of Science, v. 291, p. 339–375.

Berner, R. A., Lasaga, A. C., and Garrels, R. M., 1983, The carbonate-silicate geochemical cycle and its effect on atmospheric carbon dioxide over the past 100 million years: American Journal of Science, v. 283, p. 641–683.

Blatt, H., 1982, Sedimentary petrology: New York, W. H. Freeman, 564 p.

Blatt, H., and Jones, R. L., 1975, Proportions of exposed igneous, metamorphic, and sedimentary rocks: Geological Society of America Bulletin, v. 86, p. 1085–1088.

Bluth, G.J.S., and Kump, L. R., 1991, Phanerozoic paleogeography: American Journal of Science, v. 291, p. 284–308.

Brady, P. V., 1991, The effect of silicate weathering on global temperature and atmospheric CO2: Journal of Geophysical Research, v. 96, p. 18101–18106.

Burbank, D. W., and Johnson, G. D., 1983, The late Cenozoic chronologic and stratigraphic development of the Kashmir Intermontane Basin, Northwestern Himalaya: Palaeogeography, Palaeoclimatology, Palaeoecology, v. 43, p. 205–235.

Chamberlin, T. C., 1899, An attempt to frame a working hypothesis of the cause of glacial periods on an atmospheric basis: Journal of Geology, v. 7, p. 545–584, 667–685, 751–787.

CLIMAP, 1976, The surface of the ice-age earth: Science, v. 191, p. 1131–1144.

Crowell, J. C., 1983, Ice ages recorded on Gondwanan continents: Transactions of the Geological Society of South Africa, v. 86, p. 237–262.

Crowley, T. J., and North, G. R., 1991, Paleoclimatology: Oxford, Oxford University Press, 339 p.

Crowley, T. J., Mengel, J. G., and Short, D. A., 1987, Gondwanaland's seasonal cycle: Nature, v. 329, p. 803–807.

Curray, J. R., and Moore, D. G., 1974, Sedimentary and tectonic processes in the Bengal deep sea fan and geosyncline, _in_ Burk, C. A., and Drake, C. L., ed., The geology of continental margins: New York, Springer-Verlag, p. 617–627.

Davies, T. A., Hay, W. W., Southam, J. R., and Worsley, T. R., 1977, Estimates of Cenozoic oceanic sedimentation rates: Science, v. 197, p. 53.

Delaney, M. L., and Boyle, E. A., 1988, Tertiary paleoceanic chemical variability: Unintended consequences of simple geochemical models: Paleoceanography, v. 3, p. 137–156.

Doig, R., Nance, R. D., Murphy, J. B., and Casseday, R. P., 1990, Evidence for Silurian sinistral accretion of Avalon composite terrain in Canada: Journal of the Geological Society of London, v. 147, p. 927–930.

Edmond, J. M., 1992, Himalayan tectonics, weathering processes, and the strontium isotope record in marine limestones: Science, v. 258, p. 1594–1597.

Elderfield, H., 1986, Strontium isotope stratigraphy: Palaeogeography, Palaeoclimatology, Palaeoecology, v. 57, p. 71–90.

Fischer, A. G., 1984, The two Phanerozoic supercycles, _in_ Berggren, W. A., and Van Couvering, J. A., eds., Catastrophies and earth history: The new uniformitarianism: Princeton, Princeton University Press, p. 129–150.

Frakes, L. A., 1979, Climates throughout geologic time: New York, Elsevier, 310 p.

Frakes, L. A., and Francis, J. E., 1988, A guide to Phanerozoic cold polar climates from high-latitude ice-rafting in the Cretaceous: Nature, v. 333, p. 547–549.

Garrels, R. M., and MacKenzie, F. T., 1971, Evolution of sedimentary rocks: New York, W. W. Norton, 197 p.

Harrison, C.G.A., Brass, G. W., Saltzman, E., Sloan, J., Southam, J., and Whitman, J. M., 1981, Sea level variations, global sedimentation rates and the hypsographic curve: Earth and Planetary Science Letters, v. 54, p. 1–16.

Harrison, T. M., Copeland, P., Kidd, W.S.F., and Yin, A., 1992, Raising Tibet: Science, v. 255, p. 1663–1670.

Harwood, D. M., Webb, P. N., and Barrett, P. J., 1989, Multiple Cenozoic glaciations of Antarctica from terrestrial and continental shelf data: Terra Abstracts, v. 1, p. 2.

Hatcher, R. D., and Odem, A. L., 1980, Timing of thrusting in the southern Appalachians, USA: Model for orogeny?: Journal of the Geological Society of London, v. 137, p. 321–328.

Hsu, J., 1978, On the paleobotanical evidence for continental drift and Himalayan uplift: Paleobotany, v. 25, p. 131–142.

Jipa, D., and Kidd, R. B., 1972, Sedimentation of grained interbeds in the Arabian Sea and sedimentation processes of the Indus Cone, _in_ Suptko, P. R., and Weser, O. E., eds., Initial reports of the Deep Sea Drilling

Project, v. 23: Washington, D.C., National Science Foundation, p. 471–495.

Johnsson, M. J., Stallard, R. F., and Lundberg, N., 1991, Controls on the composition of fluvial sands from a tropical weathering environment: Sands of the Orinoco River drainage basin, Venezuela and Colombia: Geological Society of America Bulletin, v. 103, p. 1622–1674.

Kennett, J. P., and Barker, P. F., 1990, Latest Cretaceous to Cenozoic climate and oceanographic developments in the Weddell Sea, Antarctica: An ocean-drilling perspective, *in* Barker, P. F., and Kennett, J. P., eds., Proceedings of the Ocean Drilling Program, Scientific Results, v. 113: College Station, Texas A&M University, p. 937–960.

Koepnick, R. B., Denison, R. E., and Dahl, D. A., 1988, The Cenozoic seawater $^{87}Sr/^{86}Sr$ curve: Data review and implications for correlation of marine strata: Paleoceanography, v. 3, p. 743–756.

Kuhn, W. R., Walker, J.C.G., and Marshall, H. G., 1989, The effect on Earth's surface temperature from variations in rotation rate, continent formation, solar luminosity, and carbon dioxide: Journal of Geophysical Research, v. 94, p. 11129–11136.

Larson, R. L., 1991a, Latest pulse of earth: Evidence for a mid-Cretaceous superplume: Geology, v. 19, p. 547–550.

Larson, R. L., 1991b, Geological consequences of superplumes: Geology, v. 19, p. 963–966.

Leg 105 Shipboard Scientific Party, 1986, High-latitude palaeoceanography: Nature, v. 320, p. 17–18.

Marshall, H. G., Walker, J.C.G., and Kuhn, W. R., 1988, Long-term climate change and the geochemical cycle of carbon: Journal of Geophysical Research, v. 93, p. 791–801.

Mercier, J. L., Armijo, R., Tapponnier, P., Carey-Gailhardis, E., and Lin, H. T., 1987, Change from late Tertiary compression to Quaternary extension in southern Tibet during the India-Asia collision: Tectonics, v. 6, p. 275–304.

Miller, K. G., and Fairbanks, R. G., 1983, Evidence for Oligocene–middle Miocene abyssal circulation changes in the western North Atlantic: Nature, v. 306, p. 250–253.

Miller, K. G., Fairbanks, R. G., and Mountain, G. S., 1987, Tertiary oxygen isotope synthesis, sea level history, and continental margin erosion: Paleoceanography, v. 1, p. 1–19.

Molnar, P., 1986, The structure of mountain ranges: Scientific American, v. 255, p. 70–79.

Molnar, P., and England, P., 1990, Late Cenozoic uplift of mountain ranges and global climate change: Chicken or egg?: Nature, v. 346, p. 29–34.

Molnar, P., and Tapponnier, P., 1978, Active tectonics of Tibet: Journal of Geophysical Research, v. 83, p. 5361–5375.

Moore, T. C., and Heath, G. R., 1977, Survival of deep-sea sedimentary sections: Earth and Planetary Science Letters, v. 37, p. 71–80.

Palmer, M. R., and Elderfield, H., 1985, Sr isotope composition of sea water over the past 75 Myr: Nature, v. 314, p. 526–528.

Potter, P. E., 1978, Petrology and chemistry of modern big river sands: Journal of Geology, v. 86, p. 423–449.

Powell, C. M., and Veevers, J. J., 1987, Namurian uplift in Australia and South America triggered the main Gondwanan glaciation: Nature, v. 314, p. 526–528.

Ramanathan, V., 1988, The greenhouse theory of climate change: A test by an inadvertent global experiment: Science, v. 240, p. 293–299.

Raymo, M. E., 1991, Geochemical evidence supporting T. C. Chamberlin's theory of glaciation: Geology, v. 19, p. 344–347.

Raymo, M. E., and Ruddiman, W. F., 1992, Tectonic forcing of late Cenozoic climate: Nature, v. 359, p. 117–122.

Raymo, M. E., Ruddiman, W. F., and Froelich, P. N., 1988, Influence of late Cenozoic mountain building on ocean geochemical cycles: Geology, v. 16, p. 649–653.

Retallack, G. J., 1990, Soils of the past: Boston, Unwin Hyman, 520 p.

Robinson, J. M., 1990, Lignin, land plants and fungi: Biological evolution affecting Phanerozoic oxygen balance: Geology, v. 18, p. 607–610.

Robinson, J. M., 1991, Fire in Phanerozoic cybernetics, *in* Schneider, S. H., and Boston, P. J., eds., Scientists on Gaia: Cambridge, MIT Press, p. 362–374.

Ruddiman, W. F., and Kutzbach, J. E., 1991, Plateau uplift and climatic change: Scientific American, v. 264, p. 66–75.

Saini, H. S., Waraich, R. S., Malhotra, N. K., Nagpaul, K. K., and Sharma, K. K., 1979, Cooling and uplift rates and dating of thrusts from Kinnaur, Himachal, Himalaya: Himalayan Geology, v. 9, p. 549–567.

Savin, S. M., Douglas, R. G., and Stehli, F. G., 1975, Tertiary marine paleotemperatures: Geological Society of America Bulletin, v. 86, p. 1499–1510.

Schmitz, B., 1987, TiO_2/Al_2O_3 ratio in the Cenozoic Bengal Abyssal Fan sediments and its use as a paleostream indicator: Marine Geology, v. 76, p. 195–206.

Scotese, C. R., and Golonka, J., 1992, PALEOMAP paleogeographic atlas: Department of Geology, University of Texas at Arlington PALEOMAP Progress Report 20, 32 p.

Stallard, R. F., and Edmond, J. M., 1983, Geochemistry of the Amazon. 2: The influence of geology and weathering environment on the dissolved load: Journal of Geophysical Research, v. 88, p. 9671–9688.

Veizer, J., Compston, W., Clauer, N., and Schidlowski, M., 1983, $^{87}Sr/^{86}Sr$ in late Proterozoic carbonates: Evidence for mantle event at ~900 Ma ago: Geochimika et Cosmochimika Acta, v. 47, p. 295–302.

Volk, T., 1987, Feedbacks between weathering and atmospheric CO_2 over the last 100 million years: American Journal of Science, v. 287, p. 763–779.

Walker, J.C.G., Hays, P. B., and Kasting, J. K., 1981, A negative feedback mechanism for the long term stabilization of Earth's surface temperature: Journal of Geophysical Research, v. 86, p. 9776–9782.

Wedepohl, K. H., 1969, Handbook of geochemistry, 1: Berlin, Springer, 244 p.

West, R. M., 1984, Siwalik fauna from Nepal: Paleoecological and paleoclimatic interpretations, *in* Whyte, R. O., Chiu, T. N., Leung, C. K., and So, E. L., eds., The evolution of the East Asian environment: Hong Kong, University of Hong Kong Centre of Asian Studies, p. 724–744.

Williams, H., and Hatcher, R. D., 1983, Appalachian suspect terranes, *in* Hatcher, R. D., Williams, H., and Zietz, I., eds., Contributions to the tectonics and geophysics of mountain ranges: Geological Society of America Memoir 158, p. 33–53.

Windley, B. F., 1984, The evolving continents: New York, John Wiley and Sons, 399 p.

Worsley, T. R., and Kidder, D. L., 1991, First-order coupling of paleogeography and CO_2, with global surface temperature and its latitudinal contrast: Geology, v. 19, p. 1161–1164.

Worsley, T. R., and Nance, R. D., 1989, Carbon redox and climate control through earth history: A speculative reconstruction: Palaeogeography, Palaeoclimatology, Palaeoecology, v. 75, p. 259–282.

Worsley, T. R., Nance, D., and Moody, J. B., 1984, Global tectonics and eustasy for the past 2 billion years: Marine Geology, v. 58, p. 373–400.

Worsley, T. R., Moody, J. B., and Nance, R. D., 1985, Proterozoic to Recent tectonic tuning of biogeochemical cycles: The carbon cycle and atmospheric CO_2: Natural Variations Archean to Present, v. 32, p. 561–572.

Worsley, T. R., Nance, R. D., and Moody, J. B., 1986, Tectonic cycles and the history of the earth's biogeochemical and paleoceanographic record: Paleoceanography, v. 1, p. 233–263.

MANUSCRIPT ACCEPTED BY THE SOCIETY MAY 14, 1993

Geological Society of America
Special Paper 288
1994

General circulation model simulations of Triassic climates: Preliminary results

Kevin M. Wilson*
Department of Geology, Bryn Mawr College, Bryn Mawr, Pennsylvania 19010
David Pollard
National Center for Atmospheric Research, P.O. Box 3000, Boulder, Colorado 80307-3000
William W. Hay
Department of Geological Science, C/B 250, University of Colorado, Boulder, Colorado 80309
Starley L. Thompson
National Center for Atmospheric Research, P.O. Box 3000, Boulder, Colorado 80307-3000
Christopher N. Wold
GEOMAR, Wishhofstrasse 1-3, W-2300, Kiel 14, Federal Republic of Germany

ABSTRACT

The climates of two realistic geographic representations of the Triassic earth, corresponding in age to the Scythian (245 Ma) and the Carnian (225 Ma), are explored using a new atmospheric general circulation model (AGCM) called GENESIS. The GENESIS AGCM is coupled to a slab ocean 50 m thick, with prescribed heat transport; it also incorporates three types of cloud cover and new models for vegetation effects, soil hydrology, snow cover, and sea-ice formation and melting. Boundary conditions prescribed in the separate Scythian and Carnian experiments include realistic paleogeography and estimates of paleotopography, solar insolation, atmospheric CO_2 concentration, vegetation and soil types, and oceanic heat flux. Seasonal simulations of Triassic climate were performed using a horizontal spectral resolution of R15 (4.5 degrees latitude by 7.5 degrees longitude) and 12 levels in the vertical for the atmosphere and $2° \times 2·$ for the surface.

Results for both time intervals suggest that most of the seasonal precipitation fell on major highland areas of Pangea. Dry continental climates with very large seasonal temperature ranges (>45°C) were modeled in the dominantly lowland interior of Pangea. Carnian continental climates predicted by the AGCM were wetter than those of the Scythian; however, both time intervals were characterized by strongly monsoonal circulation. Comparison of these results with lithologic and fossil proxy climatic indicators suggests reasonably good correlations. However, the extreme temperature variations predicted for both Scythian and Carnian are somewhat difficult to reconcile with the fossil record, although accurate interpretation of fossil proxy climatic indicators is not a simple matter. Additional AGCM sensitivity studies may be necessary to resolve this problem.

---

*Present address: Wildhorse Exploration, Inc., 3305 Rock Creek Road, Edmond, Oklahoma 73013.

Wilson, K. M., Pollard, D., Hay, W. W., Thompson, S. L., and Wold, C. N., 1994, *in* Klein, G. D., ed., Pangea: Paleoclimate, Tectonics, and Sedimentation During Accretion, Zenith, and Breakup of a Supercontinent: Boulder, Colorado, Geological Society of America Special Paper 288.

INTRODUCTION

Ever since the advent of plate tectonics, paleoclimatologists have speculated on the probable nature of Pangean climates (Robinson, 1973). Early, qualitative estimates were improved in recent years by more sophisticated numerical climate model simulations pioneered by Crowley et al. (1987), Kutzbach and Gallimore (1989), and Crowley et al. (1992). Results from these studies and others suggested that Pangean climates were marked by strong seasonal temperature contrast and well-developed monsoonal circulation patterns. However, detailed predictions that could be compared with the geologic and fossil records (for the Triassic in particular) have not been forthcoming, because of the inherent limitations of the preliminary models employed to date. Most prior studies either used idealized continental paleogeography or modeled a limited number of variables using two-dimensional Energy Balance Models (EBM's).

Pangean climate during the Triassic interval is of particular interest in the study of paleoclimates, owing to several perhaps unique features of that period of earth history. For example, the Triassic was probably the most arid period during the Phanerozoic, as shown by the widespread deposition, at low to mid-latitudes, of great quantities of evaporites (Gordon, 1975; Habicht, 1979; Busson, 1982). The relative ubiquity of similarly distributed red bed deposits and the common occurrence of eolian sand deposits (Habicht, 1979; Crowley, 1983; Ronov et al., 1989) lend support to this interpretation. Nevertheless, Triassic humid zones occurred at high latitudes, as shown by coals and bauxite deposits (Robinson, 1973; Habicht, 1979; Hallam, 1985; Ronov et al., 1989). In spite of the general aridity assumed for the Triassic, good evidence exists for a global humid ("pluvial") episode during the Carnian (Sims and Ruffell, 1990).

Vegetation covering the land surface was considerably different during the Triassic, with a predominance of ferns, cycadophytes, and lycopods (Traverse, 1990). Virtually no angiosperms or grasses were present to bind the soil in semiarid regions (Marzolf, 1988). The Triassic oceans and atmosphere experienced significant changes in chemical cycling, as shown by large perturbations in the long-term trends of carbon and sulphur isotope ratios measured in the marine sedimentary record (Holser, 1977). Holser suggested that the large Scythian sulphur isotope excursion (the "Rot event") was the result of catastrophic mixing of two previously separated oceanic reservoirs. Milankovitch (orbital) forcing of climate during the Triassic is suggested from cyclic deposition (Van Houten, 1964; Fischer, 1964; Olsen, 1986); if present, orbital forcing would certainly have modulated long-term climate on Pangea, especially during "hot orbit" configurations (Crowley et al., 1992).

Other features of the Triassic world make it interesting as a subject for numerical climate modeling. Sediment mass-balance considerations suggest that the average elevation of

Pangea was about 1,500 m, in contrast to the present average elevation of the ice-free continents of 740 m (Hay and Southam, 1977; Hay et al., 1981). Kutzbach and Gallimore included the high supercontinent configuration in one of their Pangea experiments, finding that the increased elevation intensified the monsoonal circulation relative to the low continent case.

The Triassic was also the time of development of the rift system that ultimately ruptured Pangea to form the present continents. The rift system was well developed on the site of the future Central Atlantic, where its orography influenced the regional climate (Manspeizer, 1982; Hay et al., 1982). Sims and Ruffell (1990) suggested that the rift uplift might have been a causative factor in the Carnian "pluvial" episode.

The mass/age distribution of sediment and sedimentary flux estimates (Hay et al., 1988) show that a major peak in sediment accumulation developed during the Early Triassic. This corresponds to a peak in volcanic activity (Budyko and Ronov, 1979; Frakes, 1986) that has been taken as an indication of elevated atmospheric CO_2 levels at that time. Popp et al. (1989) and Berner (1990) estimated from geochemical models that pCO_2 of the later Triassic atmosphere may have been four to five times greater than the present-day value.

Early plate tectonic reconstructions (Dietz and Holden, 1970) suggested that a nearly monolithic Pangean supercontinent existed during the Triassic. However, terrane theory (e.g., Coney et al., 1980) suggests more complex tectonic models due to the inclusion of multiple "suspect" terranes and drifting microcontinents (Wilson, 1987; Burke, 1988; Van der Voo, 1988). For example, Wilson et al. (1989a) showed scores of terranes and microcontinents, completely separate from the Pangean landmass, drifting across the surface of the Triassic earth.

A minimum of 110 terranes and blocks must be used to model Triassic paleogeography adequately; many of these terranes drifted across major climate zones during Triassic time (Wilson, 1989).

In the present study, we examine the sensitivities of Early (Scythian; 245 Ma) and Late (Carnian; 225 Ma) Triassic climates to changes in realistic paleogeography and estimated paleotopography using an atmospheric global climate model (AGCM). The simulations employed a new circulation model called GENESIS (Version 1.02), recently developed at the National Center for Atmospheric Research (NCAR). Results are readily compared with proxy climatic indicators from the lithologic and fossil record, permitting evaluation of the viability of the modeling approach.

MODEL DESCRIPTION

The simulations employed a general circulation model, GENESIS version 1.02, recently developed at NCAR by two of the authors (DP and SLT). The atmospheric part of the model is a heavily modified version of the NCAR Community Climate Model CCM1 (Williamson et al., 1987) and is coupled to a slab ocean and new models of vegetation, soil, snow, and sea ice. The model and results for the present day will be described in more detail in forthcoming articles by Pollard and Thompson, and here we briefly summarize the main features that are different from the standard CCM1.

- The atmospheric model (AGCM) uses the solar radiation scheme of Thompson et al. (1987), which performs delta-Eddington calculations for all layers, then combines the clouds into a single effective layer for ray-tracing calculations. Aerosols can be taken into account, although none are specified for the Triassic.
- The AGCM and surface models have a diurnal cycle, with solar-radiation calculations performed every 1.5 hours. Full infrared-radiation calculations are performed by the AGCM every model time step of 0.5 hours, except for the costly computations of absorptivities and emissivities of H_2O, CO_2, and O_3 gases, which are done once every 24 hours.
- The AGCM advects water vapor by a semi-Lagrangian method, essentially as described in Williamson and Rasch (1989), Rasch and Williamson (1990), and Williamson (1990). This is done to avoid difficulties caused by spectral transport of water vapor, which produced negative holes and ripples that needed to be "fixed" at each time step in the standard CCM1.
- The AGCM uses a cloud parameterization similar to that of Slingo and Slingo (1991), with three possible types of clouds: stratus, anvil cirrus, and convective. We added a new constraint on stratus clouds when the specific humidity is very low, in order to achieve realistically low amounts in the polar regions in winter (motivated by Curry and Herman, 1985). To allow for the three-dimensional blocking effect of clouds at low zenith angles, we added a term that increases the solar-effective cloud fraction in each layer, depending on the instantaneous solar zenith angle (Davis et al., 1979; cf. Henderson-Sellers and McGuffie, 1990).
- Convection in the atmosphere is treated using an explicit sub-grid plume model along the lines of Anthes (1977, section 4.a) and Gregory and Rowntree (1990), for instance. At each time step, a column model of sub-grid rising thermals is solved, including saturation and precipitation. From this solution the implied large-scale vertical fluxes, latent heating, and precipitation are deduced. The same model is also used to simulate the planetary boundary layer by initiating dry Planetary Boundary Layer (PBL) thermals at the center of the lowest model layer using scaled values from the constant-flux region immediately below, as done somewhat more implicitly in Troen and Mahrt (1986) and Holtslag et al. (1990).
- The AGCM grid is independent of the surface grid. Fields are transferred between the AGCM and the surface by bilinear interpolation (AGCM to surface) or straightforward area-averaging (surface to AGCM) at each time step. For the Triassic simulations the AGCM used a horizontal spectral resolution of R15 (~4.5° latitude by 7.5° longi-

tude) and 12 levels in the vertical. The surface-model resolution was 2° by 2°.

- A land-surface transfer model (LSX) accounts for the physical effects of vegetation. LSX is based on the earlier models of Biosphere-Atmosphere Transfer Schome (BATS) (Dickinson et al., 1986) and Simple Biosphere Model (SiB) (Sellers et al., 1986) and is intermediate in complexity between the two. Up to two vegetation layers ("trees" and "grass") can be specified at each grid point, and the radiative and turbulent fluxes through these layers to the soil or snow surface are calculated. Rain or snow can be intercepted by the vegetation and subsequently drips or blows off.
- A six-layer soil model extends from the surface to 4.25-m depth. Heat is diffused linearly, and soil moisture is diffused highly nonlinearly (Clapp and Hornberger, 1986). Surface runoff occurs if the precipitation minus evaporation exceeds the maximum possible infiltration rate. Soil ice is predicted for each soil layer, with the latent heat of fusion accounted for explicitly.
- A standard three-layer snow model is used for snow cover on soil, ice-sheet, and sea-ice surfaces, including fractional areal cover when the snow thickness is less than 15 cm. Heat is diffused linearly through the snow, and the total thickness changes as a result of melting or snowfall on the upper layer Fractional snow cover is accounted for by imposing a minimum snow thickness of 15 cm and adjusting the fractional area to conserve snow mass.
- A standard six-layer sea-ice thermodynamic model predicts the local melting and freezing of ice, essentially as in Semtner (1976). Heat diffuses linearly through the ice, and the total thickness can change by melting of the upper layer and freezing or melting on the bottom surface. Fractional areal cover is included as in Hibler (1979) and Harvey (1988). Sea-ice advection can be included using the "cavitating-fluid" model of Flato and Hibler (1990, 1992), but it was not used for the Triassic, as explained below.
- The ocean is represented by a thermodynamic slab, which crudely captures the seasonal heat capacity of the ocean mixed layer. The thickness of the slab is 50 m. Poleward oceanic heat transport is prescribed as a zonally symmetric function of latitude based on present-day observations (Covey and Thompson, 1989), modified for the Triassic as described in the next section.

BOUNDARY CONDITIONS

The only changes to the present-day GENESIS model were the prescription of solar insolation, atmospheric CO_2 amount, land-ocean distribution, topography, vegetation types, soil properties, and oceanic heat flux. These changes are described below.

The solar constant was reduced from its present value of 1370 W m^{-2} by 2%, based on the linear solar-luminosity trend shown in Crowley and Baum (1991, their Fig. 5 alternate scale). Orbital variations have a significant effect on supercontinent climates and can bias the interpretation of geologic data (Crowley et al., 1992), but since we were limited by computer resources to just one simulation per age, we chose a "mean" orbital configuration. We used an eccentricity of zero and obliquity of 23.4°; although the actual mean eccentricity is non-zero, the choice of seasonal precession would have been arbitrary for all but zero eccentricity.

The atmospheric CO_2 volume mixing ratio was set at 1,360 ppm, ~four times the present value, based on results of the geochemical model of Berner (1990) as shown in Crowley and Baum (1991, their Fig. 3.a).

The Scythian and Carnian land-ocean distribution and el-

evation classes were prescribed on the surface-model 2° by 2° grid as described in a later section. The land-ocean map and elevation classes are shown in Fig. 1. Uniform elevations of 1,000, 2,000 and 3,000 m were assigned to the three elevation classes, guided mainly by the requirement that the average land elevation of Pangea was ~1.5 km (Hay and Southam, 1977; Hay et al., 1981). The resulting mean land elevations are 1,374 m for the Scythian and 1,260 m for the Carnian.

In the absence of substantial paleobotanical data for the Triassic, the choice of vegetation types was fairly arbitrary. A single vegetation type was assigned to each elevation class, assuming that elevation was a more dominant control than latitude. The lowest (1,000-m) class was assigned a modern "Sonoran-desert" vegetation, the intermediate (2,000-m) class

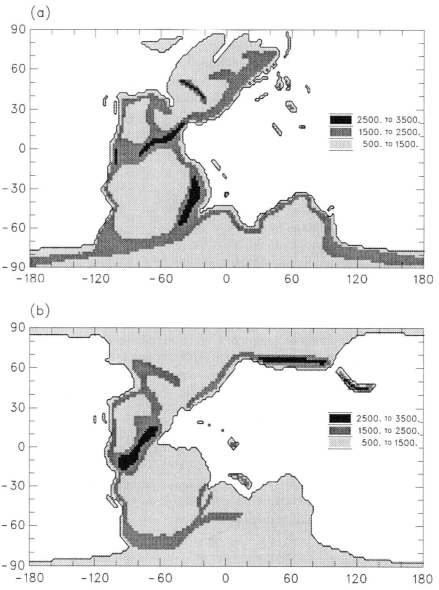

Figure 1. Land-ocean maps used for the simulations. Also shown are the three elevation classes, with uniform heights above sea level of 1,000, 2,000 and 3,000 m. (a) Scythian; (b) Carnian.

was assigned an evergreen forest, and the highest (3,000-m) class was assigned tundra. The specific vegetation attributes are obtained from Dorman and Sellers (1989), with our three classes (Sonoran desert, forest, tundra) corresponding to their biome numbers 8, 4, and 10 respectively. However, we did not use their seasonal cycles of leaf area index or fractional cover but instead used their annual mean values for types 8 and 4. For type 10 (tundra) we used constant fractional cover of 0.9, leaf area index (green) of 0.5, stem area index (total minus green) of 1.5, and no upper-story shrubs; we feel these are more realistic values for modern low-Arctic tundra.

Soil properties in the model are specified as in BATS, by assigning a texture class and an albedo class to each grid point and obtaining the physical values (porosity, hydraulic conductivity, albedo, etc.) from the appropriate BATS table (Dickinson et al., 1986, Table 3; Wilson et al., 1987, Table II). A single mid-range soil texture class was used globally for the Triassic (#6 in the BATS texture table, corresponding to a loam soil). A single soil-albedo class was also used globally, and guided by the prevalence of red beds in the Triassic, this was chosen to be quite light (#2 in the BATS color table, corresponding to the albedo of modern sandy soils).

The oceanic heat flux is prescribed in the model as a zonally asymmetric function of latitude based on present-day observations. By default, 0.3 times the "0.5 × OCNFLX" function of Covey and Thompson (1989) is used, but for the Triassic simulations this was made symmetric about the equator and uniformly doubled under the assumption that the more extensive Triassic oceans would have transported heat more efficiently than is the case today. It should be observed, however, that Kutzbach et al. (1990), using a coarse-grid oceanic GCM with idealized Pangean geography, predicted net poleward oceanic heat transport similar to modern values. Our Triassic oceanic transport implies convergence values of -30 W m^{-2} at the equator, increasing to 30 W m^{-2} at $\sim50°$, and decreasing to 16 W m^{-2} poleward of $\sim60°$. Where sea ice occurs, the convergence values under sea ice are weighted by the sea-ice fraction toward a value of 8 W m^{-2} for 100% ice cover. An additive global adjustment is made at each step to ensure that the global integral of the convergence is zero.

Although the model has an option of advecting sea ice due to wind stress and ocean currents, this was turned off for the Triassic, since the ocean current field is unknown.

SUMMARY OF TECTONIC MODEL

To set boundary conditions for the climate model runs, we used new reconstructions (Figs. 1, 2, 3) for the continental blocks at 245 Ma (Scythian) and 225 Ma (Carnian). These continental reconstructions differ from earlier attempts in the following ways: (1) they show an improved, tighter fit of the blocks that surround the sites of the future Atlantic and Indian Ocean basins, and (2) they show the positions of the larger terranes and microcontinents that existed at each time interval

(Wilson, 1989). All terrane/block names and configurations, except where noted, are taken from Wilson (1989) and Wilson et al. (1989a, 1989b, 1991). The improved fit of the tectonic elements that comprised Gondwana and Laurasia results from taking into account Mesozoic-Cenozoic internal and marginal deformation of the continental blocks. The reference frame for pole positions and paleolatitudes is that of Harrison and Lindh (1982), who established a paleomagnetic polar wander curve for North America. All other blocks were rotated in plate circuits relative to North America. The zonal character of the distribution of Carnian coals indicates that this paleolatitudinal reference frame is approximately correct.

The two reconstructions differ from each other because (1) the younger (Carnian) one shows some initial stretching that took place between West and East Antarctica (Wilson et al., 1989b), (2) the positions and numbers of terranes change, and (3) their paleolatitudinal orientations change.

In the two reconstructions, the Arctic region is occupied by the early Mesozoic Paleoarctic Ocean. This was later subducted by the "windshield wiper" motion of the Arctic-Alaska-Chukotka terrane (Wilson et al., 1991). During the opening of the Labrador Sea, the Canadian Shield was slightly deformed. Geological evidence for this exists in the thinned crust that now separates the Arctic Islands Block, the Ellesmere Block, and the Baffin Block from the Shield proper. These changes slightly altered the shape of North America and have been removed to allow a palinspastic fit for the Triassic.

During the Laramide Orogeny, the western part of North America was rotated clockwise a few degrees relative to the stable continental platform. The rotation pole lay in Guatemala and included an apparent northwest-southeast compression. We used a rotation of 5 degrees about a point southwest of Yucatan to restore the western part of the continent to its original position. To the south, the Yucatan Block fits well against the Gulf Rim (Balcones) Fault System. This implies that it is not necessary to translate the Yaqui (Mexico) Block to the west, along the proposed "Mojave-Sonora Megashear," as previous reconstructions have done (Ross and Scotese, 1988; Wilson et al., 1989a). The evidence for a "Megashear" is perhaps less than compelling, as discussed elsewhere (Cohen et al., 1986). A small translation of the Oaxaca and Chortis blocks is still required for fit. During the early Mesozoic the terranes that today form California, Oregon, Washington, British Columbia, and southern Alaska were island arcs off North and South America (Wilson et al., 1991).

During the rifting of South America from Africa during the Early Cretaceous, South America was deformed in several areas, "unwrapping" from a rigid Africa. Four sedimentary basins formed in the aulacogens extending into the continent: the Parana, Salado, Colorado, and San Jorge basins. The amount of stretching involved in producing these basins can be calculated from the present thicknesses of sediment within them and the properties of the underlying crust. Removing the stretching from these basins causes the outline of the South American con-

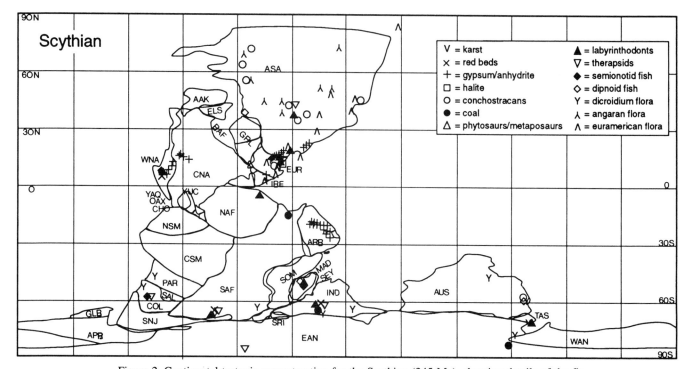

Figure 2. Continental tectonic reconstruction for the Scythian (245 Ma), showing details of the fit of the major blocks and the locations of the various geologic and fossil proxy climatic indicators. Note that terrane data are not plotted. Sources for proxy indicators are Ronov and others (1989) and Table 1 herein. Symbols for indicators are as follows: V = Karst (rainfall); X = Red beds (warm, dry); + = Gypsum/Anhydrite (warm, dry); open square = Halite (hot, dry); open circle = Conchostracans (seasonal dry); filled circle = Coal (humid); open triangle = Phytosaurs/Metaposaurs (runoff/precip.); filled triangle = Labyrinthodonts (runoff/precip.); inverted open triangle = Therapsids (temperate); filled diamond = Semionotid Fish (runoff/precip.); open diamond = Dipnoid Fish (seasonal runoff); Y (Scythian map) = Dicroidium (Gondwanan) flora (warm, temperate); Y (Carnian map) = Dictyophyllum (Gondwanan) flora (warm, temperate); inverted Y (Scythian map) = Angaran flora (cool, humid); inverted V (Scythian map) = Euramerican flora (warm temperate); tree (Carnian map) = Petrified Forest of Arizona. Symbols for major continental and terrane blocks are as follows: AAK = Arctic-Alaska-Chukotka Block; APB = Antarctic Peninsula Block; ARB = Arabian Block; ASA = Asia; AUS = Australia; BAF = Baffin Block; CHO = Chortis; CNA = Central North America Block; COL = Colorado Block; CSM = Central South America; EAN = East Antarctica; ELS = Ellesmere Block; EUR = European Block; GLB = Graham Land Block; GRL = Greenland; IBE = Iberian Block; IND = Indian Block; MAD = Madagascar; NAF = Northwest Africa; NSM = Northern South America; OAX = Oaxaca Block; PAR = Parana Block; SAF = Southeast Africa; SAL = Salado Block; SEY = Seychelles; SNJ = San Jorge Block; SOM = Somalian Block; SRI = Sri Lanka Block; TAS = Tasmanian Block; WAN = West Antarctica; WNA = Western North American Accreted Terranes; YAQ = Yaqui Block; YUC = Yucatan Block.

tinent to become more strongly concave to the east. In this reconstruction the Maurice Ewing Bank overlaps Africa, suggesting that it may have formed during the rifting phase.

The Australian sector of Pangea was bordered by a fringe of terranes in the early Mesozoic: the Samba, Timor, Indo-Burman Ranges, Buru-Seram-Janimbar, West Irian–Jaya, Hunstein-Jimi-Bismark, and Gympie terranes (Wilson, 1987, 1989; Wilson et al., 1989a). The Exmouth Plateau is the only remnant of this fringe that did not drift away from the continent during the post-Triassic. The India, Himalaya, and Lhasa blocks fit against Antarctica and Australia in the early Meso-

zoic. The Madagascar, Iran, and Afghanistan blocks appear to have filled the gap between India and Somalia during the Triassic. The Iran and Afghanistan blocks broke away from the Gondwanan portion of Pangea, drifting northward, during the Early Triassic (Wilson and others, 1989a). Madagascar later drifted southward with southeastern Gondwana during the Jurassic.

South of the main Atlas Fault, the continent of Africa was only slightly deformed. The large-scale stretching of the Benoue Trough, assumed by most geologists in order to fit Africa and South America, is not required. The present reconstruction

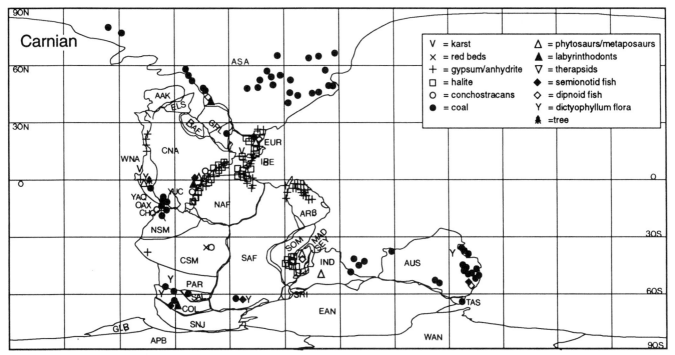

Figure 3. Continental tectonic reconstruction for the Carnian (225 Ma), showing details of the fit of the major blocks and the locations of the various geologic and fossil proxy climatic indicators. Note that terrane data are not plotted. Sources for proxy indicators are Ronov and others (1989) and Table 1 herein. Key to symbols given in Figure 2. Key to symbols for major continental and terrane blocks is given in Figure 2.

restores Somalia to its original position, removing the stretching associated with the formation of the East African Rift System. The Red Sea and Gulf of Aden close tightly, with even Socotra fitting into a notch on the Arabian block.

The quasi-transform deformation that produced the North Sea and the North German basins and caused overthrusting of the Harz Mountains has been removed. This rotates Eastern Europe and nuclear Asia counterclockwise, placing them in a more north-south orientation than in earlier reconstructions. We have not yet attempted to quantitatively remove the complex deformation of Asia that resulted from the collision of India in the Paleogene, although terrane positions for this area are based on the work of Wilson (1989), who made certain qualitative corrections to the shape of Triassic Asia. The North China, South China, and Indochina blocks, together with associated smaller blocks, collided with Asia in the Triassic and Early Jurassic; they are here shown in their presumed Scythian and Carnian positions (Wilson, 1987, 1989; Wilson et al., 1989a).

The new reconstructions show a remarkable planet. It has a pole-to-pole continent with a western margin that has an almost perfect meridional orientation. On the east, the Tethys Ocean basin forms an embayment in Pangea that is nearly symmetrical about the equator; this wedge-shaped ocean opens eastward to connect with Panthalassa, the nearly global Triassic Pacific Ocean.

SUMMARY OF PALEOGEOGRAPHY AND PALEOTOPOGRAPHY

The shorelines and locations of paleoclimatic indicator sediments were added to the continental base maps (Figs. 2, 3) using the Early and Late Triassic maps of Ronov et al. (1989) as guides. Because we did not know the transformation for the projection used by Ronov and his colleagues, the latitudes and longitudes of critical points were determined by measuring and interpolation within the 20 × 20 degree squares marked on their maps. It must be recognized that shoreline positions are always very difficult to determine and therefore must be regarded as only approximate. The locations of fossil faunas and floras, also plotted on Figures 2 and 3, were estimated in much the same way as were the sediment indicators, except that these were taken from the primary literature (for a listing of sources, see Wilson, 1989).

The paleotopography was initially estimated using the proposition of Hay (1981), Southam and Hay (1981), and Hay et al. (1987) that major features of continental topography are a result of only three factors related to plate tectonic processes: (1) subduction of young lithosphere, (2) collisions of continental fragments or oceanic plateaus with continental blocks, and (3) thermal uplift prior to and following continental rifting. It is assumed that subduction of young (< 20 m.y. old) lithosphere creates an uplift of 1.5 km in the adjacent continent. It is further assumed that collisions of continental fragments or oceanic plateaus (terranes) with continental blocks produces an uplift whose dimensions are related to the size of the colliding block, viz: those having an area of 1×10^6 km^2 produce an uplift of 1 km, whereas those with an area the size of India (4×10^6 km^2) produce an uplift of 4 km (Hay, 1983, Fig. 2).

For the thermal uplift associated with rifting, we assume that the ultimate width on each side of the rift is 1,000 km, that the uplift mimics the shape of a mid-ocean ridge, and that at the time of initial separation the density of the lithosphere lying beneath the rift is the same as that of lithosphere lying beneath a mid-ocean ridge. We also assume that the time constant associated with rifting continental lithosphere is 100 m.y.—that is, that the uplift begins 100 m.y. before actual drift onset and that the rate of uplift is the inverse of postrift subsidence.

Using these guidelines and plate boundary maps with terranes prepared by Wilson (1989) and Wilson et al. (1989a, 1991), we prepared preliminary paleotopographic maps for the Triassic earth, including all major terranes and Pangea. The paleogeographic maps of Ronov and others (1989) also show areas of uplift, but they used accumulated volumes and grain sizes of sediments in adjacent basins to differentiate between low and high uplifts. Many of their uplifts duplicate those we had proposed based on plate tectonic considerations, but there are also others that we had not suspected. We incorporated the other uplifts suggested by Ronov et al. (1989), giving the higher ones an arbitrary elevation of 1.5 km.

We then gridded the preliminary paleotopographic maps into 2×2 degree squares and determined the continental hypsography. The average elevation of land for the Scythian (245 Ma) reconstruction was 874 m and that for the Carnian (225 Ma) reconstruction was 760 m. However, based on mass balance of the sediments that have accumulated in the passive margins formed during and since the breakup of Pangea, Southam and Hay (1981) estimated Pangea's average elevation prior to breakup to have been about 1,400 m above sea level. To more closely approximate their estimate, we arbitrarily raised the elevations of the reconstructions to 1,000, 2,000, and 3,000 m for each class, which yielded average elevations of 1,374 m for the Scythian and 1,260 m for the Carnian.

In the case of the preliminary Carnian paleotopographic map we did not show the narrow rift valley between North America and Africa. In any case, it would have disappeared in the conversion to 2×2 degree square average elevations necessary for running the AGCM. Ronov et al. (1989) present a map showing the evaporites that accumulated in this rift valley, along the entire margin of northwest Africa as far south as the Guinea Plateau. We have included these marine evaporites as climatic indicators on the Carnian map (Fig. 3) even though they are probably mostly younger than Carnian. The Osprey Salt of the Grand Banks is also Carnian (Schlee et al., 1988), but the age of the salts to the south on both the North American and African margins is poorly known. It has been assumed that

the flooding of the southern part of the rift valley did not occur until the Early Jurassic (Manspeizer et al., 1978; Hay et al., 1982), but recently some workers place the salt deposition as far south as Baltimore Canyon–Cap Blanc during the Late Triassic, probably Norian (Tucholke and McCoy, 1986; Grant and McAlpine, 1990). On our Carnian reconstruction, the position of the rift valley is indicated by the symbols for halite (Fig. 3). It is located east of the crest of the uplift on the site of separation of North America from northwest Africa, using a paleogeography similar to that suggested by Hay et al. (1982).

MODEL RESULTS

Two 15-year runs were performed, one for the Scythian and one for the Carnian. Each run was started from a fairly arbitrary zonally symmetric initial state. All results shown here are monthly or annual means, averaged over the last five years of the simulations. The preceding 10-year spin-up period is necessary for the model ocean temperature, sea-ice, and deep-soil conditions to approach their climatic equilibrium values, and all of these fields did equilibrate adequately except for soil ice and liquid in the deep soil (permafrost), as discussed further below.

Figures 4 and 5 show the surface air temperature for January and July, and the annual range (January to July) is shown in Figure 6. The large seasonal range in the continental interiors is evident, especially in the larger southern land mass. For instance, in widespread interior areas poleward of ~40°S, the annual range is around 50 to 70°C, which is approached today only in central Siberia, Mongolia, and central Canada. This extreme range is due to both the small thermal inertia of the land mass and the desertlike dryness of most lowland regions (see below). The local topographic cooling due to the intermediate and high elevation regions ($\geq$ 2,000 m, termed "mountain ranges" or "highlands" below) can clearly be seen in both hemispheres in Figures 4 and 5. However, the January-to-July values in Figure 6 are not appropriate for the open ocean, where the maximum and minimum seasonal temperatures are lagged by ~2 months compared to land. Thus the true annual ranges for almost all of the present-day ocean are still less than ~10°.

Figures 7 through 10 show precipitation for the Scythian and Carnian and wind fields for two different levels in the Scythian. By comparing the Scythian precipitation patterns in Figures 7a and 8a with the corresponding low-level winds in Figures 9a and 10a, it is clear that the mountain ranges exert dominant influences over both the winds and precipitation. The winds at this height (~600 m) are steered parallel to the ranges in many locations, and heavy precipitation occurs where the winds bring oceanic moisture to the upwind side of a range. The most extreme example is at ~30°W, 20°S in January in Figure 7a, where the summertime heating of the continental interior to the west causes low-level monsoonal convergence that brings moisture from the oceans to the north and east onto the slopes of the highlands at that location. In

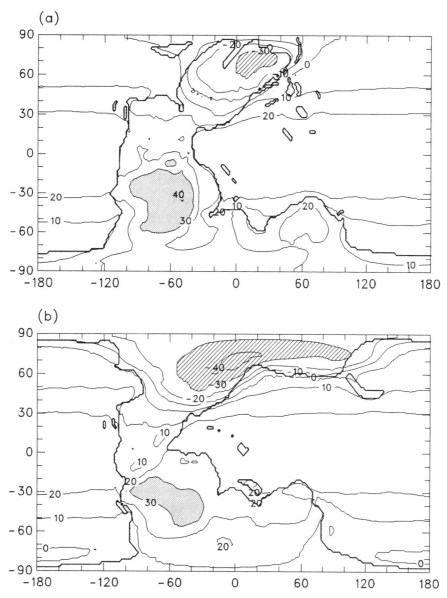

Figure 4. Surface-air (2-m screen-height) temperatures for January, in °C. Areas with temperatures >30°C are shaded and <–30°C are hatched. (a) Scythian; (b) Carnian.

addition, the trade winds are diverted by the eastern slope, a condition that presumably adds to the precipitation there. Elsewhere, appreciable amounts of precipitation are limited to mountain ranges in the summer hemisphere. Smaller amounts than shown in the figures (~1.5 mm day^{-1}) do occur in most interior lowland regions, but only in the summer months.

The mid-tropospheric winds are less influenced by topography, and the lower levels of the mid-latitude jet streams become evident, as shown in Figures 9b and 10b at the ~5,000-m level for the Scythian.

Degradation in the R15 AGCM topography fields in Figures 9 and 10 compared to the prescribed 2° by 2° fields is

shown in Figure 1. The smoothed fields are those actually seen by the AGCM and differ significantly from the prescribed fields both in the horizontal extents of the highlands and in the spectral ripples in the elevation fields (not shown).

The corresponding wind fields for the Carnian (not shown) show the same patterns, although the most intense precipitation now occurs in January over the equatorial mountain range on the west side of Pangea at ~95°W, 15°S (Fig. 7b). Interestingly, the global mean precipitation *over land* for the Carnian is ~10% more than for the Scythian (annual means of 3.28 and 2.93 mm day^{-1} respectively), probably as a result not of any difference in the global climate but simply of the Car-

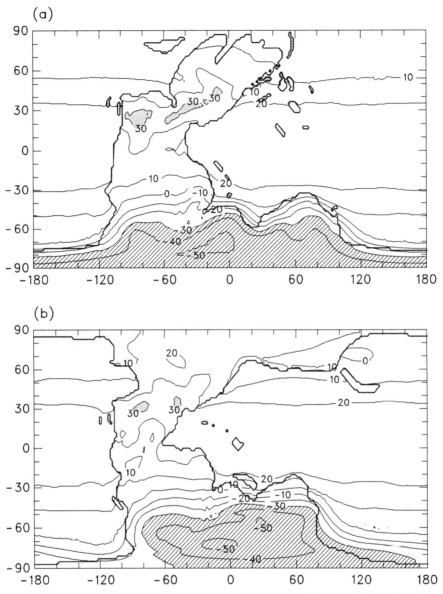

Figure 5. Surface-air (2-m screen-height) temperatures for July, in °C. (a) Scythian; (b) Carnian.

nian having a greater percentage of its highlands in the path of prevailing onshore winds. (Both ages have virtually the same global mean precipitation of 4.45 and 4.49 mm day^{-1} over land and ocean combined.) The difference in land precipitation is reflected in slightly higher annual mean values of soil moisture and runoff for the Carnian.

In the annual and zonal mean, the equatorial Intertropical Convergence Zone (ITCZ) precipitation maximum is displaced northward to 10°N (not shown). This displacement occurs more over ocean than land but is still present (to ~5°N) in the zonal mean over land alone.

The model overestimates precipitation by ~25% for the present-day climate, although the geographic distribution is largely correct. Assuming the same error applies to the Triassic, the fields of precipitation, soil moisture, and runoff would all be overestimated by roughly that amount, and the climate over the lowland regions would be even drier than shown here.

Soil moisture in the upper soil layer is shown in Figures 11 and 12. Soil moisture closely follows the patterns of precipitation, and again the effect of topography is obvious: Interior lowland regions are very dry (values ≤ 0.25) and the relatively narrow highland regions are quite wet (≥ 0.65). Since *liquid* soil water is shown, blank regions poleward of ~40° in the winter hemisphere indicate snow cover under which any soil moisture is frozen. Snowmelt in the spring produces large

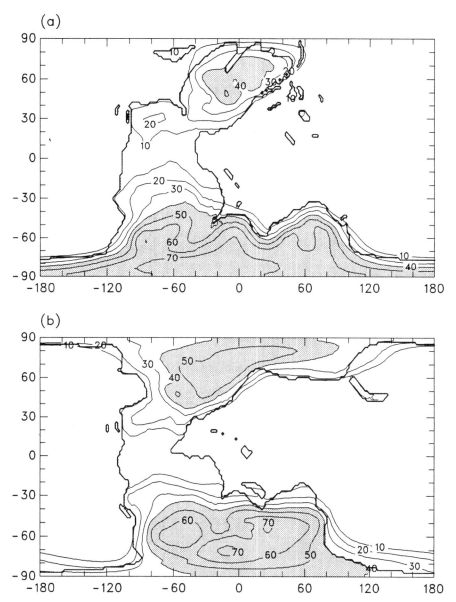

Figure 6. Annual range (January to July) of surface-air temperature, in °C. Areas with ranges >40° are shaded. (a) Scythian; (b) Carnian.

amounts of runoff and high soil moisture for a few months (not shown), but by the summer (January or July) all snow has melted and the lowland soils have dried out. Since no snow survives through the summer at any location, this implies that no ice sheets would form.

The annual-mean discharge (surface runoff plus bottom drainage) in Figure 13 also reflects the influence of precipitation, with high values occurring only on the highlands. Runoff in the model occurs when the precipitation minus evaporation exceeds the current maximum infiltration rate, so requires either short periods of intense precipitation or extended periods with moderate precipitation to first saturate the upper soil. Some runoff also occurs from the spring snowmelt in both hemispheres, as seen in the high latitudes in Figure 13. Gravitational drainage occurs from the bottom soil layer and is about equal in magnitude to runoff in the global mean.

The soil-ice fraction in the lowest soil layer is shown in Figure 14. At these depths (1.75 to 4.25 m) there is very little seasonal variation, and this field represents the extent of permafrost predicted by the model. Even after 15 years, this field still has a slow annual trend that would require several more decades of integration to reach equilibrium. However, by inspection of the trends we feel that the permafrost boundaries in Figure 14 are quite close to their final equilibrium; globally, deep soil-ice volume is gradually increasing in the Southern Hemisphere and increasing in the North, but the boundaries

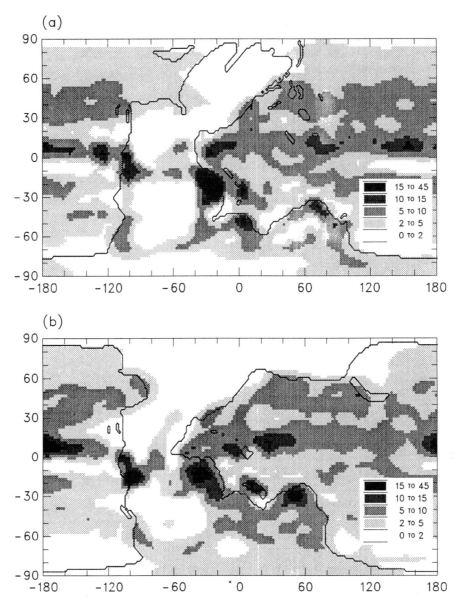

Figure 7. Precipitation for January, in mm day^{-1}. (a) Scythian; (b) Carnian.

are almost constant. The general values of ~0.6 in Figure 14 still reflect the arbitrary initial conditions of the runs when the soil water (liquid or ice) was set to 0.6. Except near the boundaries, no liquid water coexists with the deep ice, and the deep soil temperature is presumably well below zero.

Figures 15 and 16 show sea-ice fractional cover (i.e., 1 minus the areal fraction of leads). Results are shown for April and October when the extents are near minimum and maximum. Maximum thicknesses (not shown) are ~1 m in the Northern Hemisphere and ~3 m in the Southern Hemisphere. In the Southern Hemisphere the ice behaves similarly to today,

expanding to ~60°S in October. In the Northern Hemisphere there is no equivalent of the modern Arctic Ocean surrounded and cooled in winter by large land masses, so the Triassic sea ice forms only in close proximity to the land. In the open ocean its advance beyond ~80°N is checked by the seasonal thermal inertia of the wide ocean and the prescribed high-latitude oceanic heat convergence of 16 W m^{-2}. It should be emphasized, however, that sea-ice dynamics was turned off for these simulations (because of the lack of prescribed ocean current fields). It is likely that advection would significantly alter the sea-ice distribution, probably in the same way as around

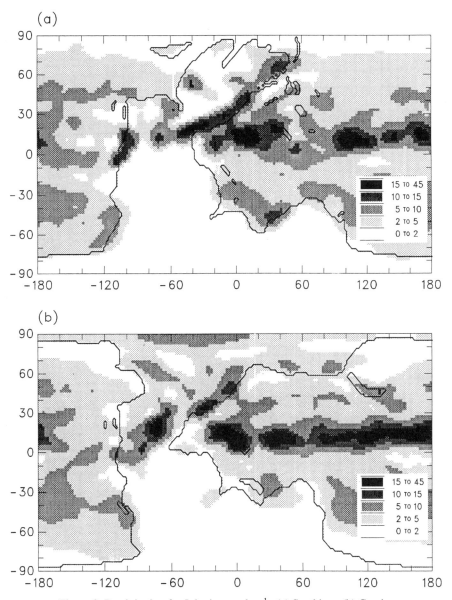

Figure 8. Precipitation for July, in mm day^{-1}. (a) Scythian; (b) Carnian.

Antarctica today, that is, cyclonic winds in winter causing an equatorward drift that expands the boundaries while decreasing the average thickness and increasing the fraction of leads.

DISCUSSION

Comparison with Scythian proxy climatic indicators

Geologic data. The most distinctive paleoclimatic feature of the Scythian reconstruction is the presence of evaporites on the eastern margin of Pangea at 5° to 20°N and 15° to 25°S and on the western margin at 5° to 15°N (Fig. 2). The evaporites are mainly sulphates; halite occurs rarely, occurring only in Europe during the Scythian. These occurrences are closer to the equator than the present zones of highest aridity, which are at 25° to 35°N and S. A single coal occurrence, in Asia at a paleolatitude of 45°N, was reported by Ronov et al. (1989). They also show an occurrence of halite and gypsum in Tasmania on their Early Triassic lithofacies map. However, we have not been able to find the source for this, and because it would have been at a paleolatitude of about 70°S, we have not shown it on Figure 2.

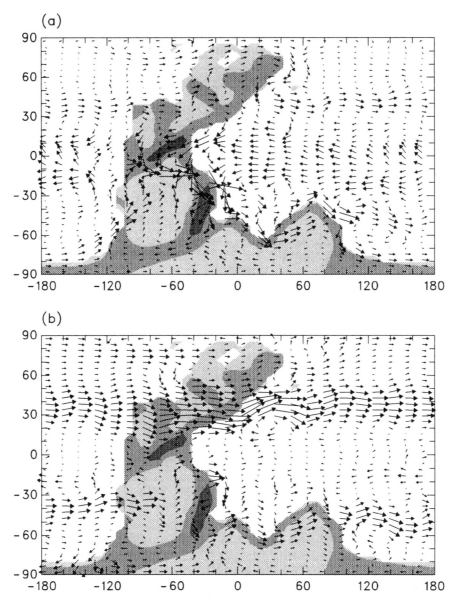

Figure 9. Wind fields and topography for the Scythian in January. The vector scale is such that a speed of 1 m s^{-1} corresponds to an arrow length of 1° of latitude. σ = (pressure/surface pressure) is the AGCM vertical coordinate. (a) σ = 0.926,, at ~600 m above surface (second-lowest AGCM layer). (b) σ = 0.500, at ~5,000 m above surface.

The model results indicate that the evaporites were deposited in areas that presumably had the highest oceanic summer surface temperatures on the eastern margin of Pangaea; although the temperatures shown in Figure 4a and 5a are for the air only, they would nevertheless closely correspond in latitude areas to the temperature of the ocean surface (SST). The evaporite localities also correspond to winter precipitation minima shown on Figures 7a and 8a. Paradoxically, the land areas adjacent to the sites of evaporite deposition have relatively high precipitation and soil moisture (Figs. 11a and 12a).

The site of Scythian coal deposition in Asia, north of the present Pamirs, has high soil moisture (Fig. 12a).

The Scythian model results suggest a strong monsoonal circulation with oscillation of the ITCZ over land from 15°N to 15°S with the seasons; note, however, that overall the ITCZ is shifted to the north of the equator (Figs. 7a and 8a).

Fossil data. Table 1 summarizes the paleoclimatic indicators suggested by the fossil record for the Scythian and Carnian (data adapted from tables in Wilson [1989] and references therein). The data are plotted on Figures 2 and 3; how-

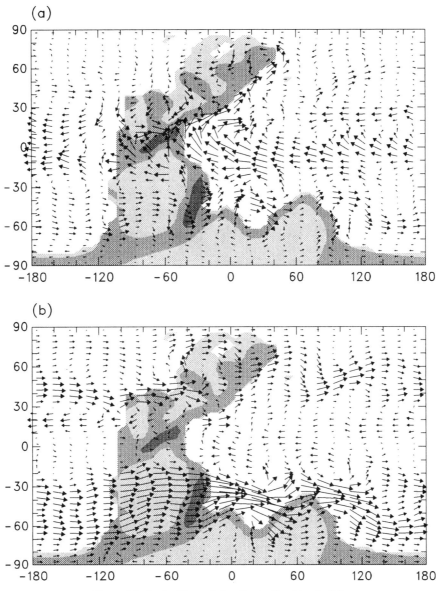

Figure 10. As for Figure 9, but for the Scythian in July.

ever, the terrane climatic data were not plotted because of uncertainty in achieving proper computer rotations for terranes on the simplified continental tectonic base.

Both faunal and floral fossil data serve to test the validity of the Scythian climate model results presented here. For example, R. T. Bakker (1989, personal communication) suggested that large amphibians such as the labyrinthodonts probably required standing water (i.e., runoff/precipitation) for survival. This is an interpretation similar to that made by Buffetaut and Martin (1984) for the particular case of the metoposaurid family of the labyrinthodonts. Many examples of labyrinthodont fossils have been found in Scythian rocks around the world (Table 1). Comparison with the climate model results for the Scythian in-

dicates a generally good correlation with soil moisture (Figs. 11a and 12a); however, different fossil localities correlate with different seasons. In general, Southern Hemisphere labyrinthodont localities correlate with January model results, that is, summer in both hemispheres. The same is true for both precipitation (Figs. 7a and 8a) and surface runoff (Fig. 13a). This is consistent with the markedly seasonal Pangean climates predicted by the model results.

Fossil semionotid fish have often been considered as integral parts of freshwater (aquatic) faunas of the Triassic (cf. Buffetaut, 1983). They therefore are suggested to be indicative of standing water (runoff/precipitation) in areas with wet climates. Scythian semionotid fish localities in Europe, Mada-

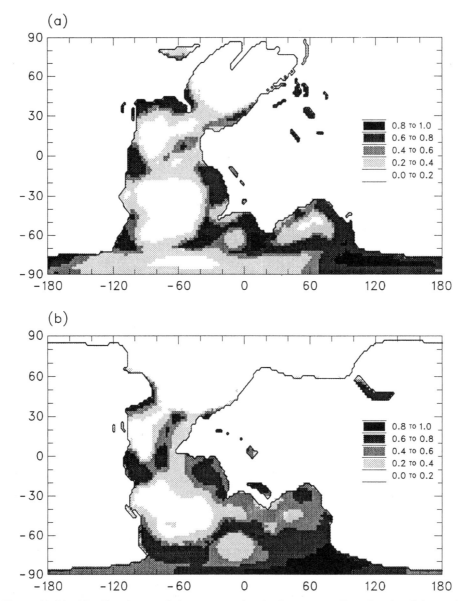

Figure 11. Liquid soil moisture relative to saturation in the topmost (0 to 5 cm) soil layer, for January. (a) Scythian; (b) Carnian.

gascar, and South America support the seasonally wet climates suggested for these areas by the soil moisture, precipitation, and surface runoff model results.

Dipnoid fish (lungfishes) have long been considered as indicators of seasonal runoff and/or interannual dry cycles (cf. Romer, 1966). Scythian dipnoid fish fossils have been located on five continents (Table 1; Fig. 2). Most of these locations show strong seasonality on the model output maps of soil moisture, precipitation, and runoff. This also supports the markedly seasonal Pangean climates predicted by the model results.

The occurrence of another vertebrate group, the therapsid (mammal-like) reptiles, was suggested by Parrish et al. (1986) to indicate temperate climates during the Scythian. Scythian

therapsids have been found in Antarctica, South Africa, Argentina, India, Siberia, and Northwest China (Fig. 2). Comparison of these localities with model results for temperature (Figs. 4a, 5a, and 6a), however, suggests a very poor correlation. In fact, in several of these localities the model seasonal temperature variation reaches 45°C, and in one (Antarctica), it exceeds 65°C. This lack of correlation suggests either that (1) the therapsids were superbly adapted endotherms whose distribution must not have been limited to temperate climates alone, (2) the therapsids of the Scythian were capable of large-scale seasonal migration, (3) the distribution of therapsid fossils is an artifact of orbitally forced (Milankovitch) modulation of summer warming, which might have allowed this animal to

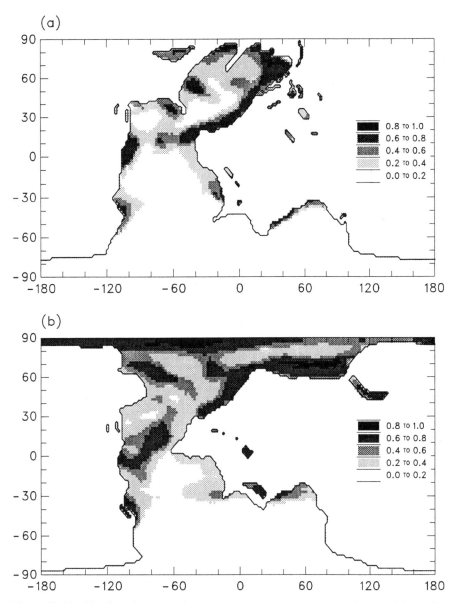

Figure 12. Liquid soil moisture relative to saturation in the topmost (to 5 cm) soil layer, for July. (a) Scythian; (b) Carnian.

migrate into higher latitudes during precession "hot orbit" configurations of 10 kyr duration (cf. Crowley et al., 1992), (4) the earth was warmed at the poles as a result of elevated methane concentrations that prevented severe winter cooling due to cloud formation (cf. Sloan et al., 1992), or (5) the model results are in serious error with respect to seasonal temperature ranges, perhaps as a result of inadequate modeling of poleward oceanic heat transport.

It is not clear which of these alternatives is valid, given the present data set. Certainly the present authors are unable to judge whether therapsids were superbly adapted endotherms or whether they were capable of large-scale seasonal migration. However, consider the model of Crowley et al. (1992)

concerning the Milankovitch modulation of summer warming. They estimated, on the basis of an energy balance model (EBM), that the modulation approached 16°C on Pangea during the Early Jurassic. The 25°C isotherm for summer reached 65° paleolatitude during "hot orbit" configurations in their model. We have not included Milankovitch forcing in the present study, but we may nevertheless evaluate its potential effect on therapsids by extrapolating from the results of Crowley et al. (1992). If we subtract the 16°C warming figure given by Crowley et al. from the total 45° to 65°C annual range observed in the present study, we can reduce that range to 29° to 49°C. The lower end of this range may well be considered temperate, but we still have a problem with the Antarctic ther-

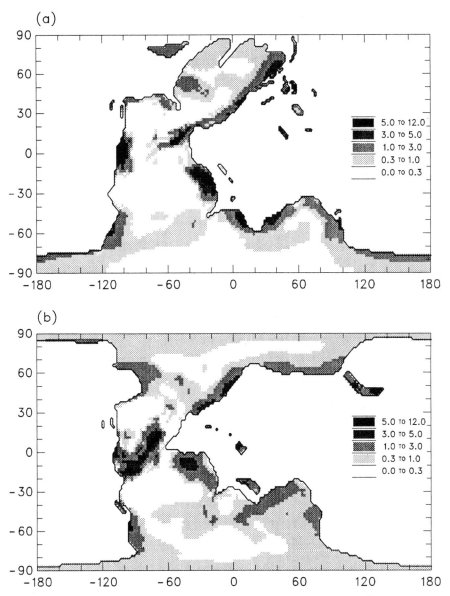

Figure 13. Annual mean surface runoff plus bottom drainage, in mm day^{-1}. (a) Scythian; (b) Carnian.

apsids, which were apparently capable of withstanding seasonal temperature variations of about 50°C, equivalent to the highest ranges on earth today.

We can also evaluate the potential for methane-induced amelioration of severe winter cooling, as suggested by Sloan et al. (1992) as an explanation for high-latitude faunas and floras in the Eocene. Sloan and her colleagues calculated their hypothetical methane flux for the Eocene atmosphere by using the known areal extent of "coaly continental clastics" as a representation of wetland environments capable of methane production. If we attempt the same for the Scythian, this approach will not work, because only one report of a coal deposit exists for the entire Scythian earth.

The final possibility with regard to the therapsid distribution is that the temperature results are in error, owing to inadequate modeling of oceanic heat transport. This is certainly possible; however, the prescribed heat transport used in this study was arbitrarily set at twice that of the present day. It is very difficult to explain how higher transport than used here could be modeled dynamically (Covey and Thompson, 1989; Sloan et al., 1992).

The occurrence of conchostracans (clam-shrimp) in modern semiarid ponds and lakes, and their persistence even at high pH and salinity, suggests that fossil forms are good indicators of seasonal runoff and/or dry cycles (Frank, 1988; Tasch, 1987). Scythian conchostracans are known from many

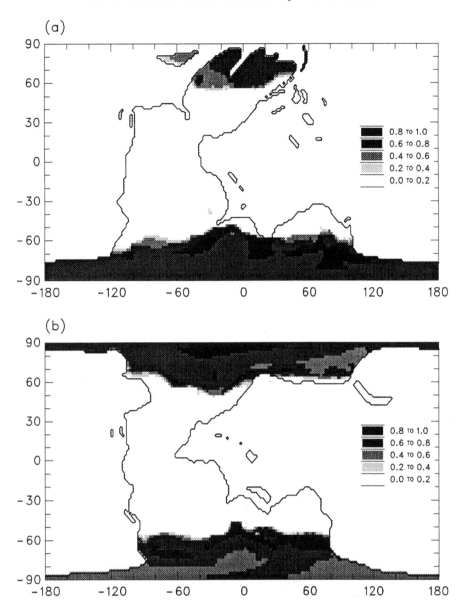

Figure 14. Annual mean soil-ice content, i.e., fraction relative to total pore space, of the bottom soil layer (1.75 to 4.25 m depth). (a) Scythian; (b) Carnian.

localities in Europe, Asia, and Australia (Table 1). Comparison with model results for soil moisture, precipitation, and surface runoff indicates a generally good correlation of conchostracan localities with dry or seasonally dry areas.

Several major floral zonations have been suggested to indicate broad climatic zonation during the Triassic (Barnard, 1973; Wang, 1985; Dobruskina, 1987). For example, the Southern Hemisphere *Dicroidium* (seed-fern) flora is considered by some to have been limited to warm temperate climates, generally south of the arid zone in southern Pangea (Gondwana). However, a comparison of the model temperature data (Figs. 4a, 5a, and 6a) and the location data in Table 1 suggests that, as with the therapsids, a significant problem ex-

ists. The minimum annual temperature range predicted for the *Dicroidium* flora is 35°C, but the maximum range exceeds 70°C. The lack of correlation suggests that either (1) the interpretation of floral habitats is poorly constrained, (2) Milankovitch modulation of summer warming (Crowley et al., 1992) affected the distribution of this flora, or (3) the model temperature data are seriously in error.

Perhaps the totipotency, hybridity, dormancy, and heterochrony typical of plants has allowed major groups to survive great extremes in climate and habitat throughout the Phanerozoic (Traverse, 1990). Interpretations of plant habitat may thus always be problematical. Furthermore, Traverse has shown that little correlation exists between the degrees of fau-

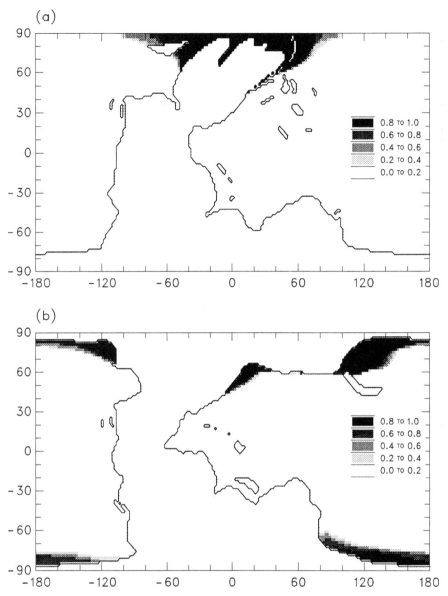

Figure 15. Sea-ice fractional cover, for April. (a) Scythian; (b) Carnian.

nal and floral extinction at the Permo-Triassic boundary, suggesting that plants have evolved almost independently of animals, regardless of shared stresses. The efficacy of Milankovitch modulation of summer warming as an explanation for the floral distribution must also be considered. As discussed above for the therapsids, one can calculate the residual annual temperature range, which in this case was still on the order of 19° to 54°C. The lower end of this range is again acceptable, but the higher figure is again difficult to explain.

In the high-latitude Northern Hemisphere, the dominant Scythian plant zone was occupied by the Angaran flora (Dobruskina, 1987). This flora is suggested by many workers to indicate cool, humid paleoclimates. Comparison of fossil occurrences (Table 1) with the model temperature data for the Scythian (Figs. 4a, 5a, and 6a) indicates a reasonably good correlation in this case.

A third and final Scythian paleofloristic zone is represented by the euramerican flora (Barnard, 1973). This zone lies between the Angaran and *Dicroidium* floras and is considered to again indicate warm temperature climates. However, this floral zone crosses a broad range of paleolatitudes on our reconstructions. Comparison of fossil localities with model temperatures indicates only partial correlation. Parts of this flora zone may have experienced more than a 50°C annual variation in temperature, if model results are correct. Again, this is difficult to evaluate given present knowledge.

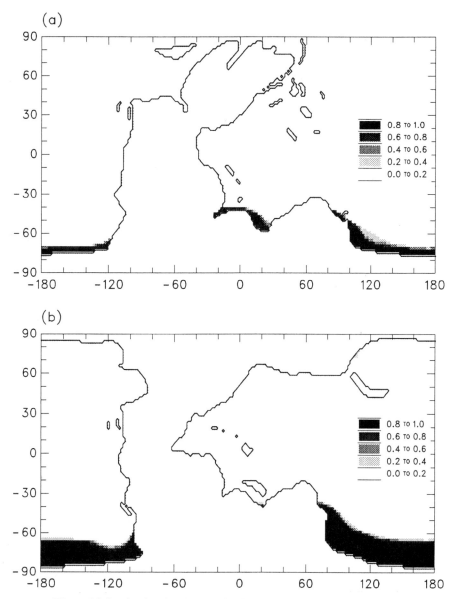

Figure 16. Sea-ice fractional cover, for October. (a) Scythian; (b) Carnian.

Comparison with Carnian proxy climatic indicators

Geologic data. The Carnian geologic record contains a greater variety of proxy paleoclimatic indicators, including extensive halite deposits and widespread coals (Fig. 3). The evaporites are concentrated on the eastern margin of the supercontinent, from 10°S to 30°N, extending directly into the equatorial zone. The rift valley on the site of later separation of North America and Africa has evaporites lining its floor from 10°N to 10°S. Halite occurs on the East African margin (Tanzania) at a paleolatitude of 45°S. These evaporites must have accumulated in a rift basin associated with the separation of Madagascar from Africa. Some occurrences of evaporites are located on the western margin of Pangea at 15° to 25°N and 35°S. Coals occur in bands from 45° to 70°N and S on both the eastern and western margins of the supercontinent. They also occur close to the equator on the western side of the continent; two occurrences in the Culpepper and Connecticut rift basins of eastern North America straddle the paleoequator. The Petrified Forest of Arizona is indicated by a triangular tree symbol on Figure 3; it lies just south of the Carnian equator on the west side of Pangaea.

Again, the model results indicate that the areas of evaporite deposition correspond to the presumed highest summer surface temperatures in the oceans (Figs. 4b, 5b) and to winter precipitation minima (Figs. 7b, 8b). The coal deposits of the

TABLE 1. CHARACTERISTICS OF PALEOCLIMATIC INDICATORS SHOWN IN FIGURES 2 AND 3*

Indicator	Use	Age	Location	Present Lat. (°)	Present Long. (°)	Indicator	Use	Age	Location	Present Lat. (°)	Present Long. (°)
Karst	Rainfall	U. Carn.	SW U.K.	51N	004W	Dipnoid Fish (continued)	Seasonal runoff	U. Tr.	Aus	32S?	150E?
		Carn.	NW Nev.	41N	119W			U. Tr.	NW Eur.	79N	015E
		M. Carn.	Alps	47N?	010E?	Conchos-tracans	Seasonal dryness	Scyth.	Yakutsk	62N	129E
Calcretes/ Redbeds	Warm, dry	Scyth.	S. Africa	28S	026E			Scyth.	Kama	56N	054E
		U. Cn-Nor.	Brazil	13S	048W			Scyth.	Vetluga	58N	045E
Redbeds/ Gypsum	Warm, dry	Scyth.	CO Plat	36N	112W			Scyth.	Pechora	65N	057E
								Scyth.	Taimyr	76N	105E
Redbeds + Coal	Warm, w/alt. dry/ humid	Scyth.	C. India	20N?	077E?			Scyth.	Lena	70N	126E
								Scyth.	France	48N	003E
								Scyth.	E. Aus.	32S	150E
Coal	Humid	L. Scyth	Trsant.	83S	160E			Cn-Nor.	NE Thai.	17N	103E
		Carn.	W. Arg.	38S?	069W?			Carn.	Yamaguc.	34N	131E
		Carn.	E. Grnld.	67N	035W			U. Tr.	Sarawak	02N	112E
		L. Scyth.	S. Africa	28S	026E			Carn.	France	48N	003E
								Carn.	Mex.	22N	101W
Phytosaurs + Metaposaurs	Runoff/ precip.	Carn.	W. Eur.	50N	010E			U. Carn.	Brazil	13S	048W
		U. Tr.	Morocco	32N	006W	Dicroidium Flora (Gondwanan)	Warm, temperate	Scyth.	E. India	18N	082E
		U. Tr.	Madagas.	18S	046E			Scyth.	NE India	25N	085E
		Cn-Nor.	NE Thai.	17N	103E			Scyth.	N. Qnsld.	17S	143E
		Carn.	Newark	40N	075W			Scyth.	NSW	32S	150E
		Carn.	Arizona	36N	112W			Scyth.	Tasmania	43S	147E
		Carn.	India	20N?	077E?			Scyth.	E. Ant.	78S	165E
Labyrinth-odonts	Runoff/ precip.	Carn.	NW Eur.	79N	015E			Scyth.	S. Africa	28S	026E
		Scyth.	N. China	39N	115E			Scyth.	SE Af.	18S	032E
		L. Scyth.	Tasmania	43S	147E			Scyth.	NW Argnt.	27S	067W
		Carn.	Newark	41N	075W			Scyth.	Chile	33S	071W
		Scyth.	India	20N?	077E?	Angaran Flora	Cool, humid	Scyth.	NW Sib.	68N	060E
		Scyth.	S. Africa	28S	026E			Scyth.	C. Sib.	51N	080E
		Scyth.	Madagas.	18S	046E			Scyth.	C. Sib.	55N	079E
		Scyth.	Poland	52N	020E			Scyth.	SE Sib.	50N	115E
		Scyth.	Arizona	36N	112W			Scyth.	Taimyr	76N	105E
		Scyth.	Grnld.	67N	035W			Scyth.	Nv. Zem.	75N	057E
		Scyth.	Germany	50N	010E			Scyth.	Verkhoy.	65N	130E
		Scyth.	N. Africa	32N	006W			Scyth.	Arkhang.	66N	045E
		Scyth.	Arc. Can.	65N?	070W?	Euramerican Flora	Warm, temperate	Scyth.	Spain	40N	002W
		Carn.	Argent.	38S?	069W?			Scyth.	SW Fr.	44N	002E
Therapsid Repts.	Temper-ate	Scyth.	S. Africa	28S	026E			Scyth.	C. Fr.	47N	003E
		Scyth.	Antarct.	83S	160E			Scyth.	NE Fr.	48N	005E
		Scyth.	Argent.	38S?	069W?			Scyth.	C.U.K.	52N	002W
		Scyth.	India	20N?	077E?			Scyth.	Poland	53N	020E
		Scyth.	Siberia	62N	060E			Scyth.	Romania	45N	023E
		Scyth.	Sinkiang	40N	090E			Scyth.	Volga R.	48N	045E
Semionotid Fish	Runoff/ precip.	Scyth.	Europe	50N?	010E?			Scyth.	S. Urals	51N	057E
		Scyth.	Madagas.	18S	046E			Scyth.	W. Sib.	51N	076E
		Scyth.	S. Amer.	38S?	069W?			Scyth.	Tadzhik	39N	070E
		U. Tr.	N. Amer	41N?	075W?			Scyth.	Kazakh	42N	074E
		U. Tr.	Aus.	32S?	150E?			Scyth.	Sikhote	44N	134E
		U. Tr.	Europe	50N?	010E?			Scyth.	Laos	21N	101E
		U. Tr.	NE Thai.	17N	103E	Dictyophyllum Fl. (Gondwanan)	Warm,, temperate	Carn.	Ariz.	36N	112W
		U. Tr.	Africa	28S?	026E?			Carn.	NW Arg	27S	067W
		U. Tr.	S. Amer.	38S?	069W?			Carn.	N. Qnsld.	17S	143E
Dipnoid Fish	Seasonal runoff	Scyth.	N. China	39N	115E			Cn-Nor.	SE Asia	22N	107E
		Scyth.	Europe	50N?	010E?			Carn.	Yamaguc.	34N	131E
		Scyth.	Madagas.	18S	046E			Carn.	S. Africa	28S	026E
		Scyth.	N. Amer.	36N?	112W?			Carn.	Chile	33S	071W
		Scyth.	Aus.	32S?	150E?			Carn.	Austria	47N	015E
		Scyth.	NW Eur.	79N	015E			Carn.	Switz.	47N	007E
		U. Tr.	NE Thai.	17N	103E						
		U. Tr.	Europe	50N?	010E?						
		U. Tr.	Madagas.	18S	046E						
		U. Tr.	Newark	41N	075E						

*Locations and ages of geologic and fossil proxy climatic indicators taken from the literature. Sources listed in Wilson (1989). Question marks after some latitudes and longitudes denote uncertainty in location as provided by the primary reference source. Locations are plotted on Figures 2 and 3 and discussed in the text.

Southern Hemisphere lie just north of the permafrost boundary, indicated (Fig. 14b) by the persistence of soil ice in the summer. The coal deposits of the Northern Hemisphere also tend to lie along the permafrost boundary but also extend in places into the southern part of the permafrost region. There are again very strong indications of monsoonal circulation in the model results.

Fossil data. Buffetaut and Martin (1984) suggested that the association of phytosaurid amphibians during the Triassic is an indicator of runoff/precipitation (standing water). This association has been found in a number of locations (Table 1; Fig. 3) containing Carnian age fossils. Comparison with the climate model data suggests a generally good correlation of fossils with soil moisture (Figs. 11b, 12b) and precipitation (Figs. 7b, 8b) results and a somewhat weaker correlation with surface runoff (Fig. 13). Most locations indicate strong seasonality.

Only three fossil labyrinthodont locations exist for the Carnian (Europe, Newark Basin, and Argentina). These are consistent with model data for soil moisture, precipitation, and surface runoff, just as they were in the Scythian for this group.

There are a number of semionotid fish occurrences in the Carnian (Table 1). Comparison with model results indicates only a moderate correlation with runoff, soil moisture, and precipitation. This result may be due to the fact that many fish localities occur in lacustrine sediments that have shown strong evidence of Milankovitch (orbital) forcing (Van Houten, 1964). Carnian dipnoid fish are known from many of the same locations as the semionotids. This suggests that conditions (e.g., lake levels) were highly variable.

Carnian conchostracans have been reported from four continents (Asia, Europe, Central America, and South America). All of these locations show good correlations with dry or seasonally dry climates, as indicated by runoff, soil moisture, and precipitation model data.

Another data comparison involves the Carnian paleofloristic zone defined by the *Dictyophyllum* (Gondwanan) flora (cf. Barnard, 1973). This flora is interpreted to indicate warm, temperate climates; thus it replaces the earlier *Dicroidium* flora as a climate indicator. In contrast to the poor correlation of the Scythian, the Carnian flora appears to be better correlated. A maximum annual temperature range of 45° or more exists in the South African sector of Pangaea, but most other localities show a reasonable correlation with model temperature data.

On the other hand, coals and numerous preserved logs in the Upper Triassic of Antarctica (Francis, 1992) suggest that at the location with maximum model temperature extremes, plants were flourishing. Fortunately, there is a hypothesis to explain this anomaly, given the Carnian data base. The general abundance and wide areal distribution of coals in the Carnian suggest that the methane-induced amelioration of polar winters (cf. Sloan et al., 1992) could have been operating. Work on a more quantitative evaluation, which could lend support to this theory, is currently in progress.

Comparison of the Scythian and Carnian results

The Scythian and Carnian results both show presumably ice-cap-free polar regions and similar large-scale continental aridity. They differ in that the Carnian global mean for precipitation over land is about 10% higher than for the Scythian. The Carnian humid episode proposed by Sims and Ruffell (1990) is thus confirmed by the model results presented here. Part of this difference could be due to changing pCO_2, as suggested by Berner's (1990) geochemical modeling. Both the Scythian and Carnian model results exhibit strong monsoonal circulations, each with a tendency to focus their energy on the major uplift areas; monsoonal precipitation is thereby brought far inland in some locations. This suggests that the strength of this circulation is a function not only of the extent of continental land area but also of the extent of highland regions.

During the Scythian, relatively light seasonal precipitation was concentrated on the northern end of the incipient North America–Africa rift uplift (Figs. 7a, 8a). However, by Carnian time the model results (Figs. 7b, 8b) suggest that significant seasonal precipitation fell on both the northernmost and southernmost portions of the rift system; the existence of the southern humid zone is supported by geologic and floral data (Fowell et al., 1992). It is also possible that the Carnian monsoonal circulation (Figs. 9, 10) distributed significant amounts of precipitation along the western side of the North America–Africa rift uplift (Figs. 7b, 8b), although the observed record of lacustrine sedimentation, faunas, and floras on the western rift shoulder may also be due to local orographic modification of climate (cf. Hay et al., 1982). In either case, the lake record also shows a spectacular sequence of Van Houten cycles caused by orbital forcing (Olsen, 1986), a factor not evaluated in the present study.

SUMMARY AND RECOMMENDATIONS

Three major aspects of Triassic paleoclimate are correctly reproduced by the model results: no apparent polar ice sheets, widespread and dominantly seasonal aridity within continental interiors, and land in the Carnian simulation that is distinctly wetter than that in the Scythian simulation. The simulations portray two distinct types of climates, one for the lowland interior regions (with average elevations of 1,000 m) and one for the relatively narrow highland areas (with average elevations of 2,000 to 3,000 m). The lowland regions experience extreme continental climates with very large ranges in seasonal temperature and are generally very dry except for moderate snowmelt in the spring. Seasonal precipitation followed by extreme heat and aridity is a climate that does not exist over any very large areas of the earth today, but these were the characteristic conditions of the tropics on the Triassic earth.

The Triassic highlands, especially near the coasts, have considerably smaller temperature ranges and are much wetter than the lowlands. Precipitation patterns are controlled in large part by topography, which tends to steer the low-level winds and causes much of the available moisture to rain out on upwind highland slopes in summer. The largest patches of precipitation in both ages occur on tropical or subtropical highlands, which are in the path both of the trade winds and also of monsoonal circulations set up by heating of the nearby landmass.

Comparison of these results with lithologic and fossil proxy climatic indicators suggests reasonably good correlations. However, the extreme temperature variations predicted for both Scythian and Carnian are somewhat difficult to reconcile with the fossil record. Accurate interpretation of fossil proxy climatic indicators is not a simple matter, however, and further research may be necessary to resolve this problem.

The two simulations for the Triassic to date are preliminary. We outline several caveats and suggestions for further work that will be needed in order to confirm or modify the current conclusions.

1. The AGCM used a relatively coarse horizontal resolution of R15, corresponding to 4.5° latitude by 7.5° longitude. This is close to the width of some of the prescribed mountain ranges, so the topography actually seen by the model dynamics is quite degraded (cf. Figs. 1, 9, and 10). Because the low-level winds and precipitation are strongly influenced by topography, it would be desirable to increase the atmospheric resolution and extend the simulations for several model years.

2. Clearly the lack of an ocean model is a potentially serious omission, and the choice of prescribed oceanic heat transport is highly speculative. One could either perform a series of simulations bracketing the conceivable range of values or couple the AGCM to an oceanic general circulation model (OGCM) such as the ones used by Barron and Peterson (1989) or Kutzbach et al. (1990); however, one would have to face the attendant problem of "spinning up" the deep ocean.

3. The vegetation types were prescribed to coincide with the elevation classes as described in the section, "Boundary Conditions." The lowlands had "grasses" and shrubs, the intermediate highlands had "evergreen" forest, and the highest elevations had tundra. In the discussion above we have assumed that topography itself is mainly responsible for the differences between lowland and highland climates, but some of the difference might be caused directly by vegetation via albedo, transpiration rates, intercepted rainfall, and so on. Additional sensitivity test runs could be made to distinguish the two effects, for instance, by simply prescribing the same vegetation type everywhere.

4. We did not model the effects of Milankovitch forcing in the present work. Strong evidence exists for orbital modulation of Triassic climate; however, the relative contributions of orbital forcing modulation and monsoonal circulation will be difficult to discriminate in the geologic and fossil record for the Triassic. The effort should be made nevertheless, and it would be prudent also to include a "hot orbit" configuration in future model runs of the AGCM (cf. Crowley et al., 1992).

5. The extreme temperature variations predicted for both Scythian and Carnian are somewhat difficult to reconcile with part of the fossil record. Accurate interpretation of fossil proxy climatic indicators is not a foregone conclusion, however, and further research on the habits and physiology of key plant and animal groups may be in order.

ACKNOWLEDGMENTS

We thank the reviewers and editor G. D. Klein for their valuable comments and suggestions. This study was funded by Grant EAR-9007202 from the U.S. National Science Foundation. We are grateful for computer time provided by the National Center for Atmospheric Research and for logistical support from GEOMAR.

REFERENCES CITED

Anthes, R. A., 1977, A cumulus parameterization scheme utilizing a one-dimensional cloud model: Monthly Weather Review, v. 105, p. 270–286.

Barnard, P.D.W., 1973, Mesozoic floras, in Hughes, N. F., ed., Organisms and continents through time: The Palaeontological Association Special Paper 12, p. 174–187.

Barron, E. J., and Peterson, W. H., 1989, Model simulation of the Cretaceous ocean circulation: Science, v. 244, p. 684–686.

Berner, R. A., 1990, Atmospheric carbon dioxide over Phanerozoic time: Science, v. 249, p. 1382–1386.

Budyko, M. I., and Ronov, A. B., 1979, Atmospheric evolution in the Phanerozoic: Geochemistry International, v. 16, p. 1–9.

Buffetaut, E., 1983, Mesozoic vertebrates from Thailand: A review: Acta Palaeontologica Polonica, v. 28, p. 43–53.

Buffetaut, E., and Martin, M., 1984, Continental vertebrate distribution, faunal zonation and climate in the Late Triassic, in Reif, W.-E., and Westphal, F., eds., Third Symposium on Mesozoic Terrestrial Ecosystems, Short Papers: Tubingen, Attempto Verlag, p. 25–29.

Burke, K., 1988, Tectonic evolution of the Caribbean: Annual Reviews in Earth and Planetary Sciences, v. 16, p. 234–278.

Busson, G., 1982, Le Trias comme periode salifere: Geologische Rundschau, v. 71, p. 857–880.

Clapp, R. B., and Hornberger, G. M., 1986, Empirical equations for some soil hydraulic properties: Water Resources Research, v. 14, p. 601–604.

Cohen, K. K., Anderson, T.H., and Schmidt, V. A., 1986, A paleomagnetic test of the proposed Mojave-Sonora megashear in northwestern Mexico: Tectonophysics, v. 131, p. 23–51.

Coney, P. J., Jones, D. L., and Monger, J.W.H., 1980, Cordilleran suspect terranes: Nature, v. 288, p. 329–333.

Covey, C., and Thompson, S. L., 1989, Testing the effects of ocean heat transport on climate: Palaeogeography, Palaeoclimatology, Palaeoecology, v. 75, p. 331–341.

Crowley, T. J., 1983, The geologic record of climatic change: Reviews of Geophysics and Space Physics, v. 21, p. 828–877.

Crowley, T. J., and Baum, S. K., 1991, Toward reconciliation of late Ordovician (~440 Ma) glaciation with very high CO_2 levels: Journal of Geophysical Research, v. 96, p. 22597–22610.

Crowley, T. J., Mengel, J. G., and Short, D. A., 1987, Gondwanaland's seasonal cycle: Nature, v. 329, p. 803–807.

Crowley, T. J., Baum, S. K., and Hyde, W. T., 1992, Milankovitch fluctuations on supercontinents: Geophysical Research Letters, v. 19, p. 793–796.

Curry, J. A., and Herman, G. F., 1985, Relationships between large-scale heat and moisture budgets and the occurrence of Arctic stratus clouds: Monthly Weather Review, v. 113, p. 1441–1457.

Davis, J. M., Cox, S. K., and McKee, T. B., 1979, Vertical and horizontal distributions of solar absorption in finite clouds: Journal of Atmospheric Science, v. 36, p. 1976–1984.

Dickinson, R. E., Henderson-Sellers, A., Kennedy, P. J., and Wilson, M. F., 1986, Biosphere-Atmosphere Transfer Scheme (BATS) for the NCAR Community Climate Model: Boulder, Colorado, NCAR Technical Note NCAR/TN-275+STR, 69 p.

Dietz, R. S., and Holden, J. C., 1970, Reconstruction of Pangaea: Breakup and dispersion of continents, Permian to Present: Journal of Geophysical Research, v. 75, p. 4939–4956.

Dobruskina, I. A., 1987, Phytogeography of Eurasia during the Early Triassic: Palaeogeography, Palaeoclimatology, Palaeoecology, v. 58, p. 75–86.

Dorman, J. L., and Sellers, P. J., 1989, A global climatology of albedo, roughness length and stomatal resistance for atmospheric general circulation models as represented by the Simple Biosphere Model (SiB): Journal of Applied Meteorology, v. 28, p. 833–855.

Fischer, A. G., 1964, The lofer cyclothems of the alpine Triassic: Kansas Geological Survey, v. 169, p. 107–149.

Flato, G. M., and Hibler, W. D., 1990, On a simple sea-ice dynamics model for climate studies: Annals of Glaciology, v. 14, p. 72–77.

Flato, G. M., and Hibler, W. D., 1992, Modeling pack ice as a cavitating fluid: Journal of Physical Oceanography, v. 22, p. 626–651.

Fowell, S. J., Cornet, B., and Olsen, P. E., 1992, Late Triassic palynofloral evolution and climate cyclicity, eastern North America, *in* Proceedings, Project Pangea Workshop, Lawrence, Kansas: International Union of Geological Sciences, Global Sedimentary Geology Program, p. 17.

Frakes, L. A., 1986, Climates throughout geologic time (second edition): New York, Elsevier Scientific Publishing, 310 p.

Francis, J., 1992, Palaeoclimates of Pangea, *in* Proceedings, Project Pangea Workshop, Lawrence, Kansas: International Union of Geological Sciences, Global Sedimentary Geology Program, p. 11.

Frank, P. W., 1988, Conchostraca: Palaeogeography, Palaeoclimatology, Palaeoecology, v. 62, p. 399–403.

Gordon, W. A., 1975, Distribution by latitude of Phanerozoic evaporite deposits: Journal of Geology, v. 83, p. 671–684.

Grant, A. C., and McAlpine, K. D., 1990, The continental margin around Newfoundland, *in* Keen, M. J., and Williams, G. L., eds., Geology of the continental margin off eastern Canada: Geological Survey of Canada Special Publication 2, p. 239–292.

Gregory, D., and Rowntree, P. R., 1990, A mass flux convection scheme with representation of cloud ensemble characteristics and stability-dependent closure: Monthly Weather Review, v. 118, p. 1483–1506.

Habicht, J.K.A., 1979, Paleoclimate, paleomagnetism, and continental drift: American Association of Petroleum Geologists Studies in Geology 9, p. 1–32.

Hallam, A., 1985, A review of Mesozoic climates: Journal of the Geological Society, London, v. 142, p. 433–445.

Harrison, C.G.A., and Lindh, T., 1982, A polar wandering curve for North America during the Mesozoic and Cenozoic: Journal of Geophysical Research, v. 87B, p. 1903–1920.

Harvey, L.D.D., 1988, Development of a sea ice model for use in zonally averaged energy balance climate models: Journal of Climate, v. 1, p. 1221–1238.

Hay, W. W., 1981, Sedimentological and geochemical trends resulting from the breakup of Pangaea: Proceedings, 26th International Geological Congress, Geology of Oceans Symposium: Oceanologica Acta, v. SP, p. 135–147.

Hay, W. W., 1983, Significance of runoff to paleoceanographic conditions during the Mesozoic and clues to locate sites of ancient river inputs: Proceedings, 5th Joint Oceanographic Assembly: Ottawa, Canadian Department of Fisheries and Oceans, p. 9–17.

Hay, W. W., and Southam, J. R., 1977, Modulation of marine sedimentation by the continental shelves, *in* Anderson, N. R., and Malahoff, A., eds., The role of fossil fuel CO_2 in the oceans: New York, Plenum, p. 569–605.

Hay, W. W., Barron, E. J., Sloan, J. L., and Southam, J. R., 1981, Continental drift and the global pattern of sedimentation: Geologische Rundschau, v. 70, p. 302–315.

Hay, W. W., Behensky, J. F., and Barron, E. J., 1982, Late Triassic-Liassic paleoclimatology of the proto-central North Atlantic rift system: Palaeogeography, Palaeoclimatology, Palaeoecology, v. 40, p. 13–30.

Hay, W. W., Rosol, M. J., Sloan, J. L., and Jory, D. E., 1987, Plate tectonic control of global patterns of detrital and carbonate sedimentation, *in* Doyle, L. J., and Roberts, H. H., eds., Carbonate clastic transitions, Developments in Sedimentology, 42: Amsterdam, Elsevier Scientific Publishing, p. 1–34.

Hay, W. W., Sloan, J. L., and Wold, C. N., 1988, Mass/age distribution and composition of sediments on the ocean floor and the global rate of sediment subduction: Journal of Geophysical Research, v. 93B, p. 14933–14940.

Henderson-Sellers, A., and McGuffie, K., 1990, Basis for integration of conventional observations of cloud into global nephanalyses: Journal of Atmospheric Chemistry, v. 11, p. 1–25.

Hibler, W. D., 1979, A dynamic thermodynamic sea ice model: Journal of Physical Oceanography, v. 9, p. 815–846.

Holser, W. T., 1977, Catastrophic chemical events in the history of the ocean: Nature, v. 267, p. 403–408.

Holtslag, A.A.M., de Bruijn, E.I.F., and Pan, H.-L., 1990, A high resolution air mass transformation model for short-range weather forecasting: Monthly Weather Review, v. 118, p. 1561–1575.

Kutzbach, J. E., and Gallimore, R. G., 1989, Pangaean climates: Megamonsoons of the megacontinent: Journal of Geophysical Research, v. 94D, p. 3341–3357.

Kutzbach, J. E., Guetter, P. J., and Washington, W. M., 1990, Simulated circulation of an idealized ocean for Pangaean time: Paleoceanography, v. 5, p. 299–317.

Manspeizer, W., 1982, Triassic-Liassic basins and climate of the Atlantic passive margins: Geologische Rundschau, v. 71, p. 895–917.

Manspeizer, W., Puffer, J. H., and Cousminer, H. L., 1978, Separation of Morocco and eastern North America: A Triassic-Liassic stratigraphic record: Geological Society of America Bulletin, v. 89, p. 901–920.

Marzolf, J. E., 1988, Controls on late Paleozoic and early Mesozoic eolian deposition of the western United States: Sedimentary Geology, v. 56, p. 167–191.

Olsen, P. E., 1986, A 40-million-year lake record of early Mesozoic orbital climatic forcing: Science, v. 234, p. 842–848.

Parrish, J. M., Parrish, J. T., and Ziegler, A. M., 1986, Permian-Triassic paleogeography and paleoclimatology, and implications for therapsid distribution, *in* Hotlow, V., Roth, J. J., and Roth, L. C., eds., Ecology and biology of the mammal-like reptiles: Washington, D.C., Smithsonian Institution Press, p. 109–131.

Popp, B. N., Takigiku, R., Hayes, J. M., Louda, J. W., and Baker, E. W., 1989, The post-Paleozoic chronology and mechanism of (13)C depletion in primary marine organic matter: American Journal of Science, v. 285, p. 436–454.

Rasch, P. J., and Williamson, D. L., 1990, Computational aspects of moisture transport in global models of the atmosphere: Quarterly Journal of the Royal Meteorological Society, v. 116, p. 1071–1090.

Robinson, P. L., 1973, Paleoclimatology and continental drift, in Tarling, D. H., and Runcorn, S. K., eds., Implications of continental drift to the earth sciences, vol. 1: London, Academic Press, p. 449–476.

Romer, A. S., 1966, Vertebrate paleontology (Third edition): Chicago, University of Chicago Press, 468 p.

Ronov, A., Khain, V., and Balukhovsky, A., 1989, Atlas of lithological-paleogeographical maps of the world: Mesozoic and Cenozoic of continents and oceans: Leningrad, Ministry Geology, USSR, 79 p.

Ross, M. I., and Scotese, C. R., 1988, A hierarchical tectonic model of the Gulf of Mexico and Caribbean region: Tectonophysics, v. 155, p. 139–168.

Schlee, J. S., Manspeizer, W., and Riggs, S. R., 1988, Paleoenvironments:

Offshore Atlantic U.S. margin, *in* Sheridan, R. E., and Grow, J. A., eds., The Atlantic continental margin, The Geology of North America, vol. M: Boulder, Colorado, Geological Society of America, p. 365–385.

Sellers, P. J., Mintz, Y., Sud, Y. C., and Dalcher, A., 1986, A simple biosphere model (SiB) for use within general circulation models: Journal of Atmospheric Science, v. 43, p. 505–531.

Semtner, A. J., 1976, A model for the thermodynamic growth of sea ice in numerical investigations of climate: Journal of Physical Oceanography, v. 6, p. 379–389.

Sims, M. J., and Ruffell, A. H., 1990, Climate and biotic change in the late Triassic: Journal of the Geological Society, London, v. 147, p. 321–327.

Slingo, A. and Slingo, J. M., 1991, Response of the National Center for Atmospheric Research Community Climate Model to improvements in the representation of clouds: Journal of Geophysical Research, v. 96, p. 15341–15357.

Sloan, L. C., Walker, J.C.G., Moore, T. C., Jr., Rea, D. K., and Zachos, J. C., 1992, Possible methane-induced polar warming in the early Eocene: Nature, v. 357, p. 320–322.

Southam, J. R., and Hay, W. W., 1981, Global sedimentary mass balance and sea level changes, *in* Emiliani, C., ed., The sea. vol. 7: The oceanic lithosphere: New York, John Wiley and Sons, p. 1617–1684.

Tasch, P., 1987, Fossil Conchostraca of the Southern Hemisphere and continental drift: Geological Society of America Memoir 165, 290 p.

Thompson, S. L., Ramaswamy, V., and Covey, C., 1987, Atmospheric effects of nuclear war aerosols in general circulation model simulations: Influence of smoke optical properties: Journal of Geophysical Research, v. 92, p. 10942–10960.

Traverse, A., 1990, Plant evolution in relation to world crises and the apparent resilience of Kingdom Plantae: Palaeogeography, Palaeoclimatology, Palaeoecology, v. 82, p. 203–211.

Troen, I., and Mahrt, L., 1986, A simple ml of the atmospheric boundary layer: Sensitivity to surface evaporation: Boundary Layer Meteorology, v. 37, p. 129–148.

Tucholke, B. E., and McCoy, F. W., 1986, Paleogeographic and paleobathymetric evolution of the north Atlantic Ocean, *in* Vogt, P. R., and Tucholke, B. E., eds., The eastern North Atlantic region, Geology of North America, vol. M.: Boulder, Colorado, Geological Society of North America, p. 589–602.

Van der Voo, R., 1988, Paleozoic paleogeography of North America, Gondwana and intervening displaced terranes: Comparisons of paleomagnetism with paleoclimatology and biogeographical patterns: Geological Society of America Bulletin, v. 100, p. 311–324.

Van Houten, F. B., 1964, Origin of red beds: Some unsolved problems, *in* Nairn, A.E.M., ed., Problems in paleoclimatology: London, Academic Press, p. 647–659, 669–672.

Wang, Z., 1985, Palaeovegetation and plate tectonics: Palaeophytogeography of North China during Permian and Triassic times: Palaeogeography, Palaeoclimatology, Palaeoecology, v. 49, p. 25–45.

Williamson, D. L., 1990, Semi-Lagrangian moisture transport in the NMC spectral model: Tellus, v. 42A, p. 413–428.

Williamson, D. L., and Rasch, P. J., 1989, Two-dimensional semi-Lagrangian transport with shape-preserving interpolation: Monthly Weather Review, v. 117, p. 102–129.

Williamson, D. L., Kiehl, J. T., Ramanathan, V., Dickinson, R. E., and Hack, J. J., 1987, Description of NCAR Community Climate Model (CCM1): Boulder, Colorado, NCAR Technical Note NCAR/TN-285+STR, 112 p.

Wilson, K. M., 1987, Circum-Pacific suspect terranes and lost microcontinents: Chips off the old blocks, *in* Proceedings of Pacific Rim Congress 87: Victoria, Australasian Institute of Mining and Metallurgy, p. 927–930.

Wilson, K. M., 1989, Mesozoic suspect terranes and global tectonics [Ph.D. thesis]: Boulder, University of Colorado, 372 p.

Wilson, K. M., Rosol, M. J., and Hay, W. W., 1989a, Global Mesozoic reconstructions using revised continental data and terrane histories: A progress report, *in* Hillhouse, J. W., ed., Deep structure and past kinematics of accreted terranes: American Geophysical Union Geophysical Monograph 50, p. 1–40.

Wilson, K. M., Rosol, M. J., Hay, W. W., and Harrison, C.G.A., 1989b, New model for the tectonic history of West Antarctica: A reappraisal of the fit of Antarctica in Gondwana: Eclogae Geologicae Helvetiae, v. 82, p. 1–36.

Wilson, K. M., Hay, W. W., and Wold, C. N., 1991, Mesozoic evolution of exotic terranes and marginal seas, western North America: Marine Geology, v. 102, p. 311–361.

Wilson, M. F., Henderson-Sellers, A., Dickinson, R. E., and Kennedy, P. J., 1987, Investigation of the sensitivity of the land-surface parameterization of the NCAR community climate model in regions of tundra vegetation: Journal of Climatology, v. 7, p. 319–343.

Manuscript Accepted by the Society May 14, 1993

Geological Society of America
Special Paper 288
1994

Depiction of modern and Pangean deserts: Evaluation of GCM hydrological diagnostics for paleoclimate studies

Mark A. Chandler
NASA, Goddard Institute for Space Studies, 2880 Broadway, New York, New York 10025

ABSTRACT

Hydrologic patterns are imprinted in the geologic record and play a prominent role in the investigations of Pangean climate. However, the hydrologic aspects of climate are complex (1) many variables are required to analyze hydrology, (2) hydrologic processes act on spatial scales that are smaller than GCM (General Circulation Model) grid spacing, and (3) observational data bases for calibrating modern climate simulations are few. This study, which uses a GCM to depict arid climates of the past and present, is designed to evaluate a variety of simulated hydrologic variables that are becoming increasingly available for paleoclimate model/data comparison studies.

Simulations of the current climate show that there are quantifiable levels of precipitation (P), soil moisture, and surface runoff that delineate the locations of modern deserts. However, in a Pangean simulation, using the same model, the threshold values of these variables reveal disparate views of desert extent. Altered boundary conditions and atmospheric circulation can invalidate thresholds based on modern climatology. The credibility of these variables thus rests heavily on the accuracy of reconstructed boundary conditions. A more fundamental meteorological approach defines deserts as regions where the atmospheric demand for moisture (potential evapotranspiration, E_p) exceeds the supply (precipitation, P). GCM values of E_p are overestimated; thus simulated $P–E_p$ fields are unusable. However, simulated E_p values can be derived independently using GCM-produced temperature values in empirically derived equations (E_{T_p}). Similar methods, using observed temperatures, are employed by atmospheric scientists to construct global and regional E_p data sets. The results of this study indicate that $P–E_{T_p}$ is more accurate than other individual variables for calculating moisture balance and is more useful for paleoclimate model/data comparisons because of its fundamental meteorological basis and lack of dependence on prescribed vegetation and soil conditions. Ultimately, hydrological misinterpretations can be avoided by understanding the limitations of GCM parameterizations and by strictly cross-checking variables with each other and with available paleoclimate data.

INTRODUCTION

During the Triassic and Early Jurassic, Pangea was characterized by globally warmer temperatures and extreme hydrological conditions. Several paleoclimate modeling experiments have investigated the first phenomenon, past global warming, but only recently has an increasing accessibility to general circulation models (GCMs), which explicitly calculate the hydrological cycle, allowed modelers to present hydrological results. In part, the focus has been directed by an immediate need to understand the processes involved in global warming but it is also true that most climate models are particularly suited to

Chandler, M. A., 1994, Depiction of modern and Pangean deserts: Evaluation of GCM hydrological diagnostics for paleoclimate studies, in Klein, G. D., ed., Pangea: Paleoclimate, Tectonics, and Sedimentation During Accretion, Zenith, and Breakup of a Supercontinent: Boulder, Colorado, Geological Society of America Special Paper 288.

temperature studies: GCMs can produce realistic likenesses of observed temperature fields but are inherently less accurate at simulating hydrological conditions (Rind, 1990). The reasons for this are numerous; three of the most important are that (1) many variables are required to analyze hydrological conditions, (2) critical hydrological processes act on small spatial scales and give rise to fields with spatial variability that is not resolvable by GCM grid spacings, and (3) global hydrological data bases for the modern climate are sparse, making model calibration difficult. Ultimately, these complexities have forced the use in most GCMs of extremely simplified parameterizations for hydrological processes. Despite the model limitations, many paleoclimate studies are regularly presenting simulation results for variables such as precipitation, evaporation, soil moisture, and surface runoff. Moreover, model experiments are a necessary step in order to analyze the processes that connect cause (climate forcings) and effect (the geologic record).

In this chapter I use a GCM to depict arid regions in the modern climate and to define the locations of Early Jurassic arid zones. Although it is important to consider whether a GCM can help locate specific Pangean environments, the primary purpose of this study is to evaluate the simulated hydrologic fields, as these fields are becoming increasingly available for model/data comparisons. Arid climate depiction presents several advantages for discussing a variety of diagnostics. For one thing, annually averaged results can be used to distinguish arid regions, since true deserts are dry year round. In addition, modern desert boundaries are easier to define than most other hydrological zones. Arid systems are also less affected by vegetation-atmosphere interactions; thus results presented here are less dependent on the GCM's vegetation scheme. These advantages imply that the GCM solutions may be comparable to observations, and therefore conclusions might apply to a variety of GCMs.

GCM DESCRIPTION AND HYDROLOGICAL PARAMETERIZATIONS

The model used for the simulations presented in this paper is the Goddard Institute for Space Studies (GISS) atmospheric general circulation model. This version of the GISS GCM has nine vertical layers in the atmosphere and an $8° \times 10°$ horizontal resolution. It uses realistic topography and a fractional grid system, which allows coastal grid boxes to contain portions of both land and ocean. The GCM solves the conservation equations for mass, energy, momentum, and moisture. Radiation equations account for aerosols and trace gases as well as for cloud cover. Clouds are predicted and include both convective and large-scale varieties. The annual results presented in this chapter are averaged from full seasonal cycle simulations that included seasonal heat storage and diurnal temperature variations. Ground hydrology and surface albedo are functions of specified vegetation types and are discussed in more detail below. Atmospheric CO_2 was fixed at

1958 levels (315 ppm) for both experiments, and current orbital configurations were used. A complete model description and results from the modern climate control experiment are presented in Hansen et al. (1983). Chandler and others (1992) present a detailed description of the Early Jurassic simulations.

Most GCMs employ simple ground hydrology and land surface schemes that promote moisture and heat feedbacks without necessarily recreating the true physical processes. Table 1 summarizes a few of the common parameterizations used in GCMs during the past decade. Vegetation distributions in these models are represented by variations in ground albedo, whereas groundwater and soil moisture are represented using constant-depth reservoirs or ""buckets" to simulate the water-holding capacity of upper ground layers. Groundwater reservoirs and subsurface flow are ignored. Surface runoff occurs when a grid cell's ground reservoir becomes saturated and precipitation exceeds evaporation over that cell. The GISS GCM has a slightly more complex parameterization, using two layers in the ground with water-holding capacities that vary by vegetation type and season (Hansen et al., 1984; Hansen et al. 1983). Vegetation types may be specified from any of eight categories (Table 2). Soil moisture in the GISS GCM is defined as the time-averaged amount of water residing within the two ground hydrology layers. Moisture exchange from the upper layer takes place via precipitation, evaporation, and surface runoff, and water is immediately available for evaporation from the upper layer during all seasons. In an attempt to mimic transpiration, the moisture of the lower layer is available in vegetated regions only and only during the growing season (defined as year-round, equatorward of 30°; May through August from 30 to 90°N; November–February from 30 to 90°S). At other times no water escapes the lower layer, although water may still diffuse in from the upper layer. Curiously (and probably incorrectly), the parameterization implies that in desert regions, which are assumed to have no growing season, water can never escape the second layer, a fact that creates a lower limit for desert dryness equal to the amount of water initialized in the second layer. Ground albedo is also a function of vegetation type (Table 2), and in winter vegetation partially masks the high albedo characteristics of snow. Surface runoff depends on precipitation rate as well as absolute soil moisture, in an attempt to represent the lower infiltration rates that exist during downpours. Although more detailed, this scheme does not include realistic physical representations of ground-vegetation-atmosphere interactions.

Detailed hydrological schemes, which contain explicit representations of components such as vegetation canopies, rooting depths, soil infiltration, and plant physiology, have been developed for use in several GCMs (Abramopoulos et al., 1988; Dickinson, 1984; Sellers and others, 1986). Such schemes should be incorporated as they become available because the added realism allows for process-oriented studies. However, by themselves, more realistic land surface schemes do not necessarily lead to improved climate simulations. Th

TABLE 1. GENERAL CIRCULATION MODEL GROUND HYDROLOGY SCHEMES*

Methods

GISS[†]	GFDL[§]	NCAR[**]	UKMO[‡]
Determined prognostically from two-layer model with upper/lower field capacities in cm prescribed as 1/1 desert, 3/20 tundra, 3/20 grassland, 3/30 shrub covered grassland, 3/30 scattered trees on grassland, 3/45 deciduous forest, 3/45 evergreen forest, 20/45 rainforest (14/45 in Jurassic simulation).	Determined prognostically from one-layer model with 15-cm field capacity.	Determined prognostically from one-layer model with 15-cm field capacity.	Determined prognostically from one-layer model with 15-cm field capacity.

Formula

Upper layer: $$\frac{\delta W_1}{\delta t} = \frac{(P - E - R_0)}{W_{k1}} + \frac{(W_2 - W_1)}{\tau}.$$ Lower layer: $$\frac{\delta W_2}{\delta t} = \frac{W_{k1}}{W_{k2}} \times \frac{(W_2 - W_1)}{\tau}.$$	Over land: if $W = W_k$ and $P > E_0$, $\frac{\delta W}{\delta t} = 0$ and $R_0 = P - E_0$; if $W < W_k$, $\frac{\delta W}{\delta \tau} = P - E$. Over snowcover: if $W < W_{k_9}$ $\frac{\delta W}{\delta t} = S_m + P$; if $W = W_k$, $\frac{\delta W}{\delta t} = 0$ and $R_0 = S_m + P$.	$\frac{\delta W}{\delta t} = (P - E + S_m)$ Runoff is computed when $W > W_k$ then, $R_0 = P - E$.	Over land: if $W = W_k$ and $P > E_0$, $\frac{\delta W}{\delta t} = 0$ and $R_0 = P - E_0$; if $W < W_k$, $\frac{\delta W}{\delta t} = P - E$. Over snowcover: if $W < W_k$, $\frac{\delta W}{\delta t} = S_m + P$; if $W = W_k$, $\frac{\delta W}{\delta t} = 0$ and $R_0 = S_m + P$.

*After Kellogg and Zhao, 1988.
[†]Goddard Institute for Space Studies (Hansen and others, 1983; Matthews, 1984).
[§]Geophysical Fluid Dynamics Laboratory (Manabe and Wetherald, 1986; Manabe, 1969).
[**]National Center for Atmospheric Research (Washington, 1983; Washington and Meehl, 1984).
[‡]United Kingdom Meteorological Office (Mitchell, 1983; Mitchell and others, 1987; Wilson and Mitchell, 1986).

complex physical processes are not easily scaled to the coarse resolutions of a GCM (Rind et al., 1992), and for most GCMs the altered hydrology will require model "retuning" to achieve the best possible modern climatology. Further studies are required to evaluate whether or not these schemes will be useful for paleoclimate simulations. Many of the required input parameters are difficult, if not impossible, to estimate from the geologic record, and the trade-off between increasing process reality and decreasing boundary condition reality has unknown ramifications. A likely benefit of the new schemes is that they should act to encourage detailed investigations of paleofloras and paleosols.

DESERTS: DEFINING ARID REGIONS

Modern deserts and their causes

By most definitions, deserts make up approximately 20 to 25% of the present-day land surface (excluding Antarctica). Figure 1 shows the modern distribution of arid and semiarid continental regions as compiled from meteorological data and proxy characteristics. Aridity in these regions results from several factors (see Table 2). Most low-latitude deserts, located between latitudes 10°N and 35°N and between 10°S and 35°S (e.g., Sahara and Kalahari deserts, Africa), result from large-

TABLE 2. VEGETATION CHARACTERISTICS USED IN THE GISS GCM

	Desert*	Tundra	Grass	Shrub	Woodland	Deciduous	Evergreen	Rain Forest
Visual Albedo	(%)	(%)	(%)	(%)	(%)	(%)	(%)	(%)
Winter	0.35	0.07	0.09	0.09	0.08	0.10	0.07	0.06
Spring	0.35	0.06	0.10	0.10	0.07	0.05	0.07	0.06
Summer	0.35	0.08	0.09	0.14	0.08	0.06	0.08	0.06
Autumn	0.35	0.08	0.09	0.11	0.06	0.05	0.06	0.06
Near-IR Albedo	(%)	(%)	(%)	(%)	(%)	(%)	(%)	(%)
Winter	0.35	0.20	0.27	0.27	0.23	0.30	0.20	0.18
Spring	0.35	0.21	0.35	0.30	0.24	0.22	0.20	0.18
Summer	0.35	0.30	0.36	0.42	0.30	0.29	0.25	0.18
Autumn	0.35	0.25	0.31	0.33	0.20	0.22	0.18	0.18
Water Field Capacity	(cm)	(cm)	(cm)	(cm)	(cm)	(cm)	(cm)	(cm)
Layer 1	1	3	3	3	3	3	3	20
Layer 2	1	20	20	30	30	45	45	45
Masking Depth	(m)	(m)	(m)	(m)	(m)	(m)	(m)	(m)
	0.1	0.2	0.2	0.5	2.0	5.0	10	25
Roughness Length	(m)	(m)	(m)	(m)	(m)	(m)	(m)	(m)
	0.005	0.01	0.01	0.018	0.32	1.0	1.0	2.0

*Desert albedo is reduced by ground wetness by a factor $(1 - 0.5 W_1)$.

scale atmospheric subsidence associated with the poleward limb of the Hadley cell. This subsidence reduces relative humidity by heating the air adiabatically, suppressing cumulus convection and precipitation along with cloud cover. The lack of clouds allows the intense low-latitude solar radiation to reach the surface, elevating ground temperatures and evaporation rates (Wallace and Hobbs, 1977, p. 429–430). Once developed, positive feedbacks help to maintain desert conditions. Desert pavements, bare sand, and high albedo vegetation reflect up to 35% of the incoming solar radiation, reducing sensible heat flux and convection, and low ground-moisture levels keep evaporation at a minimum, thus sustaining a dry atmosphere above the desert.

Arid regions may also exist outside of the subtropical latitudes (Fig. 1 and Table 3). For example, extensive deserts are located in the interiors of large continents where moisture sources are distant (e.g., Taklimakan and Gobi deserts, Asia), in the rainshadows of mountain ranges (e.g., Patagonian and Monte regions, South America), and adjacent to zones of ocean upwelling, where cool waters reduce evaporation and convection (e.g., Peruvian and Atacama Desert, South America). The world's most arid conditions result from a combination of effects. The central Sahara, for example, is located beneath the descending limb of the Northern Hemisphere Hadley cell and is within the continental interior of north Africa. In southwestern Africa, the Namib desert lies beneath the descending limb of the Southern Hemisphere Hadley cell and is adjacent to a cool upwelling zone associated with the Benguela Current (Zinderen Bakker, 1975).

Any attempt to use computer models to predict the distribution of past or future deserts first requires an objective defi-nition of an arid region. Furthermore, any diagnostics that are applied from GCM simulations must, as an initial test, successfully reproduce the distribution of present-day deserts. A good starting point, therefore, is to ask, What constitutes an arid region in the modern climate and to what extent can a GCM depict modern arid regions?

Defining aridity

From a meteorological standpoint, arid zones are defined as regions in which the atmospheric demand for water exceeds the supply. Thus, direct measurements of hydrological parameters should provide the most definitive and quantitative estimates of aridity in the current climate. The balance of atmospheric moisture can be obtained by differencing the rate of precipitation (P) and the potential rate of evapotranspiration (E_p), with P representing the atmospheric supply of water and E_p being the theoretical atmospheric demand for moisture (Thornthwaite, 1948). Depiction of deserts, following this definition, requires detailed observations of precipitation as well as of ground temperature, surface air temperatures, wind velocity, and an estimate of the turbulent transfer coefficient, since these values are used in the calculation of potential evaporation (E_p):

$$E_p = C_Q V(q_g - q_s) \qquad (1)$$

where

C_Q = turbulent transfer coefficient
V = surface windspeed
q_g = specific humidity at ground level
q_s = specific humidity of the atmosphere at
     30-m-height above ground

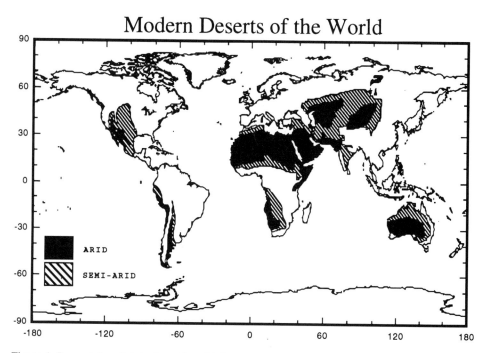

Figure 1. Present-day distribution of world deserts showing arid and semiarid regions. Based on a combination of climate data and proxy information (after Glennie, 1987; Rasool, 1984; and Greeley and Iversen, 1985).

These values are not monitored at most locations, and when vegetation interactions (particularly transpiration) are included, "observed" values of E_p are virtually unobtainable. This fact has led several researchers to derive empirical formulas for the calculation of potential evapotranspiration based on studies of bioclimatic interactions (see Holdridge, 1959; Köppen, 1936; Penman, 1948; Thornthwaite, 1948). In practice, arid regions generally are identified by the use of more traditionally measured hydrological variables, such as precipitation, evaporation, soil moisture, and runoff. Maps of these variables reveal a reasonable degree of correspondence with the location of modern deserts.

ARID REGIONS: GCM RESULTS VERSUS MODERN CLIMATOLOGIES

The diagnostics that are most commonly used to assess continental moisture balance in GCM simulations are precipitation (e.g., Manabe et al., 1965; Pitcher et al., 1983), the difference between precipitation (P) and evaporation or evapotranspiration (E) (e.g., Rind, 1984; Shukla and Mintz, 1982; Sud and Smith, 1985; Voice and Hunt, 1984), soil moisture (S_m) (e.g., Kellogg and Zhao, 1988; Milly, 1992; Rind, 1982; Zhao and Kellogg, 1988), and surface runoff (R_s) (e.g., Rind, 1984; Russell and Miller, 1990). More recently, several studies (Delworth and Manabe, 1988; Milly, 1992; Rind et al., 1990) have discussed the use of potential evapotranspiration as a diagnostic variable in GCM experiments, stressing the im-

portant distinction between the potential and actual rates of evapotranspiration for evaluating moisture balance. However, these studies also point out some severe problems with using GCM-calculated Ep values, a matter discussed in detail below.

In the following sections global distributions of the above hydrologic fields are presented for a current climate GCM simulation. The accuracy of simulations is commonly assessed by comparing simulated results with global observational data bases. Unfortunately, excepting precipitation, global data bases for hydrological variables do not exist. Instead, global data for evapotranspiration, soil moisture, and surface runoff are calculated from a combination of analytical and empirical techniques (e.g., Korzun, 1978; Thornthwaite, 1948; Willmott et al., 1985) that use observed temperature and precipitation to estimate water balances. The global data bases, which represent long-term temporal averages, are referred to as climatologies in the following sections. Readers should be aware that the difference between hydrological climatologies and true measurements may, at some locations, exceed the difference between climatologies and GCM results; there is, however, no way to accurately evaluate the magnitude of the errors. The lamentable state of current global-monitoring projects suggests that this will be a problem for many years to come.

Precipitation

Precipitation is the most reliable of the hydrological global climatologies and the quality of other hydrologic fields

TABLE 3. CAUSES AND LOCATIONS OF MODERN ARID REGIONS

Cause	Description	Examples
Subsiding or stabilized air masses	Subtropical regions.	Sahara, Namib, Kalahari (Africa);
	Specifically, regions located beneath the descending limbs of the Hadley cells (approximately 25° to 30° latitude north and south).	Chihuahuan, Sonoran (North America);
		Simpson, Great Sandy (Australia);
		Arabian, Iranian, Thar (Middle East and India).
Continentality	Regions within the continental interiors.	Saharan (Africa);
		Turkestan, Taklimakan, Gobi (Asia);
	Locations isolated by distance from moisture sources, principally the oceans.	Great Basin (North America).
Rainshadows	Regions located leeward of topographic barriers, such as mountains and plateaus.	Turkestan, Taklimakan (Asia);
		Great Basin, Colorado Plateau (North America);
	As air masses climb in elevation they cool, thus losing the ability to hold moisture in vapor form. Moisture falls out as precipitation. Leeward of barriers, subsidence occurs, thus warming and drying the air mass.	Monte, Patagonian (South America).
Cool sea surface temperatures	Regions adjacent to cool SSTs.	Namib, Western Sahara (Africa);
	The amount of moisture evaporated from the ocean surface is less under cooler conditions yielding drier air. Cool SSTs also stabilize air masses, reducing convective rainfall.	Peruvian, Atacama (South America);
		Rab'Al Khali (Saudi Arabia).

relies heavily on the precipitation climatology. The Legates and Willmott (1990) data base, used here, consists of measurements made at 26,858 stations, 91% of which are land based. Figure 2a shows the global mean annual precipitation based on these data. The standard deviation of the annual precipitation is commonly 25% of the absolute measurements and exceeds 50% in some tropical locations (compare Figs. 3 and 4 in Legates and Willmott, 1990).

Comparing the observed precipitation rates in Figure 2a with the GISS GCM simulated modern precipitation (Fig. 2b) shows that the 8° × 10° version of the GISS GCM generally reproduces the Earth's major precipitation zones. In particular, the precipitation values over the major deserts are similar to observations, although the difference map (Fig. 2c) shows that most arid and semiarid regions are slightly wetter than observations indicate. A comparison of the precipitation results with the distribution of modern world deserts (Fig. 1), using a limit

of 25 cm of rain (0.7 mm/day) to define arid climates (Glennie, 1987), shows that the GCM simulates aridity in the Sahara as well as in deserts such as the Peruvian and Atacama and the Namib, which are downwind of cool ocean currents. The deserts of central Asia, southwest North America, and Australia are dry relative to surrounding regions, yet they receive more than 0.7 mm/day of rain and are wetter than observed. Excess rainfall in Australia is likely a response to the altered position of the intertropical convergence zone (ITCZ) that, in the simulation, is displaced too far north in the Pacific and Indian oceans. This decreases the amount of atmospheric subsidence occurring over Australia (as compensation to convection in the ITCZ) and reduces drying that, in the real world, occurs as a result of that subsidence. Central Asia and the southwestern United States are drier in finer resolution (4° × 5° and 2° × 2.5°) versions of the GISS GCM, suggesting that the lack of simulated aridity in those regions is caused by the inability of the coarser grid to resolve the Himalayan and coastal Californian ranges, thus reducing their rainshadow effect.

The precipitation diagnostic apparently yields a reasonable first-order estimate of the distribution of arid regions. However, pitfalls certainly exist when using precipitation patterns alone. Precipitation represents only the supply portion of

PRECIPITATION
(mm/day)

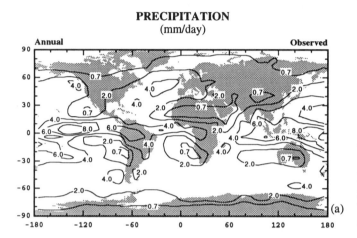

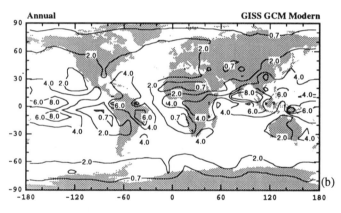

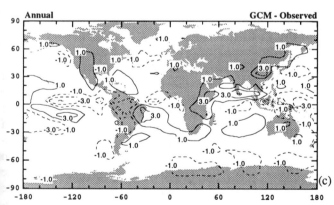

Figure 2. a, Observed precipitation from the global climatology of Legates and Willmott (1990). b, Simulated precipitation from a modern climate control experiment using the GISS GCM. c, The difference between simulated and observed precipitation. Results shown are global annually averaged fields.

the moisture balance calculation (Glennie, 1987; Rind et al., 1990), and in GCMs the moisture supply is typically dependent on parameterizations of convection and cloud formation, which are heavily tuned to the present-day climate. In addition to the moisture supply, most climatologists prefer to consider moisture losses (i.e., evaporation, transpiration) when interpreting hydrological patterns from climate change simulations.

Precipitation minus evaporation

The evaporation field calculated by the GISS GCM differs from the evapotranspiration climatology of Willmott and others (1985) by approximately the same order of magnitude as did simulated precipitation values (Fig. 3a). The tendency, in arid regions particularly, is for the evaporation to balance the overestimated precipitation. Many paleoclimate studies have used the difference between precipitation and evaporation rates (P–E) as a diagnostic for determining patterns of aridity from GCM simulations (Barron et al., 1990; Chandler et al., 1992; Kutzbach and Gallimore, 1989; Voice and Hunt, 1984). As Figures 3b and 3c show, negative P-E values are located primarily in subtropical regions and identify those deserts that lie beneath the large-scale atmospheric subsidence associated with the poleward limbs of the Hadley cells. Nevertheless, difficulties arise when interpreting the GCM P-E fields.

Over continents, GCM evaporation rates (E) are calculated as,

$$E = \beta E_p \qquad (2)$$

where

β = ground wetness factor (1 for saturated soils, 0 for dry soils)
E_p = potential evaporation

The factor β is limited by the moisture supply (Hansen et al., 1983), which includes precipitation, soil moisture, and the influx of runoff from regions up slope. If no soil moisture is available, as in deserts, the evaporation is limited to precipitation plus runoff. In current GCMs, runoff is calculated for diagnostic purposes but is not included in moisture-supply calculations because GCM Cartesian grid arrangements do not resolve drainage basin patterns or hydrology. For a simulation that has reached equilibrium, continental deserts are not identifiable using this method because, without soil moisture or runoff, evaporation is limited by precipitation, and by definition, P-E cannot be negative. An analysis method sometimes employed with GCM paleoclimate simulations involves initializing all soils with a large supply of moisture, then comparing the precipitation and evaporation rates as the simulation approaches an equilibrium state (but before soil moisture has been depleted in any location). Of course, since results may be affected by initial conditions (e.g., Shukla and Mintz, 1982), the method is of questionable use for paleoclimate experiments, where soil boundary conditions are poorly known.

Soil Moisture

The soil moisture (S_m) climatology shown in Figure 4a was calculated using water-balance equations that rely on observed precipitation and surface air temperature values (Willmott et al., 1985). Error estimates for the data are unavail-

EVAPORATION
(mm/day)

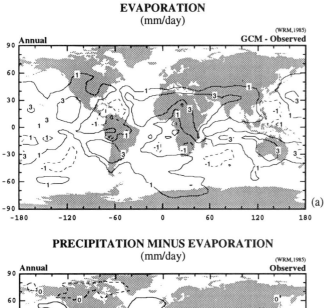

PRECIPITATION MINUS EVAPORATION
(mm/day)

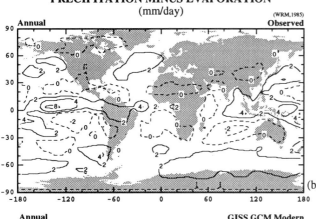

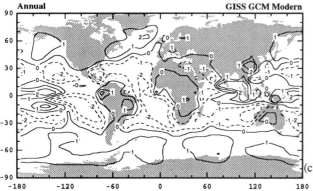

Figure 3. a, The difference between GCM evaporation rates and evaporation rates calculated from observed temperature and precipitation fields (Willmott et al., 1985). b, Precipitation minus evaporation from the global data base of Willmott et al. c, Precipitation minus evaporation from the GISS GCM modern climate simulation. Results shown are global annually averaged fields.

able because of the lack of true measurement control; thus quantitative evaluation of the GCM's performance versus reality is not possible. Adding to the complexity, values used to represent "soil moisture" in a GCM are not necessarily directly comparable to the S_m climatology. Still, a qualitative comparison between the GISS GCM soil-moisture values (Fig. 4b) and the S_m climatology is possible. GCM values of S_m are relatively dry over observed arid regions, implying that the soil-moisture parameterization does respond to both atmospheric supply and demand: absorbing precipitated water and releasing it again through evapotranspiration. GCM values are wetter (10 to 30 mm) in most desert regions than the climatological data, which lie between 5 and 10 mm. This is consistent with the GCM's overestimated precipitation. Not surprisingly, regions that should reside in rainshadows (southwest United States, central Asia, southern Patagonia) are the most poorly resolved by the GCM, again because the poorly resolved topographic barriers do not sufficiently intercept water vapor transports.

Qualitative comparability between simulated S_m values and modern desert locations does not necessarily make this a useful paleoclimate diagnostic. Simulated soil moistures can be sensitive to the model's specified water-field capacities, a fact that Kellogg and Zhao (1988) and Zhao and Kellogg (1988) showed. In their studies, the GISS GCM, with variable field capacities from 2 to 65 cm, gave consistently higher soil-moisture values than NCAR (National Center for Atmospheric Research, UKMO (United Kingdom Meteorological Office), and GFDL (Geophysical Fluid Dynamics Laboratory), GCMs, which have 15-cm field capacities. One might suspect that the GISS GCM, with variable capacities based on vegetation type, might give a better quantitative representation of S_m, but that is difficult to conclude based on available experiments. The concern remains, however, that positive feedbacks such as high albedo and low water-field capacities, which tend to keep deserts arid, could bias model results if ground conditions are assigned incorrectly. The desert ground hydrology in the GISS GCM has a low soil-moisture capacity compared with the other categories in the model (Table 2) and is generally initialized with lower amounts of groundwater. For current climate experiments, such specifications are justified, since they approximate known ground conditions. However, for paleoclimate simulations, where initial ground conditions are largely unknown, specified conditions, whether uniform or variable, may force the result unrealistically. Regardless, many paleoclimate experiments have reported soil-moisture values and will continue to do so, because they offer a single value that represents the GCM's regional supply and demand for water (e.g., Moore et al., 1992; Valdes and Sellwood, 1992).

Surface runoff

Surface runoff (R_s) values, like soil moisture, can be qualitatively correlated with moisture availability; the lowest values do approximate desert locations in the current climate.

A global surface-runoff climatology, produced by Korzun (1978) for use with the NCAR 4.5° × 7.5° GCM (Fig. 5a), was calculated using river discharge records modified by a "runoff coefficient"—a factor based on observed P–E values. Although not strictly observational, Korzun's data set provides one comparison for GCM runoff results (Fig. 5b). Compared to Korzun's climatology, the GISS GCM simulates R_s values that are higher across North America and lower in Amazonia. However, basic patterns of wet and dry are similar in both results and the absolute range of values is very close.

Like soil moisture, the GCM runoff diagnostic is not necessarily defined in a manner comparable to the Korzun clima-

tology. Field measurements of R_s include data for stream and river outflow rates and are averages over individual drainage basins. Currently, GCM ground hydrology schemes do not distinguish the hydrological aspects of drainage divides; therefore, simulated R_s values are contoured from the model's grid system without regard to directional flow. The surface runoff calculated by most GCMs is a function of precipitation and evaporation rates as well as of the saturation of the ground layer(s). In the GISS GCM, runoff is parameterized as,

$$R_s = 1/2\, W_1 P \qquad (3)$$

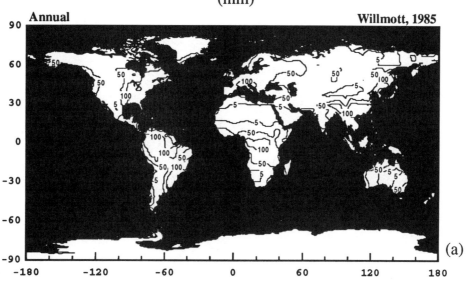

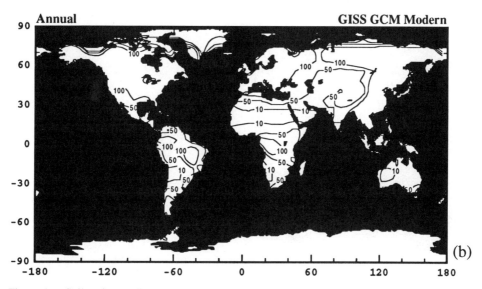

Figure 4. a, Soil moisture climatology based on the water budget analyses of Willmott et al. (1985). b, Soil moisture results from the GISS GCM modern climate experiment. Simulated soil moisture is the total water stored in the two ground layers of the GCM.

where W_1 is the water-field capacity of ground layer 1 and P is the precipitation rate. Such simple parameterizations obviously do not capture the complexity of ground hydrological processes, but they were originally incorporated into GCMs as a means of supplying a reasonable moisture feedback to the atmosphere.

A more appropriate surface runoff diagnostic can be computed based on the aerial extent of drainage basins. Russell and Miller (1990) grouped the grid boxes in the GISS GCM by their locations with respect to drainage-basin geography. They then compared the GCM results with the outflow from 33 of the world's largest rivers. Their comparison shows that, for some basins, the model yields reasonable results; however,

R_s from the arid climate drainage basins is conspicuously overestimated (Fig. 6). The combination of too much precipitation in desert regions, the small water-holding capacities of the desert ground hydrology layers, and the fact that surface runoff is not allowed to evaporate while in transit to the oceans is the likely cause for this overestimation. It is not known how the GISS GCM compares to other GCMs in this respect, since similar experiments are not available for comparison. Unfortunately, the extent of ancient drainage basins is difficult to predict and the effective overall outflow of past river systems is even more difficult to estimate. Thus, even if the simulated R_s values can be improved to a point at which

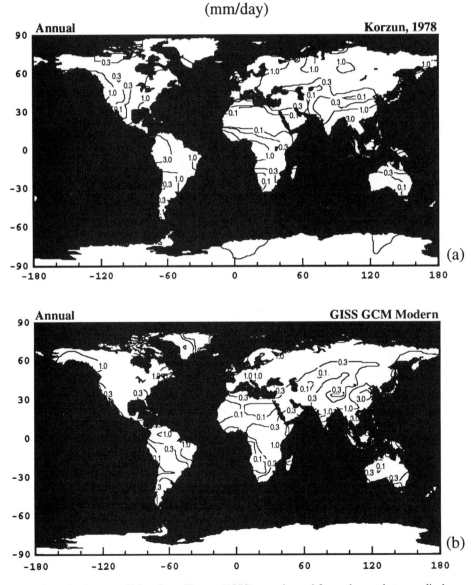

Figure 5. a, Surface runoff data from Korzun (1978) as estimated from observed stream discharge, precipitation, and evaporation values. b, Surface runoff results from the GISS GCM modern climate experiment.

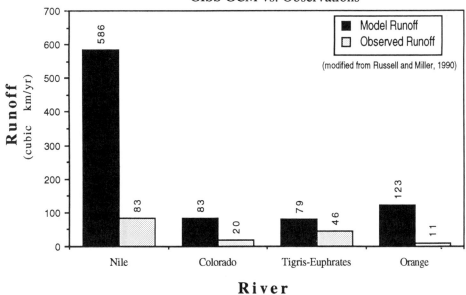

Figure 6. Simulated versus observed annually averaged runoff from four of the Earth's major arid-climate rivers (after Russell and Miller, 1990). The GCM's calculated river runoff is higher than observed values because, in the model, precipitation rates over arid regions are overestimated, runoff is not allowed to reevaporate, and runoff is not allowed to recharge down-slope ground hydrology layers.

they match modern values, it will be difficult to validate paleoclimate counterparts. In some experimental situations, R_s values may have an additional analytic importance, a factor I will discuss for the Early Jurassic experiments.

Drought indices and the significance of potential evapotranspiration

Drought indices (Palmer, 1965; Rind et al., 1990) are commonly used to analyze the intensity of atmospheric moisture deficits over land. They act as indicators of relative moisture availability, since they have climatological means that equal zero for the current climate. Such indices calculate moisture balance using the *potential* rate of evapotranspiration (Alley, 1984) (E_p) rather than the *actual* rate of evapotranspiration (E_a). Thornthwaite (1948) showed that when moisture is deficient, E_a is limited, because plants close their stomatal openings in order to conserve water. This condition limits E_a to some value beneath the true atmospheric demand for moisture. E_a is only equivalent to E_p (the true atmospheric demand for moisture) over free water surfaces or when water is plentiful in the ground, because then evaporation and transpiration are not restricted. The dependence of E_a on available moisture suggests, therefore, that the true moisture balance of a region

is obtained by comparing E_p (demand) with the rate of precipitation (supply).

Since a climate is arid when moisture demand exceeds supply ($P-E_p <0$) over long periods of time, it would seem simple to compare the GCM-simulated P and E_p values to define regions of aridity, either in current or paleoclimate settings. Unfortunately, this is not the case. Model-calculated values of E_p, over continental regions, tend to be much larger than estimated values (Delworth and Manabe, 1988), for reasons that are only recently being addressed (see Rind et al., 1990; Milly, 1992). Figure 7a shows the simulated precipitation minus potential evapotranspiration ($P-E_p$) from the GISS GCM current climate control run. The resulting $P-E_p$ field indicates that all continental regions should be interpreted as arid. The problem arises because the GCM calculates high gradients between the ground temperature (T_g) and the surface air temperature (T_s); this calculation leads to an increase in the specific humidity gradient (q_g-q_s), resulting in elevated values of E_p (see Equation 3). As Rind and others (1990) have shown, the real world, unlike the simulated world of the GCM, contains a vegetated surface, or "canopy." The canopy is cooled by the process of transpiration, therefore T_g does not become large. This keeps the ground-to-surface temperature gradient small, which in turn keeps the value of (q_g-q_s) low, reducing values of E_p. Future versions of most GCMs will include a simulated vegetation canopy in order to combat this problem. Developmental versions of such routines tested in the GISS GCM show that they improve the potential evaporation estimates but do not completely solve the problem.

Precipitation minus Thornthwaite's potential evapotranspiration

Although E_p values generated by the GCM are not directly useful, potential rates of evapotranspiration can be cal-

PRECIPITATION MINUS SIMULATED POTENTIAL EVAPORATION
(mm/day)

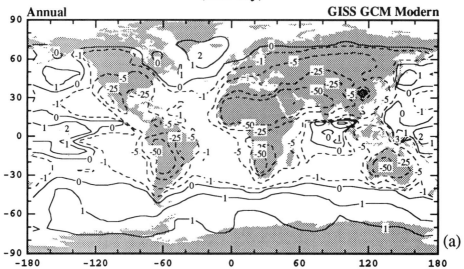

PRECIPITATION MINUS THORNTHWAITE POTENTIAL EVAPOTRANSPIRATION
(mm/day)

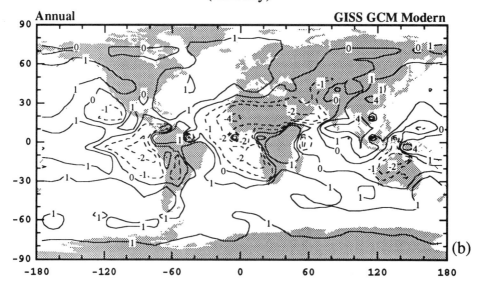

Figure 7. a, Simulated precipitation minus the GCM's calculated potential evaporation. b, Simulated precipitation minus potential evapotranspiration (E_p), where E_p is calculated from simulated surface air temperatures using the method of Thornthwaite (see text).

ulated using the GCM's simulated surface temperature results together with empirical bioclimatic formulas, such as those of Thornthwaite (1948) or Penman (1948). Willmott et al. (1985) employed such a technique, using observed temperature and precipitation fields, to derive their soil-moisture estimates, discussed above. In their work they used a modified version of Thornthwaite's (1948) equation:

$$E_{TP}(M) = 1.6(10T(M)/I)^m \times (dayl/12) \times (daym/30) \quad (4)$$

where

$T(M)$ = long-term mean monthly temperature (°C)
I = annual heat index, $\sum_{12}^{1} (T(M))/5)^{1.514}$
m = $(6.75 \times 10^{-7}) I^3 - (7.71 \times 10^{-5}) I^2$
$\quad + (1.79 \times 10^{-2}) I + 0.492$
$dayl$ = daylength (hours)
$daym$ = number of days in month

which yields monthly average potential evapotranspiration $E_{T_P}(M)$) values. An important advantage of using the empirical equation is that E_{T_P} can be derived using only the simulated surface air temperatures as input (Hillel, 1971). This is especially useful since surface air temperatures are considered to be a robust diagnostic field in GCMs. Differences between the E_{T_P} values and the GCM precipitation field are shown in Figure 7b, giving a new estimate of the distribution of arid regions. P-E_{T_P} produces a reasonably good estimate of the distribution of aridity, showing dry conditions in all of the major deserts worldwide. The index slightly overestimates the dryness of southern Amazonia and underestimates the aridity of eastern Africa; both of these deviations are caused by inaccuracies in the simulated precipitation rates over those regions. The P-E_{T_P} field also predicts drier than observed conditions in the southeastern United States and in the Congo.

Although this technique is widely used for hydrological studies of the modern climate, rarely is it used in paleoclimate experiments. Advantages of the technique for paleoclimate model/data comparisons include an ability to successfully depict modern arid regions, a basis on fundamental meteorological principles, and the chance to calculate GCM moisture balance while largely circumventing the dependence on simplistic ground hydrology parameterizations

ARID REGIONS: GCM RESULTS FOR THE EARLY JURASSIC

The expansion of desert regions into tropical and mid-latitude zones during the early Mesozoic is a climatically dramatic event. Of course, regions of aridity have changed, both in their expanse and in their distribution, throughout geologic time and even within human history. Modern deserts are subject to large-scale moisture fluctuations over periods of only a few thousands of years (Glennie, 1987; Lézine et al., 1990), and on slightly longer time scales, lake levels, dune development, and fossil pollen reveal that rainfall amounts oscillate significantly in association with orbital variations (Nicholson and Flohn, 1980; Street-Perrott and Harrison, 1984; Kutzbach and Street-Perrott, 1985). However, during the past 200 million years, the geologic record indicates no desert expansion as extensive as that which occurred in the Triassic and Jurassic. A supercontinental configuration increases the distance to moisture sources and enhances aridity, but as Hallam (1984) points out, the greatest latitudinal expanse of evaporites occurred well after Pangean breakup had begun. Rind et al. (1990) suggest that the expansion may be related to the warmer air temperatures, which would have enhanced potential evaporation. If so, then regions that are today characterized by humid rain forests and rain-fed agricultural belts might face severe moisture deficits should global warming predictions come to pass.

Determining the causes of past large-scale hydrologic changes is difficult because precipitation, potential evapotranspiration, soil moisture, and runoff cannot be measured directly. Proxy data, such as evaporites, eolian deposits, and xeromorphic vegetation characteristics, are used to recognize the distribution of past arid zones, but they are qualitative to semiquantitative representations of climate, offering few options for analyzing causal mechanisms. And yet, the proxy data do provide a means of validating numerical climate simulations; thus they are indispensable for studying changes in the Earth's hydrological system.

A summary map of paleoclimatically significant Early Jurassic sediments is shown in Figure 8. The first-order hydrologic framework of Pangea is apparent; wet climates in eastern Pangea are attested to be extensive peat deposition (Parrish et al., 1982), and arid environments in western Pangea are delineated by evaporite (Gordon, 1975) and eolian deposits (Hallam, 1975, 1985; Kocurek, 1988). Several GCM simulations have shown that the basic hydrological structure reflected by the geologic data can be reproduced by numerical models (Chandler et al., 1992; Kutzbach and Gallimore, 1989; Moore et al., 1992; Valdes and Sellwood, 1992). It can also be shown, however, that discerning even first-order hydrological regimes depends greatly upon the definitions applied. The following section reviews the hydrological results from an Early Jurassic simulation conducted using the GISS GCM. The primary boundary conditions used in the experiment are presented in Figure 9; detailed descriptions are available in Chandler et al. (1992). Figures 10 through 12 show the distribution of hydrological characteristics for the Early Jurassic simulation, which are similar to those discussed previously for the modern climate. It should be apparent from the following section that developing the capability to distinguish regional hydrological characteristics from paleoclimate simulations will require a selective and informed approach to analyzing GCM results.

Early Jurassic Indicators of Aridity and Humidity

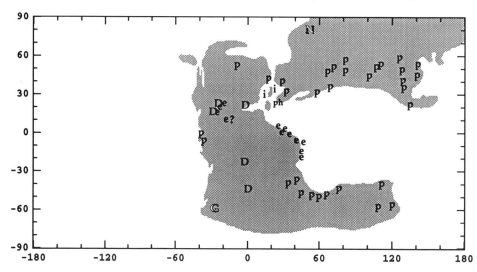

Figure 8. Distribution of aridity and humidity indicators from the Early Jurassic paleoclimate record. Evaporites (e); eolian "dune" sandstones (D); peats or coals (p); ironstones (i); phosphates (Ph); Novosibirskiye paleoflora (N); Graham Land paleoflora (G). Novosibirskiye and Graham Land are the highest known latitudinal positions of Early Jurassic paleofloras.

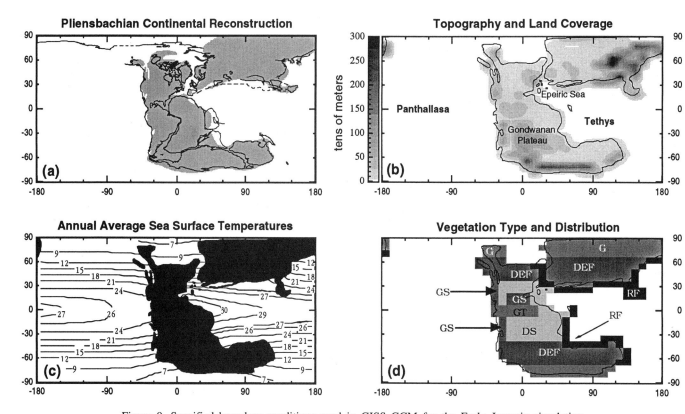

Figure 9. Specified boundary conditions used in GISS GCM for the Early Jurassic simulation. a, Early Jurassic (Pliensbachian) paleocontinental reconstruction. Shading indicates position of paleoshoreline (Ziegler et al., 1983; D. Rowley and others, unpublished data). b, Continental elevations. c, Sea surface temperatures. d, Terrestrial vegetation. The vegetation categories include desert (DS), savanna-type vegetation (G), savanna with scattered shrubs (GS), savanna with scattered trees (GT), mixed deciduous-evergreen forest (DEF), rain forest (RF).

EARLY JURASSIC GCM SIMULATIONS: HYDROLOGICAL RESULTS

The most striking aspect of the precipitation field from the Early Jurassic simulation (Fig. 10a) is the low rate of precipitation that existed over western Pangea in low and middle latitudes. Because evaporites and eolian dune deposits (Fig. 8) attest to the desert conditions that must have existed in those regions during the Early Jurassic, the simulated precipitation field qualitatively identifies a first-order hydrologic characteristic of the climate of that period. Applying the conventional definition of modern desert precipitation rates (<25 cm/yr; 0.7 mm/day) reveals that the precipitation field underestimates aridity in western Pangea and overestimates drying in north-

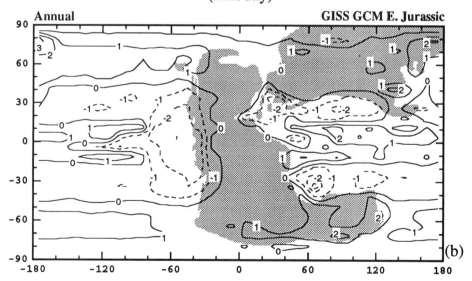

Figure 10. a, Simulated precipitation field for the Early Jurassic. b, Precipitation minus evaporation from the Early Jurassic simulation.

central Pangea. Additionally, the coastal zone of the south-western Tethys Ocean is simulated as having had annually averaged precipitation rates of >4 mm/day—difficult to imagine for a region that supported major evaporite deposition. Minor peat deposits on the equatorial west coast of Pangea are

SOIL MOISTURE
(mm)

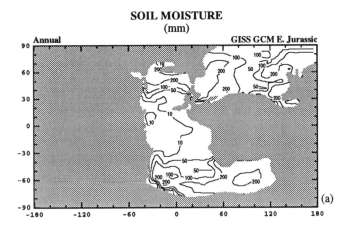

SURFACE RUNOFF
(mm/day)

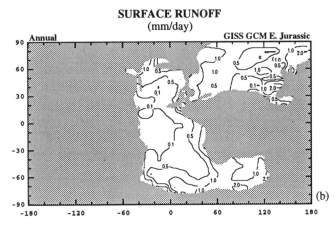

SOIL MOISTURE CHANGE
Uniform Grassland - Realistic Vegetation
(mm)

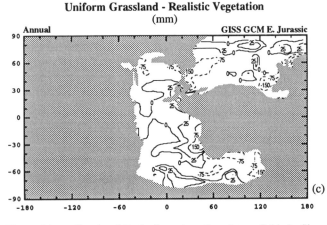

Figure 11. a, Simulated Early Jurassic soil-moisture field. b, Simulated surface runoff field. c, The soil-moisture change between the Early Jurassic simulation with "realistic" vegetation and an Early Jurassic simulation having uniform grassland-type (see Table 2) vegetation cover.

also poorly corroborated by the Early Jurassic simulation, although minor peats could easily be related to orographic, fluvial, or convective phenomena that are below GCM resolution (Chandler et al., 1992). Differencing the precipitation and evaporation fields yields a very poor representation of the sedimentary deposits, underestimating the extent of continental desert. As explained for the modern climates, the GCM formulation for evaporation does not allow evaporation to exceed precipitation in the absence of soil moisture; negative values of P-E are thus impossible over the continents for a model in equilibrium. Only coastal grid cells, which in the GISS GCM are defined to contain a fractional amount of ocean, have unlimited moisture availability for evaporation and can, therefore, have negative P-E values (Fig. 10b).

Soil moisture contours from 10 to 50 mm and surface runoff contours between 0.1 and 0.5 mm/day, which correctly define modern desert distributions, compare qualitatively to Early Jurassic aridity indicators in low-latitude western Pangea (Fig. 11a, b). Again, the central interior of northern Pangea is probably drier than indicated, considering the peat deposits found in that zone, a situation that mirrors a problem found with most of the hydrological variables over this region. Simulated Early Jurassic soil moisture and surface runoff values are, however, strongly controlled by the specified boundary conditions. Altering Pangea's vegetation characteristics, from those used in the original Jurassic experiment (see Fig. 9d) to a uniform grassland vegetation type, changes the specified water-field capacity of the ground (Table 2) and leads to a marked shift in the simulated soil moisture contours (Fig. 11c). Consequently, the usefulness of soil moisture and surface runoff in paleoclimate experiments is limited by the accuracy of the specified ground hydrology/land surface boundary conditions. The Pangean P-E$_p$ results are no more useful than they were for the present day; the entire supercontinent appears arid by this definition (Fig. 12a). Finally, Early Jurassic P-E$_{T_P}$ values (Fig. 12b) define the low-latitude and mid-latitude aridity in western Pangea, yet, as with other variables, north-central Pangea is simulated as semiarid, in defiance of the sedimentary record.

DISCUSSION

Ultimately, knowing which method to use in the depiction of hydrological regimes from simulated variables is difficult. Specific values, which approximately delineate desert boundaries, exist for precipitation, soil moisture, and surface runoff. Although variation from one desert to another exists, and researchers could select from a range of possible quantities, reasonable values are: P = 0.7 mm/day, S_m = 10 to 50 mm, and R_s = 0.3 mm/day. In addition, meteorological moisture balance diagnostics, such as P-E, P-E$_p$, or P-E$_{T_P}$ imply that an absolute value of zero should distinguish desert boundaries, although the modern simulations show inherent problems with using these differences. Working without being aware of these difficulties or of the complications associated with boundary condition dependence could make many disparate views of past desert extent possible: each supported, in some way, by GCM results. Figure 13 shows how, using the standard definitions for desert climatology given above, one might draw very different conclusions about the possible locations of Pangean deserts.

Although a reasonable amount of understanding about the models helps avoid blatant misinterpretations, regional desert extent would be nearly impossible to interpret based on the GCM results alone. Clearly, model/data comparisons are required, at this stage, to validate model representations of hydrological patterns.

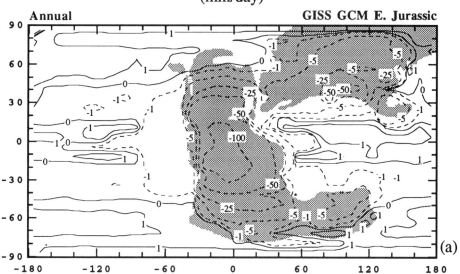

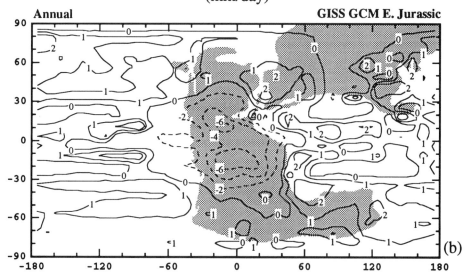

Figure 12. a, Simulated precipitation minus the GCM's calculated potential evaporation from the Early Jurassic experiment. b, Simulated precipitation minus Thornthwaite potential evapotranspiration (E_{Tp}). E_{Tp} is calculated from simulated surface air temperatures using the method of Thornthwaite (see text).

The missing moisture of north-central Pangea

The arid to semiarid depiction that the Early Jurassic simulation shows for the north-central region of Pangea is particularly troubling since most of the hydrological variables generally agree on the lack of moisture in that region. Yet, the existence of extensive peat and coal deposits in that region attests to the humid conditions that must have existed there during the Early Jurassic. Sensitivity experiments using altered topography, altered vegetation characteristics, and various sea surface temperature gradients fail to create moist conditions in the Pangean interior (M.A. Chandler, 1992, unpublished results). Increased levels of CO_2 might alter the moisture levels in this region; however, increased CO_2 poses additional difficulties for maintaining arid climates and realistic temperatures over low-latitude Pangea. The correlation between monsoon intensity and precessional cycles, identified by Kutzbach and Otto-Bliesner (1982), suggests the possibility that the geologic record in the north-central interior is biased toward a particular orbital configuration. However, their is another possible cause

of the erroneous arid climate depiction that is related to the GCM hydrological parameterization.

The GCM assumes that all surface runoff returns to the ocean (an infinite source and sink for water in the model). This parameterization is reasonable only for rivers that do not exchange significant amounts of water with aquifers or with the atmosphere prior to reaching the ocean. In some systems that is clearly not the case; for example, the White Nile loses approximately 60% of its water through evaporation in swamplands upstream from the city of Khartoum (Chan and Eagleson, 1980), and continental interior basins lose water solely through evaporative processes. If not included in the moisture balance for "downstream" grid boxes, an important aspect of regional water supplies may go unaccounted for. To test the importance of this distinction, the moisture balance for the interior of northern Pangea was reexamined (Fig. 9). Perhaps not coincidentally, this region is the only area in the reconstruction of Pangean continental topography surrounded entirely by grid cells containing higher elevations. In the GCM such a location is the equivalent of an interior drainage basin.

An estimate of the water that would collect in such a basin can be made by summing the surface runoff over all grid boxes of the interior drainage basin, R_{Sdb}, then dividing by the area of water accumulation, A_{ib},

$$(\textstyle\sum R_{Sdb}) / A_{ib} \tag{5}$$

In this case the region of water accumulation is defined as those grid boxes containing major peat deposits. Defined thus, the area of accumulating water is enormous ($A_{ib} = 3.33 \times 10^{12}$ m^2, or roughly 75% the size of the United States). Since it is assumed that the water covers that entire region uniformly, the value obtained should represent a minimum depth. Subgrid-scale topographic highs and lows would allow ponding in some localities, but in order to explain the peat accumulations, it will be enough to determine whether or not north-central Pangea could have sustained swampy conditions. Thus, the above equation provides a minimum estimate of the total amount of water that would be available, per day, to the peat depositional environments of north-central Pangea.

Figure 14 shows, schematically, the interior drainage ba-

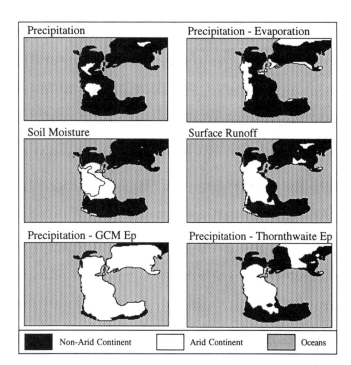

| Non-Arid Continent | Arid Continent | Oceans |

Figure 13. Hydrological variables that can be used to locate deserts in the modern climate or in modern climate simulations are not easy to interpret for paleoclimate scenarios. This figure shows how six diagnostic techniques yield drastically different views of Jurassic desert extent. Precipitation (0.7 mm/day), soil moisture (10 and 50 mm), and surface runoff (0.3 mm/day) values were chosen to coincide with values that gave reasonable depictions of desert extent in a modern climate simulation. Precipitation minus evaporation, precipitation minus GCM potential evaporation, and precipitation minus Thornthwaite potential evapotranspiration are moisture balance diagnostics that should, theoretically, be less than zero for arid climate locations. For several reasons this is not always the case (see text).

Figure 14. Diagram showing the values, by grid box, of boundary conditions and hydrologic variables that form the interior basin of northern Pangea (inset map shows location of grid boxes). Tabulated values are, from top to bottom: topography, percentage of grid box within the drainage basin, percentage land coverage in each grid box, aerial extent of each grid box (corrected for spherical geometry of the Earth), aerial extent of each grid box that drains toward the interior, surface runoff rate calculated by GCM for each grid box, and amount of surface runoff that drains toward interior. Surface runoff values from grid boxes that form the border of the basin are weighted to reflect the percentage of runoff flowing toward the interior. For example, a grid box with three out of four sides adjacent to other interiorly draining grid boxes would be multiplied by 0.75 before being added to the total amount of interiorly draining runoff.

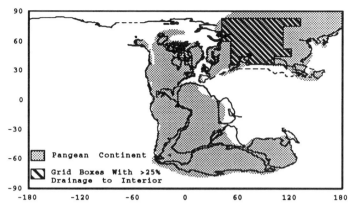

Topography (meters)									
lat/long	50	60	70	80	90	100	110	120	130
74	200	200	200	200	200	200	290	790	1100
67	200	200	200	200	200	390	2970		
59	360	200	200	200	850	1260	2860		
51		400	200	200	200	310	390		
43		280	200	200	200	280	1040	2480	
35		340		220	1050	880			

Percentage of Each Grid Box in Drainage Basin									
lat/long	50	60	70	80	90	100	110	120	130
74	0.50	0.75	0.75	0.75	0.75	0.75	0.75	0.50	0.25
67	0.75	1.00	1.00	1.00	1.00	1.00	0.75		
59	0.50	1.00	1.00	1.00	1.00	1.00	0.75		
51		0.75	1.00	1.00	1.00	1.00	0.75		
43		0.75	0.75	1.00	1.00	1.00	0.75	0.25	
35		0.25		0.50	0.75	0.50			

Percentage of Each Grid Box Covered by Land									
lat/long	50	60	70	80	90	100	110	120	130
74	1.00	1.00	1.00	1.00	1.00	1.00	1.00	1.00	1.00
67	1.00	1.00	1.00	1.00	1.00	1.00	1.00		
59	1.00	1.00	1.00	1.00	1.00	1.00	1.00		
51		1.00	1.00	1.00	1.00	1.00	1.00		
43		1.00	1.00	1.00	1.00	1.00	1.00	1.00	
35		0.82		0.87	0.50	0.58			

Area of Each Grid Box (square meters)									
lat/long	50	60	70	80	90	100	110	120	130
74	2.6E+11	2.6E+11	2.6E+11	2.6E+11	2.6E+11	2.6E+11	2.6E+11	2.6E+11	2.6E+11
67	3.8E+11	3.8E+11	3.8E+11	3.8E+11	3.8E+11	3.8E+11	3.8E+11		
59	5.0E+11	5.0E+11	5.0E+11	5.0E+11	5.0E+11	5.0E+11	5.0E+11		
51		6.1E+11	6.1E+11	6.1E+11	6.1E+11	6.1E+11	6.1E+11		
43		7.1E+11	7.1E+11	7.1E+11	7.1E+11	7.1E+11	7.1E+11	7.1E+11	
35		7.9E+11		7.9E+11	7.9E+11	7.9E+11			

Area of Each Grid Box Draining Towards Interior (square meters)									
lat/long	50	60	70	80	90	100	110	120	130
74	1.3E+11	2.0E+11	2.0E+11	2.0E+11	2.0E+11	2.0E+11	2.0E+11	1.3E+11	6.5E+10
67	2.9E+11	3.8E+11	3.8E+11	3.8E+11	3.8E+11	3.8E+11	2.9E+11		
59	2.5E+11	5.0E+11	5.01E+11	5.01E+11	5.01E+11	5.0E+11	3.8E+11		
51		4.6E+11	6.09E+11	6.09E+11	6.09E+11	6.1E+11	4.6E+11		
43		5.3E+11	5.3E+11	7.1E+11	7.1E+11	7.1E+11	5.3E+11	1.8E+11	
35		1.6E+11		3.4E+11	3.0E+11	2.3E+11			

Surface Runoff Rate Per Grid Box (mm/day)									
lat/long	50	60	70	80	90	100	110	120	130
74	1.11	0.94	0.75	0.58	0.33	0.40	0.07	0.50	1.30
67	0.93	0.79	0.68	0.46	0.24	0.40	0.81		
59	1.03	0.87	0.84	0.56	0.61	0.81	1.40		
51		0.93	0.77	0.18	0.47	0.25	0.51		
43		0.94	0.61	0.17	0.16	0.08	0.09	1.82	
35		1.01		0.08	0.38	1.01			

Surface Runoff Per Grid Box Draining Towards Interior (cubic meters)									
lat/long	50	60	70	80	90	100	110	120	130
74	1.4E+08	1.8E+08	1.5E+08	1.1E+08	6.4E+07	7.8E+07	1.4E+07	6.5E+07	8.5E+07
67	2.7E+08	3.0E+08	2.6E+08	1.8E+08	9.2E+07	1.5E+08	2.3E+08		
59	2.6E+08	4.4E+08	4.2E+08	2.8E+08	3.1E+08	4.1E+08	5.3E+08		
51		4.2E+08	4.7E+08	1.1E+08	2.9E+08	1.5E+08	2.3E+08		
43		5.0E+08	3.2E+08	1.2E+08	1.1E+08	5.6E+07	4.8E+07	3.2E+08	
35		1.6E+08		2.7E+07	1.1E+08	2.3E+08			

Total Volume of Water Draining to Interior (cubic meters)
8.70E+09

Amount of Surface Runoff Collecting In Interior Basin (mm/day)

2.61

sin of northern Pangea and includes values for the topography, land coverage, grid box areas (corrected for spherical geometry), and surface runoff amounts. Applying Equation 5 indicates that the moisture balance over the peat deposits within the interior of northern Pangea should include an additional 2.61 mm/day that is not accounted for by the model's current runoff parameterization. To put this into perspective, the total outflow from this drainage basin is approximately one-half that of the modern Amazon River basin or six times the size of the Mississippi (Fig. 15a). Even if the values are normalized to account for the large land area being drained (compared to the smaller, present-day continental drainage basins), the northern Pangean river outflow would still be comparable in magnitude to the outflow from major basins of the present (Fig. 15b). Assuming the runoff would drain toward the lowest points of the basin, it seems likely that some regions in north-central Pangea could have accumulated more than enough standing water to have maintained large lakes or swamps, a scenario more in agreement with the Early Jurassic coal deposits found in that region.

If ground hydrology models were capable of accounting for horizontal transport of runoff and subsequent ponding in low regions, then accumulations of standing water or increased ground moisture could generate feedbacks that might alter the simulated climate over northern Pangea. For example, studies indicate that climate feedbacks resulting from deforestation in the Amazon basin could increase surface temperature by up to 3°C and decrease precipitation by over 25%. Although this is not a one-to-one analogy, it serves to emphasize the potential importance of modeling ground hydrology appropriately and correctly specifying the boundary conditions.

SUMMARY AND CONCLUSIONS

Unlike temperature fields, several diagnostics are required in order to describe the hydrological state of the continents. The diagnostic fields most commonly used include precipitation, precipitation minus evaporation, soil moisture, surface runoff, and precipitation minus potential evapotranspiration. In this chapter I also present a method commonly used for modern hydrological analyses but, unfortunately, rarely applied to paleoclimate experiments. This technique uses an empirical equation for calculating potential evapotranspiration from the GCM's simulated surface air temperatures. Differencing this potential evaporation with the simulated precipitation field (P-E$_{T_P}$) yields a physically realistic diagnostic for analyzing model-derived moisture balances.

Each of the above hydrologic diagnostics supplies information about arid climate distribution, yet some of the diagnostics could be misleading, particularly in paleoclimate simulations. Some inaccuracies may be due to our incomplete knowledge of the past surface and subsurface conditions, which must be specified in order to initialize a GCM experiment. For example, soil moistures simulated by the model are

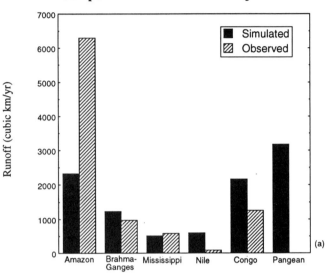

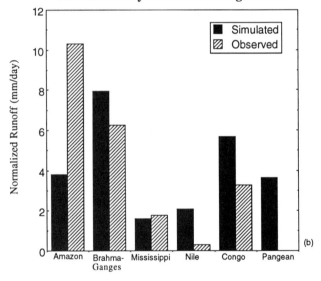

Figure 15. a, A comparison of total river runoff for major rivers of the present-day continents with a hypothetical Pangean river draining the northcentral interior basin. Both simulated and observed values are shown for current rivers (values for current rivers from Russell and Miller, 1990). b, As above, except runoff values are normalized by the size of each river's drainage basin. The large area drained by the Pangean river reduces its runoff/area but the river is still comparable to other major rivers of the present day. Considering that this runoff would all have gone into an interior basin, it seems likely that the north-central interior of Pangea must have contained numerous swamps and/or lakes.

not independent of the specified water-field capacities of ground layers. Such difficulties could increase as more physically realistic ground hydrology schemes, which require detailed specifications of soil and vegetation characteristics, become standard in GCMs. Other model-data mismatches are likely related to the GCM's imperfectly parameterized or absent physical processes. For example, the lack of a realistic treatment for surface runoff in the northern Pangean interior basin seems to have caused the GISS GCM to overestimate the aridity of that region; overestimated potential evaporation values cause P-E$_p$ results to give grossly inaccurate estimates of arid region extent.

To the first order, it is apparent that precipitation alone provides a minimum estimate of continental aridity, whereas P-E$_p$ yields the extreme overestimate. The P-E field appears to be accurate over the oceans but underestimates continental aridity. Soil moisture and surface runoff pinpoint deserts more accurately, but they are simplistically parameterized in models, reflecting a lack of observational data. P-E$_{T_p}$ provides a reasonable option for distinguishing modern arid regions, and it is a good candidate for use in paleoclimate experiments because of its close relation to physically based moisture balance calculations. P-E$_{T_p}$ is also desirable because it depends only upon simulated precipitation and surface air temperatures fields. Although precipitation fields are not as accurate as temperature fields, the current climate precipitation tendencies of most GCMs are well documented.

Above all, when examining simulation results, modelers and nonmodelers alike should remember that GCM diagnostics, like properties in the real climate, are potentially ambiguous, and no individual hydrological variable can be used to describe all climates, at all times. Paleoclimate model-data comparisons are likely to increase in the future, and it will be important to be selective, as well as inventive, in our analyses of simulated hydrological characteristics. In addition, the need for quantitative paleohydrological data must be stressed if we hope to advance our understanding of past climate processes to new levels of detail.

ACKNOWLEDGMENTS

This study was supported by the Climate Research Program at NASA. The author thanks D. Rind, T. Crowley, and an anonymous reviewer for their comments on earlier versions of the manuscript. C. Rosenzweig supplied the climatological data bases, and R. Ruedy and G. Russell provided advice on GCM operation. I am grateful to them all.

REFERENCES CITED

Abramopoulos, F., Rosenzweig, C., and Choudhury, B., 1988, Improved ground hydrology calculations for global climate models (GCMs): Soil water movement and evapotranspiration: Journal of Climate, v. 1, p. 921–941.

Alley, W. M., 1984, The Palmer drought index: Limitations and assumptions: Journal of Climatology and Applied Meteorology, v. 23, p. 1100–1109.

Barron, E. J., Hay, W. W., and Thompson, S., 1990, The hydrologic cycle: A major variable during Earth history: Palaeogeography, Palaeoclimatology, Palaeoecology (Global and Planetary Change Section), v. 75, p. 157–174.

Chan, S.-O., and Eagleson, P. S., 1980, Water balance studies of the Bahr El Ghazal Swamp: Cambridge, Massachusetts, MIT, Ralph M. Parsons Laboratory for Water Resources and Hydrodynamics Report 161.

Chandler, M. A., Rind, D., and Ruedy, R., 1992, Pangean climate during the Early Jurassic: GCM simulations and the sedimentary record of paleoclimate: Geological Society of America Bulletin, v. 104, p. 543–559.

Delworth, T., and Manabe, S., 1988, The influence of potential evaporation on the variabilities of simulated soil wetness and climate: Journal of Climate, v. 1, p. 523–547.

Dickinson, R. E., 1984, Modeling evapotranspiration for three-dimensional global climate models, in Hansen, J. E., and Takahashi, T., eds., Climate processes and climate sensitivity, Geophysical Monograph 29, Maurice Ewing vol. 5: Washington, D.C., American Geophysical Union, p. 58–72.

Glennie, K. W., 1987, Desert sedimentary environments, present and past—A summary: Sedimentary Geology, v. 50, p. 135–165.

Gordon, W. A., 1975, Distribution by latitude of Phanerozoic evaporite deposits: The Journal of Geology, v. 83, p. 671–684.

Greeley, R., and Iversen, J. D., 1985, Wind as a geological process on Earth, Mars, Venus, and Titan: Cambridge, Cambridge University Press, 333 p.

Hallam, A., 1975, Jurassic environments: Cambridge, Cambridge University Press, 269 p.

Hallam, A., 1984, Continental humid and arid zones during the Jurassic and Cretaceous: Palaeogeography, Palaeoclimatology, Palaeoecology, v. 47, p. 195–223.

Hallam, A., 1985, A review of Mesozoic climates: Journal of the Geological Society of London, v. 142, p. 433–445.

Hansen, J. E., and seven others, 1983, Efficient three-dimensional global models for climate studies: Models I and II: Monthly Weather Review, v. 111, p. 609–662.

Hansen, J. E., and seven others, 1984, Climate sensitivity: Analysis of feedback mechanisms, in Hansen, J. E., and Takahashi, T., eds., Climate processes and climate sensitivity, Geophysical Monograph 29, Maurice Ewing vol. 5: Washington, D.C., American Geophysical Union, p. 130–163.

Hillel, D., 1971, Soil and water: Physical principles and processes: New York, Academic Press, 288 p.

Holdridge, L. R., 1959, Simple method for determining potential evapotranspiration from temperature data: Science, v. 105, p. 367–368.

Kellogg, W. W., and Zhao, Z.-C., 1988, Sensitivity of soil moisture to doubling of carbon dioxide in climate model experiments. Part I: North America: Journal of Climate, v. 1, p. 348–366.

Kocurek, G., 1988, Sedimentary geology (special issue devoted to Eolian sandstones of the western United States): v. 56, Amsterdam, Elsevier.

Köppen, W., 1936, Das geographische system der klimate, in Köppen, W., and Geiger, R., eds., Handbuch der klimatologie: Berlin, Borntraeger, p. 46.

Korzun, V. I., 1978, World water balance and water resources of the earth: Paris, UNESCO Press.

Kutzbach, J. E., and Gallimore, R. G., 1989, Pangean climates: Megamonsoons of the megacontinent: Journal of Geophysical Research, v. 94, p. 3341–3357.

Kutzbach, J. E., and Otto-Bliesner, B. L., 1982, The sensitivity of the African-Asian monsoonal climate to orbital parameter changes for 9000 years B.P. in a low-resolution general circulation model: Journal of the Atmospheric Sciences, v. 39, p. 1177–1188.

Kutzbach, K. E., and Street-Perrott, F. A., 1985, Milankovitch forcing of fluctuations in the level of tropical lakes from 18 to 0 kyr BP: Nature, v. 317, p. 130–134.

Legates, D. R., and Willmott, C. J., 1990, Mean seasonal and spatial variability in gauge-corrected, global precipitation: International Journal of

Climatology, v. 10, p. 111–127.

Lézine, A.-M., Casanova, J., and Hillaire-Marcel, C., 1990, Across an early Holocene humid phase in western Sahara: Pollen and isotope stratigraphy: Geology, v. 18, p. 264–267.

Manabe, S., 1969, Climate and ocean circulation. I: The atmospheric circulation and the hydrology of the earth's surface: Monthly Weather Review, v. 97, p. 739–774.

Manabe, S., and Wetherald, R., 1986, Reduction in summer soil wetness induced by an increase in atmospheric carbon dioxide: Science, v. 232, p. 626–628.

Manabe, S., Smagorinsky, J., and Strickler, R. F., 1965, Simulated climatology of a general circulation model with a hydrologic cycle: Monthly Weather Review, v. 93, p. 769–798.

Matthews, E., 1984, Prescription of land-surface boundary conditions in GISS GCM II: A simple method based on high-resolution vegetation data bases: NASA Goddard Space Flight Center Institute for Space Studies, NASA Technical Memorandum 86096, 20 p.

Milly, P.C.D., 1992, Potential evaporation and soil moisture in general circulation models: Journal of Climate, v. 5, p. 209–226.

Mitchell, J.F.B., 1983, The seasonal response of a general circulation model to changes in CO_2 and sea surface temperature: Journal of the Royal Meteorological Society, v. 109, p. 113–152.

Mitchell, J.F.B., Wilson, C. A., and Cunnington, W. M., 1987, On climate sensitivity and model dependence of results: Quarterly Journal of the Royal Meteorological Society, v. 113, p. 1–30.

Moore, G. T., Hayashida, D. N., Ross, C. A., and Jacobson, S. R., 1992, Paleoclimate of the Kimmeridgian/Tithonian (Late Jurassic) world. 1: Results using a general circulation model: Palaeogeography, Palaeoclimatology, Palaeoecology, v. 93, p. 113–150.

Nicholson, S. E., and Flohn, H., 1980, African environmental and climatic changes and the general atmospheric circulation in Late Pleistocene and Holocene: Climatic Change, v. 2, p. 313–348.

Palmer, W. C., 1965, Meteorological drought: U.S. Weather Bureau (available from Library and Information Service Division, NOAA, Washington, D.C.).

Parrish, J. T., Ziegler, A. M., and Scotese, C. R., 1982, Rainfall patterns and the distribution of coals and evaporites in the Mesozoic and Cenozoic: Palaeogeography, Palaeoclimatology, Palaeoecology, v. 40, p. 67–101.

Penman, H. L., 1948, Natural evaporation from open water, bare soil, and grass: Proceedings of the Royal Society A, London Series, v. 193, p. 102–122.

Pitcher, E. J., Malone, R. C., Ramanathan, V., Blackmon, M. L., Puri, K., and Bourke, W., 1983, January and July simulations with a spectral general circulation model: Journal of the Atmospheric Sciences, v. 40, p. 580–604.

Rasool, S. I., 1984, On dynamics of deserts and climate, Houghton, J. T., ed., The global climate: Cambridge, Cambridge University Press, p. 107–120.

Rind, D., 1982, The influence of ground moisture conditions in North America on summer climate as modeled in the GISS GCM: Monthly Weather Review, v. 110, p. 1487–1494.

Rind, D., 1984, The influence of vegetation on the hydrologic cycle in a global climate model, in Hansen, J. E., and Takahashi, T., eds., Climate processes and climate sensitivity, Geophysical Monograph 29, Maurice Ewing vol. 5: Washington, D.C., American Geophysical Union, p. 73–91.

Rind, D., 1990, The paleo-record: How useful is it in testing Models? in Bradley, R. S., ed., Global changes of the past (papers arising from the 1989 OIES Global Change Institute, Snowmass, Colorado): Boulder, Colorado, UCAR/Office of Interdisciplinary Earth Studies, p. 397–420.

Rind, D., Goldberg, R., Hansen, J., Ruedy, R., and Rosenzweig, C., 1990, Potential evapotranspiration and the likelihood of future drought: Journal of Geophysical Research, v. 95, p. 9983–10004.

Rind, D., Rosenzweig, C., and Goldberg, R., 1992, Modelling the hydrological cycle in assessments of climate change: Nature, v. 358, p. 119–122.

Russell, G. L., and Miller, J. R., 1990, Global river runoff calculated from a global atmospheric general circulation model: Journal of Hydrology, v. 117, p. 241–254.

Sellers, P. J., Mintz, Y., Sud, Y. C., and Dalcher, A., 1986, A simple biosphere model (SiB) for use within general circulation models: Journal of the Atmospheric Sciences, v. 43, p. 505–531.

Shukla, J., and Mintz, Y., 1982, Influence of land-surface evapotranspiration on the Earth's climate: Science, v. 215, p. 1498–1501.

Street-Perrott, F. A., and Harrison, S. P., 1984, Temporal variations in lake levels since 30,000 yr BP—An index of the global hydrological cycle, in Hansen, J. E., and Takahashi, T., eds., Climate processes and climate sensitivity: Washington, D.C., American Geophysical Union, Geophysical Monograph 29, Maurice Ewing v. 5, p. 118–129.

Sud, Y. C., and Smith, W. E., 1985, The influence of surface roughness of deserts on the July circulation: Boundary Layer Meteorology, v. 33, p. 15–49.

Thornthwaite, C. W., 1948, An approach toward a rational classification of climate: Geographical Review, v. 38, p. 55–89.

Valdes, P. J., and Sellwood, B. W., 1992, A palaeoclimate model for the Kimmeridgian: Palaeogeography, Palaeoclimatology, Palaeoecology, v. 95, p. 47–72.

Voice, M. E., and Hunt, B. G., 1984, A study of the dynamics of drought initiation using a global general circulation model: Journal of Geophysical Research, v. 89, p. 9504–9520.

Wallace, J. M., and Hobbs, P. V., 1977, Atmospheric Science: An Introductory Survey: Orlando, Academic Press, 467 p.

Washington, W. M., 1983, Surface hydrology and ocean coupling to the community climate model (CCM): Boulder, Colorado, NCAR 8041/82-2E.

Washington, W. M., and Meehl, G. A., 1984, Seasonal cycle experiment on the climate sensitivity due to a doubling of CO_2 with an atmospheric general circulation model coupled to a simple mixed-layer ocean model: Journal of Geophysical Research, v. 89, p. 9475–9503.

Willmott, C., Rowe, C., and Mintz, Y., 1985, Climatology of the terrestrial seasonal water cycle: Journal of Climatology, v. 5, p. 589–606.

Wilson, C. A., and Mitchell, J.F.B., 1986, A $2 \times CO_2$ sensitivity experiment with a global climate model coupled to a simple ocean: Bracknell, England, United Kingdom Meteorological Office, Dynamical Climatology Technical Note.

Zhao, Z.-C, and Kellogg, W. W., 1988, Sensitivity of soil moisture to doubling of carbon dioxide in climate model experiments. Part II: The Asian monsoon region: Journal of Climate, v. 1, p. 367–378.

Ziegler, A. M., Scotese, C. R., and Barrett, S. F., 1983, Mesozoic and Cenozoic Paleogeographic Maps, in P. Brosche, and Sündermann, J., eds., Tidal friction and the earth's rotation II: Berlin, Springer-Verlag, p. 240–252.

Zinderen Bakker, E. M., van, 1975, The origin and palaeoenvironment of the Namib Desert biome: Journal of Biogeography, v. 2, p. 65–73.

MANUSCRIPT ACCEPTED BY THE SOCIETY MAY 14, 1993

Geological Society of America
Special Paper 288
1994

The climatic evolution of India and Australia from the Late Permian to mid-Jurassic: A comparison of climate model results with the geologic record

Peter J. Fawcett and Eric J. Barron
Earth System Science Center and Department of Geosciences, The Pennsylvania State University, University Park, Pennsylvania 16802
Vaughn D. Robison and Barry J. Katz
Texaco Inc., Exploration and Production Technology Division, 3901 Briarpark, Houston, Texas 77042

ABSTRACT

The climatic evolution of the Indian and Australian continents from the Late Permian to Jurassic is simulated using a version of the National Center for Atmospheric Research Community Climate Model (CCM). The purpose is to evaluate the effects of changing model boundary conditions on climate for the time of the supercontinent Pangea. The results of four simulations for three time slices (Permian, Triassic, and Jurassic) address the importance of changes in paleogeography (land-sea distribution or topography) and atmospheric CO_2.

The CCM simulations predict significant changes in a number of climatic variables through time. The predominant feature of the Pangean simulations is a pronounced continental seasonality in temperature, especially at mid-latitudes. For India and Australia, the seasonality is most pronounced for the high CO_2 Permian simulation with warm to hot summers and winters well below freezing. As the southern Pangean landmass drifts northward during the Triassic and Jurassic, this seasonality is reduced.

In all four simulations, most of the Pangean interior is predicted to be very dry. India and Australia, however, are predicted to be consistently wet, being located on the southern margin of the Tethys Sea. This corresponds well with large coal deposits found on both continents, particularly Australia. A large summer thermal low-pressure cell over the southern hemisphere landmass brings monsoonal rains to the southwestern margin of Tethys (India and East Africa). For the two Permian simulations this monsoonal circulation is sensitive to the presence of seaways and atmospheric CO_2 levels. The simulated summer monsoon is most intense for the Triassic over India, which corresponds well with numerous features in Triassic Indian sediments indicative of a monsoonal climate. The strong winter temperature contrasts between the southern Gondwana landmass and the subtropical Tethys Ocean forces a zone of intense storm activity along the continental margin. This corresponds well with a number of storm deposits found in the geologic record at these locations from the Permian through the Jurassic.

The CCM predictions correlate with the paleoclimatic records of India and Australia to a first order over this time interval. The results provide many insights into the sensitivity of climate to boundary conditions typical for the Pangean time period.

Fawcett, P. J., Barron, E. J., Robison, V. D., and Katz, B. J., 1994, The climatic evolution of India and Australia from the Late Permian to mid-Jurassic: A comparison of climate model results with the geologic record, *in* Klein, G. D., ed., Pangea: Paleoclimate, Tectonics, and Sedimentation During Accretion, Zenith, and Breakup of a Supercontinent: Boulder, Colorado, Geological Society of America Special Paper 288.

INTRODUCTION

Physically based climate models have a growing role as predictive tools in sedimentology, as is evident from demonstrated capabilities to predict past storm tracks and storm sedimentation (Barron, 1989a) and ancient upwelling-related regions associated with the deposition of elevated concentrations of organic matter (Kruijs, 1989; Kruijs and Barron, 1990). Although numerical models are dynamic in their computation of oceanic and atmospheric circulation, they are static at the scale of geologic time. Because of their complexity, they are executed for a "snapshot" of time based on specified conditions of geography and topography. For this reason, their verification has largely been limited to comparing predictions and characteristics spatially for particular time intervals. This is a major shortcoming because sequences of events are fundamental aspects of the geologic record. Thus, a temporal aspect become essential if the capabilities of climate models are to be utilized and evaluated fully.

The primary goal of this study is to simulate the climatic evolution of India and Australia, from the Late Permian to mid-Jurassic, during the time of the nonglacial supercontinent Pangea. Four time slices incorporating changes in paleogeography (topography and land-sea distribution) and atmospheric CO_2 content through this time span are presented. The climate model simulations are compared with the geologic records of India and Australia for each time slice to evaluate the predictions. We try to address three questions: Are first-order climatic effects (which should be observable in the geologic record) reproducible by the model? Can the model be used to evaluate possible mechanisms of long-term climatic change? If so, can the model climatic patterns for the supercontinent Pangea help explain aspects of the sedimentary record for this time range?

This last point raises an additional important question. Just how precisely can we define the climatic component of the multivariable sedimentary record? Many workers have addressed this question in the context of tectonic versus climatic control in sedimentary basins on scales ranging from the architecture of the basin itself down to the facies and petrology of the sediments within it (e.g., Dickinson and Suczek, 1979; Dutta and Laha, 1979; Suttner et al., 1981; Suttner and Dutta, 1986; Gaetani and Garzanti, 1991). They have shown that the complexity of the interactions between tectonics and climate makes it difficult to clearly separate their relative importance to the sedimentary record. By using a physically based climate model, we shall attempt to isolate the climatic component of the geologic record.

Several characteristics of India and Australia make these continents an ideal focus for this study. They have similar geographic "starting" points in the Permian from which they evolve through different tectonic/paleogeographic histories. Both are characterized by substantial changes in climate from the Permian to Jurassic, and both have a geologic record suitable for comparison with the model results.

Previous climate model studies relevant to Pangea

The Pangean supercontinent existed for some 100 million years from the time of its accretion in the Early Permian to its final breakup in the Jurassic. It stretched nearly from pole to pole and, except for the partially enclosed Tethys Sea, occurred in a single world ocean. As such, it should have produced climatic conditions very different from the present day.

There have been several efforts at reconstructing the paleoclimates of this time period, but only recently have various types of climate models been applied to the problem of Pangean climates. These studies range from qualitative models based on analogy with the present day (Parrish and Curtis, 1982; Parrish et al., 1986; Patzkowsky et al., 1991) to energy-balance models that describe climate as a steady-state balance between incoming solar radiation, outgoing terrestrial radiation, and poleward heat transport (e.g., Crowley et al., 1987; Crowley et al., 1989; Hyde et al., 1990) to fully resolved general circulation models of the atmosphere and ocean (Kutzbach and Gallimore, 1989; Kutzbach et al., 1990; Moore et al., 1992; Valdes and Sellwood, 1992).

Differences in the types of models used and in boundary conditions selected to constrain the modeled climates (i.e., continental configuration, topography, atmospheric CO_2) make specific comparison of different studies difficult. Nevertheless, a number of large-scale, important features do stand out consistently from these model studies.

The most consistent feature of modeled Pangean climates is a pronounced seasonal cycle in temperature. Crowley et al. (1989) used a two-dimensional energy-balance model with a Late Permian continental configuration and predicted that the largest seasonal range in temperature for these boundary conditions was 50°C for a region of central Gondwana. Their model showed Gondwana summer temperatures exceeding 35°C for large areas of the continental interior. Kutzbach and Gallimore (1989) used a full seasonal cycle general circulation model with a more idealized Pangea (the supercontinent was symmetric about the equator) for both present-day CO_2 values and five times present CO_2 values. Their results showed a seasonal range of temperature exceeding 40 to 50°C over much of the continental interiors. Summer temperatures in both hemispheres exceeded 30°C at mid-latitudes, and for winter, freezing temperatures extended well into mid-latitude regions. The addition of higher CO_2 values increased summer temperatures but also warmed continental interiors somewhat during the winter.

Model results showing a high seasonal range of temperatures for the Pangean supercontinent are not surprising. Continents have a very small heat capacity, so their temperatures are mainly a function of solar insolation (dependent on latitude) and the advection of warm or cool air from oceanic areas by the atmosphere. With increasing continental size, the role of advection in moderating continental interior temperatures decreases. Thus, large continents at middle to high latitudes, where seasonal variations in solar insolation are most pronounced, will have large seasonal cycle amplitudes. This is a conclusion that apparently holds for so-called equable climate time periods, including the mid-Cretaceous and Eocene. Sloan and Barron (1990) described a series of sensitivity experiments with major climatic forcing factors, including oceanic temperatures, meridional temperature gradients, and continental topography. They found that subfreezing, continental interior, winter temperatures at middle and high latitudes could not be eliminated from the model results with any reasonable scenario.

Kutzbach and Gallimore (1989) also showed a pronounced seasonality in precipitation on the northern and southern margins of the Tethys Sea. In effect, the seasonal change in temperature drove a seasonal shift in large-scale surface pressure patterns from a low in the summer to a high in the winter. Because Pangea was specified in the model as being symmetric about the equator, the summer low-pressure cell was equally strong in both hemispheres and brought summer monsoonal precipitation to both Tethyan margins. This simulation also showed that because of the size of the landmass, most of the Pangean interior was very dry. In the higher CO_2 simulation for the same geography, the hydrologic cycle was intensified but the continental P-E balance did not change significantly. Moore et al. (1992) reported precipitation patterns for a Late Jurassic Pangean configuration using an early version of the National Center for Atmospheric Research (NCAR) community climate model. Their simulations showed that large parts of the Pangean interior were still quite arid and that the Tethys margin monsoons were restricted to the western margin of Tethys and to the southeastern margin of Asia.

In summary, a variety of climate model simulations suggest that the size and configuration of the Pangean supercontinent had a significant impact on the climates of that time, including a pronounced seasonal cycle in temperature, widespread aridity in the continental interior, and wet Tethyan margins with alternating summer monsoons.

Climate model description

The model used in this study is an early version of the NCAR Community Climate Model (CCM). It is a three-dimensional time-dependent atmospheric general circulation model based on the spectral climate model of Bourke et al. (1977) and McAvaney et al. (1978). The vertical extent of the model is 33 km with nine layers, and the horizontal dimension is represented by a global spherical grid with a resolution of 4.5° latitude by 7.5° longitude. Surface temperature is calculated from surface energy fluxes, and clouds are determined using the radiation-cloudiness formulation of Ramanathan et al. (1983). The model includes an explicit surface hydro-

logic cycle with soil moisture, surface runoff, and snow cover after Washington and Williamson (1977). The oceanic portion of the model consists of an energy-balance mixed layer that includes heat storage. This allows a realistic simulation of the full seasonal cycle (cf. Washington and Meehl, 1984). Sea ice forms and grows when surface temperature drops below −1.2°C.

For a typical full seasonal cycle simulation, the model is spun up for 12 annual cycles, after which the climatic parameters are in equilibrium. The results presented here are averages of the final three years of a 15-year run. The one exception to this is the high CO_2 version for the Permian, which was run for eight years only, with one year of climate statistics taken.

PANGEAN BOUNDARY CONDITIONS

Many factors that are external to the climate system must be specified in order for the model climatology to be appropriate for the time period considered. These factors, known as boundary conditions or forcing factors, include features such as land-sea distribution, topography, extent of land and sea ice, land surface albedo due to vegetation, amounts of radiatively active atmospheric trace gases (e.g., CO_2, CH_4,) solar radiation, and the seasonal distribution of solar radiation over the globe as modified by orbital parameters.

Paleogeography

We present here four simulations for three time periods: the Late Permian, the Late Triassic, and the mid-Jurassic. Paleogeographies (land-sea distribution and topography) used in these simulations, which are adapted from Ziegler et al. (1979) and Zieger et al. (1983), are shown in Figures 1 through 3. Although the paleogeographic maps shown here are for the entire world, we will focus mainly on the Indian and Australian regions for the maps of climatic parameters (below).

Figure 1 shows the two paleogeographic representations used for the Late Permian simulations. The Pangean landmass is asymmetric about the equator, with much more land in the southern hemisphere (Gondwana). In both cases, eastern Gondwana is centered roughly over 70°S latitude and extends over the South Pole. Topography is represented as low in the southern hemisphere, with the exception of a mountain range in eastern Australia. Figure 1a shows Gondwana as a large, contiguous landmass, whereas Figure 1b has prominent seaways between Africa and India/Antarctica and between Australia and Antarctica. For the purposes of this chapter, this is the major difference in geographies for the late Permian simulations. A second major difference in the two Permian simulations is the amount of atmospheric CO_2 used, and this will be discussed below.

Figure 2 shows the paleogeographic representation used for the Late Triassic simulation. Pangea is more symmetric

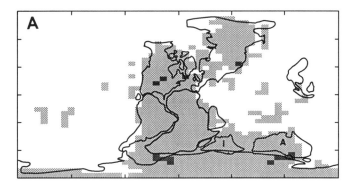

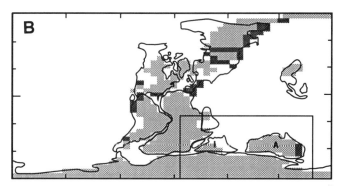

Figure 1. A, Late Permian paleogeography used for the high CO_2 simulation, showing paleopositions of the modern continents (solid lines) and the continents in model resolution (shaded). The light shade represents elevations of 400 m, the darker shade elevations of 1 km. I = India, A = Australia. B, Late Permian paleogeography used for the low CO_2 simulation, showing paleopositions of the modern continents (solid lines) and the continents in model resolution (shaded). Shading is as in Figure 1a. Differences between this paleogeography and that of Figure 1a are discussed in the text. The box outline shows the area of Figures 8 and 9.

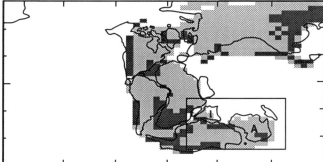

Figure 2. Late Triassic paleogeography showing paleopositions of the modern continents (solid lines) and the continents in model resolution (shaded). Light shade represents 400-m elevations, the darker shade elevations of 2 km. The box outline shows the area of Figures 10, 11, and 12.

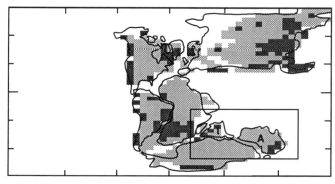

Figure 3. Mid-Jurassic paleogeography showing paleopositions of the modern continents (solid lines) and the continents in model resolution (shaded). Shading is as in Figure 2. The box outline shows the area of Figures 13, 14, and 15.

about the equator, with the Tethys Sea extending between 30°N and 30°S. Gondwana has moved north off the South Pole and has an extensive central plateau (southern Africa). Elevated topography is also present in southern India and southeastern Australia.

The mid-Jurassic continental configuration is shown in Figure 3. Of all the Pangean geographies represented here, this one is the most symmetric about the equator in amount of land area. The beginning of the breakup of Pangea is shown with the opening of the North Atlantic Ocean and a discontinuous seaway between Africa and India/Antarctica. The central Gondwanan plateau is still present as is the elevated topography in India and eastern Australia.

Carbon dioxide

The second primary forcing factor that is varied among the simulations is the amount of atmospheric carbon dioxide. Prior to the Pleistocene, no direct measurements of atmo-

spheric CO_2 and only a few indirect measurements using carbon isotopes are available (e.g., Cerling, 1991; Mora et al., 1991; Yapp and Poths, 1992). Various mass-balance models based on rock types and abundances have been used to reconstruct the history of CO_2 throughout the Phanerozoic. Budyko et al. (1987) used global volumes of carbonate and volcanic rocks at different time intervals to estimate pCO_2. Berner et al. (1983) and Berner (1991) developed CO_2 models for the last 100 million years and for the whole Phanerozoic, respectively. These models incorporate rates of sea-floor spreading (effective volcanic outgasing of CO_2) and the weathering of continental silicate minerals on the million-year time scale (effective removal of CO_2 from the atmosphere). The later version of the model (Berner, 1991) also incorporates rates of burial and weathering of organic carbon.

The amounts of atmospheric CO_2 explicitly used in these simulations are taken from Budyko et al. (1987) and are shown in Table 1. Although the exact numbers are not the

**TABLE 1. AMOUNT OF ATMOSPHERIC CO$_2$ SPECIFIED FOR
EACH OF THE FOUR SIMULATIONS**

Simulation	Atmospheric CO$_2$ Specified (ppm)
Late Permian, high CO$_2$	2,000
Late Permian, low CO$_2$	280
Late Triassic	1,000
Mid Jurassic	1,500

same as for the Berner (1991) analysis, the trends in rising and falling levels of CO$_2$ are of the same sense and magnitude. For the Permian continental configurations, we specified two very different levels of CO$_2$, one at preindustrial (Neftel et al., 1985) levels and one at approximately six times present day. This allows us to test the sensitivity of the model climate to CO$_2$ for this supercontinent configuration. The values for the Triassic and Jurassic simulations are higher than the present day—about three times and five times, respectively.

Other forcing factors

All other boundary conditions that must be set to constrain the modeled climate were held constant for the four simulations. Surface albedo was held constant for all land area, which means that no permanent land ice was specified and potential changes due to different vegetation zones were ignored. The condition of no land ice for the Late Permian and early-middle Mesozoic is supported by the disappearance of continental ice-sheet deposits by the Kazanian in Australia and other parts of Gondwana (Crowell and Frakes, 1975; Frakes, 1979). No evidence of land ice exists during any other of the time intervals of interest here. The formation of seasonal sea ice, however, seems to be a possibility for some of this time span, as shown by ice-rafted deposits reported by Frakes and Francis (1988) for the Middle Jurassic of Siberia. Although abundant evidence exists of very distinct floral zones during the Permian (e.g., Ziegler, 1990) and probably for the Triassic and Jurassic as well, we have chosen to ignore these in the model boundary conditions. For the present day, different vegetation types have a complex effect on climate in terms of albedo, evapotranspiration rates, water-balance feedbacks, and so on. Most of these features cannot be known for vegetation types from the Paleozoic and Mesozoic, so we have chosen a constant surface type to simplify this complex boundary condition. The amount of solar radiation is set at present-day values and current orbital parameters of eccentricity, precession, and obliquity are used to generate the latitudinal radiation distribution.

By choosing the above suite of boundary conditions, we are testing only the effect of changes in paleogeography and atmospheric CO$_2$ on simulated climates for Pangean time. As shown below, these changes in boundary conditions do produce

first-order changes in the simulated climates that can be tested against paleoclimatic reconstructions from the rock record.

CLIMATE MODEL RESULTS

The model results are presented as averages representing the seasonal extremes of June, July, August (JJA) and December, January, February (DJF). The CCM calculates a number of different climatic variables, but in this discussion we concentrate on surface temperature, precipitation, winter storm tracks, and sea-level pressure, because these have the most significance for the geologic record. In presenting these results, we focus mainly on the regions of interest: India and Australia. We do show the entire globe for the high-CO$_2$, Late Permian simulation to illustrate the effect of the supercontinent Pangea on global climate patterns.

The Late Permian (2,000 ppm CO$_2$) simulation

All previous climate model studies using a Pangean geography showed a pronounced seasonal cycle over land. So it is not surprising that the large landmass represented in this simulation also forces extreme seasonality in continental temperature, particularly at mid-latitudes. Figure 4 shows the seasonal sur-

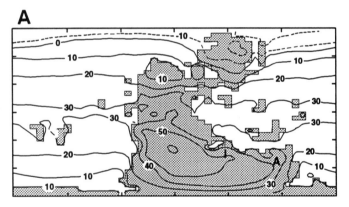

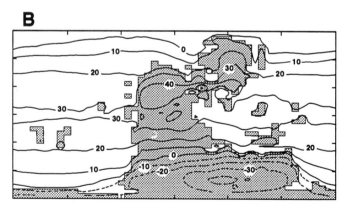

Figure 4. The simulated average surface temperatures for the Late Permian world (high CO$_2$ simulation): A, December, January, February (DJF); B, June, July, August (JJA). Temperatures are in °C, and the contour interval is 10°C.

face temperature distribution for the world. One of the most prominent features is the extremely high temperature (large areas of greater than 40°C and 50°C) of interior Gondwana for the southern hemisphere summer (Fig. 4a). These temperatures are higher than for any other Pangean simulation. Kutzbach and Gallimore (1989) showed summer temperatures in both hemispheres exceeding 40°C but not 50°C. This condition is undoubtedly due to the combination of the very large landmass and relatively high amount of specified CO_2. Most of Gondwana is well below freezing in the southern hemisphere winter (Fig. 4b). Again, this is a direct result of the large landmass with a low thermal capacity. The seasonal range in temperature for the interior of Gondwana goes from about 40°C to as high as 70°C. Note that large temperature gradients occur along the Tethyan margin of Gondwana in both seasons, but the steepest occurs in the southern hemisphere winter when the contrast between the warm, subtropical Tethys Sea and the very cold Gondwanan interior is greatest.

Equatorial land-surface temperatures remain fairly constant from season to season, ranging from 30 to 40°C. The northern hemisphere landmass also shows high summer temperatures in mid-latitude interior regions, but they are not as extreme or extensive as for the southern hemisphere. Most of present-day Siberia is below freezing in winter, whereas the rest of Laurasia is above freezing. The decreased seasonal range in temperatures for the northern hemisphere is attributed to the smaller Laurasian landmass. Equatorial sea-surface temperatures are just over 30°C—an increase of about 4°C relative to present-day observations. This is attributed to the higher atmospheric CO_2 levels.

Figure 5 shows the sea-level pressure patterns for the Late Permian geography. In the southern hemisphere, a large region of low pressure is centered over Gondwana for the DJF season. This region is produced by the high summer temperatures in the continental interior. High-pressure regions are found at the same latitude over the oceans. In the northern hemisphere a very zonal subtropical high pressure dominates at about 30 to 40°N. Poleward of this are two low-pressure regions over oceanic areas at about 60°N.

During JJA, northern Gondwana is dominated by a zonal subtropical high-pressure region, and the rest of the southern land area sits under high pressure produced by the cold continental interior temperatures. The northern Laurasian landmass is dominated by two low-pressure regions—one centered over North America and the other over Siberia.

The large variations in continental sea-level pressure from DJF to JJA illustrate the very seasonal nature of Pangean climates. The results of this simulation are similar to the sea-level patterns of the Kutzbach and Gallimore (1989) experiment, but the larger seasonal difference in the southern hemisphere reflects the presence of a larger landmass there.

Precipitation is one of the more difficult climatic parameters to predict accurately in a general circulation model (GCM) because it has a high spatial and temporal variability

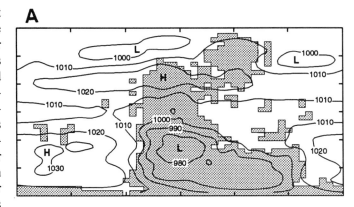

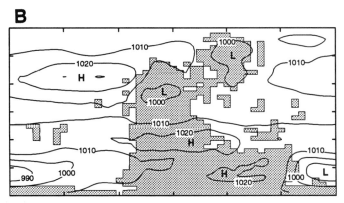

Figure 5. The simulated global distribution of Late Permian (high CO_2) sea-level pressure: A, DJF; B, JJA. Contour interval is 10 millibars.

in nature. The processes that govern precipitation occur at scales smaller than the coarse resolution of the model and hence must be parameterized. Previous modeling studies with the NCAR CCM have shown that large-scale features of precipitation are well simulated (Barron, 1989b; Barron et al., 1989). The major global precipitation regimes occur at the rising branch of the low-latitude Hadley Cell circulation (the Inter-Tropical Convergence Zone or ITCZ) and at mid-latitudes associated with the secondary meridional circulation and the position of cyclonic storm tracks. Desert regions are associated with the descending branch of the Hadley Cell in the subtropics. Areas of geographically forced precipitation, including orographic precipitation and monsoonal circulations associated with large land-sea thermal contrasts, are also well simulated by the CCM (e.g., Barron, 1989b; Schultz et al., 1992). Small-scale convective precipitation, an important component of the summer hydrologic cycle of some land areas (e.g., the southeastern United States), is poorly simulated (simulation results are too low).

Figure 6 shows the model-predicted precipitation patterns for Pangea. The most prominent feature is the extremely low continental precipitation. The ITCZ is well developed over the oceans in both seasons but breaks up over the equatorial land

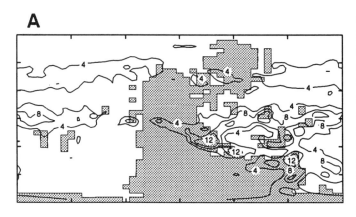

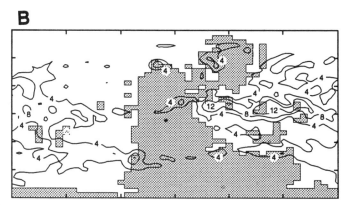

Figure 6. The simulated global distribution of Late Permian (high CO_2) precipitation rates (in mm/day): A, DJF; B, JJA. The contour interval is 4 mm/day.

area because the presence of land at the low latitudes severely restricts the availability of water for the atmosphere. The extreme aridity of the Laurasian and Gondwanan interiors is largely due to the size of the landmasses. Not only does their size produce high summer temperatures and consequently high evaporation rates, but the long distances from the oceans mean that most of the atmospheric moisture is lost well before reaching the interiors.

The deep thermal low-pressure region over central Gondwana in DJF brings summer monsoonal precipitation to the southern margin of Tethys, particularly over eastern Africa and northern India. Most of Australia is humid, with the highest levels of precipitation to the east due to the orographic forcing of the specified topography. Only a small portion of the northern Tethys margin is affected by summer monsoons, as the thermal lows of the northern hemisphere are evidently not deep enough to pull the monsoon far enough north. Precipitation associated with the mid-latitude storm tracks (see also Figure 7) occurs across the northern margin of North America, across northern Europe and Siberia, and across Gondwana at 40 to 55°S, centered over the India-Australia margin of Tethys.

Mid-latitude cyclonic storm systems are closely associ-

ated with the jet stream, which occurs where the average equator-to-pole temperature gradient is at a maximum. The greatest frequency and intensity of storms occur in the regions of strongest temperature contrast. The jets are not zonally symmetrical but are clearly linked to both land-sea distributions and associated thermal contrasts and the presence of significant topography (Blackmon et al., 1977; Reiter, 1961). Changes in paleogeography have been shown to have a significant effect on the location and intensity of the mid-latitude storm tracks in CCM simulations for the mid-Cretaceous and Eocene (Barron, 1989a).

The storm tracks calculated for the Late Permian paleogeography are shown in Figure 7. The northern hemisphere track is centered at about 50°N, with storms impinging on the Arctic coast of North America and cutting through the central Siberian block. The southern hemisphere storm track crosses central Gondwana through southern South America and southern Africa at about 40 to 50°S. It crosses northern India and Australia and is strongest off northeastern Australia. This southern hemisphere storm track is predicted to be much stronger than that for the northern hemisphere because the larger Gondwanan landmass produced much colder winter temperatures and hence a steeper temperature gradient.

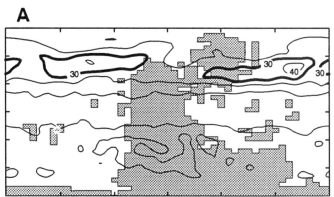

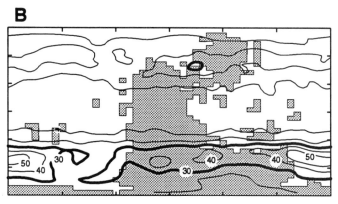

Figure 7. The time-filtered (2.5 to 6 days) standard deviation of the geopotential height (meters) field at 500 millibars, indicating the track of winter storms: A, DJF, B, JJA. Regions greater than 30 (heavy line) are considered significant storm tracks.

The Late Permian (280 ppm CO₂) simulation

As outlined above, the major differences between the two Late Permian simulations are in the amount of atmospheric CO₂ specified and in the seaways present between India/Antarctica and Africa and between Australia and Antarctica. This combination of factors does produce a significant change in the simulated climates for India and Australia.

Figure 8 shows the surface temperatures for northeastern Gondwana. Despite the reduced CO₂ relative to the first Permian simulation, there is still a pronounced seasonal cycle in temperature of up to 50 to 60°C in the continental interiors (e.g., central Antarctica). Summer (DJF) temperatures in central Antarctica exceed 30°C and reach 50°C in central Africa. Winter (JJA) temperatures drop to well below freezing in Antarctica and down to freezing in southern Africa. Although this temperature range is not quite as extreme as for the high CO₂ simulation (roughly 5 to 10°C less at mid-latitudes), it is still greater than any seasonal temperature range for the present day. Even though atmospheric CO₂ is a significant factor, the dominant control on the surface temperature of the supercontinent is evidently the size of the landmass.

An important difference for this simulation is that temperatures are significantly moderated for both seasons in the regions of the specified seaways. Summer temperatures do not rise above 20°C, and winter temperatures are just at or just below freezing. These temperatures are much more conducive to present-day plants and animals and, as will be discussed below, match the geologic record of life better in these areas.

The proximity of India and Australia to these seaways means that their summer and winter temperatures are moderated relative to the high CO₂/no-seaway simulation. Interior temperatures for both do not rise above 30°C for the summer, and winter temperatures are at or below freezing. Eastern Australia is colder than the rest of the continent in winter.

Because the temperature structure of central and eastern Gondwana has changed substantially in this simulation, the precipitation patterns should be expected to change also. Figure 9 shows the precipitation fields for DJF and JJA. The prominent monsoonal rains that were present over the southeastern margin of Tethys in DJF are much reduced over the margin of eastern Africa and no significant monsoonal precipitation affects India. We attribute this to a significant weakening of the Gondwanan summer low-pressure region produced by the splitting of high summer interior temperatures by the specified seaways. Australia is still relatively humid owing to its proximity to the Tethys Sea and its position with respect to the westerlies and has a regional precipitation high to the east, again as a result of the orographic forcing. In JJA, a broad band of precipitation that occurs over the northern margins of India and Australia is associated with the mid-latitude winter storm tracks. So, like the high CO₂ simulation, both India and

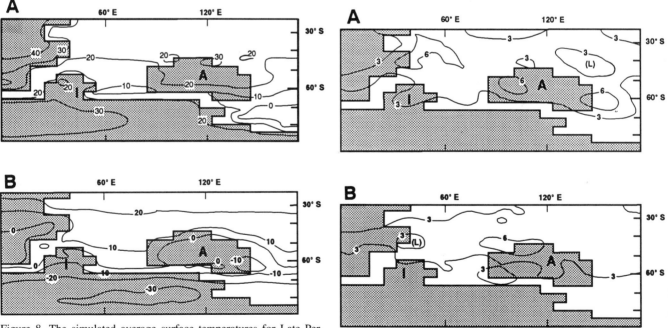

Figure 8. The simulated average surface temperatures for Late Permian (low CO₂ simulation) India and Australia: A, DJF; B, JJA. Parts of Antarctica and Africa are also shown. Land area is shaded (see Fig. 1b for continental outlines), and the contour interval is 10°C.

Figure 9. The simulated distribution of precipitation over India and Australia for the Late Permian (low CO₂): A, DJF; B, JJA. Contour interval is 3 mm/day.

Australia have an annually uniform precipitation regime, although the amount of summer precipitation is significantly reduced. India does not experience a monsoonal circulation.

The Late Triassic (1,000 ppm CO₂) simulation

The paleogeography used for the Triassic simulation has two major changes from the Permian paleogeographies: the representation of high topography for the central Gondwanan plateau (see Fig. 2; cf. Ziegler et al., 1983) and the more northerly position of Gondwana. Pangea is still a large, contiguous landmass (Fig. 2). The seaways present in the second Permian simulation are not specified here.

Again, the size of the landmass leads to a pronounced seasonal cycle at the mid-latitudes. Summer temperatures in central Antarctica (Fig. 10a) exceed 30°C, with a smaller area of temperatures greater than 40°C. The southern coast of Gondwana is much cooler because of its proximity to the sea-ice–covered South Pole. Both India and Australia experience moderate to warm summer temperatures. Winter temperatures over most of Gondwana are well below freezing (Fig. 10b). Only northern India and the northern Tethyan coast of Australia are above freezing. Note that the seasonality in temperature for India has decreased relative to Australia in this simulation and to that of India in both Permian simulations.

The continental interiors are still quite arid in this simulation, again because of the size of the landmass. Eastern Africa and India, however, are the sites of very high summer monsoonal rains (Fig. 11a). The strength of this monsoonal circulation is attributed to a very strong low-pressure region over south-central Gondwana, which is produced by the combination of high summer temperatures and the extensive plateau. This geographic situation is very analogous to the present-day effect on the Indian monsoon of the size of the Asian landmass in combination with the Tibetan Plateau. Most of Australia is also humid, with a precipitation maximum to the east, again produced by orographic effects. The only significant winter precipitation for Gondwana is associated with the winter storm track running along the southern margin of Tethys (Fig. 11b). The precipitation over India is limited whereas Australia is wetter. Thus, for this simulation, Australia is in an annually wet precipitation regime, whereas India goes through a pronounced seasonal cycle for precipitation due to the monsoon.

The close proximity of the warm, subtropical Tethys sea to the very cold interior of Gondwana in JJA produces a very steep temperature gradient across the Gondwana-Tethys mar-

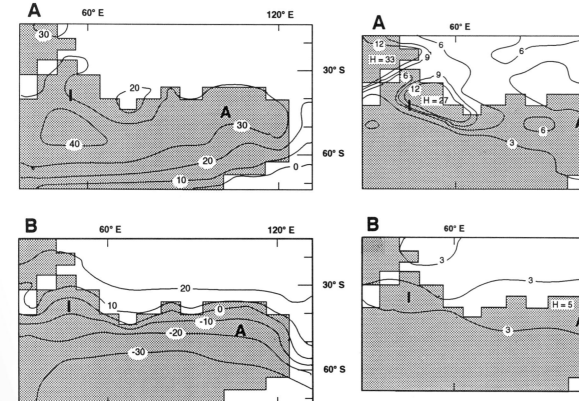

Figure 10. The simulated average surface temperature for Late Triassic India and Australia: A, DJF; B, JJA. Parts of Antarctica and Africa are also shown. Contour interval is 10°C.

Figure 11. The simulated distribution of precipitation over India and Australia for the Late Triassic: A, DJF; B, JJA. Contour interval is 3 mm/day. The highest contour shown is 12, and maximum values over this are indicated.

gin (Fig. 10b). This results in a very strong storm track that runs from southern India through central Australia. The track intensifies moving to the east (Fig. 12).

The mid-Jurassic (1,500 ppm CO₂) simulation

The paleogeography specified for the mid-Jurassic is not substantially different from that for the Triassic for Gondwana but does change considerably in the northern hemisphere (compare Figs. 2 and 3). Gondwana sits at roughly the same latitude, and the central Gondwanan Plateau is still present. There is a partial seaway between Africa and India/Antarctica.

The biggest difference between the Triassic and Jurassic simulations is in winter (JJA) surface temperatures. For the Jurassic case, over half of Australia is still below freezing but does not drop below –10°C (Fig. 13b). The Triassic case was much colder, with most of Australia well below –10°C. India's winter temperature pattern for the Jurassic (Fig. 13b) is not much different than that for the Triassic. The summer temperatures of both India and Australia for the Jurassic (Fig. 13a) are also not much different from the Triassic.

This difference in Australian winter temperatures is something of an enigma because the regional (Gondwanan) geography has not changed significantly from the Triassic to Jurassic, and as already reported for the Permian case, changing atmospheric CO₂ does not affect continental interior temperatures this much. We can only postulate that the specified higher CO₂ in the Jurassic kept winter sea-surface temperatures at high latitudes above freezing. Sea ice did not form south and east of Australia, and thus temperatures on the southern margin were considerably moderated relative to the Triassic.

The summer monsoons over India and east Africa are present again in this simulation (Fig. 14a). Although not quite as intense as for the Late Triassic case, they are still quite strong. Australia is wet once again, with abundant orographic precipitation to the east. The continental interiors (e.g., Antarctica) are fairly arid. As for the Triassic, the combination of warm summer temperatures and the Gondwanan Plateau makes the southern margin of Tethys quite humid.

The winter precipitation pattern for the Jurassic is shown in Figure 14b. For this simulation, both India and Australia lie under the mid-latitude storm track and receive 3 mm/day or more precipitation. Higher values of precipitation occur in central India and along the northern coast of Australia. Thus, both continents can be characterized as annually wet, although both receive significantly more precipitation in the summer months.

The winter temperature gradient between the interior of Gondwana and the Tethys Sea is reduced relative to the Triassic simulation. The winter storm track associated with this gradient is therefore also reduced in intensity and shows a slight shift in location from southeastern India to north-central Australia (Fig. 15).

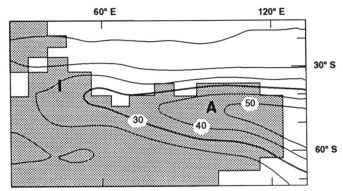

Figure 12. The simulated track of winter storms (JJA) over India and Australia for the Late Triassic.

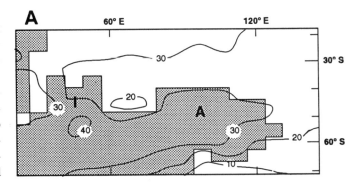

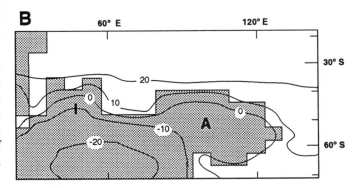

Figure 13. The simulated average surface temperature for mid-Jurassic India and Australia: A, DJF; B, JJA. Parts of Antarctica and Africa are also shown. Contour interval is 10°C.

RECONSTRUCTION OF PANGEAN PALEOCLIMATES

Several reviews of the climates of Pangea have been reconstructed from the geologic record. Robinson (1973) used the distribution of evaporites and coals to infer arid and humid zones and the distribution of continental red beds to infer regions of alternating wet and dry seasons. Gordon (1975)

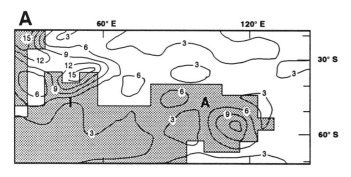

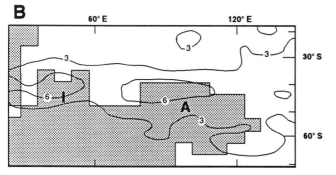

Figure 14. The simulated distribution of precipitation over India and Australia for the mid-Jurassic: A, DJF; B, JJA. Contour interval is 3 mm/day.

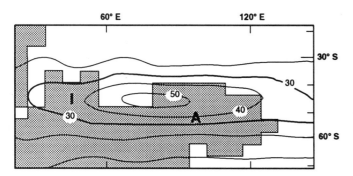

Figure 15. The simulated track of winter storms (JJA) over India and Australia for the mid-Jurassic.

examined the distribution of evaporites throughout the Phanerozoic and found that the Permian to Jurassic was characterized by a higher rate of evaporite accumulation than times before or after. These results were attributed to the presence of Pangea, with its exceptional expanse of land in the tropics and subtropics. Van Houten (1982) also inferred widespread low-latitude aridity, based on the dominance of calcrete in the continental tropics. Frakes (1979) described Permian climates as cool and humid, with a warming and drying trend into the

Triassic. Both the Triassic and Jurassic were inferred to have been much warmer and drier than the present day, based on a variety of indicators. Frakes (1979) and Hallam (1985) have described climates of the Triassic and Jurassic as being appreciably more equable than the Quaternary. This interpretation is based in part on warm oxygen-isotope paleotemperatures and diverse fossil forests at relatively high latitudes. However, modeling results by Chandler et al. (1992) and Moore et al. (1992) for the Early and Late Jurassic respectively show mid-to high-latitude continental interior temperatures to be strongly seasonal. Ziegler (1990) gives a detailed phytogeographic reconstruction for the Permian that shows a very strong climatic differentiation for Pangea.

The Permian

The Permian is one of the most interesting time intervals in the Phanerozoic from a paleoclimatic perspective. It contains a variety of climatic indicators, including tillites, coals, and unique floras in Gondwana and evaporites, red beds, coals, and reefs in Laurasia. Together, these indicators show a profound change in climate from widespread glaciation in the southern hemisphere at the start of the Permian to warm, generally dry conditions at the close of the period.

The classic Permian stratigraphic sequence for the southern Gondwanan continents starts at the base with glacial tillites that pass upward into fluvial sandstones, shales, and very extensive coal deposits. The coals on all of these continents are largely composed of *Glossopteris,* a seedfernlike plant.

The distribution of coals and evaporites for the Permian is shown in Figure 16 (data from Habicht, 1979). When compared with the CCM-predicted precipitation fields (Fig. 6), a striking correspondence in wet and dry regions is noted. Evaporites are found in Europe, western North America, and throughout central South America. All of these regions were predicted to be very dry. Two major coal belts are present, one running through central Siberia in the northern hemisphere and the other running through northeastern and central Gond-

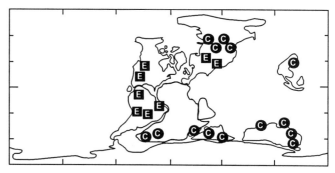

Figure 16. A global distribution of coals (C) and evaporites (E) in the Late Permian. Data from Habicht (1979).

wana. Both of these belts correspond to predicted zones of high annual (everwet) precipitation at the mid-latitudes.

As a proxy indicator for large storms in the Permian we use hummocky cross-stratification (HCS). Its mode of formation, either by severe winter storms or by hurricanes, has been the subject of some debate (Marsaglia and Klein, 1983; Duke, 1985, 1986; Klein and Marsaglia, 1986; Swift and Nummedal, 1986). Both types of storms generate surface waves large enough to produce oscillatory-dominant or multidirectional flows at the base of the water column to depths greater than normal shallow marine processes. Thus, the type of generating storm cannot be distinguished by features in the sedimentary structure itself, so the above debate has centered on paleogeographic and paleoclimatic controls on severe storms. In a previous climate model study for the Cretaceous, Barron (1989a) found that changing climate and geography does strongly affect the rates of generation and the distributions of severe storms.

Figure 17 shows the distribution of shallow marine hummocky cross-stratified sandstones and siltstones reported for the Late Permian by Arditto (1985), Bull and Cas (1989), and Moore and Hocking (1983) for Australia; Bhattacharya et al. (1989) for India; Vos and Hobday (1977) for South Africa; Della-Favera (1987) for Brazil; Kaldi (1980) for England; and B. Beauchamp, personal communication (1992) for the Sverdrup Basin, Northwest Territories. The most striking feature of this compilation is the preponderance of HCS reported in the southern hemisphere, in particular along the southern margin of the Tethys Sea. A comparison with the model predictions for the Late Permian (Figs. 7a and b) shows that all of the southern hemisphere localities fall under the winter (JJA) storm track running along the Gondwana-Tethys margin. The example reported from the Sverdrup Basin in the northern hemisphere is just east of the winter (DJF) storm track. The one example found in England at a low paleolatitude was almost certainly formed by hurricane activity.

The Permian winter storm tracks were predicted to be more intense for the southern hemisphere than for the northern hemisphere because the larger Gondwanan landmass produced colder winter temperatures and hence a steeper temperature

gradient (Fig. 4b). This prediction is apparently borne out by the concentration of HCS in the southern hemisphere, although this represents a relatively small data base of points and the trend may reflect a preservational bias.

Paleoclimatic indicators for peninsular India are preserved in the Gondwana basins. These basins contain up to a 3-km-thick continental succession ranging in age from the Permian to Early Cretaceous (Albian). Information about the late Paleozoic and Mesozoic has more recently become available through studies of sedimentary successions preserved in the Himalayas (e.g., Gaetani and Garzanti, 1991; Gradstein et al., 1991). Australian paleoclimatic information is preserved in numerous sedimentary basins, from those fringing the stable, western craton on the western and northwestern coasts to the foreland basins in the east.

The Late Permian is one of the most important intervals of coal deposition for both India and Australia in the Phanerozoic. Thick coals interbedded with fluvial sands and mudstones characterize the Barakar and Raniganj formations of the Gondwana basins, and coals are widespread throughout Australia, especially in the eastern basins (Cooper, Bowen, and Sydney basins). The humid climate interpretation of these coals is also supported by the presence of enormous delta complexes in the Fitzroy basin and Bonaparte basin along the northwestern coast. These deltas indicate a well-developed drainage for a large part of Australia (Veevers, 1984). Other indicators from the same-aged rocks in India also show climates that are humid but cool to moderate in temperature. For example, the compositional maturity of sandstones interbedded with the coals of the Baraker Formation (expressed as quartz, feldspar, and rock fragment ratios) is indicative of a cool, yet very wet climate (Suttner and Dutta, 1986). A decrease in compositional maturity of sandstones in the Raniganj Formation relative to the younger Barakar Formation indicates a warming and drying of the Indian climate in the latest Permian. Detailed studies of the flora and fauna of this time range (Kar, 1976; Lele, 1976; Shah, 1976) also support a cool, humid climate for the Late Permian, with a subsequent warming and drying into the Triassic.

Analysis of marine faunal types and diversity throughout Australia shows a progressive warming from the Early Permian glacial phase to latest Permian warm temperate to tropical conditions (Dickins, 1978). During the Late Permian, eastern Australia was interpreted to be cooler than western Australia because of a lower faunal diversity and the presence of cold-water forms, including the pelecypod *Eurydesma* and the gastropod *Keeneia*. Several features of the coal-bearing rocks in the interior of Australia point to a seasonally cold climate. Most prominent of these is the predominance of the fossil plant *Glossopteris* in the coals themselves. *Glossopteris* is considered to have been a deciduous plant because numerous leaves have been found in fall-winter varved sediments, with no leaves found in the spring-summer varves (Gould and Delevoryas, 1977). The main trunk of *Glossopteris* also has

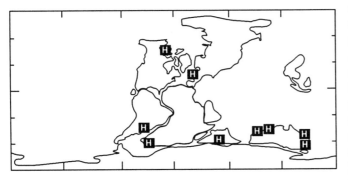

Figure 17. A global distribution of hummocky cross-stratification (H) reported for the Late Permian. Data from several sources listed in text.

prominent growth rings. The deciduous aspect of this plant is indicative of a strong seasonal cycle, and the association of *Glossopteris* with sedimentary periglacial features (cf., Archangelsky, 1990) has led to a cool temperate interpretation for climate. *Glossopteris* is in fact the dominant plant constituent of Late Permian coals throughout Gondwana.

Another feature of some Australian Permian coals thought to reflect paleoclimate is an unusually high amount (in some cases over 50%) of the coal maceral inertinite. Inertinite is thought usually to be produced by fire (i.e., charcoal), but in these particular coals, Taylor et al. (1989) attribute its formation to freezing winter temperatures. Their interpretation is based on the unoxidized nature of inertodetrinite (a form of inertinite unlike charcoal, which is highly oxidized) and an unusual structural alteration of the coal that is attributed to progressive gelification of the inertinite precursor by freeze drying. As additional evidence of freezing winter temperatures, Taylor et al. (1989) show imprints of ice crystals in sandstone above the Balmoral Coal Seam in the Hunter Valley of New South Wales.

The overall picture of India and Australia during the Late Permian is a cool temperate, humid climate. Several features are indicative of a seasonal range in temperature with cool to freezing winters. The widespread presence of coal and evidence of large continental drainage systems are indicative of annually high precipitation. Storm deposits are characteristic of the shallow marine fringes of both continents.

The Triassic

For the Triassic, abundant evidence exists for warm, dry climates over much of the Pangean landmass (e.g., Gordon, 1975; Frakes, 1979). The global extent of evaporite deposits reached a maximum in the Triassic, whereas coal deposition was reduced relative to the late Paleozoic and to later in the Mesozoic. Diverse fossil communities at high latitudes indicate temperatures not greatly different than equatorial temperatures (Frakes, 1979), so an overall global warmth has been inferred. However, most of these localities are proximal to the oceans and probably do not reflect conditions in the interior.

A drying of the Indian climate in the Triassic is suggested by the lack of coal deposits. The *Dicroidium* macroflora replaces the *Glossopteris* flora in the Indian Gondwana basins, and Lele (1976) interprets this flora as being indicative of widespread aridity and irregular rainfall. The Triassic sandstones of India have mature framework mineralogies that are indicative of warm, humid climates (Suttner and Dutta, 1986). However, these same sandstones contain significant amounts of early chlorite and smectite cements along with kaolinite. Dutta and Suttner (1986) interpret this cement assemblage to be a result of relative aridity where the ionic concentration of groundwater was high and smectite and chlorite formed in very early diagenesis.

Perhaps the most climatically diagnostic feature of the Indian Triassic sediments is the presence of continental red beds. Robinson (1967) describes a sequence of fluvial sandstones (containing channel forms and large- to medium-scale cross-bedding) and shales that contain a variety of semiaquatic vertebrates, including *Chasmatosaurus* and *Lystrosaurus* along with lungfish. The hematite cement that gives color to the red beds requires seasonal, high rainfall to leach iron out of the source rock, followed by a period of dryness to fix the iron in the oxidized state. These features, along with the presence of fern spores in the same rocks (Kar, 1976), led Robinson (1967) to infer a monsoonal climate with heavy seasonal rainfall followed by an extended period of dryness. The marine portion of the Indian Tethyan margin consists of carbonate ramp and platform sediments (Gaetani and Garzanti, 1991) that were deposited in a storm-dominated shallow marine environment.

An Early Triassic dry phase in Australia is shown by the lack of coal deposits. Coals reappear in eastern Australia during the Middle Triassic and become more extensive by the Late Triassic (Traves and King, 1975). Two plant microfossil assemblages are described by Dolby and Balme (1976) for the Middle and Late Triassic of Australia. In the Carnarvon basin of western Australia, the Onslow Microflora contains a diverse mixture of Gondwanan and European forms and is taken to represent a temperate rain forest. The Ipswich Microflora of southeastern Australia contains Gondwanan elements only, and its composition is not as diverse. It is taken to represent cooler temperatures than for the west. A detailed study of paleosols in eastern Australia shows a dominance of podzols, which Retallack (1977) ascribes to a cool temperate climate.

In summary, Triassic strata in India show a significant change in climate from annually humid conditions to pronounced seasonality in precipitation. Temperatures do not appear to have changed greatly, apart from some warming associated with increased aridity, and the Tethyan margin is still storm dominated. For Australia, an Early Triassic dry phase is succeeded by a more humid climate, and a temperature gradient is apparently developed from warmer to cooler, west to east across the continent.

The Jurassic

Like the Triassic, many features have been cited for Jurassic global equability in temperature (e.g., Frakes, 1979; Hallam, 1985) and for widespread aridity in the Pangean interior (e.g., Hallam, 1984). Although the oceans were apparently quite warm relative to today, the continental climates were not as uniform as earlier supposed, as shown by evidence of floral provinciality (e.g., Traverse, 1988). This calls into question the concept of climatic equability for the Jurassic.

The Indian climate evidently became warmer and more humid in the Jurassic, with a minor period of coal deposition in the Early Jurassic, although coal deposits are not found in the mid to Late Jurassic. Lele (1976) describes the characteristic Jurassic *Ptilophyllum* flora, which consists in part of cy-cadophytes and ferns, as suggestive of a hot, moist subtropical to tropical climate. The additional presence of conifers and Ginkophytes in this flora, however, reflects a more temperate climate. There is still evidence of seasonality in the Jurassic, as shown by prominent growth rings in woods (e.g., *Sahnioxylon*, Lele, 1976).

Jurassic-aged sediments in the Gondwana basins of peninsular India consist of supermature (99% quartz) quartz arenites with kaolinite and silica cements. These are inferred to have been formed in a very warm, humid climate capable of producing first-cycle quartz arenites (Dutta, 1976; Suttner and Dutta, 1986; Dutta and Suttner, 1986). Shallow-marine storm deposits including hummocky cross-stratification are reported from northwestern India, which was the Tethyan margin of the continent (Bose et al., 1986). A sequence of Upper Jurassic sandstones and shales preserved in the Himalayas was interpreted by Gaetani and Garzanti (1991) to represent a storm-dominated shelf.

Australia experienced a more humid climate in the mid to Late Jurassic, as shown by increased coal deposition relative to the Triassic, especially in the east (Traves and King, 1975). Filatoff (1975) describes the palynoflora of the Perth basin of Western Australia as indicative of a hot and wet climate for the mid to Late Jurassic. The deposition of a thick sequence of clastic sediments off the northwest coast of Australia (Habicht, 1979; Veevers, 1984) in the Jurassic indicates a well-developed drainage system and high runoff from the interior. The Early Jurassic experienced a drier phase, as shown by a period of reduced coal deposition (Traves and King, 1975) and a more arid palynoassemblage in the Perth basin (Filatoff, 1975).

Winter temperatures evidently were not as cold as in the Permian or Triassic because the inertinite component of Australian coals is much reduced relative to those earlier time periods (cf. Taylor et al., 1989). Although winter temperatures apparently were not as severe as for earlier Pangean times, storm beds with hummocky cross-stratification are reported from the Surat basin in Queensland (Fielding, 1989).

In summary, the geologic record shows a warm temperate to subtropical humid climate for both India and Australia in the mid to Late Jurassic. Winter temperatures were not as severe as in the earlier time periods considered, although the Tethyan margin of both continents still experienced severe storms. Coal deposition on Australia and first-cycle quartz arenites on India are both indicative of the high precipitation received by this region.

DISCUSSION

One of the major purposes of this study is to evaluate the model predictions of climate and climate change over geologic time for the supercontinent Pangea in general, and for India and Australia specifically. Here we address the questions of how much change in climate the CCM predicts in response to chang-

ing boundary conditions from the Late Permian to mid-Jurassic and how well the predictions match the geologic record. Also, we comment on what inferences can be made about the major controls on Pangean climates and how these affect the formation and distribution of climatically influenced sediments.

Predictions of climate change through time

When examined in chronological sequence, the four simulations discussed above do show significant changes in predicted climates for India and Australia (see Table 2 for a summary). Also some important aspects of the modeled climates remain fairly constant over this time interval. The changes in modeled climate occur in response to changes in particular forcing factors, including exposed land area, geography, topography, and atmospheric CO_2.

The Late Permian 2,000-ppm CO_2 simulation shows an extreme seasonal range in surface temperatures, especially at mid-latitudes. The interiors of India and Australia are hot in the summer months (although temperatures are not as exceedingly high as other parts of south-central Gondwana) and fall to well below freezing in the winter months. This extreme range in temperatures for central Gondwana controls the other major aspects of the modeled climate, namely the relatively high summer monsoonal rains over India and the location and intensity of the winter storm tracks along the Tethyan margin. Australia is humid overall, with the wettest region in the east due to orographic precipitation.

The second Late Permian simulation, with 280 ppm CO_2 and a modified geography, shows significant changes in both surface temperature and in precipitation amounts and location. The addition of the seaways in the vicinity of India and Australia reduces the seasonal cycle of this portion of Pangea dramatically. Winter temperatures still drop below freezing, but summer temperatures are much reduced relative to the first simulation. Moving away from the regional influence of the seaways, the interior temperatures of other parts of Pangea still experience a large seasonal cycle. The lower amount of CO_2 represented in this simulation does not appear to be a significant control on continental surface temperatures for the supercontinent, as the maximum temperature of this simulation was only 4°C less than that for the high CO_2 simulation. These results are in accord with some of the results of Chandler et al. (1992). In a series of sensitivity tests for the Jurassic using the GISS GCM, they found that increasing CO_2 to six times present-day value raised the maximum temperature of the continental interior by only 2.3°C. They also found that adding a large "hypothetical" lake in a sensitivity test produced the warmest continental interior temperatures in winter.

The reduction in summer temperatures in south-central Gondwana results in the disappearance of the Indian monsoon and a significant reduction in the amount of precipitation received. Relative to the rest of Pangea, however, precipitation is still quite high, and India remains wet in both summer and

TABLE 2. MODEL-PRODUCED TIME SERIES FOR INDIA AND AUSTRALIA vs. THE ENVIRONMENTAL RECORD

Time Interval		Model Climate	Reconstructed Climate
Mid-Jurassic	India	DJF: <30 to 40 °C As much as 15 mm/day precipitation JJA: -15 to 10 °C 3 to 6 mm/day precipitation	Humid, subtropical
	Australia	DJF: 20 to 30+ °C As much as 10 mm/day precipitation JJA: -10 to 5 °C 3 to 6 mm/day precipitation	Humid, warm temperate to subtropical
Late Triassic	India	DJF: 20 to 35 °C Very wet, as much as 21 mm/day JJA: -20 to 10 °C 3 mm/day precipitation	Warm, monsoonal
	Australia	DJF: 10 to 30 °C 3 to 6 mm/day precipitation JJA: -30 to 0 °C As much as 3 mm/day precipitation	Humid temperate
Late Permian (High CO_2)	India	DJF: 30 to 40+ °C As much as 12 mm/day precipitation JJA: -20 to 10 °C As much as 4 mm/day precipitation	Humid, cool temperate
	Australia	DJF: 20 to 40 °C 4 to 12 mm/day precipitation JJA: -30 to 0 °C As much as 4 mm/day precipitation	Humid, cool temperate subfreezing winters
Late Permian (Low CO_2)	India	DJF: 15 to 30 °C 3 to 6 mm/day precipitation JJA: -25 to 0 °C As much as 3 mm/day precipitation	Humid, cool temperate
	Australia	DJF: 10 to 25 °C 4 to 8 mm/day precipitation JJA: -10 to 5 °C As much as 4 mm/day precipitation	Humid, cool temperate subfreezing winters

winter. Eastern Australia remains wet as a result of the orographic precipitation. Discussion of which Permian simulation better fits the geologic record is deferred to the next section.

The Late Triassic simulation shows a high seasonal range in surface temperature—greater than the low CO_2 Permian simulation but less than the high CO_2 Permian case. Summer temperatures are warm to hot for India and Australia because this part of Gondwana has moved about 10 degrees closer to the equator since the Permian. Winter temperatures are very cold, especially for Australia, again because of the size of the landmass. The storm track over India and Australia is predicted to be the most intense for this time period because Gondwana has moved closer to the equator and sits adjacent to warmer waters, whereas its interior is still very cold.

The combination of Gondwana moving closer to the equator and the development of the central Gondwanan plateau produced a very strong summer monsoon over India. This monsoon is much more intense than that simulated in the first Permian case or for the Jurassic. India's winter precipitation is limited to a small portion intersected by the winter storm track. Precipitation over Australia in the Triassic looks

much as it did in both Permian simulations—high summer rainfall with the highest values in the east associated with the specified topography. Apart from these two areas, much of the rest of Pangea is very arid in both seasons, as in the Permian simulations.

The Jurassic simulation is similar in most respects to the Triassic for India and Australia because the geography of Gondwana has not changed significantly. The biggest differences between the two simulations are the warmer Australian winter temperatures and the higher Indian winter precipitation values, both in the Jurassic case. As discussed above, the warmer winter temperatures are most likely due to the higher CO_2 specified (five times the 280-ppm value), generating warmer sea-surface temperatures at high latitudes. This condition may also be responsible for shifting the location of the Jurassic winter storm track farther over India (relative to the Triassic case), which resulted in higher winter precipitation in that area.

In summary, we list those features of the simulated climates that do not change substantially over the time interval of interest, followed by those aspects of climate that are predicted to change over time. For all of the simulations, the seasonal surface temperature cycle is very pronounced at the middle latitudes of continental interiors. Widespread aridity in most of Pangea's interior is also common to all simulations. In contrast, the southern margin of Tethys receives DJF precipitation, with less in JJA over this time span—in particular, eastern Australia is an area of geographically (orographically) focused precipitation. The eastern Gondwana-Tethys margin is the focus of mid-latitude winter storm tracks that vary in intensity from simulation to simulation.

The addition of seaways to the Permian geography caused major changes in the predicted climate for India and Australia, including warmer winter temperatures, a dampened seasonal temperature cycle, and loss of the Indian monsoon and consequently reduced precipitation. Other areas of significant change include the development of a very strong monsoon over India in the Triassic and an intensification of the Gondwanan winter storm tracks, both due in large part to the migration of Gondwana closer to the equator. The specification of the central Gondwanan Plateau in the Late Triassic simulation is largely responsible for the divergence in predicted climates for India and Australia at this time slice. The proximity of this plateau to paleo-India in conjunction with the large Gondwanan landmass changes the climate of India from everwet to monsoonal. Australia, being some distance removed from the effects of the plateau, keeps largely the same climate regime. The Jurassic saw a decrease in the seasonal temperature cycle of India and Australia, largely due to a pronounced warming of interior winter temperatures. This result appears to be a function of increased atmospheric CO_2 rather than of any changes in geography.

Time-slice comparisons of simulations with the geologic record

A comparison of the major features of the Late Permian climate simulations with global distributions of climatically sensitive sediments has already been made. It was found that the distribution of coals and evaporites largely matched the model-predicted continental humid and arid zones and that the distribution of shallow marine hummocky cross-stratification matched the winter storm track belts surprisingly well. This gives us confidence that the CCM is indeed capturing at least the large-scale features of the Pangean climate. Table 2 gives an abbreviated summary comparison of the model climate predictions for India and Australia with the reconstructed climates.

Two simulations for the Late Permian have been presented here that show markedly different predictions of climate for India and Australia. The geologic record of both continents for this time indicates a cool temperate, humid climate. The deciduous nature of the *Glossopteris* plant and prominent growth rings in fossil woods of this time are the best indicators of a pronounced seasonal cycle in temperature. Subfreezing temperatures in Australia are apparently indicated

by the high inertodetrinite content of coals as well as by the report of ice crystal impressions. Both Permian simulations show substantial portions of India and Australia to be below freezing in winter, but the high CO_2/no seaway version predicts extremely high summer temperatures in the continental interiors. This prediction seems quite incompatible with a cool temperate climate. The problem of extreme summer and winter temperatures in this simulation is further exacerbated by the interpretation of a cool temperate climate for southern Africa from therapsid localities (cf. Parrish et al., 1986) and a sedimentological and palynological study of Late Permian lake sediments (Yemane, 1991). Neither of these studies shows evidence of hot or cold temperature extremes, and southern Africa sits in the heart of the Gondwanan seasonal temperature variation for this simulation. However, the presence of the seaway between Africa and India/Antarctica in the second Permian simulation moderates the seasonal cycle in these regions and thus fits the geologic record much better.

The northern margin of Gondwana was a very wet region in the Late Permian, in distinct contrast to the dryness of the rest of Pangea. Coal deposition was at a maximum in both India and Australia, and there are several other indicators of high annual precipitation. Both Permian simulations predict high annual rainfall for this region. Winters are wet, as a result of mid-latitude storm systems along the southern margin of Tethys, and summers are wetter still, with the subtropical Tethys Sea acting as a local moisture source. Summer precipitation is higher over India in the high CO_2/no seaway simulation because of the monsoonal circulation, but the amount of precipitation of the low CO_2/seaway simulation is sufficient to explain the humid indicators preserved in the rocks. The predicted high orographic precipitation over eastern Australia in both simulations coincides with the maximum thickness and extent of Australian coals. Although both Permian simulations capture the major aspects of the Late Permian Pangean climates, the low CO_2/seaway version fits the geologic records of India and Australia much better, in particular for the temperature inferences.

The climatic predictions for India and Australia start to diverge for the Triassic simulation. Compared to Australia, India has a reduced seasonal temperature cycle and warmer winters, but the biggest difference is in its strong monsoonal precipitation regime. Large quantities of rain are predicted for the summer months, whereas precipitation is reduced in the winter. Australia receives high amounts of rainfall in the summer and moderate amounts in the winter, characterizing it as everwet. The Indian Triassic record shows strong evidence for a seasonal alternation between high precipitation and relative aridity. Thus the predicted monsoon matches the record very well in this case. The Australian record shows strong evidence for annually humid conditions with rain forests and coal swamps, and it is again noteworthy that the greatest extent of Triassic coals on this continent are found in the east, where rainfall was predicted to be greatest.

The temperature predictions for both continents are largely in keeping with the cool temperate to temperate interpretations of the geologic record. The west-to-east, warm-to-cool temperature gradient inferred from microfloras across Australia matches a similar temperature gradient predicted by the CCM. Unfortunately, there are no reported HCS localities from either India or Australia for the Triassic, so the storm track predictions cannot be evaluated at this time. The Indian Tethyan margin, however, was interpreted to be storm dominated. Thus, the major aspects of the Late Triassic climatic predictions for India and Australia are borne out by comparison with the geologic records.

As discussed above, the Jurassic predictions for India and Australia do not differ greatly from the Triassic predictions, except for warmer Australian winter temperatures. This aspect of the Jurassic predictions seems to be borne out by the reduction in the amount of (cold-climate) inertodetrinite in coals of this age. The seasonal range in predicted temperatures matches growth rings in fossil woods.

Once again, the model prediction of high annual precipitation for Australia is well matched by features in the sedimentary record, the extensive coals in particular. In addition, the first-cycle quartz arenites and floras of the Indian Jurassic that are suggestive of warm, everwet conditions match the model temperature and precipitation predictions quite well. Hummocky cross-stratification localities are reported for the Jurassic Tethyan margin of both India and Australia and match the predicted storm track. Thus, many features predicted for the Jurassic climates of India and Australia are consistent with climates reconstructed from the rock record.

CONCLUSIONS

The climate predictions presented here are a first-order view of climatic change computed from basic physical principles in response to specific forcing factors. The model results suggest large and well-defined climate changes as a function of changing geography and atmospheric CO_2, which can be compared with the geologic record. The first-order predictions of climate and climate change for India and Australia from the Late Permian to Jurassic largely match the climates reconstructed from the geologic record. These results provide insight into the climate sensitivity of the supercontinent Pangea.

The most important control on Pangean climates was the size of the supercontinent itself, a factor that generated pronounced seasonality in continental surface temperatures at extratropical latitudes, controlled the locations of continental humid and arid zones, and controlled the location and intensity of winter storm tracks. The climatic changes experienced by India and Australia within the Pangean time frame are largely due to changes in geography, including the presence or absence of seaways, topography (i.e., Gondwanan plateau), and the drift of Gondwana toward the equator. Atmospheric CO_2 is apparently a secondary control on continental climates, mainly

because of the size of the supercontinent and its dominant influence on temperatures and aridity. This idea needs to be examined further, however, by testing the sensitivity of different CO_2 levels for the same geography on predicted climates.

All of the predicted climatic parameters discussed here significantly affect the generation and location of climatically sensitive sediments. The degree to which the supercontinent Pangea affected climates of the Permian to Jurassic is clearly reflected in patterns of sedimentation during this time range. This underscores the importance of considering climate in addition to tectonics when analyzing ancient sedimentary sequences. The use of physically based models can be a powerful tool of prediction for this type of analysis.

ACKNOWLEDGMENTS

This chapter forms part of a doctoral dissertation of the senior author, who gratefully acknowledges the generosity and assistance of Texaco Exploration and Production Technology Division, Houston, Texas, in providing three of the simulations discussed here (the Late Permian low carbon dioxide, the Late Triassic, and the mid-Jurassic simulations). The fourth simulation (Late Permian high carbon dioxide) was provided by the Earth System Science Center at Penn State. The manuscript was improved considerably after helpful reviews by R. Slingerland, M. Patzkowsky, T. Crowley, and G. Moore.

REFERENCES CITED

Archangelsky, S., 1990, Plant distribution in Gondwana during the Late Paleozoic, *in* Taylor, T. N., and Taylor, E. L., eds., Antarctic paleobiology: Its role in the reconstruction of Gondwana: New York, Springer-Verlag, p. 102–117.

Arditto, P. A., 1985, Hummocky cross-stratification as an environmental indicator in the Late Permian Shoalhaven Group, southern Sydney Basin, *in* Moelle, K.H.R., ed., Advances in the study of the Sydney Basin: Newcastle, New South Wales, University of Newcastle, Proceedings of the Symposium, 19, p. 33–36.

Barron, E. J., 1989a, Severe storms during Earth history: Geological Society of America Bulletin, v. 101, p. 601–612.

Barron, E. J., 1989b, Climate variations and the Appalachians from the Late Paleozoic to the Present: Results from model simulations: Geomorphology, v. 2, p. 99–118.

Barron, E. J., Hay, W. W., and Thompson, S., 1989, The hydrologic cycle: A major variable during earth history: Global and Planetary Change, v. 1, p. 157–174.

Berner, R. A., 1991, A model for atmospheric CO_2 over Phanerozoic time: American Journal of Science, v. 291, p. 339–376.

Berner, R. A., Lasaga, A. C., and Garrels, R. M., 1983, The carbonate-silicate geochemical cycle and its effect on atmospheric carbon dioxide over the past 100 million years: American Journal of Science, v. 283, p. 641–683.

Bhattacharya, H. N., Mukhopadhyay, G., and Bose, P. K., 1989, Hummocky cross-stratification and its hydraulic and climatic implications in Talchir Formation, Dudhi Nala, Hazaribagh, Bihar: Journal of the Geological Society of India, v. 34, p. 398–404.

Blackmon, M. L., Wallace, J. M., Lau, N. C., and Muller, S. L., 1977, An observational study of the northern hemisphere wintertime circulation: Journal of the Atmospheric Sciences, v. 34, p. 1040–1053.

Bose, P. K., Shome, S., Bardhan, S., and Ghosh, G., 1986, Facies mosaic in the Ghuneri member (Jurassic) of the Bhuj Formation, western Kutch, India: Sedimentary Geology, v. 46, p. 293–309.

Bourke, W., McAvaney, B., Pure, K., and Thurling, R., 1977, Global modeling of atmospheric flow by spectral methods, *in* Chiang, J., ed., Methods in computational physics. Vol. 17: General circulation models of the atmosphere: New York, Academic Press, p. 267–324.

Budyko, M. I., Ronov, A. B., and Yanshin, A. L., 1987, History of the Earth's atmosphere: Berlin, Springer-Verlag, 139 p.

Bull, S. W., and Cas, R.A.F., 1989, Volcanic influences in a storm- and tide-dominated shallow marine depositional system: The Late Permian Broughton Formation, southern Sydney Basin, Kiama, NSW: Australian Journal of Earth Sciences, v. 36, p. 569–584.

Cerling, T. E., 1991, Carbon dioxide in the atmosphere: Evidence from Cenozoic and Mesozoic paleosols: American Journal of Science, v. 291, p. 377–400.

Chandler, M. A., Rind, D., and Ruedy, R., 1992, Pangaean climate during the Early Jurassic: GCM simulations and the sedimentary record of paleoclimate: Geological Society of America Bulletin, v. 104, p. 543–559.

Crowell, J. C., and Frakes, L. A., 1975, The Late Paleozoic glaciation, *in* Campbell, K.S.W., ed., Gondwana geology: Canberra, Australian Capital Territory, Australian National University, p. 313–331.

Crowley, T. J., Mengel, J. G., and Short, D. A., 1987, Gondwanaland's seasonal cycle: Nature, v. 329, p. 803–807.

Crowley, T. J., Hyde, W. T., and Short, D. A., 1989, Seasonal cycle variations on the supercontinent of Pangaea: Geology, v. 17, p. 457–460.

Della-Favera, J. C., 1987, Tepestades como agents de poluicao ambiental e mortandade em massa no passado geologico; caso das formaçoes Santana (Bacia do Ararip) e Irate (Bacia do Parana): Boletim de Geoscienceias da Petrobras, v. 1, p. 239–240.

Dickins, J. M., 1978, Climates of the Permian in Australia: The invertebrate faunas: Palaeogeography, Palaeoclimatology, Palaeoecology, v. 23, p. 33–46.

Dickinson, W. R., and Suczek, C. A., 1979, Plate tectonics and sandstone composition: American Association of Petroleum Geologists Bulletin, v. 63, p. 2164–2182.

Dolby, J. H., and Balme, B. E., 1976, Triassic palynology of the Carnarvon Basin, Western Australia: Review of Palaeobotany and Palynology, v. 22, p. 105–168.

Duke, W. L., 1985, Hummocky cross-stratification, tropical hurricanes, and intense winter storms: Sedimentology, v. 32, p. 167–194.

Duke, W. L., 1986, Reply: Hummocky cross-stratification, tropical hurricanes, and intense winter storms: Sedimentology, v. 34, p. 344–359.

Dutta, P. K., 1976, Climate during Upper Gondwana sedimentation in peninsular India: Geophytology, v. 6, p. 170–173.

Dutta, P. K., and Laha, C., 1979, Climatic and tectonic influence on Mesozoic sedimentation in India, *in* Laskar, B., and Raja Rao, C. S., eds., Papers, Fourth International Gondwana Symposium: Delhi, Hindustan Publishing Corporation, p. 562–580.

Dutta, P. K., and Suttner, L. J., 1986, Alluvial sandstone composition and paleoclimate. II: Authigenic mineralogy: Journal of Sedimentary Petrology, v. 56, p. 346–358.

Fielding, C. R., 1989, Hummocky cross-stratification from the Boxvale Sandstone Member in the northern Surat Basin, Queensland: Australian Journal of Earth Sciences, v. 36, p. 469–471.

Filatoff, J., 1975, Jurassic palynology of the Perth Basin, Western Australia: Palaeontographica, v. B154, p. 1–113.

Frakes, L. A., 1979, Climates throughout geologic time: Amsterdam, Elsevier, 310 p.

Frakes, L. A., and Francis, J. E., 1988, A guide to Phanerozoic cold polar climates from high-latitude ice-rafting in the Cretaceous: Nature, v. 333, p. 547–549.

Gaetani, M., and Garzanti, E., 1991, Multicyclic history of the Northern India continental margin (Northwestern Himalaya): American Association of Petroleum Geologists Bulletin, v. 75, p. 1427–1446.

Gordon, W. A., 1975, Distribution by latitude of Phanerozoic evaporite deposits: Journal of Geology, v. 83, p. 671–684.

Gould, R. E., and Delevoryas, T., 1977, The biology of *Glossopteris:* Evidence from petrified seed-bearing and pollen-bearing organs: Alcheringa, v. 1, p. 387–399.

Gradstein, F. M., and eight others, 1991, Mesozoic Tethyan strata of Thakkhola, Nepal: Evidence for the drift and breakup of Gondwana: Palaeogeography, Palaeoclimatology, Palaeoecology, v. 88, p. 193–218.

Habicht, J.K.A., 1979, Paleoclimate, paleomagnetism, and continental drift: Tulsa, Oklahoma, American Association of Petroleum Geologists Studies in Geology 9, 31 p.

Hallam, A., 1984, Continental humid and arid zones during the Jurassic and Cretaceous: Palaeogeography, Palaeoclimatology, Palaeoecology, v. 47, p. 195–223.

Hallam, A., 1985, A review of Mesozoic climates: Journal of the Geological Society of London, v. 142, p. 433–445.

Hyde, W. T., Kim, K.-Y., and Crowley, T. J., 1990, On the relation between polar continentality and climate: Studies with a nonlinear seasonal energy balance model: Journal of Geophysical Research, v. 95, p. 18653–18668.

Kaldi, J. G., 1980, Aspects of the sedimentology of the Lower Magnesian Limestone (Permian) of Eastern England [Ph.D. thesis]: Cambridge, University of Cambridge, 165 p.

Kar, R. K., 1976, Miofloristic evidences for climatic vicissitudes in India during Gondwana: Geophytology, v. 6, p. 230–245.

Klein, G. deV., and Marsaglia, K. M., 1986, Hummocky cross-stratification, tropical hurricanes, and intense winter storms: Discussion: Sedimentology, v. 34, p. 353–359.

Kruijs, E., 1989, Predicting the locations of mid-Cretaceous wind-driven upwelling and productivity: A critical evaluation [M.S. thesis]: University Park, The Pennsylvania State University, 166 p.

Kruijs, E., and Barron, E. J., 1990, Climate model prediction of paleoproductivity and potential source rock distribution, *in* Huc, A. Y., ed., Deposition of organic facies: Tulsa, Oklahoma, American Association of Petroleum Geologists Special Volume, p. 195–216.

Kutzbach, J. E., and Gallimore, R. G., 1989, Pangaean climates; Megamonsoons of the megacontinent: Journal of Geophysical Research, v. 94, p. 3341–3357.

Kutzbach, J. E., Guetter, P. J., and Washington, W. M., 1990, Simulated circulation of an idealized ocean from Pangaean time: Paleoceanography, v. 5, p. 299–317.

Lele, K. M ., 1976, Paleoclimatic implications of Gondwana flora: Geophytology, v. 6, p. 207–229.

Marsaglia, K. M., and Klein, G. deV., 1983, The paleogeography of Paleozoic and Mesozoic storm depositional systems: Journal of Geology, v. 91, p. 117–142.

McAvaney, B. J., Bourke, W., and Puri, K., 1978, A global spectral model for simulation of the general circulation: Journal of the Atmospheric Sciences, v. 35, p. 1557–1583.

Moore, G. T., Hayashida, D. N., Ross, C. A., and Jacobson, S. R., 1992, Paleoclimate of the Kimmeridgian/Tithonian (Late Jurassic) world. I: Results using a general circulation model: Palaeogeography, Palaeoclimatology, Palaeoecology, v. 93, p. 113–150.

Moore, P. S., and Hocking, R. M., 1983, Significance of hummocky cross-stratification in the Permian of the Carnarvon Basin, Western Australia: Journal of the Geological Society of Australia, v. 30, p. 323–331.

Mora, C. L., Driese, S. G., and Seager, P. G., 1991, Carbon dioxide in the Paleozoic atmosphere: Evidence from carbon-isotope compositions of pedogenic carbonate: Geology, v. 19, p. 1017–1020.

Neftel, A., Moore, E., Oeschger, H., and Stauffer, B., 1985, Evidence from polar ice cores for the increase in atmospheric CO_2 in the past two centuries: Nature, v. 315, p. 45–47.

Parrish, J. M., Parrish, J. T., and Ziegler, A. M., 1986, Permian-Triassic paleogeography and paleoclimatology and implications for Therapsid distribution, *in* Hotton, N. II, MacLean, P. D., Roth, J. J., and Roth, E. C., eds., The ecology and biology of mammal-like reptiles: Washington, D.C., Smithsonian Institution Press, p. 109–131.

Parrish, J. T., and Curtis, R. L., 1982, Atmospheric circulation, upwelling, and organic-rich rocks in the Mesozoic and Cenozoic eras: Palaeogeography, Palaeoclimatology, Palaeoecology, v. 40, p. 31–66.

Patzkowsky, M. E., Smith, L. H., Markwick, P. J., Engbert, C. J., and Gyllenhall, E. D., 1991, Application of the Fujita-Ziegler paleoclimate model: Early Permian and Late Cretaceous examples: Palaeogeography, Palaeoclimatology, Palaeoecology, v. 86, p. 67–85.

Ramanathan, V., Pitcher, E. J., Malone, R. C., and Blackmon, M. L., 1983, The response of a spectral general circulation model to refinements in radiative processes: Journal of Atmospheric Science, v. 40, p. 605–630.

Reiter, E. R., 1961, Jet-stream meteorology: Chicago, University of Chicago Press, 515 p.

Retallack, G. J., 1977, Triassic palaeosols in the Upper Narrabeen Group of New South Wales. Part II: Classification and reconstruction: Journal of the Geological Society of Australia, v. 24, p. 19–36.

Robinson, P. L., 1967, The Indian Gondwana formations—A review, *in* Reviews prepared for the First Symposium on Gondwana Stratigraphy, 1967: Buenos Aires, International Union of Geological Sciences, p. 201–268.

Robinson, P. L., 1973, Palaeoclimatology and continental drift, *in* Tarling, D. H., and Runcorn, S. K., eds., Implications of continental drift to earth sciences, v. 1: New York, Academic Press, p. 451–476.

Schultz, P., Barron, E. J., and Sloan, J. L. II, 1992, Assessment of NCAR General Circulation Model precipitation in comparison with observations: Palaeogeography, Palaeoclimatology, Palaeoecology (Global and Planetary Change Section), v. 97, p. 269–310.

Shah, S. C., 1976, Climates during the Gondwana era in peninsular India: Faunal evidence: Geophytology, v. 6, p. 186–206.

Sloan, L. C., and Barron, E. J., 1990, "Equable" climates during earth history?: Geology, v. 18, p. 489–492.

Suttner, L. J., and Dutta, P. K., 1986, Alluvial sandstone composition and paleoclimate. I: Framework mineralogy: Journal of Sedimentary Petrology, v. 56, p. 329–345.

Suttner, L. J., Basu, A., and Mack, G. H., 1981, Climate and the origin of quartzarenite: Journal of Sedimentary Petrology, v. 51, p. 1235–1246.

Swift, D.J.P., and Nummedal, D., 1986, Hummocky cross-stratification, tropical hurricanes, and intense winter storms: Discussion: Sedimentology, v. 34, p. 338–344.

Taylor, G. H., Liu, S. Y., and Diessel, C.F.K., 1989, The cold-climate origin of inertinite-rich Gondwana coals: International Journal of Coal Geology, v. 11, p. 1–22.

Traverse, A., 1988, Paleopalynology: London, Unwin Hyman, 600 p.

Traves, D. M., and King, D., eds., 1975, Economic geology of Australia and Papua New Guinea. 2: Coal: Netley, South Australia, Griffin Press, The Australasian Institute of Mining and Metallurgy Monograph 6, 398 p.

Valdes, P. J., and Sellwood, B. W., 1992, A palaeoclimate model for the Kimmeridgian: Palaeogeography, Palaeoclimatology, Palaeoecology, v. 95, p. 47–72.

Van Houten, F. B., 1982, Ancient soils and ancient climates, *in* Climate in Earth history: Studies in Geophysics Series, Washington, D.C., National Academy Press, p. 112–117.

Veevers, J. J., ed., 1984, Phanerozoic Earth history of Australia: Oxford, Clarendon Press, Oxford Monographs on Geology and Geophysics, 418 p.

Vos, R. G., and Hobday, D. K., 1977, Storm beach deposits in the late Palaeozoic Ecca Group of South Africa: Sedimentary Geology, v. 19, p. 217–232.

Washington, W. M., and Meehl, G. A., 1984, Seasonal cycle experiment on the climate sensitivity due to a doubling of CO_2 with an atmospheric general circulation model coupled to a simple mixed-layer ocean model: Journal of Geophysical Research, v. 90, p. 9475–9503.

Washington, W. M., and Williamson, D. L., 1977, A description of the NCAR global circulation models, in Chiang, J., ed., Methods in computational physics. Vol. 17: General circulation models of the atmosphere: New York, Academic Press, p. 111–172.

Yapp, C. J., and Poths, H., 1992, Ancient atmospheric CO_2 pressures inferred from natural goethites: Nature, v. 355, p. 342–344.

Yemane, K., 1991, Sedimentological evidence for a cool-temperate and seasonal climate in southern Gondwana during the Late Permian: Geological Society of America Abstracts with Programs, v. 23, p. 302.

Ziegler, A. M., 1990, Phytogeographic patterns and continental configurations during the Permian Period, *in* McKerrow, W. S., and Scotese, C. R., eds., Palaeozoic palaeogeography and biogeography: Geological Society of London Memoir 12, p. 363–379.

Ziegler, A. M., Scotese, C. R., McKerrow, W. S., Johnson, M. E., and Bambach, R. K., 1979, Paleozoic paleogeography: Annual Reviews of Earth and Planetary Sciences, v. 7, p. 473–502.

Ziegler, A. M., Scotese, C. R., and Barrett, S. F., 1983, Mesozoic and Cenozoic paleogeographic maps, in Brosche, P., and Sundermann, J., eds., Tidal friction and the Earth's rotation, II: New York, Springer-Verlag, p. 240–252.

MANUSCRIPT ACCEPTED BY THE SOCIETY MAY 14, 1993

Geological Society of America
Special Paper 288
1994

Pangean orogenic and epeirogenic uplifts and their possible climatic significance

Gerald M. Friedman
*Department of Geology, Brooklyn College and Graduate School of the City University of New York, Brooklyn,
New York 11210; and Northeastern Science Foundation, Inc., affiliated with Brooklyn College–City University of New York,
Rensselaer Center of Applied Geology, 15 Third Street, P.O. Box 746, Troy, New York, 12181-0746*

ABSTRACT

In paleoclimatic modeling, orographic variances are a key component. The Permian was a period of elevated, lofty, and rugged topographic settings that resulted from two kinds of uplift: orogeny and epeirogeny. Pangean orogenic uplift created mountain ranges that were among the largest in the Earth's history. Epeirogenic movements resulted in uplifts of approximately 7 km of undeformed strata. Whether epeirogenic uplifts created significant elevation increase or whether sufficient denudation in the Permian accompanied uplift so that significant relief remained is difficult to determine. Yet in places epeirogenic uplift exceeded the denudation rate, resulting in elevated regions that may have been of basin to multibasin dimension.

INTRODUCTION

Facies indicative of climate changes include evaporites, coals, reefs, red beds, caliche, tillites, and phosphorites, all of which formed during the life span of the supracontinent. Based on the presence of these diverse facies, paleoclimatic modeling reveals significant ranges between temperature extremes of "icehouse" and "greenhouse" climates (Klein, 1992). Most paleoclimatic discussions involve facies and related paleogeography and plate tectonics. However, paleoclimatic reconstructions must consider important nonfacies variables: Climate is extremely sensitive to topography, especially that of elevated regions. Mountain terrain affects the circulation of air-flow systems, which in turn affect the climate (Tannehill, 1947). In paleoclimatic modeling, orographic variances are a key component; if those variances are neglected — and especially if they are overlooked—climatic concepts may be misleading because they do not include the paleotopography of elevated regions. The paleoclimatic history must include an evaluation of changing paleotopography (Kutzbach et al., 1989; Ruddiman and Kutzbach, 1989). As an example, global cooling in the Cenozoic may have been caused by the uplift of the Tibetan plateau (Raymo and Ruddiman, 1992).

Changing paleotopography commonly results from uplifts, hence "uplift is a major factor in explaining climatic deterioration" (Kerr, 1989, quoting W. F. Ruddiman). The purpose of this chapter is to show that lofty, mountainous, uplifted terrain was important in the Permian landscape.

Two recent papers relate the issue of climate sensitivity to topographic influences (Chandler et al., 1992; Kutzbach and Gallimore, 1989), and two others have discussed the importance of topography in General Circulation Model (GCM) climatic simulations of the late Jurassic (Moore et al., 1992; Vales and Sellwood, 1992). A debate currently rages in the literature regarding the effect of uplift on Cenozoic climate change (Kerr, 1989; Kutzbach et al., 1989; Molnar and England, 1990; Raymo and Ruddiman, 1992; Raymo et al., 1988; Rind and Chandler, 1991; Ruddiman and Kutzbach, 1989). These papers on uplift and Cenozoic climate point out that uplift exerts two primary influences on climate: Increased topography affects atmospheric circulation and radiation balance, and it also leads to erosion, which can affect the carbon cycle and thus the CO_2 level of the atmosphere and oceans. The effects of the latter may be as important as those of the former. Topographic relief affects global climate (Meehl, 1992). As an example, tropical topography plays an important role in pro-

Friedman, G. M., 1994, Pangean orogenic and epeirogenic uplifts and their possible climatic significance, *in* Klein, G. D., ed., Pangea: Paleoclimate, Tectonics, and Sedimentation During Accretion, Zenith, and Breakup of a Supercontinent: Boulder, Colorado, Geological Society of America Special Paper 288.

ducing tropical monsoon rainfall regimes whose heat inputs drive the global climate system (Meehl, 1992).

The Permian landscape differed radically from that which dominated most other geologic periods, and land elevations were high. Enormous uplifts created lofty topographic settings. Permian mountain systems were among the largest in the Earth's history (Znosko, 1981). The resultant environments must have been extremely seasonal, with hot summers and cold winters.

In his classic study of Lake Bonneville, G. K. Gilbert (1890) recognized two kinds of uplift: orogeny and epeirogeny. The term *orogeny* came into use before Gilbert, but he related it to deformation by which structures within fold-belt mountains resulted from lateral-compressional motions, now recognized as the effects of plate motions. By contrast, he considered epeirogeny to be a form of tectonism that has produced the larger features of continents, such as plateaus and basins. Epeirogenic movements are essentially vertical and have affected large parts of the continents, not only in cratons but also in stabilized orogenic belts. Epeirogeny may be defined as the process by which broad vertical movements of the Earth's crust take place unaccompanied by crumpling of the strata (Friedman and Sanders, 1978). Pangean uplifts resulted from both orogeny and epeirogeny. The concept of Pangean orogenic uplift is well established in regional geology (H. L. Levine, 1988), whereas that of Pangean epeirogenic uplift is only now developing.

A current controversy concerns the effect of uplift in generating topographic elevation (England and Houseman, 1989; England and Molnar, 1990, 1991; Hatfield, 1991; Pinter and Keller, 1991). In the example of Pangean orogenic uplift, the issue is not whether mountain ranges rose; geologic evidence demands that Pangean mountains were among the largest in the Earth's history (Znosko, 1981).

This chapter follows two tracks. Under the heading of "Pangean Orogenic Uplift" I discuss tectonic deformation at plate margins resulting in mountain belts of deformed strata. Under the heading "Pangean Epeirogenic Uplift" I consider vertical movements of undeformed strata in continental platform regimes and intracratonic basins and explain their mountain-building ability.

PANGEAN OROGENIC UPLIFT

The end of the Paleozoic Era was a time of unusually extensive mountain building resulting from several continental collisions (Dott and Batten, 1981). During Late Carboniferous and Permian times the encounter between Laurussia and Gondwana generated the Allegheny Mountains that, despite extensive erosion, still stand today as a prominent mountain belt (Rodgers, 1983). This collision affected a belt that extended for more than 1,600 km between New York and Alabama. The Ouachita orogenic belt that resulted from the collision of Gondwana with the North American craton like-

wise generated active mountain building. Although since Permian time erosion has leveled most of the highlands, still the Ouachita Mountains of Oklahoma and Arkansas and the Marathon Mountains of Texas remain as once-lofty ranges (H. L. Levine, 1988). The Cordilleran belt of the western United States experienced comparable surface uplift. The Antler and Cassiar orogenies created highlands that provided thick deposits of Pennsylvanian and Permian sediments. The Hercynian orogeny of Europe, active at approximately the same time as the Allegheny orogeny in North America, created a great range of mountains across southern Europe (H. L. Levine, 1988).

Figure 1 shows the distribution of mountainous terrain in and around North America during the Permian. Although no precise computation of elevation above sea level for these mountains is available, they may have been comparable, at least in part, to those of modern Tibet. Since, as previously stated, uplift is a major factor in explaining climatic deterioration that culminated in glaciation, the possibility exists that Permian glaciation may relate to a similar event of orogenic uplift.

PANGEAN EPEIROGENIC UPLIFT

General statement

In North America, Paleozoic epeirogeny was stressed by Ham and Wilson (1967), who explained that the Paleozoic areas of the North American cratons between the Appalachians and the Rocky Mountains were epeirogenically uplifted. The Paleozoic record is characterized by episodes of marine sedimentation terminated by episodes of uplift. Epeirogeny was recognized even before Gilbert introduced this term. The frontispiece of Sir Charles Lyell's *Principles of Geology* (1830–1833) shows the Temple of Jupiter Serapis near Naples, Italy, where pelecypod borings provide evidence for vertical movements; "the movement in each case exceeds 20 feet and must have been accomplished since early Christian days" (Bailey, 1962, p. 72). Lyell's experience bears comparison with the derogatory comments received at the Tenth International Congress on Sedimentology by the late E. T. Degens's presentation on the Quaternary uplifts of the Black Sea region, which included "the early Quaternary erosion plateau has been raised to +100 to +300 m in Thrace, +950 m on Tekir Dag and +1600 to +2000 m on Ulu Dag" (Degens and Paluska, 1978). Yet, modern epeirogenic uplift occurring at the rate of 3.7 mm/yr (Isachsen, 1985) would create the highest of these elevations in only 500,000 years. Quaternary earth movements, a concept known as neotectonics (Vita-Finzi, 1986), has been of recent interest for geologists.

My research and that of my students has focused on epeirogenic uplift in eastern North America (Fig. 2); no discussion of western North American epeirogenic uplift will be considered in this chapter.

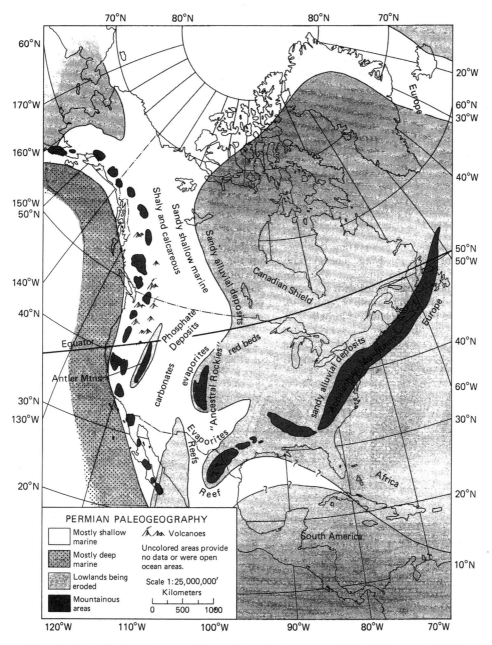

Figure 1. Generalized paleogeographic map for the Permian Period (after H. L. Levine, 1988).

Discovery of anthracite

The initial recognition of the presence of organic pyritic lenses containing coarse plant fragments in flat-lying Middle to Upper Devonian strata in the northern Appalachian Basin (Fig. 2) (Johnson and Friedman, 1969; Friedman and Sanders, 1982) showed that the woody cells of the plant debris had in part been converted to anthracite. The mean reflectivity in oil of the vitrinites in the plant debris, using light with wavelengths 546 µm, was 2.5%. This indicated that the vitrinite contains 93 to 94% so-called fixed carbon and about 3.5% hy-drogen and other volatile matter. The coalified plant chambers contained galena, pyrite, and—outside the cells—chalcopyrite and probably sphalerite. A vitrinite reflectance of 2.5% implied conditions in the upper part of the zone of metagenesis (Tissot and Welte, 1978). These results were totally unexpected, although studies of conodont color alteration had predicted a similar trend (Harris et al., 1978, sheet 2). Using a geothermal gradient of 26°C km^{-1}, the data suggested a former depth of burial of~6.5 km, consistent with the idea that the thick (~6.5 km) Carboniferous strata of northeastern Pennsylvania formerly had extended east far enough to bury the

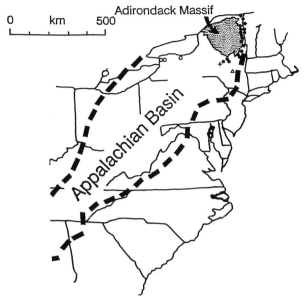

Figure 2. Index map of eastern United States showing location of Appalachian Basin and Adirondack Massif. Triangle = discovery site of anthracite; solid circles = discovery of microcline feldspar; open circles = Silurian carbonate strata; diamonds = Middle Ordovician carbonate strata; and cross = Lower and Middle Devonian carbonate strata.

Catskill Mountains of New York (Friedman and Sanders, 1982). Accordingly, it was necessary to infer not only a great depth of burial but also an equally great uplift (Friedman and Sanders, 1982, 1983). On the basis of various lines of evidence, others have confirmed deep burial and large-scale uplift (Gale and Siever, 1986; Gerlach and Cercone, 1986; Johnsson, 1986). These drastic uplifts represent crustal unroofing, with widespread implications for paleogeography of a kind only now beginning to be recognized. Pennsylvanian to Permian epeirogeny uplifted the strata (Friedman, 1990).

Discovery of microcline feldspar

Authigenic feldspars, occurring locally as microcline (alkaline feldspar) in sedimentary rocks, were discovered more than 100 years ago. Although usually they are only accessory constituents in many sedimentary deposits, in Cambrian and Ordovician rocks of the Appalachians, they may be dominant (Fig. 2). Chemical analyses of insoluble residues of Lower Ordovician (Beekmantown Group) carbonate rocks yielded 10 to 11% K_2O; the insoluble residue, for the most part composed of microcline, makes up between 35 and 67% by weight in samples studied (Braun and Friedman, 1969; Friedman and Braun, 1975). Stromatolites in Ordovician dolostones consist of alternating laminae of microcline feldspar and dolomite. Chemical analyses of more than 1,300 carbonate rock samples of Cambrian to Devonian age from the northern Appalachian Basin indicate that Cambrian and Lower Ordovician strata

contain seven times more normative K-feldspar than the younger strata (Buyce and Friedman, 1975).

Petrographic study utilizing cathodoluminescence shows that the microcline is not entirely authigenic but rather is composed of subequal amounts of detrital K-feldspar as the cores of particles and authigenic K-feldspar as overgrowths. The source of the detrital feldspar cores has been inferred as originating in volcanic terrain as tephra that were blown across the tidal flats where the carbonate sediments accumulated (Buyce and Friedman, 1975). Such tephra commonly start out as a volcanic glass that becomes successively altered to zeolites and finally to feldspar (Friedman and Sanders, 1978). The tephra at the margins of some Quaternary lakes change to K-feldspar in the center of the lakes (Sheppard and Gude, 1968). As occurrences of Lower Paleozoic zeolites are unknown, and as feldspar is the stable end product, it is probable that the cores of feldspar particles originated as zeolite precursors. After replacement by feldspar, the wind-transported detrital tephra served as surfaces of nucleation on which the authigenic feldspar grew.

$^{40}Ar/^{39}Ar$ spectrum analysis (analyst, Matt Heizler, State University of New York, Albany) shows an age minimum of 320 Ma for authigenic microcline (Friedman, 1990), which compares with $^{40}Ar/^{39}Ar$ age-spectrum analysis of authigenic K-feldspar from Cambrian carbonates of the central and southern Appalachians that yielded ages of 278 to 322 Ma (Hearn and Sutter, 1985; Hearn et al., 1987). These analyses suggest Late Carboniferous to Early Permian ages at which the authigenic feldspar formed. For carbonate rocks in Nova Scotia $^{40}Ar/^{39}Ar$ spectrum analysis shows that argon clocks in feldspars were reset in the Pennsylvanian (300 to 320 Ma). $^{40}Ar/^{39}Ar$ age-spectrum analysis suggests late Carboniferous to Early Permian ages for the uplift of these deposits to a temperature realm below 100°C, which represents cooling below argon-closure temperatures. The observation that authigenic feldspar in Cambro-Ordovician carbonates occurs along the proto-Atlantic shelf from the Appalachian Basin to Newfoundland, Scotland, and Greenland suggests active crustal uplift in Pennsylvanian-Permian time along this entire belt (Friedman, 1990). Paleomagnetic studies have documented that the magnetite carries a well-defined magnetization of Pennsylvanian-Permian age (Jackson et al., 1988). A two-stage model suggests deep burial and elevated temperature followed by uplift and in-situ growth of diagenetic magnetite (Jackson et al., 1988). Thus, following subsidence, Pennsylvanian to Permian uplift occurred. This leads to the surprising conclusion that isostatic unroofing following uplift has stripped off thick sections of strata whose presence was previously unsuspected.

Fluid-homogenization temperatures average 141°C for the formation of the coarse crystalline Cambro-Ordovician dolostones in which the microcline occurs: 223°C for calcite cement and 117 to 140°C for calcite and dolomite vein fillings. These temperatures are supported by oxygen isotope and conodont-alteration data (Harris et al., 1978; Urschel and Friedman, 1984; Friedman 1987a, b). Using a geothermal gradient of 26°C km^{-1}, a former depth of burial in excess of 7 km is implied. As the argon-age spectra show, uplift from that depth and erosion of the overlying strata occurred during Carboniferous to Permian times.

The tephra beds

Tephra are defined as particles exploded from volcanoes; in the Appalachian Basin tephra are in large part metabentonites or potassium (K)-bentonites. Middle Ordovician potassium (K)-bentonites showed K/Ar ages of illitization that are narrowly confined between 272 to 303 Ma (Late Pennsylvanian to Early Permian). This suggests that illitization was a short-lived episode coincident with the Alleghanian orogeny (Elliott and Aronson, 1987). Study of clay-mineral diagenesis and apatite fission-track data of Middle Devonian Tioga metabentonite of the northern Appalachian Basin indicated that Upper Devonian and Carboniferous strata, no longer preserved, were responsible for burial in excess of 7 km. Their uplift coincided with the Alleghany orogeny (Johnsson, 1986).

In Pennsylvania, the Middle Devonian Tioga metabentonites and the Devonian Kalkberg tephra yielded Permian dates (270 to 285 Ma), with uplift of at least 3.4 km to have begun at 251 ±25 Ma (Roden, 1989). In the Appalachian Basin of Maryland, Virginia, and West Virginia, uplift occurred in the Permian, 270 to 285 Ma (Roden, 1989).

Pennsylvanian coal-bearing strata

Coal-bearing strata of the Pennsylvanian anthracite region were once buried at depths ranging from 6 to 9 km (J. R. Levin, 1986). Paleomagnetic and paleobotanical ages delimit the maximum burial to a relatively short interval of 270 to 285 Ma (J. R. Levine, 1986), coincident with the Carboniferous/ Permian boundary and extending into the Early Permian.

Removal of post-Devonian strata from the Adirondack Massif, New York

Since the Permian—that is, during the last 255 m.y.— epeirogenic uplift has removed from the Adirondacks Massif of New York (Fig. 2) at least 7.5 km of Paleozoic strata and an unknown thickness of Precambrian basement (Sarwar, 1992; G. Sarwar and G. M. Friedman, manuscript).

Other evidence for Permian epeirogenic uplift

In the Appalachian Basin other evidence for Permian vertical uplift of undeformed strata includes (1) fission-track data on fluorite in Silurian carbonates (V. Harder and G. M. Friedman, unpublished data); (2) fluid-homogenization temperatures, vitrinite reflectance, and stable-isotope data on vein fillings and calcite cement in Middle Ordovician carbonate strata (Fig. 2) (Brockerhoff and Friedman, 1987; Friedman, 1987a, b) and in Lower and Middle Devonian carbonate strata (Fig. 2) (Gurney and Friedman, 1987; Friedman, 1987a, b); (3) paleomagnetic ages (J. R. Levine, 1986); (4) illitization (Elliot and Aronson, 1987); (5) mathematic geodynamic model (Beaumont et al., 1988); and (6) an absence of Pennsylvanian strata beneath Mesozoic basins of the eastern United States.

In the Mississippi Valley K/Ar dates for illite/smectite yielded 265 Ma (Permian) (Hay et al., 1988). In the Ouachita Mountains of Arkansas, K/Ar analysis yielded a date of 262 ±10 Ma (Permian) for an uplift of 7.6 km (Shelton et al., 1986) and a genetic tie to the formation of the Mississippi Valley Type (MVT) deposits for which a Late Pennsylvanian–Permian age was suggested (Wu and Beales, 1981). MVT deposits in the central and eastern United States are Late Pennsylvanian to Permian in age (Sharp, 1978; Leach et al., 1984; Rowan et al., 1984). Uplift and erosion removed about 3 to 4 km of Paleozoic cover from the southern tract of the Fennoscandian Shield at the beginning of the Mesozoic (Zeck et al., 1988).

Although the more-recent uplifts of the Near East influenced the present topography, the history of uplift and erosion included multiple events, including Late Devonian, Early Carboniferous, pre- or intra-Permian, and Late Jurassic–Early Cretaceous (Garfunkel and Derin, 1988; Kohn et al., 1984; Weissbrod and Gvirtzman, 1988). Apparent fission-track ages on sphene and zircon indicate erosion involving at least 5 km of strata.

Timing of epeirogeny and source of vanished strata

As Ham and Wilson (1967) observed, Paleozoic strata of the North American craton testify to several episodic intraplate epeirogenic events. Major events occurred during the Carboniferous-Permian, coinciding with the Alleghanian/ Hercynian orogeny at 320 to 250 Ma. This dating is based on techniques that have built-in uncertainties, especially fission-track annealing. The accuracy of burial temperatures inferred from annealing curves may be questionable, because closure temperatures for different minerals depend on rate of cooling (Haack, 1977). Determining the cooling rate requires that the rate of uplift be known, but of course it is initially unknown. Inferring different rates of uplift will result in different estimates of closure temperature. Yet despite these and other constraints, the data provided clusters of dated intervals that are meaningful in terms of uplift events.

What was the source of the several kilometers of strata that piled up and that following uplift have subsequently vanished? For northeastern North America, this source has been inferred as Carboniferous strata that formerly extended far enough to bury the underlying Devonian (Friedman and Sanders, 1982). In Carbon County, Pennsylvania, the Devonian strata are overlain by Carboniferous rocks 2,000 to 4,800 m thick (Behre, 1933, p. 57). In the Anthracite district of north-eastern Pennsylvania, strata overlying the Middle Devonian are as much as 6,400 m thick (Wood et al., 1969). The removal of the sedimentary section through erosion, especially for the strata of the Appalachian Basin, focuses on the opening of the Atlantic Ocean into which the removed sediment is interpreted to have been dumped.

Significance of Pangean epeirogenic uplifts

The section "Pangean Orogenic Uplift" explained that this kind of uplift generated significant mountain belts and that uplift induced climatic events (Ruddiman and Kutzbach, 1989). However, whether Pangean epeirogenic uplift created significant elevation increase or whether sufficient denudation accompanied uplift so that significant relief remained is difficult to determine. Yet epeirogenic uplift in places exceeded the denudation rate in the Adirondack Massif (Fig. 2) (Isachsen, 1992). Epeirogenic surface uplift has occurred in New York through the last 255 m.y. Lower and Middle Paleozoic rocks that were buried to depth of many kilometers are now exposed at various elevations above the present sea level: Epeirogenic uplift raised Mt. Marcy and Mt. Algonquin in the Adirondack Massif to an elevation of more than 1.5 km and the Devonian Hamilton Group rocks in the Catskills to an elevation of 1,280 m (Broughton et al., 1966). Surface uplift took place over most of New York between Middle and Late Permian and Miocene time (Rodgers, 1967; Sarwar, 1992). During this interval, the rate of "rock uplift" was greater than the rate of "exhumation" resulting in net "surface uplift" in the sense of England and Molnar (1990) (Sarwar, 1992; G. Sarwar and G. M. Friedman, manuscript). As in the example of the Adirondack Massif, epeirogenic uplift of the Precambrian basement of the Sinai subplate of the Middle East has generated particularly high peaks, for example, Santa Katarina (2,642 m) and Gebel Um Shomar (2,586 m) (Kohn and Eyal, 1981; Garfunkel, 1988). Although the time of epeirogeny was younger than the Permian that is the subject of this chapter, these examples of epeirogenic uplift illustrate its importance in creating surface uplift. The observation that such epeirogenic uplifts occurred implies that they may have generated in the Permian elevated regions of basin- to multibasin-wide dimension that need to be considered in climate modeling.

Causes of epeirogeny

Most deformations of the Earth's crust are consistent with the tenets of plate tectonics. These are expressed by Gilbert's (1890) orogeny. Yet, as we have seen, crustal deformations involving deep subsidence and large-scale uplift and erosion occurred in the past and continued to occur at present well into the interior of plates. Some epeirogenic movements may relate to plate-margin processes, but others certainly do not. "Yet intraplate tectonics constitutes more than a scientific enigma" (Brown and Reilinger, 1986). In many parts of the world,

within ocean basins as well as continental interiors, there are concentrations of earthquake and volcanic activity divorced from plate-tectonic boundaries (Brown and Reilinger, 1986). In the United States, one of the most-destructive earthquakes in history occurred not along a plate boundary but in an intraplate position: near New Madrid, Missouri, in 1811–1812. Geodetic surveys over the cratons of the United States, Europe, and Asia indicate that these regions are epeirogenically active. These motions are apart from those related to the retreat of the ice sheets since the last major continental glaciation (Isachsen, 1985, 1992).

Although intraplate epeirogenic motions are remote from plate boundaries, it does not necessarily follow that the motions are unrelated to plate-boundary forces (McGetchin et al., 1980; Hinze et al., 1980). Indeed, epeirogeny may be related to plate margins, where crustal loading by thrust sheets is being recognized as a major factor in uplifts. Such thrustloading causes isostatic downbending of the edge of the cratons, which creates a space for the accumulation of sediments to thicknesses of several thousand meters. The effects of such loading of the cratonic margin in front of a new mountain system may extend across the width of hundreds of kilometers from the mountain front. Downflexing adjacent to the mountains may produce a foreland basin with a complementary bulge or cratonic arch that represents a major uplift (Quinlan and Beaumont, 1984).

No agreement exists on the causes of epeirogenic motions that are unrelated to plate margins, such as those of the Adirondack Massif or the Arabo-Nubian Shield, or uplifts involving former belts that are now inactive. Increased mantle-plume activity may be a factor in causing uplift of extensive sectors of continents; in fact, since present-day hot spots are associated with regional topographic bulges, epeirogenic uplifts may reflect hot, low-density ridges in the asthenosphere, derived from plume convection (Vogt, 1972). Mantle activity, intraplate magmatism, lineament activation, and other poorly understood phenomena have been invoked (Bhattacharji, 1987). Dynamic flow in the lower lithosphere and asthenosphere, as well as partial melting, can produce uplift. A thinning of the lower lithosphere through diapiric rise of the asthenosphere will cause epeirogenic motions (Keene, 1987) or even domal uplift of the asthenosphere. Mantle plumes, phase changes at the boundary between crust and mantle, or partial melting processes may be responsible for epeirogeny and/or major subsidence. Epeirogenic uplift may result from the intrusion of large thicknesses of basic magma into the lower part of the continental crust, a mechanism that Gilbert (1877) had already considered (McKenzie, 1984).

CONSEQUENCES OF UPLIFT FOR CLIMATE AND EXTINCTION

The magnitude of orogeny and epeirogeny relating to Carboniferous-Permian events amounts to extensive mountain building. During the Permian continents had collided to become a supracontinent Pangea. A single continent with eleva-tions of the order indicated created widespread effects on cli-matic change. These changes, which affected both land and sea, included temperature; atmospheric circulation; heat flow between air, sea, and land; precipitation or its lack; and wind at the Earth's surface. Through uplift, large sections of Pangea became isolated; within these sections lack of moisture and circulation created desert conditions. In this mountainous desert region, temperatures must have fluctuated widely be-tween day and night and summer and winter. The environ-ments for land animals became unstable, creating extinction events over several million years (Elliott, 1986). The fusion of one continent from separate and distinct plates reduced the habitat available for marine life, but the elimination of shallow seas as a result of large-scale uplift created environmental con-ditions of receding seas that obliterated much of the then-liv-ing world. Marine invertebrates prefer shallow-water habitats, which uplifts eliminated, to deep-water habitats. The Permian extinction interval was the most profound of the entire Phan-erozoic. Drops in biologic diversity resulting from extinction exceed those of all other geologic periods. Perhaps 96% of all species disappeared (Elliot, 1986; Raup and Sepkoski, 1982). Much has been said recently about extraterrestrial extinction causes for the Cretaceous-Tertiary boundary. By comparison, the Permian extinction event must have been Earth bound, yet the Permian marked the greatest extinction event of all time.

CONCLUSIONS

Pangean orogenic deformation at plate margins resulted in lofty mountain ranges of deformed strata. Epeirogenic or vertical motion of undeformed strata created uplifts that in the Appalachian Basin approximated 7 km. The extent to which denudation kept pace with epeirogenic uplift is difficult to de-termine, but in places epeirogenic uplift exceeded denudation. Climate is sensitive to topographic relief, and orographic vari-ances must be included in climate modeling, especially con-sidering that the Pangean mountains have been described as among the mightiest in geologic history.

ACKNOWLEDGMENTS

Grateful thanks are extended to George Klein, Mark Chandler, Warren Manspeizer, and John Sanders for helpful suggestions in revising this paper.

REFERENCES CITED

Bailey, Sir Edward, 1962, Charles Lyell: London, Thomas Nelson & Sons, 214 p.

Beaumont, C., Quinlan, J., and Hamilton, J., 1988, Orogeny and stratigraphy: Numerical models of the Paleozoic in the eastern interior of North America: Tectonics, v. 7, p. 389–416.

Behre, C. H., Jr., 1933, Slate in Pennsylvania: Pennsylvania Topographic and Geologic Survey, 4th series, Bulletin M 16, 400 p.

Bhattacharji, S., 1987, Asthenospheric upwelling, lineament reactivations, magmatic episodes and ore mineral localization in Proterozoic basin evo-lution on the Archean Indian Shield: International Basement Tectonics Association, Publication 5, p. 187–200.

Braun, M., and Friedman, G. M., 1969, Carbonate lithofacies and environ-ments of the Tribes Hill Formation (Lower Ordovician) of the Mowhawk Valley, New York: Journal of Sedimentary Petrology, v. 39, p. 106–119.

Brockerhoff, F. G., and Friedman, G. M., 1987, Paleo-depth of burial of Middle Ordovician Chazy Group carbonates in New York State and Vermont: Northeastern Geology, v. 9, p. 51–58.

Broughton, J. G., Fisher, D. W., Isachsen, Y. W., and Rickard, L. V., 1966, Geology of New York, A short account: New York State Museum and Science Service, Education Leaflet 20, 45 p.

Brown, L. D., and Reilinger, R. E., 1986, Epeirogenic and intraplate move-ments, *in* Active tectonics, Studies in Geophysics: Washington, D.C., National Academy Press, p. 30–44.

Buyce, M. R., and Friedman, G. M., 1975, Significance of authigenic K-feldspar in Cambrian Ordovician carbonate rocks of the Proto-Atlantic shelf in North America: Journal of Sedimentary Petrology, v. 45, p. 808–821.

Chandler, M. A., Rind, D., and Ruedy, R., 1992, Pangean climate during the Early Jurassic: GCM simulations and the sedimentary record of paleocli-mate: Geological Society of America Bulletin, v. 104, p. 543–559.

Degens, E. T., and Paluska, A., 1978, Quaternary geology of Black Sea re-gion, *in* Friedman, G. M., ed., Abstracts, 10th International Congress on Sedimentology, v. 1, p. 162.

Dott, R. H., Jr., and Batten, R. L., 1981, Evolution of the earth: New York, McGraw-Hill, 573 p.

Elliott, D. K., ed., 1986, Dynamics of extinction: New York, John Wiley & Sons, 294 p.

Elliot, W. C., and Aronson, A. L., 1987, Alleghanian episode of K-bentonite il-litization in the southern Appalachian Basin: Geology, v. 15, p. 735–739.

England, P., and Houseman, G., 1989, Extension during continental conver-gence with application to the Tibetan Plateau: Journal of Geophysical Research, v. 94 B 12, p. 17561–17579.

England, P. C., and Molnar, P., 1990, Surface uplift, uplift of rocks, and ex-humation of rocks: Geology, v. 18, p. 1173–1177.

England, P., and Molnar, P., 1991, Comments and replies *on* 'Surface uplift of rocks, and exhumation of rocks': Geology, v. 19, p. 1051–1054.

Friedman, G. M., 1987a, Deep-burial diagenesis: Its implications for vertical movements of the crust, uplift of the lithosphere and isostatic unroof-ing—A review: Sedimentary Geology, v. 50, p. 67–94.

Friedman, G. M., 1987b, Vertical movements of the crust: Case histories from the northern Appalachian Basin: Geology, v. 15, p. 1130–1133.

Friedman, G. M., 1990, Anthracite and concentrations of alkaline feldspar (microcline) in flat-lying undeformed Paleozoic strata: A key to large-scale vertical crustal uplift, *in* Heling, D., Rothe, P., Förstner, U., and Stoffers, P., eds., Sediments and sedimentary environments: Berlin, Springer-Verlag, 317 p.

Friedman, G. M., and Braun, M., 1975, Shoaling and tidal deposits that accu-mulated marginal to the Proto-Atlantic Ocean: The Tribes Hill Formation (Lower Ordovician) of the Mohawk Valley, New York, *in* Ginsburg, R. N., ed., Tidal deposits, a source book of Recent examples and fossil counterparts: New York, Springer-Verlag, p. 307–314.

Friedman, G. M., and Sanders, J. E., 1978, Principles of sedimentology: New York, John Wiley & Sons, 792 p.

Friedman, G. M., and Sanders, J. E., 1982, Time-temperature-burial signifi-cance of Devonian anthracite implies former great (~6.5 km) depth of burial of Catskill Mountains, New York: Geology, v. 10, p. 93–96.

Friedman, G. M., and Sanders, J. E., 1983, Reply *on* 'Time-temperature-burial significance of Devonian anthracite implies former great (~6.5 km) depth of burial of Catskill Mountains, New York': Geology, v. 11, p. 123–124.

Gale, P. E., and Siever, R., 1986, Diagenesis of Middle to Upper Devonian Catskill facies sandstones in southeastern New York: American Asso-ciation Petroleum Geology Bulletin, v. 70, p. 592–593.

Garfunkel, Z., 1988, Relation between continental rifting and uplifting: Evidence from the Suez rift and northern Red Sea: Tectonophysics, v. 150, p. 33–49.

Garfunkel, Z., and Derin, B., 1988, Reevaluation of latest Jurassic–Early Cretaceous history of the Negev and the role of magmatic activity: Israel Journal of Earth Science, v. 37, p. 43–52.

Gerlach, J. B., and Cercone, K. R., 1986, Post-Devonian depositional history of northern Appalachian Basin based on regional vitrinite reflectance trends: Geological Society of America Abstracts with Programs, v. 18, p. 612.

Gilbert, G. K., 1877, Report on the geology of the Henry Mountains (Utah): Washington, D.C., U.S. Geological Survey, Rocky Mountain Region (Powell), 160 p.

Gilbert, G. K., 1890, Lake Bonneville: U.S. Geological Survey Monograph 1, 438 p.

Gurney, G. G., and Friedman, G. M., 1987, Burial history of the Devonian Cherry Valley carbonate sequence, Cherry Valley, New York: Northeastern Geology, v. 9, p. 1–11.

Haack, U., 1977, The closure temperature for fission track retention in minerals: American Journal of Science, v. 277, p. 459–464.

Ham, W. E., and Wilson, J. L., 1967, Paleozoic epeirogeny and orogeny in the central United States: American Journal of Science, v. 265, p. 332–407.

Harris, A. G., Harris, L. D., and Epstein, J. B., 1978, Oil and gas data from Paleozoic rocks in the Appalachian Basin: Maps for assessing hydrocarbon potential and thermal maturity (conodont alteration isograds and overburden isopachs): U.S. Geological Survey Miscellaneous Investigations Map I-917-E, scale 1:2,500,000, 4 sheets.

Hatfield, C. B., 1991, Comments and replies on 'Surface uplift of rocks, and exhumation of rocks': Geology, v. 19, p. 1051–1054.

Hay, R. L., Lee Mingchou, Kolata, D. R., Matthews, J. C., and Morton, J. P., 1988, Episodic potassic diagenesis of Ordovician tuffs in the Mississippi Valley area: Geology, v. 16, p. 743–747.

Hearn, P. P., and Sutter, J. F., 1985, Authigenic potassium feldspar in Cambrian carbonates: Evidence of Alleghanian brine migration: Science, v. 228, p. 1529–1531.

Hearn, P. P., Jr., Sutter, J. F., and Belkin, H. E., 1987, Evidence for Late-Paleozoic brine migration in Cambrian carbonate rocks of the central and southern Appalachians: Implications for Mississippi Valley–type sulfide mineralization: Geochimica Cosmochimica Acta, v. 51, p. 1323–1334.

Hinze, W. J., Braile, L. W., Keller, G. R., and Lidiak, E. G., 1980, Models for midcontinent tectonism, in Studies in Geophysics: Continental Tectonics: National Academy of Sciences, Washington, D.C., p. 73–83.

Isachsen, Y. W., 1985, Structural and tectonic studies in New York State: n.p., U.S. Nuclear Regulatory Commission, Field Report, 74 p.

Isachsen, Y. W., 1992, Still rising after all these years: Natural History, v. 101, p. 31–33.

Jackson, M., McCabe, C., Ballard, M. M., and Van der Voo, R., 1988, Magnetite authigenesis and diagenetic paleotemperatures across the northern Appalachian Basin: Geology, v. 16, p. 592–595.

Johnson, K. G., and Friedman, G. M., 1969, The Tully clastic correlatives (Upper Devonian) of New York State: A model for recognition of alluvial, dune (?) tidal, nearshore (bar and lagoon), and offshore sedimentary environments in a tectonic delta complex: Journal of Sedimentary Petrology, v. 39, p. 451–485.

Johnsson, M. J., 1986, Distribution of maximum burial temperatures across the northern Appalachian Basin and implications for Carboniferous sedimentation patterns: Geology, v. 14, p. 384–387.

Keene, C. E., 1987, Some important consequences of lithospheric extension, in Coward, M. P., Dewey, J. F., and Hancock, P. L., eds., Continental extensional tectonics: Geological Society Special Publication 28, p. 67–73.

Kerr, R. A., 1989, Did the roof of the world start an ice age? Science, v. 244, p. 1441–1442.

Klein, G deV., 1992, Project PANGEA: Goals and developments; tectonic-climatic discrimination of cyclic deposition: Lawrence, Kansas, International Union of Geological Societies, Global Sedimentary Program, Project PANGEA Workshop, p. 7.

Kohn, B. P., and Eyal, M., 1981, History of uplift of the crystalline basement of Sinai and its relation to opening of the Red Sea as revealed by fission track dating of apatites: Earth and Planetary Science Letters, v. 52, p. 129–141.

Kohn, B. P., Eyal, M., and Feinstein, S., 1984, Early Carboniferous fission-track ages from southern Israel and Sinai; evidence for major uplift and erosion of a thick Lower Paleozoic section: Israel Geological Society, Annual Meeting Abstracts, p. 56.

Kutzbach, J. E., and Gallimore, R. G., 1989, Pangaean climates: Megamonsoons of the megacontinent: Journal of Geophysical Research, v. 94 D 3, p. 3341–3357.

Kutzbach, J. E., Guetter, P. J., Ruddiman, W. F., and Prell, W. L., 1989, Sensitivity of climate to late Cenozoic uplift in Southern Asia and the American west: Numerical experiments: Journal of Geophysical Research, v. 94 D 5, p. 18393–18407.

Leach, D. L., Viets, J. G., and Rowan, L., 1984, Appalachian-Ouachita orogeny and Mississippi Valley–type lead-zinc deposits: Geological Society of America Abstracts with Programs, v. 16, p. 572.

Levine, H. L., 1988, The earth through time: Philadelphia, Saunders College Publishing, 593 p.

Levine, J. R., 1986, Deep burial of coal-bearing strata, Anthracite region, Pennsylvania: Sedimentation or tectonics: Geology, v. 14, p. 577–580.

Lyell, Sir Charles, 1830–1833, Principles of geology: London, John Murray, 511 p.

McGetchin, T. R., Burke, K. G., Thompson, G. A., and Young, R. A., 1980, Mode and mechanisms of plateau uplift, in Bally, A. W., Bender, P. L., McGetchin, T. R., and Walcott, R. I., eds., Geodynamics Series, v. 1, p. 99–110.

McKenzie, D., 1984, A possible mechanism for epeirogenic uplift: Nature, v. 307, p. 616–618.

Meehl, G. A., 1992, Effect of tropical topography on global climate: Annual Review of Earth and Planetary Science, v. 20, p. 85–112.

Molnar, P., and England, P., 1990, Late Cenozoic uplift of mountain ranges and global climate change: Chicken or egg?: Nature, v. 346, p. 29–34.

Moore, G. T., Hayashida, D. N., Ross, C. A., and Jacobson, S. R., 1992, Paleoclimate of the Kimmeridgian/Tithonian (Late Jurassic) world. 1: Results using a general circulation model: Palaeogeography, Palaeoclimatology, Palaeoecology, v. 93, p. 113–150.

Pinter, N., and Keller, E. A., 1991, Comments and replies on 'Surface uplift of rocks, and exhumation of rocks': Geology, v. 19, p. 1051–1054.

Quinlan, G. M., and Beaumont, C., 1984, Appalachian thrusting, lithospheric flexure, and the Paleozoic stratigraphy of the Eastern Interior of North America: Canadian Journal of Earth Sciences, v. 21, p. 973–996.

Raup, D. M., and Sepkoski, J. J., Jr., 1982, Mass extinctions in the marine fossil record: Science, v. 215, p. 1501–1503.

Raymo, M. E., and Ruddiman, W. F., 1992, Tectonic forcing of late Cenozoic climate: Nature, v. 359, p. 117–122.

Raymo, M. E., Ruddiman, W. F., and Froelich, P. N., 1988, Influence of Late Cenozoic mountain building on ocean geochemical cycles: Geology, v. 16, p. 649–653.

Rind, D., and Chandler, M. A., 1991, Increased ocean heat transports and warmer climate: Journal of Geophysical Research, v. 96 D 4, p. 7437–7461.

Roden, M. K., 1989, Apatite fission-track thermochronology of the central and southern Appalachian Basin [Ph.D. thesis]: Troy, New York, Rensselaer Polytechnic Institute, 214 p.

Rodgers, J., 1967, Chronology of tectonic movements in the Appalachian region of eastern North America: American Journal of Science, v. 265, p. 408–427.

Rodgers, J., 1983, The life history of a mountain range—The Appalachians, in Hsü, K. J., Mountain building processes: Zürich, Geologisches Institut, Eidgenössische Technische Hochschule, p. 229–241.

Rowan, L., Leach, D. L., and Viets, J. G., 1984, Evidence for a Late

Pennsylvanian–Early Permian regional thermal event in Missouri, Kansas, Arkansas and Oklahoma: Geological Society of America Abstracts with Programs, v. 16, p. 640.

Ruddiman, W. F., and Kutzbach, J. E., 1989, Forcing of Late Cenozoic Northern Hemisphere climate by plateau uplift in southeast Asia and the American southwest: Journal of Geophysical Research, v. 94 D 15, p. 18409–18427.

Sarwar, G., 1992, Geology of missing strata: The post-Devonian of New York State [Ph.D. thesis]: New York, City University of New York, 369 p.

Sharp, J. M., 1978, Energy and momentum transport model of the Ouachita Basin and its possible impact on formation of economic mineral deposits: Economic Geology, v. 73, p. 1057–1068.

Shelton, K. L., Reader, J. M., Ross, L. M., Viele, G. W. and Seidemann, D. E., 1986, Ba-rich adularia from the Ouachita Mountains, Arkansas: Implications for a postcollisional hydrothermal system: American Mineralogist, v. 71, p. 916–923.

Sheppard, R. A., and Gude, A. J., III, 1968, Distribution and genesis of authigenic silicate minerals in tuffs of Pleistocene Lake Tecopa, Inyo County, California: U.S. Geological Survey Professional Paper 597, 38 p.

Tannehill, I. R., 1947, Drought—Its causes and effects: Princeton, New Jersey: Princeton University Press, 264 p.

Tissot, B. P., and Welte, D. H., 1978, Petroleum formation and occurrence: A new approach to oil and gas exploration: Berlin, Springer Verlag, 538 p.

Urschel, S. F., and Friedman, G. M., 1984, Paleodepth of burial of Lower Ordovician Beekmantown Group carbonates in New York State: Compass, Sigma Gamma Epsilon, v. 61, p. 205–215.

Valdes, P. J., and Sellwood, B. W., 1992, A palaeoclimate model for the Kimmeridgian: Palaeogeography, Palaeoclimatology, Palaeoecology, v. 95, p. 47–72.

Vita-Finzi, C., 1986, Recent earth movements: An introduction to neotectonics: London, Academic Press, 226 p.

Vogt, P. R., 1972, Evidence for global synchronism in mantle plume convection, and possible significance for geology: Nature, v. 240, p. 338–342.

Weissbrod, T., and Gvirtzman, G., 1988, The Late Devonian event in the Near East: Cour. Forschungs Institut Senckenberg, v. 100, p. 221–233.

Wood, G. H., Trexler, J. P., and Kehn, T. M., 1969, Geology of the west-central part of the southern Anthracite field and adjoining areas, Pennsylvania: U.S. Geological Survey Professional Paper 602, 150 p.

Wu, Y., and Beales, F. W., 1981, A reconnaissance study of paleomagnetic methods of the age of mineralization along the Viburnum Trend, southeast Missouri: Economic Geology, v. 76, p. 1879–1894.

Zeck, H. P., Andriessen, P.A.M., Hansen, K., Jensen, P. K., and Rasmussen, B. L., 1988, Paleozoic paleo-cover of the southern part of the Fennoscandian Shield: Fission track constraints: Tectonophysics, v. 149, p. 61–66.

Znosko, J., 1981, Tectonic framework of the Permian events in the Polish area, *in* Proceedings, International Symposium, Central European Permian, Warsaw: Warsaw, n.p., p. 127–154.

MANUSCRIPT ACCEPTED BY THE SOCIETY MAY 14, 1993

Geological Society of America
Special Paper 288
1994

The breakup of Pangea and its impact on climate: Consequences of Variscan-Alleghanide orogenic collapse

Warren Manspeizer
Department of Geology, Rutgers University, Newark, New Jersey 07102

ABSTRACT

The breakup of Pangea in the central Atlantic occurred at a time of worldwide plate reorganization, embracing both the terminal phases of Pangean consolidation and the early phases of Pangean extension. The breakup developed along the thickened and highly elevated Variscan-Alleghanian orogen that was the site of Late Paleozoic polyphase deformation, which ultimately led to the formation of Late Paleozoic, late orogenic, wrench-formed basins. These late orogenic basins of the northern Appalachians and Morocco may have formed by tectonic escape as the collision of Gondwana and Laurasia forced the Hercynian-European plate northeast along major dextral shears.

Fission-track and isotopic data indicate that the subsequent breakup of Pangea during the Triassic was accompanied by continued northwest plate convergence in the lower crust and by large-scale vertical uplift and southeast extension in the upper crust. It is postulated that as the crust thickened beneath the leading edge of the Alleghanian orogen, topographic elevations increased so as to provide increased vertical stress needed to drive the extension. As these events were concurrent with subduction of the paleotethys plate, through the suturing of Cimmeria to Laurasia, I propose that orogenic collapse leading to the breakup may have been aided or induced by subduction rollback, initiating tectonic extrusion of a microplate bounded by the N40°-Kelvin and South Atlas fracture zone, which acted as a ridge-to-arc transform. The Late Triassic rift basins, in this view, formed along the western border of this easterwardly extruded microplate, whose detachment surface may have been composed of Carboniferous evaporites.

Breakup of the supercontinent during the Late Triassic–Early Jurassic also had major consequences on Pangean climates, as Early Mesozoic climates were substantially modified by changes in continentality, oceanography, orography, and igneous activity. In contrast to Pangean climates marked by glaciation and aridity, Late Triassic climates were markedly more equitable and characterized by more humid conditions over much of the world. The changing conditions also profoundly affected the biota, as Late Triassic strata record one of the five greatest episodes of mass extinctions in the history of the earth.

Manspeizer, W., 1994, The breakup of Pangea and its impact on climate: Consequences of Variscan-Alleghanide orogenic collapse, *in* Klein, G. D., ed., Pangea: Paleoclimate, Tectonics, and Sedimentation During Accretion, Zenith, and Breakup of a Supercontinent: Boulder, Colorado, Geological Society of America Special Paper 288.

INTRODUCTION

Consolidation of the Pangean landmass during the Early Carboniferous, through the northeast-southwest convergence of Gondwana with Laurasia, marked the onset of the Himalayan-type Variscan orogeny, which terminated about 40 million years later during the latest Westphalian (Ziegler, 1988). The final phase of the Variscan orogeny appears to have culminated along a major east-west–trending Late Variscan dextral shear zone that linked the northern and central Alleghany-Mauri-

tanides to the southern Uralides. Differential motion of the Laurasian and Gondwana plates has been postulated (Arthaud and Matte, 1977; Fig. 1) to explain crustal shortening at both ends of the megashear that led to Late Variscan and Alleghanian thrusting, which is considered by Cook et al. (1979) and Harris et al. (1982) to be in the order of 200 km in the Alleghanides-Mauritanides-Uralides.

The final phases of Late Paleozoic deformation produced a very large, broadly convex continental plate that extended almost symmetrically from the polar regions to the equator,

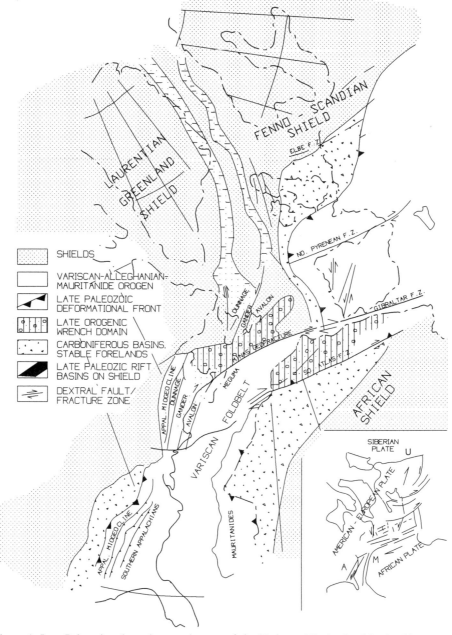

Figure 1. Late Paleozoic schematic tectonic map of the Variscan-Alleghanian-Mauritanide orogen. After Arthaud and Matte, 1977; Ziegler, 1982. Inset (modified from Arthaud and Matte, 1977), shows Variscan shear zone, interpreted as a 2,000-km-wide Reidel shear system that led to the formation of the Uralides (U) on the east and the Alleghanides (A) and Mauritanides (M) on the west.

where it flanked the tropical Tethys Seaway on the east (Scotese and McKerrow, 1990; Fig. 2). The landmass with an area about 184×10 km^2, had a broad central arch about 1.7 km high and 720 km across and had highlands ranging from 2.4 to 4.5 km above sea level (Hay et al., 1981). Dewey (1988) also reported that Late Paleozoic transpression in the Appalachians must have led to the formation of a very thick orogenic crust that, like the Tibetan Plateau, was on the order of 60 km thick and stood in excess of 3 km above sea level. Dallmeyer (1989) concluded, on the bases of isotopic data, that the near-present erosional level of the crystalline Appalachians was exhumed about 200 Ma, and thus very rapid uplift, cooling, and erosion of the metamorphic terrane must have occurred during the Late Permian and Early Triassic (Fig. 3).

The object of this chapter is to examine the tectonic and climatic consequences of a rapidly uplifted, high-standing Himalayan-type Alleghanian-Variscan orogen. The focus of the chapter is primarily on Triassic-Liassic events along the proto-Atlantic. Although no new data are presented in this chapter, the literature is reexamined in terms of what is now known from tectonically active mountain ranges, such as the Himalayas and Tibetan Plateau; new tectono-stratigraphic relationships are explored and new ideas are presented about the breakup of Pangea and the consequences thereof. My plan is to examine first how the Variscan-Alleghany orogeny impacted on Triassic extension, then to review Triassic rifting and basin filling, and finally to examine how the Early Mesozoic paleogeography impacted on Pangean climates.

VARISCAN-ALLEGHANIAN WRENCH FAULTING

During the Late Carboniferous, New England and the Maritime Provinces were situated within a complex wrench zone, whereas the central and southern Appalachians were located within a convergent tectonic zone, characterized primarily by a broad fold-and-thrust belt (Arthaud and Matte, 1977). The link between these two distinct structural domains was the east-west–trending dextral shear, the N40°-Kelvin Lineament (Fig. 1; Getty and Gromet, 1988), which when projected landward underlies the Newark rift basin of Late Triassic–Early

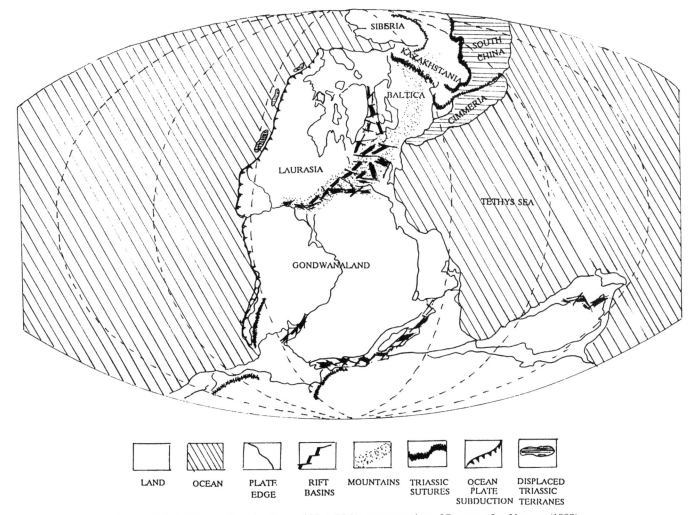

Figure 2. Late Triassic (Carnian Stage; 230 ± 5 Ma) reconstruction of Pangea, after Veevers (1989), Smith and Briden (1977), and Sengor (1984).

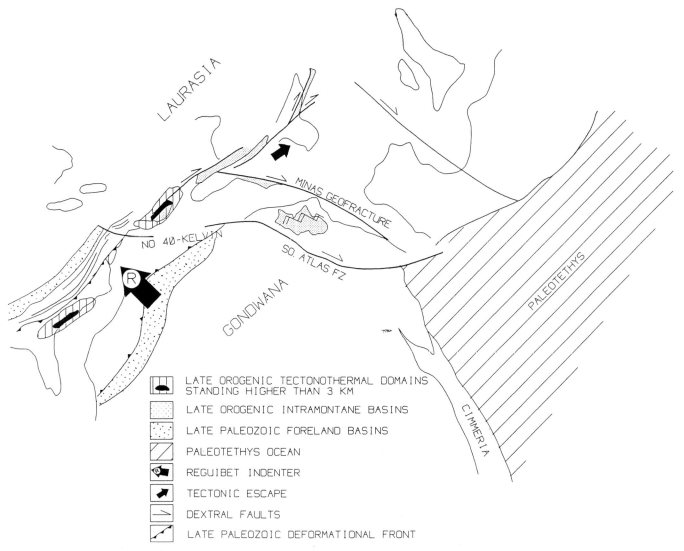

Figure 3. Schematic tectonic map of Late Paleozoic plate collision between Gondwana and Laurasia, showing regions of broad tectonothermal uplift, late orogenic Variscan-Allegheny wrench-formed basins, Late Paleozoic foreland clastic basins, Paleotethys Ocean, Cimmeria, and the Reguibet indenter; the large black arrow shows the major Gondwana plate motion with respect to Laurasia; the small black arrow shows the direction of tectonic escape.

Jurassic age and seems to be relayed en echelon as a transfer fault connecting the Newark and Gettysburg extensional basins (Fig. 4). The N40°-Kelvin Lineament is correlated (Van Houten, 1977; Manspeizer et al., 1978) to the South Atlas fracture zone, which is one of the first-order wrench faults in the megashear zone of the Arthaud and Matte model (Fig. 1). Other important zones include the Minas Geofracture (Keppie, 1982; Cobequid-Chebaducto fault system) and the Bahamas fracture zone (Klitgord et al., 1988). The megashear zone, an east-west–trending belt 10,000 km long and 1,000 km wide, may be considered a transform fault system resulting from the right-lateral displacement of two rigid plates, Gondwana and Laurasia. These first-order shears are right lateral, making a small angle with the general shear direction, and represent the

R shears of a Reidel shear system. Within the shear zone are second- and third-order wrench faults. Whereas the second-order faults typically are sinistral and make angles of 60 to 90° with the R shears and correspond to R' Reidel shears, the kinematic relationship of the third-order faults to the shear couple is unclear.

The importance of large-scale strike-slip faults in convergent orogenic terranes is well documented in the literature. Extrusion and/or escape tectonics, for example, explains how major segments of the Asian continent have moved or escaped eastward along giant strike-slip faults and how large extensional regimes (e.g., the Shansi and Baikal) formed in front of the impinging Indian subcontinent (Tapponier and Molnar, 1977; Tapponier et al., 1982; Molnar, 1989). Arthaud and

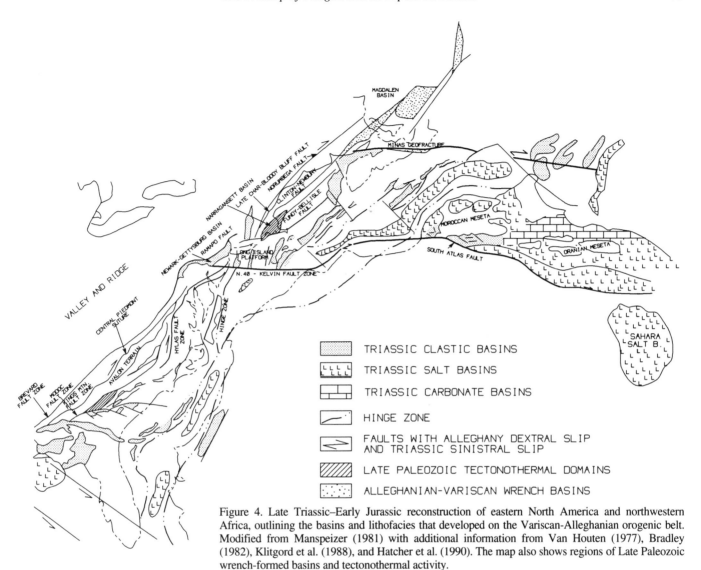

Figure 4. Late Triassic–Early Jurassic reconstruction of eastern North America and northwestern Africa, outlining the basins and lithofacies that developed on the Variscan-Alleghanian orogenic belt. Modified from Manspeizer (1981) with additional information from Van Houten (1977), Bradley (1982), Klitgord et al. (1988), and Hatcher et al. (1990). The map also shows regions of Late Paleozoic wrench-formed basins and tectonothermal activity.

Matte (1977) were two of the first workers to report the occurrence of major strike-slip faults cutting the Variscan-Alleghanian orogen on both sides of the Atlantic, and Lefort and Van der Voo (1981) were the first to propose that the continuous approach between the African and North American cratons during the Late Paleozoic forced the intervening Hercynian-European plate sideways along major east-west–trending dextral faults north of the indenter in the northern Appalachians, whereas predominantly southwest-oriented sinistral faults were postulated for the southern Appalachians west of the indenter. The problem with the model is that strike-slip faulting in both the northern and southern Appalachians is dominated by dextral slip. Hatcher (1989) has thus suggested that the rigid indenter, the Reguibat Promotory of Africa, may have collided obliquely from a more northeasterly direction, rather than head-on, with the Goochland terrane of North America just north of present Washington, D.C. (Fig. 3). In the absence of

definitive markers of strike-slip transport, primary micro- and mesoscopic shear indicators may record only the last sense of displacement along these faults and thus may be misleading. Additional problems exist with indenter models, and the interested reader is referred to Hatcher (1989) and Gates and Valentino (1991).

VARISCAN-ALLEGHANIAN OROGEN: CENTRAL ATLANTIC

Late Paleozoic polyphase deformation in the northern Appalachians, resulting from plate-boundary compression, appears to have been accompanied by tectonic escape, yielding wrench-formed basins (see references below). Alleghanian dextral transpression in the southern Appalachian Piedmont, however, produced crustal thickening and uplift associated with strike-slip shear zones (Gates et al., 1988). Rocks dated at

240 Ma in the Goochland terrane and Raleigh belt of the southern Piedmont record temperatures up to 300°C, indicating that crustal thickening and uplift continued through the latest Paleozoic into the Triassic when, as postulated by Manspeizer and Gates (1988), gravitational instability caused by the uplift produced a series of half-grabens that formed along the western edge of an east-dipping detachment zone. These workers concluded that such Alleghanian strike-slip faults as the Brookneal, Hylas, and Nutbush Creek were passively reactivated in the Late Triassic by gravitational slip, yielding the bounding border faults for the Dan River, Richmond, and Durham basins. Alleghanian deformation is also manifested in the large Appalachian foreland fold belt, where thick sequences of Alleghanian-Variscan (Westphalian and Stephanian) clastics were deposited and deformed (Fig. 3).

The northern Appalachians, including the Atlantic provinces of Canada, responded differently to Alleghanian deformation and embrace the structural zone that links the fold belt to the American craton. Here there is neither a molasse sequence west of the orogen in New England nor demonstrable Alleghanian foreland deformation (Hatcher, 1989; Fig. 3). Instead, Late Paleozoic dextral slip, coupled with a more easterly trend of the orogen, led to a series of late orogenic, nonmarine, intermontane transtensional basins (McMaster et al., 1980; Bradley, 1982; Mosher, 1983). Alleghanian polyphase deformation of the cover rocks in the Narragansett and Norfolk basins (Mosher, 1983; Snoke and Mosher in Hatcher et al., 1989; Dreier, 1984) and the high-grade metamorphic basement rocks of New England (Getty and Gromet, 1988) are compatible with the regional kinematic model proposed by Arthaud and Matte (1977).

In the Atlantic provinces of Canada, up to 9 km of primarily nonmarine clastics were deposited in a series of Late Devonian pull-apart basins that were initiated along dextral shear zones (Belt, 1968; Webb, 1969; Bradley, 1982; Keppie, 1982). Deposition continued into the Late Carboniferous–Early Permian (Stephanian-Autunian) as thermal subsidence occurred over a broad, low-lying area (Bradley, 1982). These basins are situated in a wrench zone where northeast-trending dextral faults are truncated or intersected by a major east-west–trending dextral transcurrent fault, the Cobequid-Chedabucto fault of the Minas Geofracture (Fig. 3; Bradley, 1982; Keppie, 1982). Triassic synrift strata of the Fundy basin occur entirely within the borders of the Late Paleozoic basins, where they rest unconformably on the older and slightly deformed synrift and postrift beds (Klein, 1962; Belt, 1968; Webb, 1969).

Late orogenic basin sequences also occur on the Variscan orogen of Morocco, which formed from the latest Namurian to the end of the Westphalian. From the Late Carboniferous (Stephanian) to the Early Permian (Autunian) (Cousminer and Manspeizer, 1977), the Variscan basement was marked by vertical displacement, mild compression, granitic plutonism, extrusion of acidic to intermediate lavas, and the accumulation of conglomerates up to 2,000 m thick (Van Houten, 1976). Remnants of these basins are scattered across the Moroccan and Oranian mesetas, where they were deposited in late orogenic intramontane basins that probably were fault bounded (Van Houten, 1976; Lorenz, 1988). By the Late Permian the intermontane basins were deformed, uplifted, and eroded. Deposition occurred once more on the mesetas in Triassic, but at that time it occurred under a new extensional regime. Late Variscan deformation is recorded also in the High Atlas and the Anti Atlas, where rocks of the Variscan orogen, which was deformed in Visean and Stephanian, were folded and/or faulted in a dextral shear zone of the South Atlas fault system.

THE NEW EXTENSIONAL REGIME

The Late Triassic (Carnian Age) was a time of worldwide plate reorganization that, in the central Atlantic, included tectonic phases of both Late Paleozoic collision to Early Mesozoic extension. Triassic-Liassic rift basins in northwest Africa and North America lie within the orogen and thus along the Atlantic passive margins (Fig. 4). Those of the Gulf of Mexico have a similar structural relationship to the craton, but here they lie within the Sabine plate that was thrust onto the North American craton during the Late Carboniferous (Viele and Thomas, 1989).

Tectonic evolution of the Atlantic margin, as reported by Klitgord et al. (1988), is partly due to the modification of the crust during the rifting process and is thus a record of orogenic degradation in the Triassic-Jurassic. These workers have divided the margin into three broad crustal zones, namely the continental crust, a rifted-continental crust, and a rift stage crust (which is followed seaward by the oceanic crust; Fig. 5). The thick (greater than 30 km) continental crust existed along the North American–African boundary prior to the breakup. Its thin-skinned allochthonous component of thrust slices, including the onshore rift basins (Allmendinger et al., 1987; Olsen and Van Houten, 1988), is separated from the underlying craton by low-angle, eastward-dipping detachment surfaces that steepen abruptly beneath the rifted continental crust to the east. The rifted-continental crust of accreted terranes was tectonically thinned during extension and contains most of the Triassic-Liassic rift basins. Its landward and seaward limits respectively are the westernmost deep crustal-penetrating faults of the rift basins, which may extend to the upper mantle and to the outer basement hinge zone. Seaward of the hinge zone is the rift stage crust with its substantially thicker marginal basins (e.g., the Baltimore Canyon trough and Georges Bank basin) that deepen from 2 to 4 km to more than 8 km, containing vast accumulations of synrift and postrift strata.

Extensional basins

The offshore and onshore extensional rift basins are asymmetric half-grabens, bounded on one side by a system of major high-angle listric or planar normal faults and on the

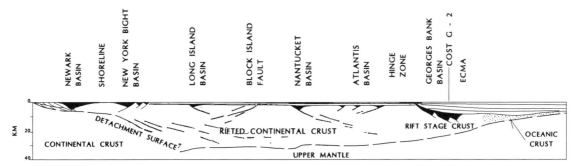

Figure 5. Schematic cross section from the Newark basin across the Long Island Platform to the Georges Bank basin and the COST G-2 well (off the coast of Massachusetts), showing zones of crustal extension, the autochthonous continental crust, and allochthonous rifted continental crust with the Triassic rift basins overlying an Alleghanian-Variscan detachment surface. In this view the western bounding border fault of the Newark basin lies along the western breakaway detachment of the allochthonous plate. Modified from Hutchinson and Klitgord, 1988.

other side by a gently sloping basement with sedimentary overlap (Manspeizer et al., 1989). The basins are aligned with right-stepping offset in the northern Appalachians and a modified left-stepping offset in the southern Appalachians. Paired asymmetric basins, such as the Newark-Gettysburg basins with their east-facing border faults and west-dipping strata and the Hartford-Deerfield basins with their west-facing border faults and east-dipping strata, are common in the offshore and onshore, giving the impression that they may have formed initially as a "broad terrane" symmetric graben that was subsequently uplifted along an axial arch and eroded (Figs. 4 and 5).

These basins may be viewed also as a series of asymmetric half-grabens or subbasins with alternating border fault polarities that are linked together by a complex zone of wrench and oblique slip transfer faults; as for instance the extensional models employed in the North Sea (Gibbs, 1984), the Gregory rift (Bosworth and others, 1986), and Lake Tanganyika (Rosendahl et al., 1986). This type of geometry is believed to result from the role of low-angle detachment surfaces in continental extensional zones (Wernicke, 1981; Bally, 1981). In this context, border faults of the Newark and Hartford basins mark the surface traces of synthetic and antithetic listric faults respectively on a southeast-dipping detachment surface (see Hutchinson and Klitgord, 1988).

Rift controls

The extensional history of the orogen was profoundly influenced by its strongly inherited anisotropic fabric. The bounding border faults of most rift basins are reactivated Alleghanian structures. For example, the Fundy basin occurs along the Avalon and Meguma suture, which according to Brown (1986) is an Alleghanian thrust fault that shows major dextral slip during the Late Paleozoic and about 75 km of sinistral slip in the Triassic (Keppie, 1982; see also Olsen and Schlische, 1990). The Middleton basin of eastern Massa-

chusetts developed along the Bloody Bluff fault (Kaye, 1983), which according to Rankin et al. (1989) is the western boundary of the Avalon Terrane. The Hartford-Deerfield basin lies on a crust of eastward-dipping, thrust-imbricated ramps of Grenville basement and younger metasediment (Ando et al., 1984). The bedrock geologic map of Zen et al. (1983) depicts the eastern border of that basin as a reactivated west-dipping listric normal fault, which according to MacFayden et al. (1978) was a high-angle reverse fault of possible Late Paleozoic age. The Ramapo border fault of the Newark basin lies along an Alleghanian thrust fault zone that separates the Precambrian Blue Ridge and Paleozoic terranes (Aggerwal and Sykes, 1978; Ratcliffe and Burton, 1985) and is considered to be the surface trace of a detachment that may extend to the mantle (Klitgord et al., 1988). The narrow neck connecting the Newark and Gettysburg basins occurs along a major Late Paleozoic–Early Mesozoic zone of dislocation, including the N40°-Kelvin lineament (Van Houten, 1977; Manspeizer, 1981). Furthermore, the Richmond-Taylorsville, Roanoke, and Scotsburg basins of the Goochland terrane of Virginia and North Carolina occur along a wrench complex that is superimposed over a reactivated Alleghanian thrust belt, including the Hylas fracture zone (Glover et al., 1980; Bobyarchick, 1981; Ressetar and Taylor, 1988; and Venkatakrishnan and Lutz, 1988). In the Carolinas, the Dan River–Danville basins lie along the Piedmont suture, separating the Avalon and Inner Piedmont terranes (see Hatcher et al., 1990).

In Morocco, major (Newark-type) detrital basins formed almost exclusively along the South Atlas fracture zone, a late Paleozoic fault system with major dextral displacement that separates the Variscan orogen from the African craton (Mattauer et al., 1972). Sinistral displacement along the suture during the Late Triassic led to the formation of transtensional basins with thick clastic sequences (Laville, 1988; Beauchamp, 1988). Elsewhere, throughout much of Morocco (Fig. 4), evaporites and carbonates formed on a denuded orogen that in places received only minor clastic sequences (Manspeizer, 1988).

Basin filling

Triassic-Liassic basin filling is characterized by what appears to be a paradoxical occurrence of primarily thick fluvial-lacustrine detrital deposits in the onshore basins and evaporite deposits in the offshore. In Morocco, clastic deposition occurred mainly in wrench-related basins along the South Atlas fracture zone; elsewhere evaporites or a hiatus was forming at that time. The distribution of these facies records a complex balance between climate and tectonics (see below).

The depositional history of the basins was strongly influenced by their half-graben geometry. Where rainfall was excessive, as along faulted margins of some basins, it fed high-discharge ephemeral streams, flowing down steep slopes and feeding coarse-grained, poorly sorted braided streams that prograded alluvial fans and/or fan-deltas into moderately deep water lacustrine basins (Olsen, 1980; Lorenz, 1988; Manspeizer, 1988). Perennial streams, because of their much larger drainage basins, developed along the more gently sloping axial or hinged margin of the basin, transporting large quantities of fine clastics from more deeply weathered and dissected uplands. The basins were largely closed hydrologic systems (see Smoot, 1985) and thus experienced cycles of drought, with arid landscapes alternating with conditions of heavy rainfall, high discharge streams, and lacustrine settings.

The other characteristic aspect of basin filling is the occurrence of tholeiitic lavas and intrusions. They are dated as Hettangian or Early Liassic and were emplaced about 20 million years after deposition began, when sediments had accumulated to about 2 to 8 km. Isotopic and paleontologic data indicate that emplacement was geologically instantaneous (about 500,000 yrs) and contemporaneous for at least 1,600 km along and 900 km across the orogen. This apparent consistency is most remarkable, given the diversity of terranes, lithologies, and crustal thicknesses of the orogen (see Manspeizer et al., 1989).

ACTIVE MOUNTAIN RANGES: IMPLICATIONS FOR TRIASSIC TECTONIC EVENTS

Recent findings from tectonically active mountain ranges (the Himalayas, the Tibetan plateau, Tien Shan in Asia) that are forming through continental plate convergence provide new insight into the origin and collapse of older orogens. Rifting within the Tibetan plateau and strike-slip faulting along its margins have been attributed both to orogenic or gravitational collapse (Burchfiel and Royden, 1985; England and Houseman, 1988; Dewey, 1988) and to tectonic escape or extrusion tectonics (Burke and Sengor, 1986; Tapponier et al., 1982). Orogens are composed of structurally weak rock (England and Houseman, 1988), and where thickened and uplifted through underplating, heating, and thrusting, they become unstable and collapse gravitationally along major normal faults. Where the crust cannot be continually thickened, it may fail

along strike-slip faults that tectonically transport crustal blocks away from converging zones and toward a subducting oceanic plate; this process, known as tectonic escape and/or extrusion tectonics, is due primarily to horizontal forces.

The Himalayan-Tibetan system (Burchfiel and Royden, 1985), like the eastern Alps (Ratschbacher et al., 1991a, b) and Alleghanides-Variscides, also records different styles of coeval deformation in different parts of the orogen. Thus, extension may be occurring in the upper crust while thrusting and compression may be occurring in the lower crust, and both tectonic escape and orogenic collapse may be contemporaneous along different segments of the orogen.

REVERSAL OF STRESS

Late Paleozoic consolidation of the Variscan-Alleghanian orogen with its characteristic dextral strike slip was due to northwest-southeast compression, whereas Early Mesozoic rifting of the orogen with its diagnostic sinistral strike slip resulted in northwest-southeast extension. A major problem for workers of this orogen is to explain these changes in the stress field.

Morgan (1981) and Crough (1981) indicated that, as the newly consolidated Pangean plate moved north about 200 Ma, Laurasia tracked northwest over the Canary hot spot while Gondwana tracked westward over the St. Helena hot spot. Heating and doming led to lithospheric attenuation through both surface erosion (as documented by the widespread Permo-Triassic unconformity) and tectonically induced listric faulting (as recorded by seismic profile). Post-orogenic igneous activity in the Appalachians (including the Early Jurassic tholeiitic flows and dikes and the mildly alkaline plutons of the White Mountain Magma Series), however, are chemically and temporally inconsistent with the hot-spot model (see McHone and Puffer in Manspeizer et al., 1989).

Another mechanism, introduced in this paper to explain the change in stress field, relates the buildup and collapse of the orogen to the subduction of the Paleotethys Ocean.

APPLICATION OF AN OROGENIC COLLAPSE–TECTONIC ESCAPE MODEL

Implicit in the rigid indenter model, as previously discussed, is the contention that the crust of the American plate was compressed and thickened as the African plate penetrated into Laurentia. A competing hypothesis postulates that crustal thickening occurred as the African plate was subducted beneath the American plate. Although this study provides no new insights, the occurrence of a thick Late Paleozoic orogenic crust is central, in my view, to the extensional history of the Triassic basins and the breakup of Pangea.

Late Paleozoic polyphase deformation in the northern and southern Appalachians was accompanied by widespread magmatic activity and high-grade metamorphism. In marked contrast to the southern and central Appalachians, where late orogenic molasse basins formed on the foreland from Alabama to Pennsylvania, high-grade ductile deformation in the northern Appalachians was accompanied by the formation of late orogenic, strike-slip, and transtensional basins (e.g., Narragansett and Magdalen) that in general formed concurrently with the final phases of Alleghany-Variscan deformation in the south. Based on $^{40}Ar/^{39}Ar$ ages on biotite in the metamorphic terranes west of the Narragansett basin that are as young as 240 Ma, Dallmeyer (1989) concluded that the very rapid cooling during the Late Permian and Early Triassic most likely resulted from large-scale vertical crustal adjustment. Permo-Triassic tectonothermal activity also was reported from syenite and alkali granite complexes of coastal New England, with K-Ar dates as young as 234 to 244 ± 5 m.y. (McHone and Puffer, in Manspeizer et al., 1989). Apatite fission-track studies the Appalachians (Roden, 1991) also indicate that the Atlantic margin experienced significant uplift during the Triassic, when extension occurred along the orogen. I postulate that as tectonothermal uplift continued, the orogen became unstable as Late Paleozoic thrust faults were reactivated as Late Triassic listric normal faults.

These Late Triassic basins (in contrast to the late orogenic Variscan basins) are marked by sinistral slip and late synrift tholeiitic lavas, indicating that the lithosphere had been sufficiently thinned so as to enhance adiabatic decompression that was accompanied by asthenospheric melting and the extrusion of tholeiitic lavas. Tectonic inversion from Late Paleozoic dextral slip to Late Triassic sinistral slip occurred virtually at the same time as south China and Cimmeria were being sutured to Laurasia, closing the Paleotethys basin (Fig. 6; Sengor, 1984; Veevers, 1989). I thus propose that subduction of the Paleotethys induced and/or aided tectonic extension in the Atlantic (see Dewey et al., 1973; Burke and Sengor, 1986; and Dewey, 1988b). Connection between the subducting Tethyan plate and the extending Atlantic plate could have occurred through the South Atlas fracture zone, which served as a ridge-to-arc transform, albeit a leaky one (Fig. 6). An appealing aspect of this model is that the subducting oceanic plate could induce deep lithospheric changes in the stress field along the orogen from northwest-southeast Alleghanian compression to northwest-southeast Triassic extension (Fig. 7). In this model the extruded microplate escaped along the east-west–trending sinistral fault systems of the N40°-Kelvin–South Atlas and the Minas Geofracture (Cobequid-Chedabucto) system, creating subhorizontal extensional stress in the brittle crust that, in Alleghanian time, yielded to ductile deformation (Fig. 7).

A further consequence of the orogenic collapse is that it gave rise to a conjugate set of asymmetric continental margins along detachment faults, which broke the crust into upper and lower plate margins (Lister et al., 1986). The Newark basin thus may have formed along the western margin of a detachment fault (Figs. 5 and 7) that slid along one of several Late Paleozoic evaporites (e.g., those of the Windsor and Horton groups). A modification of the detachment model presented by

Klitgord et al. (1988), Bosworth (1987), Bally (1981), Lister et al. (1986), and Manspeizer (1988) is shown in Figure 8.

The asymmetry of the margins is reflected by substantially different stratigraphic records at the time of breakup (Manspeizer et al., 1978; Manspeizer, 1988). The American plate clearly was dominated by high-relief, high-altitude fluvial-lacustrine clastic basins along the western edge of the orogen. By contrast, broadly subsiding marine evaporite intraplate basins and low-relief sabkhas dominated the Moroccan plate as well as the easternmost part of the American plate where it lay adjacent to the future spreading axis. Transform plate boundaries in Africa and America were dominated by strike-slip extensional basins, such as the High Atlas basins and perhaps the Newark basin (see Beauchamp, 1988; Laville, 1988, and Lucas et al., 1988). During the Late Triassic–Early Jurassic, the lower plate in North America was rapidly and isostatically uplifted into a broad central arch that migrated seaward as the load of the highly elevated overlying plate continued to be transported eastward along detachment faults. During this early phase of gravitational collapse, detrital Triassic basins formed passively along reactivated listric faults on the highly elevated western edge of the orogen while the near-sea-level marine and sabkha basins formed 250 to 500 km to the east on a fairly gentle and eroded Variscan slope. During the Lias, marine Triassic basins, lying astride of the proto Atlantic axis, were uplifted and eroded. Topographic reversal may reflect the easterly migration of upwelling asthenosphere in response to tectonic thinning or perhaps to back thrusting due to orogenic collapse. The Lias was a time of major deviatoric extension that was accompanied by crustal thinning, adiabatic decompression with upwelling of theoleiitic magma all across the orogen, and axial uplift relating to the formation of the postrift unconformity. As the upwelling asthenosphere migrated eastward in response to tectonic thinning, the abandoned rift-stage crust cooled and subsided, ushering in the drift stage of the newly forming passive margin.

TRIASSIC CLIMATES:

Another consequence of orogenic collapse is that it gave rise to a system of tectonically induced climate-forcing mechanisms. During the Triassic and Lower Jurassic, tectonism played the dominant role because it controlled the size, geometry, and migration of the plate and its igneous history, as well as the distribution and shape of basins and the relief and uplift history of the region. Climate, on the other hand, influences the type of weathering products found in the source, the type of detritus carried into the basin, and the chemical and biological processes in the basin. Indeed, Late Triassic rifting was coeval with one of the five greatest episodes of mass extinctions; at that time 24% of marine families and 43 to 58% of marine genuses became extinct (citations given below).

The Early and Middle Triassic, in brief, was a time of widespread aridity. Evaporites, alluvial fans, ephemeral stream deposits, and playa sedimentation occurred over equatorial and tropical regions, and coal, bauxite, and swamp deposits were laid down in higher latitudes (Robinson, 1973; Tucker and Benton, 1982; Hallam, 1985; Chandler et al., 1992). Apparently neither high-latitude arctic climates nor low-latitude rain-forest climates prevailed globally throughout the Triassic. Compelling geological evidence, however, indicates that a major climate change occurred during the Middle to Late Carnian when humid conditions increased markedly over much of the globe. Simms and Ruffell (1989) show that increased rainfall produced large-scale karstification, fluviatile sandstones with high kaolinite-to-illite ratios that interrupted playa deposition, depletion of ^{13}C values in Triassic carbonates with a concommitant increase of terrigenous clastics in marine sequences, and major faunal and floral changes. Whereas increased rainfall with interludes of arid climates during the Carnian characterized the southern and central rift basins of eastern North

America, semiarid to arid climates marked the northern rift basins. An increase of pluvial conditions is recorded in the offshore basins of North America and Morocco where Triassic-Liassic evaporites yield low Br/NaCl, low $\delta^{34}S$, and high $^{87}Sr/^{86}Sr$ values, suggesting a significant input of freshwater runoff from continental sources (Holser et al., 1988).

Veevers (1989) correlated the Late Triassic breakup of Pangea with a worldwide climate change from an icehouse to a greenhouse state and attributed this change to an increase of plate activity (citing Fisher, 1984; Worsley et al., 1984) and thus to mantle convection with extrusion of flood basalts. In this section I discuss how Triassic tectonics affected early Mesozoic climates of Pangea by impacting on a variety of rift-induced climate-forcing mechanisms, including changes in geography, continentality, oceanography, topography, and atmospheric composition.

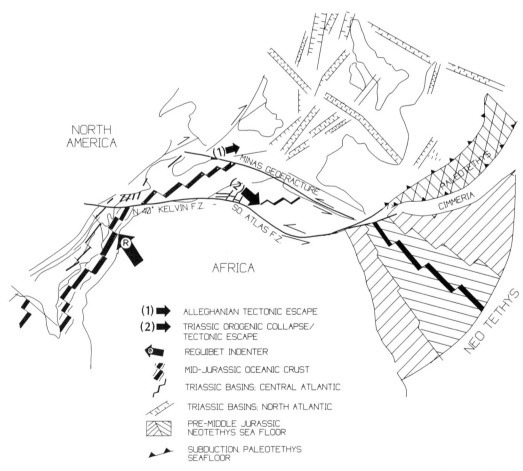

Figure 6. Reconstruction of Early Mesozoic tectonic events, depicting collapse and tectonic escape of the Variscan-Allegheny orogen in the central Atlantic, early stages of Neotethys seafloor spreading, and the culmination of subduction of the Paleotethys seafloor. The large black arrow shows major Late Paleozoic plate motion, which continued into the Triassic; the small black arrows show two stages of tectonic escape: Alleghanian and Late Triassic. Note that seafloor spreading of the Atlantic began in the Middle Jurassic and corresponds only to the youngest phase of Neotethyan rifting shown on the diagram; prior to that time, the tectonic slice in the northern Appalachians and Morocco may have been transported as one microplate with a breakaway detachment located along the western edge of the Triassic rift basins in North America (see Fig. 5).

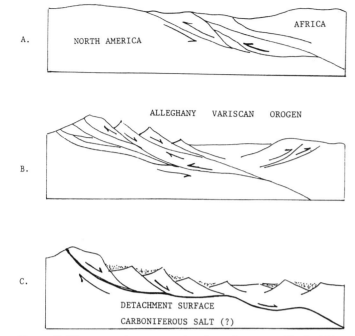

A. NORTH AMERICA   AFRICA

B.   ALLEGHANY   VARISCAN   OROGEN

C.   DETACHMENT SURFACE
              CARBONIFEROUS SALT (?)

Figure 7. Diagrammatic cross section through western North Africa and eastern North America. A, Late Paleozoic northwest-southeast compression with subduction of the North American plate beneath the leading edge of the Moroccan plate. B, Latest Paleozoic–Middle Triassic crustal thickening beneath the high-standing Allegheny tectonic front with concomitant compression and extension in the lower part of the upper plate and back thrusting within the orogen. C, Late Triassic detachment faulting along a Carboniferous salt(?), yielding northwest-southeast extension in the upper plate.

Paleogeography

During the Middle Triassic, Florida lay about 5°S of the equator, and Grand Banks was located about 20°N (Smith and Briden, 1977); the rift terrane thus encompassed meteorological zones ranging from the equatorial low-pressure to subtropical high-pressure cells. As the plate migrated north (Morgan, 1981), transgressing about 10° of latitude between the Middle Triassic and Middle Jurassic, the northern rift basins (e.g., the Fundy and Scotian) would have encountered increasing aridity while the southern and central basins would have remained under the influence of equatorial rain-forest and savannah climates. The rift facies in general is consonant with this view: Coal and gray mudstones are interbedded with playa red beds, bearing calcrete, tufa, and chert in the southern basins; thick lacustrine sequences and braided stream deposits with calcrete characterize the central basins of New Jersey and Connecticut; farther north eolian sands occur in the Fundy basin, and thick salt deposits mark the offshore Scotian basins.

Continentality

Because of the large size of the landmass, it must have been subjected to monsoon circulation, resulting in well-defined seasons across the continent (Robinson, 1973; Man-

speizer, 1982; Parrish et al., 1982). Numerical models (Kutzbach and Gallimore (1989) of the Pangean landmass also show the presence of extreme continentality, with hot summers, cold winters, and large-scale summer and winter monsoonal circulation. Winters along the future central Atlantic probably were dominated by subtropical high-pressure cells bringing in cool dry air from aloft, whereas summers were dominated by equatorial low-pressure systems bringing in warm moist air from the warm Tethys seaway to the east. Tropical and subtropical Pangea during the Late Permian and Triassic had a seasonal temperature range between 2 and 20°C, with maximum temperatures greater than 35°C. Kutzbach and Gallimore (1989) also predicted an annual precipitation for the Appalachians of about 1.5 mm/day, with precipitation exceeding 2 mm/day only during the summer months when the Northern Hemisphere received monsoonal winds from the Tethys to the east.

Oceanography: Epeiric seaways

Continuing extension of the proto-Atlantic estuarine gulf and semirestricted evaporite basins during the Triassic and Liassic led, in the Middle Jurassic, to seafloor spreading and to the occurrence of a narrow seaway extending from the western Tethys to the Pacific (Fig. 9). Jansa (1991) reported that unrestricted flow of Tethyan waters into the central Atlantic may have occurred during the early Pliensbachian and that opening of the seaway between North and South America may have been as early as Pliensbachian or as late as middle Callovian or even Oxfordian. Manspeizer and Cousminer (1988) and Cousminer and Steinkraus (1988) would argue from palynologic data in COST G-2 cores that a marine connection into the central Atlantic existed in the Late Triassic, but this is contentious (see Poag, 1982). Opening of the seaway is reflected by the cessation of evaporite deposition and by changes in ocean circulation, water chemistry, sedimentation, and faunal provinciality (Jansa, 1991). As ocean waters and epeiric seas transport heat and are the source and sink for water (Chandler et al., 1992), the opening also impacted on the climate by decreasing continentality, increasing specific humidity, creating more equable climates, and changing and reducing pressure gradient forces and wind patterns in central Pangea.

Topography: Paleoaltitude

The former presence and duration of a mountain range may be inferred through basin analyses, but no reliable data base exists from which one could estimate with any degree of certainty the height of ancient terranes. Given these shortcomings and acknowledging that the issue is fundamental to paleoclimate studies, I discuss the impact of topography on Mesozoic climates from modern-day analogs.

The onset of rifting in the Late Triassic created a basin-and-range topography that strongly modified climates within the rift and along its shoulders (Manspeizer, 1981, 1982). It is

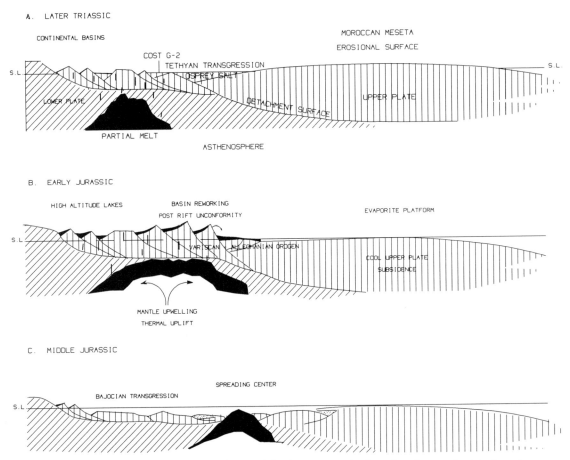

Figure 8. Crustal evolution model for the Atlantic-type margins based on low-angle detachment faulting and the formation of lower- and upper-plate margins (concept and caption modified from Klitgord et al., 1988). A, Late Triassic collapse along a detachment zone in the upper plate accompanied by heating of the lower American plate; as the load to the upper plate is tectonically transported (via orogenic collapse and subduction roll back) eastward it wedges and/or back thrusts the Moroccan plate so that North Africa becomes a broad erosional surface and/or one receiving only fine muds (except along transforms that become loci of clastic deposition). Late Triassic marine seas transgress the toe of the wedge, depositing evaporates and carbonates on the upper plate along the future spreading center. B, Early Jurassic uplift and partial melting. As tectonic thinning of the upper plate migrates eastward, the locus of partial melting and thermal uplift migrates to the proto-Atlantic axis, which is uplifted and eroded during the formation of the Post-Rift Unconformity (PRU), as seen in the COST G-2 well. C, Middle Jurassic crustal cooling and subsidence, Bajocian transgression accompanied by postrift deposition, and seafloor spreading.

thought that the Atlantic rifted terrane had substantial elevation and relief and encompassed an area of about 600 km from east to west and about 2,500 km from north to south. The trend of these basins and ranges generally lay at a moderate angle to the prevailing paleowind direction. As moist air, from either Tethys or Arctic Canada, was uplifted over the shoulders of the rifted terrane, it would have cooled adiabatically, yielding rainwater for high-discharge streams and high-altitude lakes. Conversely, as the air descended into the trough of the rift, it would have warmed adiabatically, becoming hot and dry, thus increasing the rates of evaporation and mineral precipitation. Although quantitative data about paleolatitudes are

lacking, this model suggests that Triassic-Liassic lacustrine and paludal sedimentation occurred in high-altitude rift lakes about 2,000 to 3,000 m above sea level (such as in Lake Sway, Ethiopia) and that evaporites formed concurrently in near-sea-level basins (such as in the Danakil Depression, Ethiopia/ Eritrea). Indeed, climates must have been vertically zoned with the same rift basins, as is seen today in the Dead Sea (Manspeizer, 1985) and in Lake Magadi (Kenya) of the East Africa rift system, where lacustrine and paludal basins occur behind tilted fault blocks near the shoulder of the rift and evaporites form along the deepest floor of the rift (my unpublished observations). In the Dead Sea rift, for example, ove

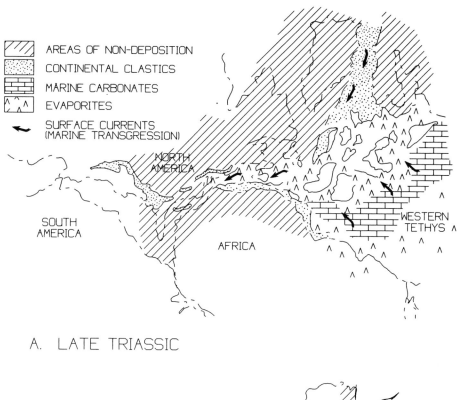

A. LATE TRIASSIC

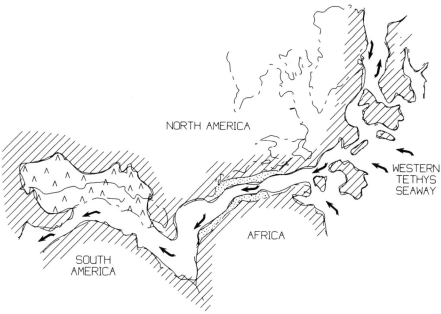

B. EARLY JURASSIC

Figure 9. Reconstructed paleogeography: A, the breakup of Pangea in the Late Triassic; B, the onset of seafloor spreading in the Atlantic and Gulf of Mexico and the opening of the western Tethys into the Pacific. The figures have been modified from Jansa (1991), with the major changes found in the southernmost extent of Late Triassic marine transgression of the central Atlantic. In this reconstruction transgression extends to the coast of Massachusetts and is based on the occurrence of marine palynomorphs from the COST G-2 well in the Georges Bank basin (see Manspeizer and Cousminer, 1988; Cousminer and Steinkraus, 1988). For a contrary view, see Poag (1982) and Jansa (1991).

900 mm of rainfall are recorded on the shoulders of the rift in Jerusalem, Israel, and Amman, Jordan, whereas in excess of 2,000 mm of evaporation occurs in the basin (Manspeizer, 1985). The rate would be in excess of 3,000 mm/yr if the waters were not saline.

Thus I postulate that the depositional surfaces of the tropical rift basins (e.g., Riddleville and Durham) with their humid climatic indicators and fine-grained clastics stood topographically high but had low relief, whereas the depositional floors of the temperate basins (e.g., Fundy and Hartford), with their pronounced arid climatic indicators and coarse-grained clastics, stood lower but had high relief. Also, whereas the presence of evaporites, bauxites, and calcrete indicates arid depositional sites, as in the Newark and Hartford basins, the presence of thick shale sequences in these same basins indicates that the shoulders of these rifts must have been humid (Van Houten, 1969). Because these rifts are largely aligned with the northeast trades and resemble a narrow corridor that is closed at its sides and open at both ends, surface winds would have been channeled along the rift axis, where local pressure systems would have impacted on them. In the Dead Sea rift, for example, the noonday heat of the desert floor is slightly moderated by incoming lake breezes carrying "cool" and "humid" air. Because of the differences in specific heat of water and land and their impact on microclimates, the flow is reversed in the evening hours. The principle of actualism provides a basis for postulating similar local wind patterns on the floor of these Mesozoic basins.

Atmospheric composition

According to Simms and Ruffel (1989), Carnian rifting in the proto-Atlantic and plate accretion in the Pacific also may have caused a global increase in rainfall, through a change in the distribution patterns of atmospheric and oceanic circulation, sea-level changes, and/or tectonically related aerosols and gases. These workers also reported that increased rainfall may have caused changes in surface ocean temperatures, increased detrital sedimentation and turbidity, and changes in pH and salinity, all of which may have been related to the major extinction of shallow marine invertebrates at the start of the Middle Carnian.

The magnitude of Late Triassic extinctions was second only to the earlier Permian-Triassic extinction, when more than 50% of marine families and 76 to 80% of marine genera became extinct (J. J. Sepkowski, University of Chicago, data cited in New York Times, December 15, 1992). The Permian mass extinction was coeval with violent eruptions of the Siberian flood basalts and the ejection of vast quantities of tuff and sulfur dioxide into the upper atmosphere, which may have led to global cooling and glaciation, fluctuations in sea level, and the precipitation of acid rain (Campbell et al., 1992). The Triassic-Liassic basalts, on the other hand, although widespread, typically are nonexplosive, nontuffaceous, and yield CO_2 to the atmosphere, thereby leading to an increase in rainfall and global warming.

Insolation

Superimposed on this assemblage of tectonically generated Triassic factors is the more subtle, but pervasive, variation of insolation due to periodic cycles between the Earth and the Sun. Triassic and Lower Jurassic lake deposits reveal a well-documented and pronounced cyclical pattern of wetting and drying, wherein lakes expanded and contracted with periodicities in the order of 23,000, 44,000, 100,000, and 400,000 years (see Van Houten, 1964, 1980; Olsen 1980, 1986). These intervals agree with the Milankovitch astronomical theory of climates, which holds that variations in net solar radiation are due to the earth's ellipticity of orbit (92,000-year cycle), obliquity of axis (40,000-year cycle), and precession of the equinoxes (21,000-year cycle). However, as the periods of these events differ, their net affect on either very small or large variations of insolation is exceedingly infrequent. Thus their impact on sedimentation seems to be important only in the presence of extreme stability, and this hardly seems to be the kind of climatologic or tectonic setting supported by the geologic record. Yet, syn rift lacustrine sequences clearly show cyclical patterns that can be correlated with Milankovitch cycles (see Van Houten, 1969; Olsen, 1980; Gore, 1988; Perlmutter and Matthews, 1989). Although the makeup of the cycles may vary according to the depositional setting (viz. lacustrine deltaic and deep water lake), the cycles are identifiable.

CONCLUSIONS

The breakup of Pangea occurred along the Variscan-Alleghanian orogen, which had been heated, tectonically thickened, and highly elevated through continental plate convergence from the late Paleozoic to the beginning of the Late Triassic. Orogens are composed of structurally weak rock, and where they cannot be further thickened and uplifted, they may become unstable and fail by tectonic escape and/or gravitational collapse along microplates that are bounded by major strike slip and extensional faults.

The geologic record indicates that the breakup followed this pattern, failing in two stages that were virtually contemporaneous with northwest-southeast plate convergence: (1) in the late Paleozoic by tectonic escape along northeast-trending dextral shears that produced late orogenic wrench-formed basins in the northern Appalachians and Hercynians, and (2) in the Late Triassic–Early Jurassic by orogenic collapse that thinned the brittle crust through northwest-southeast extension along the western edge of the N40°-Kelvin and South Atlas fracture zone, which acted as a ridge-to-arc transform connecting Atlantic extensional basins to the suturing of Cimmeria to Laurasia with subduction of the Paleotethys.

A consequence of the breakup of the supracontinent which in the Late Paleozoic was marked by extreme glacial and arid climates, was the formation of smaller Early Mesozoic landmasses with more humid and moderate climates tha became increasingly influenced by their proximity to maritime air masses. As the Late Triassic also records one of the greatest mass extinctions in history, I propose that the breakup triggered a sequence of climatic events that impacted on Triassic extinctions.

ACKNOWLEDGMENTS

I am pleased to acknowledge constructive reviews by B. A. van der Pluijm and G. D. Klein. I am particularly grateful to George Klepp for his helpful discussions and drafting, and to Liz Oldham for her patience while typing this manuscript.

REFERENCES CITED

Aggerwal, Y. P., and Sykes, L. R., 1978, Earthquakes, faults, and nuclear power-plants in southern New York and northern New Jersey: Science, v. 200, p. 425–429.

Allmendinger, R. W., Nelson, K. D., Potter, C. J., Barazangi, M., Brown, L. D., and Oliver, J. E., 1987, Deep seismic reflection characteristics of the continental crust: Geology, v. 15, p. 304–310.

Ando, C. J., and 11 others, 1984, Crustal profile of Mountain Belt: COCORP deep seismic reflection in New England Appalachians and implications for architecture of convergent mountain chains: American Association of Petroleum Geologists Bulletin, v. 68, p. 819–837.

Arthaud, F., and Matte, P., 1977, Late Paleozoic strike-slip faulting in southern Europe and northern Africa: Result of a right-lateral shear zone between the Appalachians and the Urals: Geological Society of America Bulletin, v. 88, p. 1305–1320.

Bally, A. W., 1981, Atlantic-type margins, *in* Bally, A. W., ed., Geology of passive continental margins: History, structure, and sedimentologic record: American Association of Petroleum Geologists Educational Course Note Series 19, p. 1–48.

Beauchamp, J., 1988, Triassic sedimentation and rifting in the High Atlas (Morocco), *in* Manspeizer, W., ed., Triassic-Jurassic rifting: Continental breakup and the origin of the Atlantic Ocean and passive margins: Amsterdam, Elsevier, Developments in Geotectonics, v. 22, p. 477–493.

Belt, E. S., 1968, Post-Acadian rifts and related facies, eastern Canada, *in* Zen E-an, ed., Studies in Appalachian geology, northern and maritime: New York, Wiley Interscience, p. 95–113.

Bobyarchick, A. R., 1981, The eastern Piedmont Fault System and its relationship to Alleghanian tectonism in the southern Appalachians: Journal of Geology, v. 89, p. 335–347.

Bosworth, W., 1987, Off-axis volcanism in the Gregory Rift, east Africa: Implications for models of continental rifting: Geology, v. 15, p. 397–400.

Bosworth, W., Lambiase, J., and Keisler, R., 1986. A new look at Gregory's Rift: The structural style of continental rifting. EOS, Transactions of the American Geophysical Union, v. 67, p. 582–583.

Bradley, D. C., 1982, Subsidence in late Paleozoic basins in the northern Appalachians: Tectonics, v. 1, p. 107–123.

Brown, D., 1986, The Bay of Fundy: Thin-skinned tectonics and resultant Early Mesozoic sedimentation [abs.]: Geological Society of America Basins Symposium, Halifax, Nova Scotia, Canada.

Burchfiel, B. C., and Royden, L. H., 1985, North-South extension within the convergent Himalayan region: Geology, v. 13, p. 679–682.

Burke, K., and Sengor, A.M.C., 1986, Tectonic escape in the evolution of the continental crust, *in* Barazangi, M., and Brown, L., eds., Reflection seismology: The continental crust: Washington, D.C., American Geophysical Union, Geodynamics Series, p. 41–53.

Campbell, I. H., Czamanske, E. K., Fedorenko, V. A., Hill, R. I., and Stepanov, V., 1992, Synchronism of the Siberian Traps and the Permian-Triassic boundary: Science, v. 258, p. 1760–1763.

Chandler, M.A., Rind, D., and Ruedy, R., 1992, Pangaean climate during the Early Jurassic: GCM simulations and sedimentary record of paleoclimate: Geological Society of America Bulletin, v. 104, p. 543–559.

Cook, F. A., Albaugh, S. D., Brown, L., Kaufman, S., Oliver, J. and Hatcher, R., 1979, Thin-skinned tectonics in the crystalline southern Appalachians: COCORP seismic reflection profiling of the Blue Ridge and Piedmont: Geology, v. 7, p. 563–567.

Cousminer, H. L., and Manspeizer, W., 1977, Triassic pollen date Moroccan High Atlas and the incipient rifting of Pangaea as middle Carnian: Science, v. 191, p. 943–945.

Cousminer, H. L., and Steinkraus, W. E., 1988, COST G-2 Well: Biostratigraphy and implications for the origin of the Atlantic passive margin, *in* Manspeizer, W., ed., Triassic-Jurassic rifting: Continental breakup and the origin of the Atlantic Ocean and passive margins, Amsterdam, Elsevier, Developments in Geotectonics, v. 22, p. 167–184.

Crough, S. T., 1981, Mesozoic hot spot epeirogeny in eastern North America: Geology, v. 9, p. 2–6.

Dallmeyer, R. D., 1989, Late Paleozoic thermal evolution of crystalline terranes within portions of the U.S. Appalachian orogen, *in* Hatcher, R. D., Jr., Thomas, W. A., and Viele, G. W., eds., The Appalachian-Ouachita Orogen in the United States, The geology of North America, v. F-2: Boulder, Colorado, Geological Society of America, p. 417–444.

Dewey, J. F., 1988, Extensional collapse of orogens: Tectonics, v. 7, p. 1123–1139.

Dewey, J. F., Pitman, W. C., Ryan, W.B.F., and Bonnin, J., 1973, Plate tectonics and evolution of the Alpine System: Geological Society of America Bulletin, v. 84, p. 3137–3180.

Dreier, R. B., 1984, The Blackstone Series: Evidence for Alleghanian deformation in an Avalonian terrane: Geological Society of America Abstracts with Programs, v. 16, p. 13.

England, P. C., and Houseman, G. A., 1988, The mechanics of the Tibetan Plateau: Philosophical Transactions Royal Society of London, Ser. A, v. 326, p. 301–319.

Fisher, A. G., 1984, The two Phanerozoic supercycles, *in* Berggren, W. A., and van Couvering, J. A., eds., Catastrophes and earth history: Princeton, New Jersey, Princeton University Press, p. 129–150.

Gates, A. E., and Valentino, D. W., 1991, Late Proterozoic rift control on the shape of the Appalachians: The Pennsylvania reentrant: Journal of Geology, v. 99, p. 863–872.

Gates, A. E., Speer, J. A., and Pratt, T. L., 1988, The Alleghanian Southern Appalachian Piedmont: A transpressional model: Tectonics, v. 7, p. 1307–1324.

Getty, S. R., and Gromet, P. L., 1988, Alleghanian polyphase deformation of the Hope Valley Shear Zone: Southeastern New England Tectonics, v. 7, p. 1325–1338.

Gibbs, A. D., 1984, Structural evolution of extensional basin margins: Quarterly Journal of the Geological Society of London, v. 141, p. 609–620.

Glover, L. III, Pollard, F. B., Tucker, R. D., and Bourland, W. C., 1980, Diachronous Paleozoic mylonites and structural heredity of Triassic-Jurassic basins in Virginia: Geological Society of America Abstracts with Programs, v. 12, p. 178.

Gore, P.J.W., 1988, Late Triassic and Early Jurassic lacustrine sedimentation in the Culpeper Basin, Virginia, *in* Manspeizer, W., ed., Triassic-Jurassic rifting: Continental breakup and the origin of the Atlantic Ocean and passive margins: Amsterdam, Elsevier, Developments in Geotectonics, v. 22, p. 369–396.

Hallam, A., 1985, A review of Mesozoic climates: Quarterly Journal of the Geological Society of London, v. 142, p. 433–445.

Hatcher, R. D., 1989, Tectonic synthesis of the U.S. Appalachians, *in* Hatcher, R. D., Jr., Thomas, W. A., and Viele, G. W., eds., The Appalachian-Ouachita Orogen in the United States, The geology of North America, v. F-2: Boulder, Colorado, Geological Society of America, p. 511–535.

Hatcher, R. D., Jr., Thomas, W. A., Geiser, P. A., Snoke, A. W., Mosher, S., and Wiltschko, D. V., 1989, Alleghanian orogen, *in* Hatcher, R. D., Jr., Thomas, W. A., and Viele, G. W., eds., The Appalachian-Quachita Orogen in the United States, The Geology of North America, v. F-2: Boulder, Colorado, Geological Society of America, p. 233–318.

Hatcher, R. D., Jr., Osberg, P. H., Drake, A. A., Jr., Robinson, P., and Thomas, W. A., 1989, Tectonic map of the U.S. Appalachians, *in* Hatcher, R. D., Jr., Thomas, W. A., and Viele, G. W., eds., The Appalachian-Quachita Orogen in the United States, The Geology of North America, v. F-2: Boulder, Colorado, Geological Society of America, Plate 1.

Hay, W. W., Barron, E. J., Slovan, J. L., and Southam, J. R., 1981, Continental drift and the global pattern of sedimentation: Geologische Rundschau, v. 70, p. 302–315.

Harris, L. D., DeWitt, W., Jr., and Bayer, K. C., 1982, Interpretive seismic profile along interstate I-64 from the Valley and Ridge to the Coastal Plain in central Virginia: U.S. Geological Survey, Oil and Gas Investigations Chart OC-0123.

Holser, W. T., Clement, G. P., Jansa, L. F., and Wade, J. A., 1988, Evaporite deposits of the North Atlantic rift, in Manspeizer, W., ed., Triassic-Jurassic rifting: Continental breakup and the origin of the Atlantic Ocean and passive margins: Amsterdam, Elsevier, Developments in Geotectonics, v. 22, p. 525–556.

Hutchinson, D. R., and Klitgord, K. D., 1988, Evolution of rift basins of the continental margin off southern New England, *in* Manspeizer, W., ed., Triassic-Jurassic rifting: Continental breakup and the origin of the Atlantic Ocean and passive margins, Amsterdam, Elsevier, Developments in Geotectonics, v. 22, p. 81–98.

Jansa, L. F., 1991, Processes affecting paleogeography, with examples from the Tethys: Paleogeography, Paleoclimatology, Palaeoecology, v. 87, p. 345–371.

Kaye, C. A., 1983, Discovery of a Late Triassic basin north of Boston and some implications as to post-Paleozoic tectonics in northeastern Massachusetts: America Journal of Sciences, v. 283, p. 1060–1079.

Keppie, J. D., 1982, The Minas Geofracture, *in* St. Julian, T., and Beland, J. E., eds., Major structural zones and faults of the northern Appalachians: Geological Society of Canada Special Paper 24, p. 263–280.

Klein, G. de V., 1962, Triassic sedimentation, Maritime Provinces, Canada: Geological Society of America Bulletin, v. 73, p. 1127–1146.

Klitgord, K. D., Hutchinson, D., and Schouten, H., 1988, U.S. Atlantic continental margin: Structural and tectonic framework, *in* Sheridan, R. E., and Grow, J. A., eds., The Atlantic continental margin, U.S., The Geology of North America, v. I-2: Boulder, Colorado, Geological Society of America, p. 19–56.

Kutzbach, J. E., and Gallimore, R. G., 1989, Pangaean climates: Megamonsoons of the megacontinent: Journal of Geophysical Research, v. 94, p. 3341–3357.

Laville, E., 1988, A multiple releasing and restraining stepover model for the Jurassic strike-slip basin of the central High Atlas (Morocco), *in* Manspeizer, W., ed., Triassic-Jurassic rifting: Continental breakup and the origin of the Atlantic Ocean and passive margins: Amsterdam, Elsevier, Developments in Geotectonics, v. 22, p. 499–523.

Lefort, J. P., and Van der Voo, R., 1981, A kinematic model for the collision and complete suturing between Gondwanaland and Laurasia in the Carboniferous: Journal of Geology, v. 89, p. 537–550.

Lister, G. S., Ethridge, M. A., and Symonds, P. A., 1986, Detachment faulting and the evolution of passive continental margins: Geology, v. 14, p. 246–250.

Lorenz, J. C., 1988, Triassic-Jurassic rift-basin sedimentology: History and methods: New York, Van Nostrand Reinhold, p. 315.

Lucas, M., Hull, J., and Manspeizer, W., 1988, A foreland-type fold and related structures in the Newark rift basin, *in* Manspeizer, W., ed., Triassic-Jurassic rifting: Continental breakup and the origin of the Atlantic Ocean and passive margins: Amsterdam, Elsevier, Developments in Geotec-

tonics, v. 22, p. 307–333.

MacFayden, J. A., Thomas, J. E., Jr., and Washer, E. M., 1978, A new look at the Triassic border fault of north central Massachusetts, *in* O'Leary, D. W., and Earle, J. L., eds., Proceedings, Third International Conference on Basement Tectonics, Salt Lake City, Utah: Basement Tectonics Committee Publication, v. 3, p. 363–373.

Manspeizer, W., 1981, Early Mesozoic basins of the central Atlantic passive margins, *in* Bally, A. W., ed., Geology of passive continental margins: History, structure, and sedimentologic record: American Association of Petroleum Geologists Educational Course Note Series 19, article, p. 1–60.

Manspeizer, W., 1982, Triassic-Liassic basins and climate of the Atlantic passive margins: Geologische Rundschau, v. 71, p. 895–917.

Manspeizer, W., 1985, The Dead Sea rift: Impact of climate and tectonism on Pleistocene and Holocene sedimentation, *in* Biddle, K. T., and Christie-Blick, N., eds., Strike-slip deformation, basin formation and sedimentation, a symposium (1984 joint meeting in San Antonio, Texas, of the Society of Economic Paleontologists and Mineralogists and American Association of Petroleum Geologists): Tulsa, Oklahoma, Society of Economic Paleontologists and Mineralogists, p. 144–158.

Manspeizer, W., 1988, Triassic-Jurassic rifting and opening of the Atlantic: An overview, *in* Manspeizer, W., ed., Triassic-Jurassic rifting: Continental breakup and the origin of the Atlantic Ocean and passive margins: Amsterdam, Elsevier, Developments in Geotectonics, v. 22, p. 41–80.

Manspeizer, W., and Cousminer, H. L., 1988, Late Triassic–Early Jurassic synrift basins of the U.S. Atlantic margin, *in* Sheridan, R. E., and Grow, J. A., eds., The Atlantic continental margin, U.S., The Geology of North America, v. I-2, Boulder, Colorado, Geological Society of America, p. 197–216.

Manspeizer, W., and Gates, A. E., 1988, Alleghanian transpression and Triassic gravitational tectonics: Precursors to the formation of asymmetric conjugate Atlantic Margins: Geological Society of America Abstracts with Programs, v. 20, p. A218.

Manspeizer, W., Puffer, J. H., and Cousminer, L. H., 1977, Separation of Morocco and eastern North America: Geological Society of America Bulletin, v. 89, p. 901–920.

Manspeizer, W., and eight others, 1989, Post-Paleozoic activity, *in* Hatcher, R. D., Jr., Thomas, W. A., and Viele, G. W., eds., The Appalachian-Ouachita Orogen in the United States, The Geology of North America, v. F-2: Boulder, Colorado, Geological Society of America, p. 319–372.

Mattauer, M., Proust, F., and Tapponier, P., 1972, Major strike-slip fault of Lake Hercynian age in Morocco: Nature, v. 237, p. 160–162.

McMaster, R. L., DeBoer, J., and Collins, B. P., 1980, Tectonic development of southern Narragansett Bay and offshore Rhode Island: Geology, v. 8, p. 496–500.

Molnar, P., 1989, The geologic evolution of the Tibetan Plateau: American Scientist, v. 77, p. 350–360.

Morgan, W. J., 1981, Hotspot tracks and the opening of the Atlantic and Indian oceans, *in* Emiliani, C., ed., The sea. Vol. 7: The oceanic lithosphere: New York, John Wiley, p. 443–487.

Mosher, S., 1983, Kinematic history of the Narragansett Basin, Massachusetts and Rhode Island: Constraints on late Paleozoic plate reconstruction: Tectonics, v. 2, p. 327–344.

Olsen, P. E., 1980, Fossil great lakes of the Newark Supergroup in New Jersey, *in* Manspeizer, W., ed., Field studies of New Jersey geology and guide to field trips: New York State Geological Association, 52nd Annual Meeting, Newark College of Arts and Sciences, Rutgers University, Newark, New Jersey: Newark, New Jersey, New Jersey Department of Energy, p. 352–398.

Olsen, P. E., 1986, A 40-million-year lake record of early Mesozoic climatic forcing: Science, v. 234, p. 842–848.

Olsen, P. E., and Schlische, R. W., 1990, Transtensional arm of the early Mesozoic Fundy rift basin: Penecontemporaneous faulting and sedimentation: Geology, v. 18, p. 695–698.

Olsen, P. E., and Van Houten, F. B., 1988, Field guide to the Late Triassic portion of the Newark Basin section in the Delaware Valley, New Jersey, *in* Husch, J. M., and Hozik, M. J., eds., Geology of the Central Newark Basin: Lawrenceville, New Jersey, Geological Association of New Jersey, p. 233–289.

Parrish, J. T., Ziegler, A. M., and Scotese, C. R., 1982, Rainfall patterns and the distribution of coals and evaporites: Paleogeography, Paleoclimatology, Paleoecology, v. 40, p. 67–101.

Perlmutter, M. A., and Matthews, M. D., 1989, Global cyclostratigraphy—A model, *in* Cross, T. A., ed., Quantitative dynamic stratigraphy: Englewood Cliffs, New Jersey, Prentice-Hall, p. 233–260.

Poag, C. W., 1982, Foraminiferal and seismic stratigraphy, paleoenvironments, and depositional cycles in the Georges Bank basin, *in* Scholle, P. A., and Wenkam, C. R., eds., Geological studies of the COST nos. G-1 and G-2 wells, United States North Atlantic Outer Continental Shelf: U.S. Geological Survey Circular 861, p. 11–33.

Rankin, and nine others, 1989, Pre-orogenic terranes, *in* Hatcher, R. D., Jr., Thomas, W. A., and Viele, G. W., eds., The Appalachian Quachita orogen in the United States, The Geology of North America, v. F-2: Boulder, Colorado, Geological Society of America, p. 7–100.

Ratcliffe, N. M., and Burton, W. C., 1985, Fault reactivation models for origin of the Newark basin and studies related to eastern U.S. seismicity: U.S. Geological Survey Circular 946, p. 36–44.

Ratschbacher, L., Merle, O., Davy, P., and Cobbold, P., 1991a, Lateral extrusion in the eastern Alps. Part 1: Boundary conditions and experiments scaled for gravity: Tectonics, v. 10, p. 245–256.

Ratschbacher, L., Frisch, W., Linzer, H. G., and Merle, O., 1991b, Lateral extrusion in the eastern Alps. Part 2: Structural analysis: Tectonics, v. 10, p. 257–271.

Ressetar, R., and Taylor, G. K., 1988, Late Triassic depositional history of the Richmond and Taylorsville basins, eastern Virginia, *in* Manspeizer, W., ed., Triassic-Jurassic rifting: Continental breakup and the origin of the Atlantic Ocean and passive margins: Amsterdam, Elsevier, Developments in Geotectonics, v. 22, p. 423–443.

Robinson, P. L., 1973, Paleoclimatology and continental drift, *in* Tarling, D. H., and Runcorn, S. K., eds., Implications of continental drift to the earth sciences, vol. 1: London, Academic Press, p. 451–476.

Roden, M. K., 1991, Apatite fission-track thermochronology of the southern Appalachian basin: Maryland, West Virginia, and Virginia: Journal of Geology, v. 99, p. 41–53.

Rosendahl, B. R., and seven others, 1986, Structural expressions of rifting: Lessons from Lake Tanganyika, Africa, in Frostick, L. E., et al., eds., Sedimentation in the African rifts: Geological Society of London Special Publication 25, p. 29–43.

Scotese, C. R., and McKerrow, W. S., 1990, Revised world maps and introduction, *in* McKerrow, W. S., ed., Paleozoic palaeogeography and biogeography: Geological Society of London Memoir 12, p. 1–21.

Sengor, A.M.C., 1984, The Cimmeride orogenic system and the tectonics of Eurasia: Geological Society of America Special Paper 195, 82 p.

Simms, M. J., and Ruffell, A. H., 1989, Synchroneity of climatic change and extinctions in the Late Triassic: Geology, v. 17, p. 265–268.

Smith, A. G., and Briden, J. C., 1977, Mesozoic and Cenozoic paleocontinental maps: Cambridge, Cambridge University Press, 63 p.

Smoot, J. P., 1985, The closed-basin hypothesis and its use in facies analysis of the Newark Supergroup [abs.]: *in* Robinson, G. R., Gilpin, R., et al., eds., Proceedings, Second U.S. Geological Survey Workshop on the Early Mesozoic Basins of the Eastern United States: U.S. Geological Survey Circular, 0946, p. 4–10.

Tapponnier, P., and Molnar, P., 1977, Active faulting and Cenozoic tectonics of China: Journal of Geophysical Research, v. 82, p. 2905–2930.

Tapponnier, P., Peltzer, G., Le Dain, A. Y., Armijo, R., and Cobbold, P., 1982, Propagating extrusion tectonics in Asia: New insights from simple experiments with plasticine: Geology, v. 10, p. 611–616.

Tucker, M. E., and Benton, M. J., 1982, Triassic environments, climates and reptile evolution: Palaeogeography, Palaeoclimatology, Palaeoecology, v. 40, p. 361–379.

Van Houten, F. B., 1964, Cyclic lacustrine sedimentation, Upper Triassic Lockatone Formation, central New Jersey and adjacent Pennsylvania: Kansas State Geological Survey Bulletin, v. 169, p. 497–531.

Van Houten, F. B., 1969, Late Triassic Newark Group, north central New Jersey, and adjacent Pennsylvania and New York, *in* Subitzki, S. S., ed., Geology of selected areas in New Jersey and eastern Pennsylvania: New Brunswick, New Jersey, Rutgers University Press, p. 314–347.

Van Houten, F. B., 1976, Late Variscan nonmarine deposits, northwestern Africa: Implications for pre-drift North Atlantic reconstructions: American Journal of Science, v. 276, p. 671–693.

Van Houten, F. B., 1977, Triassic-Liassic deposits, Morocco and eastern North America: A comparison: American Association of Petroleum Geologists Bulletin, v. 61, p. 79–99.

Van Houten, F. B., 1980, Late Triassic part of the Newark Supergroup, Delaware River section, west-central New Jersey, *in* Manspeizer, W., ed., Field studies of New Jersey geology and guide to field trips: New York State Geological Association, 52nd Annual Meeting, Newark College of Arts and Sciences, Rutgers University, Newark, New Jersey: Newark, New Jersey New Jersey Department of Energy, p. 264–276.

Veevers, J. J., 1989, Middle/Late Triassic (230 ± 5 Ma) singularity in the stratigraphic and magmatic history of the Pangean heat anomaly: Geology, v. 17, p. 748–787.

Venkatakrishnan, R., and Lutz, R., 1988, A kinematic model for the evolution of Richmond Triassic Basin, Virginia, *in* Manspeizer, W., ed., Triassic-Jurassic rifting: Continental breakup and the origin of the Atlantic Ocean and passive margins: Amsterdam, Elsevier, Developments in Geotectonics, v. 22, p. 445–462.

Viele, G. W., and Thomas, W. A., 1989, Tectonic synthesis of the Ouachita orogenic belt, *in* Hatcher, R. D., Jr., Thomas, W. A., and Viele, G. W., eds., The Appalachian-Ouachita Orogen in the United States, The Geology of North America, v. F-2: Boulder, Colorado, Geological Society of America, p. 695–728.

Webb, G. A., 1969, Paleozoic wrench faults in the Canadian Appalachians: American Memoir Association of Petroleum Geologists 12, p. 754–786.

Wernicke, B., 1981, Low-angle normal faults in the Basin and Range province: Nappe tectonics in an extending orogen: Nature, v. 291, p. 645–648.

Worsley, T. R., Nance, D., and Moody, J. B., 1984, Global tectonics and eustacy for the past 2 billion years: Marine Geology, v. 58, p. 373–400.

Zen, E-an, ed., Goldsmith, R., Ratcliffe, N. M., Robinson, P., and Stanley, R. S., 1983, Bedrock geologic map of Massachusetts: U.S. Geological Survey, 3 sheets, scale 1:250,000.

Ziegler, P. A., 1982, Faulting on graben formation in western and central Europe: Philosophical Transactions, Royal Society of London, Series A, v. 305, p. 113–143.

Ziegler, P. A., 1988, Post-Hercynian plate reorganization in the Tethys and Arctic–North Atlantic domains, *in* Manspeizer, W., ed., Triassic-Jurassic rifting: Continental breakup and the origin of the Atlantic Ocean and passive margins: Amsterdam, Elsevier, Developments in Geotectonics, v. 22, p. 711–749.

MANUSCRIPT ACCEPTED BY THE SOCIETY MAY 14, 1993

Geological Society of America
Special Paper 288
1994

Turning point in Pangean environmental history at the Permian/Triassic (P/Tr) boundary

J. J. Veevers, P. J. Conaghan, and S. E. Shaw
Australian Plate Research Group, School of Earth Sciences, Macquarie University, North Ryde, NSW 2109, Australia

ABSTRACT

Profound short-lived events about the Permian/Triassic (P/Tr) boundary, determined here as 250 Ma, include (1) *magmatic events:* rapid eruption of the vast flood basalt of the Siberian Traps and the peak of convergent magmatism in the Gondwanaland province along the Panthalassan margin, represented in Australia by the Dundee/Emmaville Volcanics and in South America by the Choiyoi province; (2) *paleoclimatic change:* following the last ice-rafting dropstone in eastern Australia, an abrupt change from coal measures to redbeds in the Gondwanaland province; (3) *biota extinctions:* indicated by a minimum standing diversity of marine invertebrates and by the replacement of the *Glossopteris* flora by the *Dicroidium* flora; (4) a *sea-level* minimum; (5) seawater isotope changes: a minimum $^{87}Sr/^{86}Sr$, a precipitous drop in $\delta^{13}C$, and a broad minimum in $\delta^{34}S$; (6) *magnetic polarity shift:* change from the Permo-Carboniferous Reversed Polarity Superchron to the Permo-Triassic Mixed Superchron. All but the demonstrably older magnetic polarity change are possibly synchronous, because any apparent differences in age fall within the uncertainties of measuring radiometric ages and of calibrating the biostratigraphic and radiometric timescales.

Eastern Australia, which represents the Panthalassan margin of the Gondwanaland province, has a record in this stratigraphic order of the following abrupt changes at the P/Tr boundary: (3) sediment containing redbeds with *Dicroidium* replaces (2) the last *Glossopteris* in coal measures with thick tuff from eruption of the Emmaville Volcanics, and (1) the last ice-rafted dropstones.

This chain of events is consistent with the following global model: (1) An abrupt change ~255 Ma in the heat regime at the core/mantle boundary generated a change of magnetic chron and released a mantle plume that erupted at the surface ~250 Ma as the Siberian Traps, at the same time as the peak of convergent volcanism along the Gondwanaland margin of Panthalassa. (2) The volcanics vented CO_2 that effected rapid warming by the greenhouse effect; (3) the resulting biotal extinctions and a decreased biomass caused lower organic productivity. (4) Oxidation of surface sediment, including progenitors of coal, led to a drop in seawater $\delta^{13}C$ and, in much of Gondwanaland and China, a gap in the preservation of coal. (Seawater $\delta^{13}C$ rose and the preservation of coal was resumed 20 m.y. later at 230 Ma in the Late Triassic.) (5) Warm surface water at high latitudes slowed bottom ocean-water circulation so that the ocean floor became anoxic.

Veevers, J. J., Conaghan, P. J., and Shaw, S. E., 1994, Turning point in Pangean environmental history at the Permian/Triassic (P/Tr) Boundary, *in* Klein, G. D., ed., Pangea: Paleoclimate, Tectonics, and Sedimentation During Accretion, Zenith, and Breakup of a Supercontinent: Boulder, Colorado, Geological Society of America Special Paper 288.

INTRODUCTION

The abrupt change in much of the Gondwanaland province and in China from coal measures to redbeds at the Permian/Triassic (P/Tr) boundary is consistent with a rapid increase in global surface temperature caused by a large injection of volcanic CO_2 into the atmosphere during the eruption of the Siberian Traps (Moore et al., 1990). Slow-changing effects, such as the supercontinental configuration, the release of Pangean heat, and biological evolutionary trends, are inadequate. Only a mechanism with immediate effect, such as a massive volcanic eruption or (though this is not suspected) a bolide, can explain the abrupt change in the environment.

At 250 Ma (Fig. 1), the continents, except Cimmeria, Indochina (IC), South China (SC), and North China (NC), were united in a Pangea that stretched from pole to pole on either side of the wedge-shaped Paleo-Tethys. Pangea was in the middle of the second stage (290–230 Ma) of the release of Pangean heat that generated the extension of the continental platform (Veevers, this volume) (Fig. 2). Within this long thermotectonic stage, Pangea was subjected to a conjunction of events with profound environmental impacts.

One effect was a notable low stand of the sea below the nonmarine Pangean platform that confined marine facies to the edge of the continental margins. Time-correlation by fossils is impeded by the disjunction between the vast nonmarine platform and the narrow marine margin so that time-correlation must rely on the mainly endemic nonmarine biota. A marine stratotype of the P/Tr boundary from the Tethyan margin in South China, which we accept as the standard, has been dated radiometrically and provides a time-link, independent of fossils, between the two facies. Furthermore, the P/Tr bound-

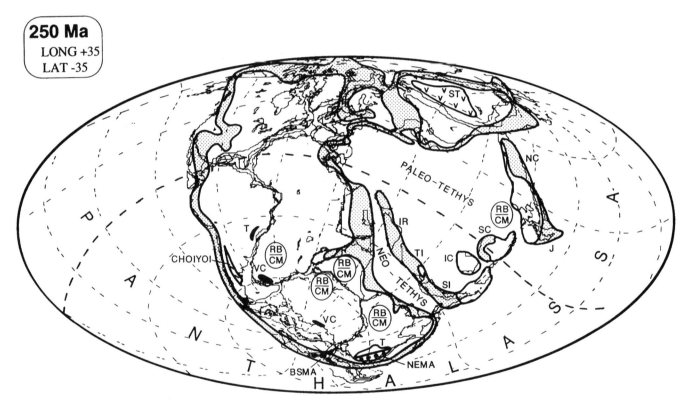

Figure 1. Mid-Pangean (P/Tr, 250 Ma) configuration. Independent continents are North China (NC), including Japan (J); South China (SC); Indochina (IC); and the narrow Cimmerian continent, comprising Iran (IR), Tibet (TI), and Sibumasu (China-Burma-Malaya-Sumatra) (SI), which was drifting northward from Gondwanaland by generation of the ocean floor of Neo-Tethys. Within the continents, the shallow sea is shown by light stipple. Base map and paleolatitude drawn by computer from the Terra Mobilis program (Scotese and Denham, 1988), with center of projection (given beneath the age) chosen to concentrate the continents in the middle. Projection: Lambert equal-area full globe. Paleogeography from Scotese et al. (1979, figs. 38 through 43, for the Kazanian), with the addition of the Siberian Traps (ST), marked by v's and the exposed parts of the Panthalassan/Gondwanaland calc-alkaline magmatic arc at the P/Tr peak of activity in Eastern Australia (granitoids and ignimbrites in New England magmatic arc [NEMA] shown by filled circle, tuff [T] in coal measures) on the east, the Choiyoi province in Argentina (O. López-Gamundí, personal communication, 1991) on the west, and in between the Late Permian volcaniclastic (VC) sandstone in the lower Beaufort of the Karoo basin and in the central Transantarctic Mountains and the Brook Street magmatic arc (BSMA) in New Zealand. Places with the P/Tr change from coal measures to redbeds are marked with RB/CM.

ary defined and dated in the stratotype coincides with other radiometrically dated events of global significance.

CALIBRATING THE P/TR BOUNDARY AT 250 Ma

As detailed below, we regard 250 Ma as the best estimate of the P/Tr boundary because this value (Fig. 3) reconciles the precise ages of (1) the boundary in the Chinese stratotype: 251.2 ± 3.4 Ma, (2) the presumed coeval Siberian Traps: 248.4 ± 2.4 Ma, and (3) tuffs in the latest Permian coal measures of eastern Australia: 249.6 to 250.1 ± 1 Ma, 252.4 ± 1 Ma, and 256 ± 4 Ma and because (4) their magmatic source, represented by the Emmaville Volcanics/Dundee Rhyodacite (248.7 ± 1, 253 ± 2.5 Ma) erupted (5) during the peak of granitoid magmatism, reflected in the peak of cooling that started at 248 ± 1 Ma, expected to lag 1 m.y. or so after the ignimbritic eruption.

The dated tuff lies in the Tuffaceous Stony Coal Facies (Beckett et al., 1983), within the Upper 5c palynological zone of eastern Australia, above the first appearance of *Microreticulatisporites bitriangularis* in the underlying Upper Delta Plain Facies (McMinn, 1993). Upper 5c is regarded as Late (but not latest) Permian (Balme, 1969; Balme and Helby, 1973, p. 439; Foster, 1983) on the basis of extended intercontinental comparison with palynomorphs in the Salt Range of Pakistan, which Balme (1969, p. 108) considered "an entirely reasonable, but not irresistible conclusion" because of diachronous ecological or environmental gradients. The radiometric data confirm the earlier conventional choice (David, 1950, cited by Retallack, 1980, p. 406) of the Newcastle Coal Measures/Narrabeen Group as marking the P/Tr boundary.

EVENTS

Magmatic

The Siberian Traps (basalt flows and minor tuffs) cover 3.4×10^5 km^2 (Fig. 1) and may have had an original volume of 1.5×10^6 km^3. Renne and Basu (1991) estimated by the laser-heating ^{40}Ar/^{39}Ar method that eruption started at 248 ± 2.4 Ma (Fig. 3) and lasted for an extremely short interval of 0.9 ± 0.8 m.y. In volume and short interval of eruption, the Siberian Traps resemble the K/T Deccan Traps, and both are attributed to the thermal anomaly generated by a subcontinental mantle plume or hot spot. Furthermore, both Siberian Traps and Deccan Traps coincide (within experimental error) with an era boundary.

Antipodal to the Siberian Traps and no less voluminous are the tuffs, ignimbrites, and parent granitoids erupted in the magmatic arc along the Panthalassan margin of the Gondwanaland province (Fig. 1). In eastern Australia, most of the calcalkaline granitoids of the New England magmatic arc were emplaced in a 4-m.y. interval that started about 250 Ma, 1 m.y. before their peak interval of cooling at 248 ± 1 Ma (Fig. 3). A related ignimbrite, the Dundee Rhyodacite, has dates of 248.7 ± 1 Ma (Rb/Sr on biotite) and 253 ± 2.5 (K/Ar, biotite). As detailed below, tuffs in the uppermost Black Jack Formation of the Gunnedah basin have dates (Rb/Sr on biotite) of $249.6/250.1 \pm 1$ and 252.4 ± 1 Ma. A tuff in the uppermost Newcastle Coal Measures in the Sydney basin has a date (U/Pb on bulk zircon) of 256 ± 4 Ma.

In southern South America, at the other end of the Panthalassan margin, the granite-rhyolite Choiyoi province ranges from Late Carboniferous (290 Ma) to Triassic (200 Ma) (Kay et al., 1989). Peak effusion of rhodacitic pyroclastics from this province is probably marked by the concentration of tuffaceous sediment in the Late Permian (Kungurian-Tatarian) (260–250 Ma) Rio Bonito and Estrada Nova formations of the Parana basin of Brazil (Coutinho et al., 1991). Likewise, the rhyodacitic volcaniclastic sediment in the Karoo basin of South Africa is coarsest and most abundant in the Kazanian-Tatarian (260–250 Ma) lower-middle Beaufort Group (D. I. Cole, personal communication, 1991), deposited at the same time as major folding and thrusting of the Cape Fold Belt, dated as 247 ± 3 Ma (Hälbich et al., 1983). The Beaufort volcaniclastic sediment was probably derived from the magmatic arc along the Panthalassan margin in West Antarctica, along strike from the Late Permian Brook Street magmatic arc of New Zealand (Korsch and Wellman, 1988), and was responsible for the pulse of Late Permian volcaniclastic sandstone in the central Transantarctic Mountains (J. W. Collinson, personal communication, 1991).

Coarse (>1 mm) biotite in tuff from the upper Black Jack Formation in the Gunnedah basin was reported by Dr. J. Byrnes in unpublished Geological Survey of New South Wales reports (Shaw et al., 1991). Details of dated samples of biotite follow.

Sample B 1. This sample is from the base of a 13-m interval of tuff (depth 30 to 43 m), 8 m below the preserved top of the Black Jack Formation in the Department of Mineral Resources Benelabri DDH 5 located at 30°56.5′S, 150°03′E, 20 km west-northwest of Gunnedah (W. J. Bamberry, personal communication, 1992). Two samples of biotite, a coarse (C) (>1 mm) and a fine (F) (<1 mm) fraction, were analyzed.

Sample C1. This sample is from a 2.4-m interval of tuff (depth 100 m), 27 m below the eroded top of the Black Jack Formation (depth 73 m) beneath the Digby Formation in the Department of Mineral Resources Clift DDH 2 located at 31°17′S, 150°17′E, 33 km south of Gunnedah (Hamilton, 1985, p. 49). A single sample was analyzed.

The biotites have a low magnesium number (32 to 37), typical of biotite from evolved (rhyolitic) calcalkaline rocks, such as the voluminous Emmaville Volcanics, which were succeeded conformably, presumably immediately after emplacement, by the Dundee Rhyodacite. The Emmaville Volcanics lack fresh biotite, probably because of hydrothermal alteration that accompanied the emplacement of the ignimbritic Dundee Rhyodacite. In contrast, the Dundee Rhyodacite contains abundant fresh biotite (this was used in dating; see Fig. 3) but with compositions (magnesium number 47 to 53) typical of rhyodacitic and dacitic rocks, probably eliminating it as a source of the biotite in the Gunnedah tuff.

The tuff biotites have a high content of Sr (36–47 ppm), much higher than biotite in evolved calcalkaline rocks (<10 ppm). The biotites are therefore less radiogenic, so that the choice of an initial ratio is critical. The range of ratios in the batholithic volcanic rocks that could provide a source of the Gunnedah biotites is 0.7042 to 0.7052 (Dundee Rhyodacite of the Moonbi Plutonic Suite) and 0.7060 (volcanics in the Uralla Suite) (Shaw and Flood, 1981, fig. 7). We choose the intermediate value of 0.7055. Increasing the initial ratio by 0.0005 decreases the calculated age by approximately 1.5 m.y. The analytical details and the calculated ages are given in Table 1.

Paleoclimatic changes

The P/Tr boundary marks the sharp change from coal-measure to redbed deposition at the base of the 250- to 230-Ma coal gap (Fig. 2, N) in China and the Gondwanaland province, except South America and Africa. The Sydney basin

in eastern Australia, representing the Panthalassan margin of the Gondwanaland province, records the following abrupt environmental changes across the lacuna at the P/Tr disconformity (Fig. 4), in this succession: (3) the Narrabeen Group sediment with the *Dicroidium* flora, containing redbeds from 20 m above its base and no coal whatever, replaces across a short lacuna at a disconformity to a very low angle unconformity) (2) the last members of the *Glossopteris* flora at the top of the regressive Newcastle Coal Measures, with thick tuff (T in Fig. 4, including the Awaba Tuff, age in Fig. 3) from eruption of equivalents of the Emmaville Volcanics, 500 m below, underlain by (1) the last-known ice-rafted dropstones (D) in the youngest (early Tatarian) transgressive marine deposit in eastern Australia, the Dempsey Formation. The changes took place during a time of apparently constant tectonic activity in an orogenic piedmont (Jones et al., 1987), so that they are not attributable to local tectonics.

According to Knoll (1984, p. 52), "In Gondwana, changing temperature regimes may have contributed to the extinc-

---

Figure 2 (on facing page). Mid-Pangean (250 Ma) sedimentary and tectonic events within the Pangean (320–160 Ma) interval. A and P: time scale (Palmer, 1983), with the Permian/Triassic (P/Tr) boundary changed here from 245 Ma to 250 Ma, as discussed in the text. B: eustatic sea level measured on the Euramerican platform, serrated line = short term, smooth line = long term. Carboniferous-Permian (360–250 Ma) from Ross and Ross (1987, figs. 2 through 4), Triassic-Jurassic from Haq et al. (1988, figs. 16 and 17). Minima from 360 Ma to 207 Ma indicated in Ma. The 250-Ma minimum lies within the negative values from 253 to 248 Ma. C: δ13C in marine carbonate (Holser et al., 1988). D: δ34S in marine sulfate (Holser et al., 1988). E: 87Sr/86Sr in marine carbonate (Koepnick et al., 1988). F: Glaciations in the Visean (345 Ma) and Pennsylvanian-Sakmarian (320–275 Ma) (Veevers and Powell, 1987); dropstones (D) are found up to the Dempsey Formation (251 Ma) in the Sydney basin (see Fig. 4). G: magnetic polarity bias: (left) superchrons (Harland et al., 1990); (right) cumulative magnetic polarity (N normal, R reversed) from Nicolaysen (1985), as explained in Veevers (1990, fig. 3, III). H: Pangean extension/shortening couplets. I: North American granite emplacement (Fischer, 1984). J: Eastern Australian granitoids, age histogram, with n = number of age determinations (stipple); Dundee (D) ignimbrite; and biotite in coal-measure tuff (T). K: Siberian Traps (ST) (Renne and Basu, 1991). L: standing diversity (number of genera) for marine genera about the Permian/Triassic boundary (stipple) from J. J. Sepkoski, cited by Holser and Magaritz, 1987, fig. 6), and percentage extinction for marine animal genera—younger than 260 Ma (Raup and Sepkoski, 1986), older (Sepkoski, 1992). M: continental combinations (Veevers, this volume). N: stages of release of Pangean heat (Veevers, 1990); bracket delimits the coal gap in India, Australia, Antarctica, Africa, and China between the P/Tr (250 Ma) and Middle (M)/Late (L) Triassic (230 Ma). O: platform sequences with transgressive (T)–regressive (R) curves; lacunas shown by stipple, tectonic shortening by wavy lines, Early Permian transtensional volcanics by v's. G = glacials, C = coal measures, C with vertical bar = carbonaceous sediment; sediment containing redbeds denoted by coarse stipple. *Gondwanaland province*—India: the Gondwana sequence, divided by the mid-Triassic lacuna into two parts—E-Early and L-Late—and the overlying sequence of the eastern margin

(Sastry et al., 1977). Australia (Veevers, 1984), east (E) and west (W): Onset of deposition on the Pangean platform (Innamincka sequence) is dated at 290 Ma (epi-Carboniferous or Gzelian, East Australian palynological stage 2) and is accompanied in eastern Australia by thick transtensional volcanics. Antarctica: Permian coal measures and Late Triassic carbonaceous sediment in Transantarctic Mountains from J. W. Collinson (personal communication, 1992); change at P/Tr boundary from coal measures to redbeds in Prince Charles Mountains, from Webb and Fielding (1991); Gondwanide deformation in the Ellsworth Mountains [EM] from Grunow et al. (1991). Southern Africa (Dingle et al., 1983): BE—Beaufort, with an exceptional coal in the coal gap; DR—Drakensberg; DW—Dwyka; EC—Ecca; ST—Stormberg; UIT—Uitenhage; start of redbeds (here denoted by vertical dotted line) in Beaufort Group from Botha and Linström (1978). Other redbeds shown are to the northeast in Tanzania, Madagascar, and Arabia (Wopfner, 1991). Brazil (Soares et al., 1978). *Laurussia*—North America: sequences from Sloss (1988), T/R curve from Vail et al. (1977); in the Permian basin of Texas and New Mexico, the earliest Permian (286 Ma) Wolfcamp Series overlaps the Central Basin Platform (Sloss, 1988, p. 265); the base of the Absaroka II subsequence (268 Ma) is marked by greatly accelerated rates of subsidence (Sloss, 1988, p. 39). Redbeds started in the Pennsylvanian, are common between 255 and 215 Ma (dotted line), and are coeval with coal measures in the Carnian Newark Group (Olsen, 1989, p. 324, 349). Europe: main phases of plate boundary reorganization, from Ziegler (1988); in the Permian basins of Europe, subsidence was initiated in the Oslo (volcanic) Graben and renewed in the half-grabens between Norway and Greenland at the same time (290 Ma, Stephanian B or Gzelian) as sagging in the south during transtension was accompanied by the eruption of flood lavas (Wopfner, 1984; Ziegler, 1988) and the deposition of the Rotliegend and later successions (Ziegler, 1988). Coal deposition ceased in the Early Permian and did not resume until the end-Triassic, and then only in the Viking Graben and Jutland (Ziegler, 1990, encl. 47–49). HERCYN = Hercynian. *China* (Zunyi et al., 1986), mid-Carboniferous through Triassic only, showing distribution of coal on either side of the interval with redbeds (coal gap) and the Indosinian Movement between the Early-Middle Triassic marine (S China) and nonmarine (N-M) (N China) redbeds and Late Triassic coal-bearing nonmarine sediments.

tion of the glossopterid pteridosperms. It is not clear that these deciduous, cold-temperature adapted plants had many avenues of migration open to them when climatic conditions became warmer and more equable. Shifting geographic patterns did provide migration routes for early corystosperm pteridosperms (*Dicroidium* and relatives), which appear to have immigrated from the Northern Hemisphere and which became dominant elements of Gondwanan Triassic floras." According to Retallack (1977), the likely ancestors of *Dicroidium* in the basal Narrabeen Group are *"Thinnfeldia" callipteroides,* which probably came from India, then in the Southern Hemisphere.

Following Knoll (1984), we interpret the *Glossopteris*- and dropstone-bearing coal measures as indicating a cold climate and the replacement by *Dicroidium*-bearing sediment containing redbeds but without coal as indicating a warm climate. The corresponding change from thick tuff in the uppermost coal measures to no tuff in the Narrabeen Group, seen throughout eastern Australia, signifies either the onset of extreme weathering or the demise of ignimbritic eruption in the

magmatic arc (but not the continuing peak intrusion of granitoids—see Fig. 3, column D) or both.

The 250-Ma beginning and 230-Ma end of the coal gap corresponds to the events shown in Fig. 2 and listed in Table 2. Further events at the P/Tr boundary, not shown in the diagram, are the 49% drop in diversity of families of terrestrial tetrapods (Benton, 1985) and the replacement of all but a few remnants of the *Glossopteris* flora by the *Dicroidium* flora (Gould, 1976; Retallack, 1980; Anderson, 1981). Unlike the marine invertebrates, the terrestrial flora in North America and western Europe did not change catastrophically at the P/Tr boundary (Knoll, 1984, p. 48). In the Gondwanaland province except South America, the coal measures with the *Glossopteris* flora were replaced by redbed sediment with the *Dicroidium* flora, with corresponding changes in the analogous microflora (R. Helby, personal communication, 1992), but without coal. In China, the coal measures with the Cathaysia flora were replaced by barren redbed sediment with the *Voltzia* flora (Zunyi and others, 1986).

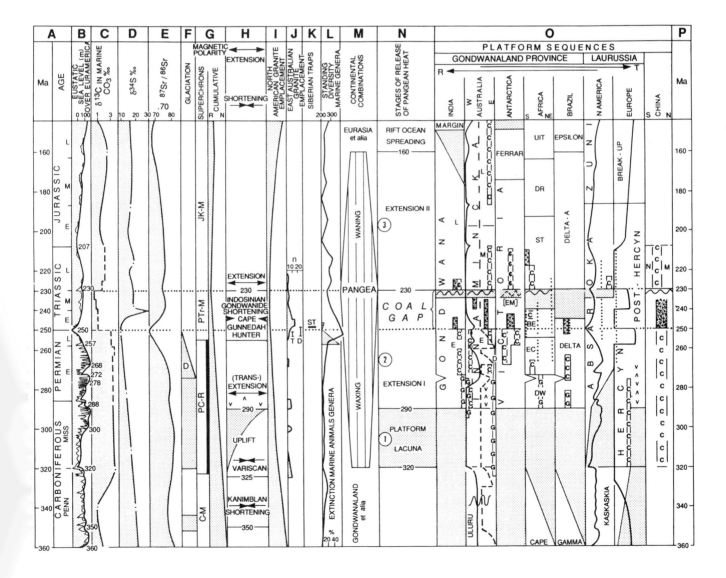

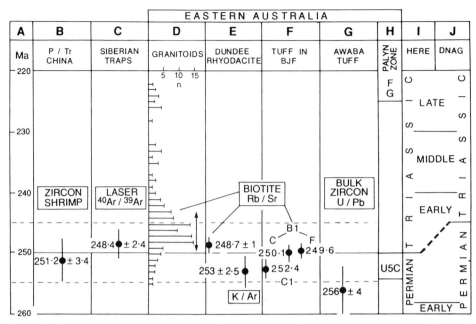

Figure 3. Time scale (A), radiometric dates B through G (method indicated in box), and biostrati-graphic divisions H through J about the P/Tr boundary. A: linear scale in Ma. B: zircons in the 5-cm-thick clay bed 30 cm above the boundary between the Chinglung Formation/Changxing Formation in the South Chinese stratotype (Claoué-Long et al., 1991). C: Siberian Traps (Renne and Basu, 1991). D–G, eastern Australia—D: 140 dates of granitoids of the southern New England orogen, arranged in a histogram to show peak cooling 248 ± 1 to 245 ± 1 Ma. E: 248.7 ± 1 Ma, oldest (preferred) date of seven samples of the Dundee Rhyodacite; 253 ± 2.5 Ma—K/Ar date of biotite from the Dundee Rhyodacite (formerly known as the Blue Granite of Wyberba), originally dated by Evernden and Richards (1962) as 242 Ma, since corrected for new constants and a new spike value (J. Richards, personal communication, 1986) to 253 Ma. F: dates of two samples of tuffaceous sandstone from near the preserved top of the Black Jack Formation (BJF) in the Gunnedah basin—B1, in duplicate of coarse (C) and fine (F) fractions of biotite, and C1 (Shaw et al., 1991)—according to McMinn (1993), both from the Upper Stage 5c palynological zone of Price et al. (1985), the base of which is marked by the first appearance of *Microreticulatisporites bitriangularis* Balme and Hennelly. G: Date by Gulson et al. (1990) of zircon in the Awaba Tuff, near the top of the Newcastle Coal Measures (see Fig. 4), also in the Upper Stage 5c palynological zone (McMinn, 1985). H: as noted above, samples dated in F and G belong to the Upper 5c paly-nological zone, only a few tens of meters below the transition from coal measures with *Glos-sopteris* to barren measures with redbeds and *Dicroidium* (see Fig. 4). I: calibration here of the P/Tr boundary at 250 Ma by moving it 5 m.y. older than in J, which is the DNAG time scale (Palmer, 1983).

The Early-Middle Triassic coal gap (Fig. 2) is found in India, East Antarctica (Amery Group), and China as well as eastern Australia. Elsewhere, the onset of redbeds is earlier. In South Africa, redbeds start in the Early Permian, and the Early Triassic upper Beaufort Group contains a rare example of coaly beds in the coal gap. Redbeds date from the mid-Per-mian in Europe and (not shown in Fig. 2) Argentina (López-Gamundí et al., 1992). In North America, redbeds start in the Pennsylvanian–Early Permian and continue through the Trias-sic and are joined by coal measures in the Carnian.

The climatic interpretations are consistent with the fol-lowing postulated course of global events. An ice age, contin-uous since 320 Ma, was terminated at 250 Ma by the onset of a greenhouse state brought about by a catastrophic injection into the atmosphere of volcanic CO_2. The cold-loving *Glos-sopteris* flora was unable to survive the abrupt warming. We follow Magaritz (1989) in interpreting the drop in the $\delta^{13}C$ curve at the P/Tr boundary (Holser and Magaritz, 1987) (Fig 2) as due to extinctions and the diminished biomass of plants that preferentially fractionated ^{12}C in the C cycle. According to our scenario, the warmer climate promoted greater oxida-tion, seen in the redbed intervals, soil profiles, and the absence of coal (= coal gap). Only after the volcanic CO_2 had been re-sorbed into the crust was coal deposition resumed in the Carnian (230 Ma) and $\delta^{13}C$ stepped upward to its previous level. The CO_2 was resorbed by the enhanced weathering of crustal silicate rocks (Worsley and Kidder, 1991), as shown by the rise of $^{87}Sr/^{86}Sr$ from the P/Tr boundary.

TABLE 1. ANALYTICAL VALUES OF THE TUFF BIOTITES*

Sample	Rb (ppm)	Sr (ppm)	$^{87}Rb/^{86}Sr$	$^{87}Sr/^{86}Sr$	Age[†]
B1 C	298.4	41.8	20.8041	0.77952	250.1
B1 F	292.3	36.6	23.3284	0.78834	249.6
C1	315.0	47.4	19.3661	0.77503	252.4

*Isotope analyses were done on a multisample fully automated VG54E mass spectrometer fitted with a single collector at the Centre for Isotope Studies, Division of Exploration Geoscience, CSIRO, North Ryde, and followed the procedures of Williams et al. (1975). Decay constant and standard values are lambda $^{87}Rb = 1.42 \times 10^{-11}a^{-1}$, $^{86}Sr/^{88}Sr = 0.1194$, and E and A $SrCO_3 = 0.708039 \pm 0.000065$ (2s external precision, population of 48). Analytical uncertainties at the 95% confidence level were calculated to be ±0.5%.
[†]I.R. = 0.7055.

Biota

The most spectacular extinctions were in marine animals (Fig. 2, L), followed by nonmarine tetrapods, with a drop in diversity at the P/Tr boundary of 49% (Benton, 1985), and plants. Knoll (1984, p. 44, 45) found that vascular plant family diversity underwent a comparable decline, but the diminution began earlier and continued longer, with a low point in the Middle Triassic. Moore and others (1990), using a General Circulation Model (GCM) experiment, suggested that the P/Tr extinction event was effected by a combination of causes, chiefly processes related directly to the formation of Pangea that altered the atmospheric composition by increasing CO_2, CH_4, and other greenhouse gases, all augmented by CO_2 from the Siberian Traps. A warmer world had a harsh arid continental interior that adversely affected the land biota; the restricted shelf and coast likewise affected the shallow marine animals.

Sea level

The P/Tr boundary is marked by an extreme low stand of the sea relative to the land platform, some 50 m below the zero datum (Ross and Ross, 1987; Haq et al., 1988). Wignall (1992) explained the fall in $\delta^{13}C$ values at the P/Tr boundary by the exposure of organic matter (coals and black shale) on the continental shelf to erosion and oxidation and the faunal extinctions that followed as due to anoxia of the Early Triassic seafloor covered by the marine transgression.

Seawater isotopes

According to Moore et al. (1990), the $\delta^{13}C$ and $\delta^{34}S$ curves reflect major shifts in the carbon and sulfur reservoirs from the reduced to the oxidized state. As reported above, we believe that the chief factor in the drop in $\delta^{13}C$ was the set of processes that brought about the coal gap. The increase in $\delta^{34}S$

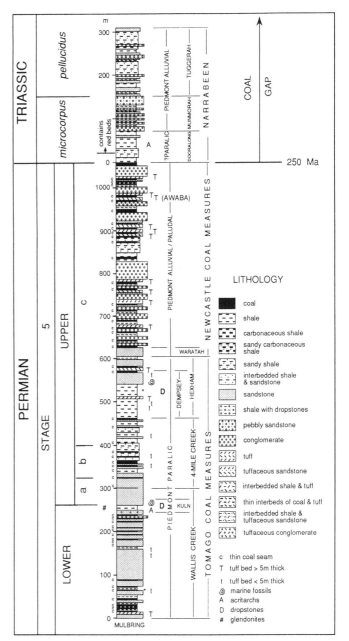

Figure 4. Composite stratigraphic column of the Upper Coal Measures (from Diessel, 1985, fig. 2; Brown and Preston, 1985, fig. 2; Brown, 1978) and the lower part of the Narrabeen Group (Uren, 1980, fig. 9.2) showing the environmental change at the P/Tr boundary from coal measures below to barren measures with redbeds above. Palynological zones from McMinn (1985) and Helby and others (1987).

after the P/Tr boundary is interpreted as being due to euxinic oceanic conditions (Holser and Magaritz, 1987), occasioned in part by the warming of high-latitude waters and the end of bottom oceanic-water circulation. The fall in $\delta^{34}S$ in the Middle Triassic indicates a return to more normal oceanic circulation.

Holser and Magaritz (1987, p. 171) identified the then poorly dated Siberian Traps as a possible source of ^{86}Sr that

TABLE 2. EVENTS AT THE PERMIAN/TRIASSIC AND MIDDLE/LATE TRIASSIC BOUNDARIES, ON EITHER SIDE OF THE COAL GAP*

Events at Permian/Triassic Boundary (250 Ma)	Events at Middle/Late Triassic Boundary (230 Ma)
B. Sea level extreme minimum	Sea level minimum
C. Drop in δ^{13}C	Rise in δ^{13}C
D. δ^{34}S minimum	Middle of δ^{34}S broad minimum
E. ^{87}Sr/^{86}Sr extreme minimum	^{87}Sr/^{86}Sr shallow minimum
F. ~251 Ma: last dropstone	
G. ~252 Ma: PC-R/PTr-M chron	Minimum cumulative mag polarity
H. ≤250 Ma: shortening Gunnedah basin	Extension in continental rifts and elsewhere after Indosinian/Gondwanide shortening
I. Broad minimum in ages of North American granites	
J. Dundee (D) Rhyodacite and other ignimbrites, tuff [T] in coal	
K. Siberian Traps	
L. Minimum standing diversity, extinction marine genera, *Glossopteris* replaced by *Dicroidium*	
N.	Stage 3 (extension II)
O. Coal measures replaced by barren redbeds	Return coal measures ± redbed sediment; marine regression

*Letters correspond to the columns in Figure 2.

causes the minimum in the ^{87}Sr/^{86}Sr curve at the P/Tr boundary. The precise dating of the Siberian Traps by Renne and Basu (1991) as P/Tr confirms this source. We suggest another likely source from mantle-derived basalt in hypothetical oceanic counterparts of the Siberian Traps, which could be compared with the huge volumes of basalt erupted on the oceanic lithosphere during the Cretaceous (Larson, 1991a, b), as mentioned next.

Magnetic polarity

Larson (1991a, b) pointed out the correlation of the Cretaceous superchron (124–83 Ma) with rapid eruption in superplumes of lava rich in volatiles derived from the lower mantle and the possibility of this kind of correlation for the Permian-Carboniferous reversed superchron (PC-R). According to Olson (1992), "by removing heat from the core-mantle boundary, plumes perturb the thermal regime of the core and may, through a process that is not well understood, switch the core dynamo from a state with frequent reversals to one without reversals." This view implies interaction between the core, mantle, crust, and atmosphere, with its history recorded in the magnetic-polarity time scale.

We interpret the switch from the Permian-Carboniferous reversed superchron (PC-R) to the Permo-Triassic mixed superchron (PTr-M) at ~255 Ma (Menning, 1986) (Fig. 2, G) as generated by a change in heat regime at the core/mantle boundary, which spawned a mantle plume. The plume took some 5 m.y. to cross the 2,500-km-thick mantle to its 250-Ma eruption as the Siberian Traps. The kind of Cretaceous oceanic activity, in particular the vast oceanic plateaus of Ontong Java and Kerguelen, is unknown (for reasons of nonpreservation) in P/Tr Panthalassa, but as suggested above, it could be represented by the minimum of the ^{87}Sr/^{86}Sr curve.

CONCLUSIONS

Constrained by the global indicators shown in Fig. 2, the P/Tr events are consistent with the following model.

1. The new magnetic chron at ~255 Ma was generated by a changed heat regime at the core/mantle boundary.

2. Also generated was a mantle plume, which erupted as the ~250-Ma Siberian Traps.

3. CO_2 from this eruption, together with that from peak explosive magmatism along the convergent Panthalassan margin of Gondwanaland, caused a climatic change from cold to warm.

4. Permian coal measures in China and much of Gondwanaland were replaced by a coal gap of barren measures with redbeds, a result of plant extinctions producing a diminished biomass oxidized in the warm climate.

5. Only by the Late Triassic (230 Ma) was sufficient CO_2 resorbed in the lithosphere to lower the temperature so that coal progenitors were preserved again in coal measures.

ACKNOWLEDGMENTS

We thank colleagues in the Panthalassan margin project—Doug Cole, Jim Collinson, Oscar López-Gamundí, and Chris Powell—for sharing their geological insights of Gondwanaland; John Hayes, Robin Helby, Ric Morante, and Malcolm Walter for discussion; Greg Retallack and Debra Willard for helpful GSA reviews; Manfred Menning for information on the magnetostratigraphic time scale and other participants of the Pangea workshop for discussion; Cec Murray for information on the age of the Dundee Rhyodacite; and W. J. Bamberry, New South Wales Department of Mineral Resources, for access to the material from drill-holes in the Gunnedah basin. Andrew Roach made the computer map from Scotese and Denham's (1988) Terra mobilis program and drew the stratigraphic column from MacDraw II. Judy Davis made the line drawing. Research was supported by the Australian Research Council, including Shaw's isotopic work done at the Centre for Isotope Studies at the Division of Exploration Geoscience, CSIRO, North Ryde. Veevers's attendance at the Pangea workshop was facilitated by a travel grant from the workshop funds of the Global Sedimentary Geology Program.

REFERENCES CITED

Anderson, J. M., 1981, World Permo-Triassic correlations: Their biostratigraphic basis, *in* Cresswell, M. M., and Vella, P., eds., Gondwana Five, selected papers and abstracts of papers presented at the Fifth International Gondwana Symposium: Rotterdam, Balkema, p. 3–10.

Balme, B. E., 1969, The Permian-Triassic boundary in Australia: Special Publications of the Geological Society of Australia, v. 2, p. 99–112.

Balme, B. E., and Helby, R. J., 1973, Floral modifications at the Permian-Triassic boundary in Australia, *in* Logan, A., and Hills, L. V., eds., The Permian and Triassic systems and their mutual boundary: Canadian Society of Petroleum Geologists Memoir 2, p. 431–444.

Beckett, J., Hamilton, D. S., and Weber, C. R., 1983, Permian and Triassic stratigraphy and sedimentation in the Gunnedah-Narrabri-Coonabarabran region: New South Wales Geological Survey Quarterly Notes, v. 51, p. 1–16.

Benton, M. J., 1985, Mass extinction among non-marine tetrapods: Nature, v. 316, p. 811–814.

Botha, B.J.V., and Linström, W., 1978, A note on the stratigraphy of the Beaufort Group in North-Western Natal: Transactions of the Geological Society of South Africa, v. 81, p. 35–40.

Brown, K., 1978, Bore log of Miller Ironbark DDH 54: Joint Coal Board of N.S.W., v. 4591.

Brown, K., and Preston, B., 1985, A revision of the stratigraphy of the Tomago Coal Measures: Newcastle Symposium on Advances in the Study of the Sydney Basin: Department of Geology, University of Newcastle, Australia, v. 19, p. 50–55.

Claoué-Long, J. C., Zichao, Z., Guogan, M., and Shaohua, D., 1991, The age of the Permian-Triassic boundary: Earth and Planetary Science Letters, v. 105, p. 182–190.

Coutinho, J.M.V., Hachiro, J., Coimbra, A. M., and Santos, P. R., 1991, Ashfall–derived vitroclastic tuffaceous sediments in the Permian of the Parana basin and their provenance, *in* Ulbrich, H., and Rocha Campos, A. C., eds., Gondwana Seven, Proceedings and Papers of the Seventh International Gondwana Symposium: Instituto de Geociencias, Universidade de São Paulo, São Paulo, Brazil, p. 147–160.

David, T.W.E., and Browne, W. R., 1950, The geology of the Commonwealth of Australia (3 vols.): London, Arnold, p. 1357.

Diessel, C.F.K., 1985, Tuffs and tonsteins in the coal measures of New South Wales, Australia: Proceedings, 10th International Congress on Carboniferous Stratigraphy and Geology, Madrid, Instituto Geologico y Minero de Espana, 1983, Volume 4, p. 197–210.

Dingle, R. V., Siesser, W. G., and Newton, A. R., 1983, Mesozoic and Tertiary geology of Southern Africa: Rotterdam, A. A. Balkema, 375 p.

Evernden, J. F., and Richards, J. R., 1962, Potassium-argon ages in eastern Australia: Journal of the Geological Society of Australia, v. 9, p. 1–49.

Fischer, A. G., 1984, The two Phanerozoic supercycles, *in* Berggren, W. A., and van Couvering, J. A., eds., Catastrophes and Earth history: Princeton, New Jersey, Princeton University Press, p. 129–150.

Foster, C. B., 1983, Review of the time frame for the Permian of Queensland in Permian geology of Queensland: Brisbane, Geological Society of Australia, Queensland Division, p. 107–120.

Gould, R. E., 1976, The succession of Australian pre-Tertiary megafossil floras: The Botanical Review, v. 41, p. 453–482.

Grunow, A. M., Kent, D. V., and Dalziel, I.W.D., 1991, New paleomagnetic data from Thurston Island: Implications for the tectonics of West Antarctica and Weddell Sea opening: Journal of Geophysical Research, v. 96, p. 17935–17954.

Gulson, B. L., Diessel, C.F.K., Mason, D. R., and Krogh, T. E., 1990, High precision radiometric ages from the northern Sydney Basin and their implication for the Permian time interval and sedimentation rates: Australian Journal of Earth Sciences, v. 37, p. 459–469.

Hälbich, I. W., Fitch, F. J., and Miller, J. A., 1983, Dating the Cape orogeny, *in* Söhnge, A.P.G., and Hälbich, I. W., eds., Geodynamics of the Cape Fold Belt: Geological Society of South Africa Special Publication 12, p. 149–164.

Hamilton, D. S., 1985, Deltaic depositional systems, coal distribution and quality, and petroleum potential, Permian Gunnedah Basin, N.S.W.: Sedimentary Geology, v. 45, p. 35–75.

Haq, B. U., Hardenbol, J., and Vail, P. R., 1988, Mesozoic and Cenozoic chronostratigraphy and cycles of sea-level change: Society of Economic Paleontologists and Mineralogists, Special Publication 42, p. 71–108.

Harland, W. B., Armstrong, R. L., Cox, A. V., Craig, L. E., Smith, A. G., and Smith, D. G., 1990, A geological time scale 1989: Cambridge, Cambridge University Press, 263 p.

Helby, R., Morgan, R. and Partridge, A. D., 1987, A palynological zonation of the Australian Mesozoic: Association of Australasian Palaeontologists Memoir 4, p. 1–94.

Holser, W. T., and Magaritz, M., 1987, Events near the Permian-Triassic boundary: Modern Geology, v. 11, p. 155–180.

Holser, W. T., Schidlowski, M., Mackenzie, F. T., and Maynard, J. B., 1988, Biogeochemical cycles of carbon and sulfur, *in* Gregor, C. B., Garrels, R. M., Mackenzie, F. T.,and Maynard, J. B., eds., Chemical cycles in the evolution of the Earth: New York, John Wiley and Sons, p. 105–173.

Jones, J. G., Conaghan, P. J., and McDonnell, K. L., 1987, Coal measures of an orogenic recess: Late Permian Sydney Basin, Australia: Palaeogeography, Palaeoclimatology, Palaeoecology, v. 58, p. 203–219.

Kay, S. M., Ramos, V. A., Mpodozis, C., and Sruoga, P., 1989, Late Paleozoic to Jurassic silicic magmatism at the Gondwana margin: Analogy to the middle Proterozoic in North America: Geology, v. 17, p. 324–328.

Knoll, A. H., 1984, Patterns of extinction in the fossil record of vascular plants, *in* Nitecki, M. H., ed., Extinctions: Chicago, The University of Chicago Press, p. 21–68.

Koepnick, R. B., Denison, R. E., and Dahl, D. A., 1988, The Cenozoic seawater $^{87}Sr/^{86}Sr$ curve: Data review and implications for correlation of marine strata: Paleoceanography, v. 3, p. 743–756.

Korsch, R. J., and Wellman, H. W., 1988, The geological evolution of New Zealand and the New Zealand region, *in* Nairn, A.E.M., Stehli, F. G., and Uyeda, S., eds., The ocean basins and margins. Vol. 7B: The Pacific Ocean: New York, p. 411–482.

Larson, R. L., 1991a, The latest pulse of the Earth: Evidence for a mid-Cretaceous superplume: Geology, v. 19, p. 547.

Larson, R. L., 1991b, Geological consequences of superplumes: Geology, v. 19, p. 963–966.

López-Gamundí, O. R., Limarino, C. A., and Cesari, S. N., 1992, Late Paleozoic paleoclimatology of central west Argentina: Palaeogeography, Palaeoclimatology, Palaeoecology, v. 91, p. 305–329.

Magaritz, M., 1989, ^{13}C minima follow extinction events: A clue to faunal radiation: Geology, v. 17, p. 337–340.

McMinn, A., 1985, Palynostratigraphy of the Middle Permian coal sequences of the Sydney Basin: Australian Journal of Earth Sciences, v. 32, p. 301–309.

McMinn, A., 1993, Permian to Jurassic palynostratigraphy of the Gunnedah-Surat Basins in northern N.S.W.: Geological Survey of New South Wales Memoir (Geology) 12, p. 135–143.

Menning, M., 1986, Zur Dauer des Zechsteins aus magnetostratigraphischer Sicht: Zeitschrift der Geologischen Wissenschaften, Berlin, v. 14, p. 395–404.

Moore, G. T., Schoell, M., and Jacobson, S. R., 1990, Pangea, an elevated greenhouse effect, and the Late Permian–Early Triassic extinction event: A cause and effect relationship: EOS, Transactions of the American Geophysical Union, v. 71, p. 1384.

Murray, C. G., 1986, Metallogeny and tectonic development of the Tasman Fold Belt System in Queensland: Ore Geology Reviews, v. 1, p. 315–400.

Nicolaysen, L. O., 1985, On the physical basis for the extended Wilson cycle, in which most continents coalesce and then disperse again: Geological

Society of South Africa Transactions, v. 88, p. 562–580.

Olsen, P. E., 1989, Stratigraphy, facies, depositional environments and paleontology of the Newark Supergroup, *in* Hatcher, R. D., Thomas, W. A., and Viele, G. W., eds., The Appalachian-Ouachita orogen in the United States, The Geology of North America, v. F-2: Boulder, Colorado, Geological Society of America, p. 343–350.

Olson, P., 1992, Superplumes from the deep mantle: EOS Transactions of the American Geophysical Union, v. 73, p. 22.

Palmer, A. R., 1983, The Decade of North American Geology 1983 geologic time scale: Geology, v. 11, p. 503–504.

Price, P. L., Filatoff, J., Williams, A. J., Pickering, S. A., and Wood, G. R., 1985, Late Palaeozoic and Mesozoic palyno-stratigraphical units: Brisbane, CSR Oil and Gas Division Palynology Facility, Report 274/25, p. 1–20.

Raup, D. M., and Sepkoski, J. J., 1986, Periodic extinction of families and genera: Science, v. 231, p. 833–836.

Renne, P. R., and Basu, A. R., 1991, Rapid eruption of the Siberian Traps flood basalts at the Permo-Triassic boundary: Science, v. 253, p. 176–179.

Retallack, G. J., 1977, Reconstructing Triassic vegetation of eastern Australasia: A new approach for the biostratigraphy of Gondwanaland: Alcheringa, v. 1, p. 247–278.

Retallack, G. J., 1980, Late Carboniferous to Middle Triassic megafossil floras from the Sydney Basin: New South Wales Geological Survey Bulletin, v. 26, p. 384–430.

Ross, C. A., and Ross, J.R.P., 1987, Late Paleozoic sea levels and depositional sequences: Cushman Foundation for Foraminiferal Research Special Publication 24, p. 137–168.

Sastry, M.V.A., and seven others, 1977, Stratigraphic index of Gondwana formations of India: Geological Survey of India Miscellaneous Publication 36, 170 p.

Scotese, C. R., and Denham, C. R., 1988, Terra Mobilis: Plate tectonics for the Macintosh: Austin, Texas, Earth in Motion Technologies, two disks.

Scotese, C. R., Bambach, R. K., Barton, C., Van der Voo, R., and Ziegler, A. M., 1979, Paleozoic base maps: Journal of Geology, v. 87, p. 217–277.

Sepkoski, J. J., 1992, Major bioevents during the Paleozoic Era: A view from global taxonomic data bases: Newsletter of the International Geological Correlation Programme, Project 303, Late Precambrian and Cambrian event stratigraphy, v. 5, p. 25–26.

Shaw, S. E., and Flood, R. H., 1981, The New England Batholith, eastern Australia: Geochemical variations in time and space: Journal of Geophysical Research, v. 86, p. 10530–10544.

Shaw, S. E., Conaghan, P. J., and Flood, R. H., 1991, Late Permian and Triassic igneous activity in the New England Batholith and contemporaneous tephra in the Sydney and Gunnedah Basins: Newcastle Symposium on Advances in the Study of the Sydney Basin: Department of Geology, University of Newcastle, Australia, v. 25, p. 44–51.

Sloss, L. L., ed., 1988, Sedimentary Cover—North American Craton: U.S., The Geology of North America, Vol. D-2: Boulder, Colorado, Geological Society of America, 506 p.

Soares, C. S., Landim, P.M.B., and Fulfaro, V. J., 1978, Tectonic cycles and sedimentary sequences in the Brazilian intracratonic basins: Geological Society of America Bulletin, v. 89, p. 181–191.

Uren, R., 1980, Notes on the Clifton Sub-Group, northeastern Sydney Basin: New South Wales Geological Survey Bulletin, v. 26, p. 162–168.

Vail, P. R., Mitchum, R. M., and Thompson, S., 1977, Seismic stratigraphy and global changes of sea level. Part 4: Global cycles of relative changes of sea level: American Association of Petroleum Geologists Memoir 26, p. 83–97.

Veevers, J. J., ed., 1984, Phanerozoic earth history of Australia: Oxford, Clarendon Press, 418 p.

Veevers, J. J., 1990, Tectonic-climatic supercycle in the billion-year plate-tectonic eon: Permian Pangean icehouse alternates with Cretaceous dispersed-continents greenhouse: Sedimentary Geology, v. 68, p. 1–16.

Veevers, J. J., and Powell, C. M., 1987, Late Paleozoic glacial episodes in Gondwanaland reflected in transgressive-regressive depositional sequences in Euramerica: Geological Society of America Bulletin, v. 98, p. 475–487.

Webb, J. A., and Fielding, C. R., 1991, Late Permian–Early Triassic stratigraphy and basin evolution of the Lambert Graben, northern Prince Charles Mountains, Antarctica, *in* Findlay, R. H., ed., Gondwana Eight Abstracts: Hobart, Tasmania, Department of Resources and Energy, p. 89–90.

Wignall, P., 1992, The day the world nearly died: New Scientist, v. 1805, p. 39–43 [Australian edition]; p. 51–55 [U.S. edition].

Williams, I. S., Compston, W., Chappell, B. W., and Shirahase, T., 1975, Rubidium-strontium age determinations on micas from a geologically controlled, composite batholith: Journal of the Geological Society of Australia, v. 22, p. 497–505.

Wopfner, H., 1984, Permian deposits of the Southern Alps as product of initial alpidic taphrogenesis: Geologische Rundschau, v. 73, p. 259–277.

Wopfner, H., 1991, Palaeoclimatic transect from Africa to the Tethys in the Permo-Triassic, *in* Findley, R. H., ed., Abstracts, Eighth International Symposium on Gondwana: Hobart, Tasmania, Department of Resources and Energy, p. 96.

Worsley, T. R., and Kidder, D. L., 1991, First-order coupling of paleogeography and CO_2, with global surface temperature and its latitudinal contrast: Geology, v. 19, p. 1161–1164.

Ziegler, P. A., 1988, Evolution of the Arctic–North Atlantic and the Western Tethys: American Association of Petroleum Geologists Memoir 43, 198 p., 30 plates.

Ziegler, P. A., 1990, Geological atlas of western and central Europe, 2d ed.: The Hague, Shell Internationale Petroleum Maatschappij B.V., 239 p., 56 enclosures.

Zunyi, Y., Yuqi, C., and Hongzhen, W., 1986, The geology of China: Oxford, Clarendon Press, 303 p.

MANUSCRIPT ACCEPTED BY THE SOCIETY MAY 14, 1993

Geological Society of America
Special Paper 288
1994

Geologically rapid Late Triassic extinctions: Palynological evidence from the Newark Supergroup

S. J. Fowell, B. Cornet,* and P. E. Olsen
Department of Geological Sciences and Lamont-Doherty Earth Observatory of Columbia University,
Palisades, New York 10964

ABSTRACT

Orbitally controlled, sedimentary cycles of the Newark Supergroup permit palyniferous Late Triassic sections to be calibrated in time. Carnian palynofloras from the Richmond basin exhibit 2-m.y. fluctuations in the spore/pollen ratio, but taxonomic composition remains stable. Diversity of Norian and Rhaetian palynofloras increases prior to a 60% reduction at the Triassic/Jurassic boundary. The extinction of Late Triassic palynomorph species is coincident with a spike in the spore/pollen ratio and approximately synchronous with the last appearances of tetrapod taxa and ichnofossil genera. This geologically brief episode of biotic turnover is consistent with bolide impact hypotheses.

INTRODUCTION

The composition and diversity of Triassic faunas and floras are of particular interest with respect to the late Norian (=Rhaetian) mass extinction, an event that culminated in a 42% decrease in the number of terrestrial tetrapod families (Olsen et al., 1987) and a 23% reduction in diversity of marine invertebrate families (Sepkoski, 1984). Although the Norian event is recognized as one of the most severe Phanerozoic mass extinction episodes, substantial disagreement remains as to the duration and synchroneity of the Late Triassic terrestrial and marine extinctions.

Multiple extinction events throughout the Carnian and Norian have been proposed for both terrestrial tetrapods (Benton, 1986) and marine invertebrates (Benton, 1986; Johnson and Simms, 1989). Hallam (1981) argued that the extinctions were concentrated in the latter part of the Norian (=Rhaetian), but he maintained that the tetrapod turnover

preceded extinction of the marine invertebrates by several million years. Olsen et al. (1987) provided evidence that Triassic vertebrate faunas persisted until the latest Triassic.

Although these hypotheses make different predictions about the Late Triassic fossil record, the dearth of Triassic/Jurassic boundary sections (Hallam, 1981), the difficulty of correlating marine and terrestrial strata, and the proliferation of Late Triassic time scales (see Kerp, 1991) render them difficult to test.

These problems can be partially surmounted in the Newark Supergroup of eastern North America (Fig. 1). Sedimentation in these rift basins was continuous from the Carnian through the Hettangian, and the Triassic/Jurassic boundary is accessible in five separate basins. The presence of dated basalt horizons, in conjunction with periodic sedimentary cycles, permits construction of a Late Triassic time scale calibrated in absolute time (Fig. 2) (Fowell and Olsen, 1993). No marine strata are present, but the variety of fossilized materials, including osseous tetrapod remains, palynomorphs, and vertebrate ichnofossils, permits comparison of a suite of organisms preserved under diverse conditions. In this chapter, we deal primarily with the palynological record. However, it is hoped that the numerous tetrapod fossils and palynomorph-bearing horizons will ultimately enable more rigorous correlations with global terrestrial and marine strata.

---

*Present address: 27 Tower Hill Avenue, Redbank, New Jersey 07701.

Fowell, S. J., Cornet, B., and Olsen, P. E., 1994, Geologically rapid Late Triassic extinctions: Palynological evidence from the Newark Supergroup, *in* Klein, G. D., ed., Pangea: Paleoclimate, Tectonics, and Sedimentation During Accretion, Zenith, and Breakup of a Supercontinent: Boulder, Colorado, Geological Society of America Special Paper 288.

CYCLICITY

The Newark Supergroup is composed predominantly of fluvial and lacustrine strata that fill a series of rift basins formed by the Pangean breakup. During the Late Triassic and Early Jurassic, this chain of elongate half grabens stretched from 4°S to 15°N (Witte et al., 1991). Climate models for idealized geographic representations of Pangea have shown that a large landmass centered on the equator will exhibit summer and winter

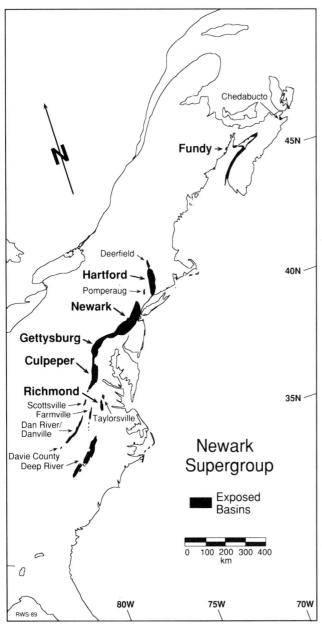

Figure 1. The early Mesozoic Newark Supergroup, showing distribution of exposed basins (from Olsen et al., 1989). Palynomorph assemblages discussed in this chapter were collected from basins shown in boldface type.

monsoon circulation patterns (Kutzbach and Gallimore, 1989; Short et al., 1991). These models are consistent with the thick lacustrine deposits of the Newark Supergroup, where long-term fluctuations of annual precipitation are indicated by the presence of hierarchical transgressive and regressive lacustrine cycles (Olsen, 1986; Olsen et al, 1989).

The shortest of these cycles are shallowing-upward packages between 1.5 and 35 m thick, identified in outcrop on the basis of rock type and fabric (Olsen, 1986; Olsen et al., 1989; Olsen, 1991). Using the rationale outlined by Olsen (1986), cycles have been calibrated via biostratigraphic age estimates and published radiometric dates. Biostratigraphic calibration and Fourier analysis of these cycles both yield an average periodicity of approximately 21 k.y. (Olsen, 1986). This value falls between the 18-k.y. and 21.5-k.y. precession periods calculated for the Early Jurassic (Berger et al., 1992).

Fourier analysis of long stratigraphic columns and cores of the entire Triassic Newark basin section reveals higher-order cycles with periodicities of 100 k.y., 400 k.y., and 2 m.y. (Olsen, 1986). The 100-k.y. and 400-k.y. cycles correspond to periodicities predicted by Milankovitch theory for the Earth's eccentricity cycles (Hays et al., 1976; Short et al., 1991), which have remained relatively constant throughout Earth history (Berger and Pestiaux, 1984). A 2-m.y. eccentricity cycle can also be shown to exist from the orbital dynamics, but unlike the other cycles its effect on climate has not been modeled.

The regularity and duration of the Newark Supergroup lacustrine cycles are compatible with the hypothesis that orbitally controlled seasonal and latitudinal variations in solar radiation determined the length and intensity of Mesozoic rainy seasons. A latitudinal climatic gradient is also apparent; differences in the type and abundance of sedimentary structures and facies indicate that southern Newark Supergroup basins were far more humid than the northern basins (Hubert and Mertz, 1980; Olsen, 1991; Olsen et al., 1989). This drier-to-the-north trend resulted in three primary types of lacustrine cycles distinguishable by the ratio of wet/dry fabrics: the humid Richmond type, the dry Fundy type, and the intermediate Newark type (Olsen, 1991). Palynologically productive horizons are generally restricted to the deeper-water lacustrine facies. Consequently, the completeness of the palynological record in stratigraphic sections from the Newark Supergroup increases with the average lake depth.

Dry lacustrine cycles occur in the Fundy basin of Nova Scotia (Fig. 1), where sedimentation rates were so low that 21-k.y. cycles cannot be identified. Higher-order cycles are manifested in the form of sand-patch cycles (Smoot and Olsen, 1985, 1988). These cycles are approximately 1 to 2 m thick and consist of sedimentary fabrics that record alterations between shallow, perennial lakes and playas with salt crusts (Olsen, 1991). Deep-water lacustrine facies are extremely rare, and preserved palynofloras are similarly sparse.

Intermediate Newark-type cycles are present in the Dan River/Danville, Culpeper, Gettysburg, Newark, Pomperaug,

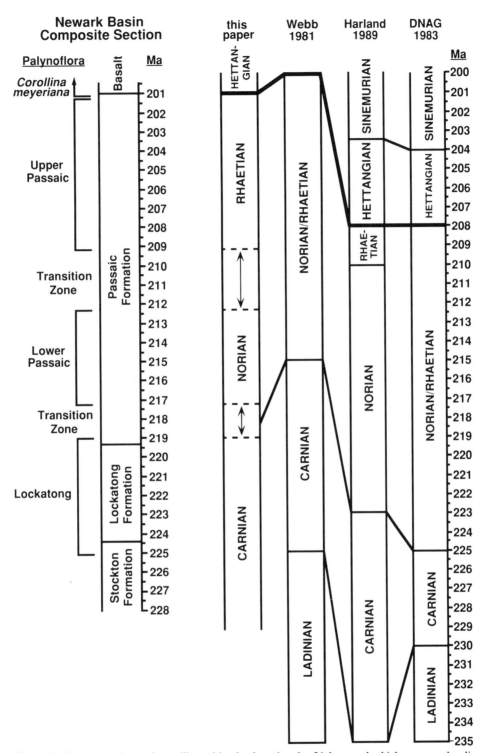

Figure 2. Newark basin section calibrated in absolute time by 21-k.y.-cycle thicknesses and radiometric dates (see text). Palynostratigraphy outlined by Cornet (1977) permits construction of a preliminary Late Triassic time scale for the Newark Supergroup. Time scales by Webb (1981), Harland et al. (1989), and Palmer (1983) (DNAG) are shown for comparison.

Hartford, and Deerfield basins (Fig. 1). These 21-k.y. cycles display a range of sedimentary fabrics, from deep-water microlaminae to subaerial desiccation cracks. Many of the cycles contain deep-water facies, but shallow-water and desiccated fabrics are more common (Olsen, 1991). Palynomorph preservation is restricted to the deep-water facies and is discontinuous within individual 21-k.y. cycles.

Humid Richmond-type cycles are present in the Richmond and Taylorsville basins of the southern Newark Supergroup (Fig. 1). Desiccated, mudcracked fabrics are rare, and 21-k.y. cycles consist primarily of microlaminated claystones, coals, and shallow-water siltstones (Olsen, 1991). The nearly continuous palynological record of the Richmond basin is ideal for studies of early Late Triassic microfloral diversity.

PALYNOFLORAL ASSEMBLAGES AND SEDIMENTARY CYCLICITY OF THE CARNIAN RICHMOND BASIN

Outcrops are rare in the Richmond basin, but a nearly complete palynological record has been obtained from the ~2,000-m-deep Horner #1 well (Fig. 3). Well cuttings of the entire middle Carnian Richmond basin section, from the Otterdale Formation to the base of the Tuckahoe Formation, were collected at 9.1-m (30-ft) intervals and processed for palynomorphs.

In contrast to Early Jurassic palynomorph assemblages, which are dominated by a single pollen genus *(Corollina)*, the morphological and generic diversity of the Richmond basin palynofloras is characteristic of Triassic assemblages throughout the Newark Supergroup. Dominance of either bisaccate or monosaccate (circumsaccate) pollen morphotypes is also typical. Spores, however, are far more abundant in the Carnian Richmond basin assemblages than in Norian palynofloras from northern basins. The Horner #1 well cuttings exhibit large fluctuations in the relative abundance of pollen and spores (Fig. 3) that appear to reflect the 2-m.y. climate cycle.

Well logs from Horner #1 indicate that the thickness of the 21-k.y. cycle increases from 7 to 10 m downsection. Adjacent to the Horner #1 well, a 150-m outcrop of the Turkey Branch Formation also exhibits an extremely regular, 7-m cycle thickness. Cores of underlying formations confirm the presence of thicker, 10-m cycles. The average 21-k.y. cycle thickness is estimated to be 8.5 m for the palynologically productive portions of the Horner well. Application of this estimate to the data in Figure 3 demonstrates that the Horner #1 well spans approximately 4 m.y. Peaks of the pollen/spore ratio, emphasized by smoothing of the data in Figure 3, occur at ~2-m.y. intervals. The spores were produced by lower vascular plants that favored high precipitation and/or humidity, whereas pollen-producing seed plants dominated during intervals of relatively arid climate.

Despite periodic fluctuations in palynomorph abundances, the taxonomic composition of the assemblages re-

mains relatively stable throughout the entire Carnian record of the Richmond basin. This indicates that the climatic variations produced gradual floral changes and were not of sufficient magnitude to cause regional extinctions.

LATE TRIASSIC AND EARLY JURASSIC PALYNOFLORAS

The youngest sediments in the Richmond basin are of Carnian age, but the palynological record is continued through Norian, Rhaetian, and Hettangian strata in basins to the north. The Triassic/Jurassic boundary in these basins has been identified by the appearance of palynofloras dominated by the circumpolloid pollen genus *Corollina*. This Early Jurassic *Corollina meyeriana* palynoflora (Fig. 2) rapidly replaces the diverse, monosaccate- and bisaccate-dominated assemblages characteristic of the Carnian, Norian, and Rhaetian (Cornet, 1977; Cornet and Olsen, 1985).

PALYNOLOGY OF HORNER # 1

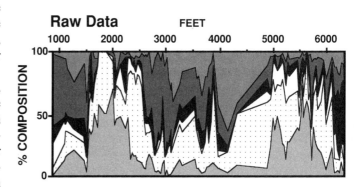

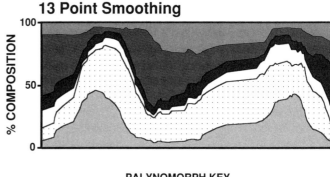

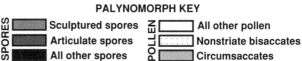

Figure 3. Composition of palynomorph assemblages from the Richmond basin Horner #1 well. Smoothing of the data via a 130-ft moving window emphasizes cyclical variations of the pollen/spore ratio. The entire palynological record (900 ft to 6,400 ft) spans an estimated 4 m.y., based on 21-k.y. cycle thicknesses from well log, core, and outcrop data.

The abrupt transition from Late Triassic to Early Jurassic palynofloras is evident in Figure 4, a composite range chart of palynomorph species from deep-water, lacustrine facies of the Culpeper, Gettysburg, Hartford, and Newark basins (see Table 1 for species names with citations). Temporal resolution of these ranges is derived from Newark basin cyclostratigraphy. Fowell and Olsen (1993) use measured cycle thicknesses from the Late Triassic and earliest Jurassic lacustrine record of the Newark basin to calibrate the stratigraphic section in relative time (Fig. 2). This section is fixed in absolute time by 202.2 ± 1.3 Ma ^{40}Ar/^{39}Ar dates (Sutter, 1988) and 201 ± 1 Ma U/Pb dates (Dunning and Hodych, 1990) of the Palisades sill, which fed the Orange Mountain basalt and the correlative Jacksonwald basalt (Ratcliffe, 1988).

The composite range chart in Figure 4 was constructed on the time-calibrated Newark basin section using the graphic correlation method outlined by Shaw (1964). As discontinuous preservation precluded calculation of continuous correlation lines from the palynological data alone, correlation lines were fixed by paleontological, stratigraphic, and palynological tie points (Fowell and Olsen, 1993).

Species' ranges for the late Carnian, Norian, and Rhaetian (Fig. 4; Table 1) indicate that palynofloral diversity increased throughout the last 24 m.y. of the Triassic (see Fig. 5 of Fowell and Olsen, 1993). The transition from diverse Triassic assemblages to *Corollina*-dominated Jurassic palynofloras occurs at approximately 201 Ma and is coincident with a loss of 13 of the 20 most common Late Triassic species. In total, 24 of the 40 species recorded from the latest Triassic palynofloras are absent from Early Jurassic assemblages. This represents a 60% regional extinction across the Triassic/Jurassic boundary.

TRIASSIC/JURASSIC BOUNDARY SECTIONS

Palynomorph assemblages from exposures in the Jacksonwald Syncline of the Newark basin further limit the Triassic/Jurassic boundary palynofloral turnover to an 11-m interval that is barren of palynomorphs. A local cycle thickness of ~20 m allows the duration of this transition to be constrained to less than 21 k.y. (Fig. 5) (Fowell and Olsen, 1993).

Palynomorph assemblages characterized by unusually high percentages (>50%) of trilete spores have been recovered from the Triassic/Jurassic boundary in three Jacksonwald syncline sections (Fig. 5a, b, and c). All three sections lie within the Passaic Formation, and two extend to the base of the ~201 Ma Jacksonwald basalt. Stratigraphic correlations are facilitated by the cyclostratigraphy of the sections and the presence in each of a black, organic-rich clay layer overlain by an unusual, blue-gray, plant-bearing sandstone. Spore-dominated assemblages Cl, EVD, 6-4, and 6-5 are composed of 50 to 89% trilete spore species of the genera *Anapiculatisporites, Converrucosisporites, Deltoidospora, Dictyophyllidites, Granulatisporites, Kyrtomisporis, Porcellispora, Reticulatisporites,*

Todisporites, and *Verrucosisporites* (R. Litwin, personal communication, 1989; Olsen et al., 1990). These palynofloras occur between the highest Triassic assemblage (A4, Fig. 5a) and the lowest Jurassic *Corollina meyeriana* palynoflora (EVC, Fig. 5b).

Palynofloras from section 6 (Fig. 5c) and the Exeter Village section (Fig. 5b) serve to bracket the stratigraphic duration of the spore-dominated assemblages. The percentage of trilete spores increases markedly between samples 6-2 and 6-4 of section 6 and decreases again from 6-5 to 6-6. The abundance of trilete spores also drops off dramatically above sample EVD of the Exeter Village section.

In Figure 6, spore percentages from all productive localities in the Jacksonwald Syncline are plotted against thickness above and below the base of the blue-gray sandstone. The spore-dominated palynofloras have a limited stratigraphic distribution (less than 0.5 m), apparently originating and terminating abruptly.

In the Grist Mills (Fig. 5a) and Exeter Village (Fig. 5b) sections, this spore spike occurs above typical Late Triassic assemblages of monosaccates and bisaccates and below *Corollina*-rich Jurassic palynofloras. This relationship is not apparent in section 6 (Fig. 5c). Samples 6-1 and 6-2, which underline the spore spike, contain the high percentages of *Corollina* typical of Jurassic assemblages. Yet these assemblages retain low abundances of the monosaccate Triassic index species *Vallasporites ignacii* and *Patinasporites densus*. The only comparable palynofloras in the Newark Supergroup are from the Fundy basin, where samples with abundant *Corollina* and rare (but clearly not reworked) *Patinasporites densus* are present 32 cm below the North Mountain basalt. This basalt has been assigned a U/Pb date of 202 ± 1 Ma (Hodych and Dunning, 1992) and is correlative with the Jacksonwald basalt. Given the low sedimentation rates in the Fundy basin (Olsen et al., 1989; Olsen, 1991), the Fundy assemblages may be time-equivalent with samples 6-1 and 6-2. We consider these palynofloras indicative of uppermost Triassic strata due to the presence of diagnostic Triassic species, which are absent from overlying assemblages in both the Newark and Fundy basins.

DISCUSSION AND CONCLUSIONS

Evidence for a geologically rapid, terminal-Triassic biotic turnover in the Newark Supergroup is not confined to the palynological record. Footprint assemblages from the Jacksonwald Syncline show that the last appearances of the Late Triassic ichnofossil genera *Gwyneddichnium, Apatopus, Brachychirotherium,* and two new genera are coincident with the palynologically defined Triassic/Jurassic boundary (Silvestri, 1991; Silvestri and Szajna, 1993). Absence of these five footprint taxa from Early Jurassic assemblages corresponds to the disappearance of previously abundant tetrapod trackmakers and constitutes a decrease of approximately 50% in the diversity of Newark basin ichnofossil genera (Silvestri, 1991; Silvestri and Szajna, 1993).

Composite Range Chart

SPECIES

tetrad type 39
Retisulcites sp. 126
Microcachryidites doubingeri
Lunatisporites acutus
Vallasporites sp. 68
Camerozonosporites rudis
Microcachryidites sp. 143
Plicatisaccus badius
Camerosporites pseudoverrucatus
Triadispora cf. T. obscura
Guthoerlisporites cancellosus
Trilites klausii
Colpectopollis sp. 142
Carnisporites granulatus
Verrucosisporites morulae
Conbaculatisporites mesozoicus
Tigrisporites halleinis
Osmundacidites cf. O. alpinus
Foveolatitrilete sp. 235
Retimonocolpites sp. 173
Sulcatisporites kraeuselii
Carnisporites leviornatus
Pseudenzonalasporites summus
Uvaesporites argentiformis
Triadispora modesta
Spiritisporites spirabilis
Kyrtomisporis laevigatus
Lycopodiumsporites cf. L. semimuris
Triadispora verrucata
Alisporites opii
Alisporites cf. A. perlucidus
Camerosporites verrucosus
Pyramidosporites traversei
Triadispora sp. 165
Alisporites parvus
Granuloperculatipollis rudis
Triadispora stabilis
Alisporites toralis
Colpectopollis cf. C. ellipsoedeus
Ovalipollis ovalis
Vallasporites ignacii
Patinasporites densus
Distaverrusporites sp. 167
Enzonalasporites vigens
Rugubivesiculites sp. 183
Rugubivesiculites sp. 225
cf. Triadispora sp. 202
Pretricolpipollenites ovalis
Alisporites similis
Tsugaepollenites pseudomassulae
Chasmatosporites sp. N
Lycopodiacidites rhaeticus
Alisporites giganteus
Carnisporites spiniger
Pityosporites scaurus
Chasmatosporites sp. R
Lygodioisporites cf. L. perverrucatus
Trilobosporites sp. 305
Alisporites grandis
Triletes cf. T. lygodioides
Ischyosporites marburgensis
Lycopodiacidites rugulatus
Cycadopites andrewsii
Pityosporites parvisaccatus
Rugubivesiculites sp. 303
Convolutispora klukiforma
Araucariacites punctatus
Gleicheniidites cf. G. nilssonii
Araucariacites fissus
Corollina meyeriana
Corollina simplex
Granulatisporites infirmus
Converrucosisporites cameronii
Corollina torosa
Corollina murphyi
Alisporites thomasii
Verrucosisporites cheneyi
Perinopollenites elatoides
Araucariacites australis
Corollina itunensis
Callialasporites trilobatus
Callialasporites cf. C. dampieri
Platysaccus cf. P. lopsiensis
Leptolepidites cf. L. major
Staplinisporites caminus
Anapiculatisporites cf. A. dawsonensis

225   220   215   210   205   200

MILLION YEARS AGO

Triassic/Jurassic
boundary

Figure 4. Time-calibrated range chart of palynomorph species collected by Cornet (1977) from the Newark, Culpeper, Gettysburg, and Hartford basins. Solid lines denote composite ranges within the four basins. Dashed lines extend the ranges of species present in older strata of the Richmond basin. The Triassic/Jurassic boundary coincides with a 60% regional extinction of common Triassic species at approximately 201 Ma.

◄─────────────────────────────────────

Terrestrial tetrapod fossils of Late Triassic age are preserved throughout the Newark Supergroup. However, no characteristic Triassic taxa are found among abundant osseous remains from the earliest Jurassic strata of the Fundy basin. Calibration of the ranges of the Late Triassic vertebrate families by lacustrine cycles indicates that the last appearances of domi-

nant Triassic taxa occurred within an interval of 850 k.y. that brackets the Triassic/Jurassic boundary (Olsen et al., 1987).

The abruptness and apparent synchroneity of the tetrapod, ichnofossil, and palynofloral extinctions in the Newark Supergroup are consistent with catastrophic extinction scenarios involving volcanism or bolide impacts. Fowell and Olsen (1993) previously rejected volcanism as a catalyst for Late Triassic palynological turnover in the Newark Supergroup on the grounds that the first basalt flows lie 7 to 10 m above the transition from Triassic to Jurassic palynomorph assemblages and ash-fall horizons have not been observed.

Bice et al. (1992) report the discovery of multiple shocked quartz horizons from the Triassic/Jurassic boundary in Tuscany, Italy; the uppermost horizon coincides with the

TABLE 1. ALPHABETICAL LIST OF PALYNOMORPH SPECIES IN FIGURE 4

Alisporites giganteus (Danzé-Corsin and Laveine) Cornet 1977
Alisporites grandis (Cookson) Dettman 1963
Alisporites opii Daugherty 1941
Alisporites parvus de Jersey 1963
Alisporites cf. *A. perlucidus* (Pautsch) Pautsch 1973
Alisporites similis (Balme) Dettman 1963
Alisporites thomasii (Couper) Nilsson 1958
Alisporites toralis (Leschik) Clarke 1965
Anapiculatisporites cf. *A. dawsonensis* Reiser and Williams 1969
Araucariacites australis Cookson 1947
Araucariacites fissus Reiser and Williams 1969
Araucariacites punctatus (Nilsson) Cornet and Traverse 1975
Callialasporites cf. *C. dampieri* (Balme) Sukh Dev 1961
Callialasporites trilobatus (Balme) Sukh Dev 1961
Camerosporites pseudoverrucatus Scheuring 1970
Camerosporites verrucosus Mädler 1964
Camerozonosporites rudis (Leschik) Klaus 1960
Carnisporites granulatus Schulz 1967
Carnisporites leviornatus (Levet-Carette) Morbey 1975
Carnisporites spiniger (Leschik) Morbey 1975
Chasmatosporites sp. N Cornet 1977
Chasmatosporites sp. R Cornet 1977
Colpectopollis cf. *C. ellipsoideus* Visscher 1966
Colpectopollis sp. 142 Cornet 1977
Conbaculatisporites mesozoicus Klaus 1960
Converrucosisporites cameronii (de Jersey) Playford and Dettman 1965
Convolutispora klukiforma (Nilsson) Schutz 1967
Corollina itunensis (Pocock) Cornet and Traverse 1975
Corollina meyeriana (Klaus) Venkatachala and Góczán 1964
Corollina murphyae Cornet and Traverse 1975
Corollina simplex (Danzé-Corsin and Laveine) Cornet and Traverse 1975
Corollina torosa (Reissinger) Klaus 1960
Cycadopites andrewsii Cornet and Traverse 1975
Distaverrusporites sp. 167 Cornet 1977
Enzonalasporites vigens Leschik 1955
Foveolatitriletes sp. 235 Cornet 1977
Gleicheniidites cf. *G. nilssonii* Pocock 1977
Granulatisporites infirmus (Balme) Cornet and Traverse 1975
Granuloperculatipollis rudis Venkatachaia and Góczán 1964
Guthoerlisporites cancellous Playford and Dettmann 1965
Ischyosporites marburgensis de Jersey 1963
Kyrtomisporis laevigatus Mädler 1964
Leptolepidites cf. *L. major* Couper 1958

Lunatisporites acutus Leschik 1955
Lycopodiacidites rhaeticus Schulz 1967
Lycopodiacidites rugulatus (Couper) Schulz 1967
Lycopodiumsporites cf. *L. semimuris* Danzé-Corsin and Laveine 1963
Lygodioisporites cf. *L. perverrucatus* Couper 1958
Microcachryidites doubingeri Klaus 1964
Microcachryidites sp. 143 Cornet 1977
Osmundacidites cf. *O. alpinus* Klaus 1960
Ovalipollis ovalis Krutzsch 1955
Patinasporites densus Leschik 1955
Perinopollenites elatoides Couper 1958
Pityosporites parvisaccatus de Jersey 1959
Pityosporites scaurus (Nilsson) Schulz 1967
Platysaccus cf. *P. lopsiensis* (Malyavkina) Pocock 1970
Plicatisaccus badius Pautsch 1971
Pretricolpipollenites ovalis Danzé-Corsin and Laveine 1963
Pseudenzonalasporites summus Scheuring 1970
Pyramidosporites traversei Dunay and Fisher 1979
Retimonocolpites sp. 173 Cornet 1977
Retisulcites sp. 126 Cornet 1977
Rugubivesiculites sp. 183 Cornet 1977
Rugubivesiculites sp. 225 Cornet 1977
Rugubivesiculites sp. 303 Cornet 1977
Spiritisporites spirabilis Scheuring 1970
Staplinisporites caminus (Balme) Pocock 1962
Sulcatisporites kraeuselii Mädler 1964
tetrad type 39 Cornet 1977
Tigrisporites halleinis Klaus 1960
Triadispora cf. *T. obscura* Scheuring 1970
Triadispora modesta Scheuring 1970
Triadispora stabilis Scheuring 1970
Triadispora verrucata (Schulz) Scheuring 1970
Triadispora sp. 165 Cornet 1977
cf. *Triadispora* sp. 202 Cornet 1977
Triletes cf. *T. lygodioides* Mai 1967
Triletes klausii Bharadwaj and Singh 1964
Trilobosporites sp. 305 Cornet 1977
Tsugaepollenites pseudomassulae (Mädler) Morbey 1975
Uvaesporites argentiformis (Bolchovitina) Schultz 1967
Vallasporites ignacii Leschik 1955
Vallasporites sp. 68 Cornet 1977
Verrucosisporites cheneyi Cornet and Traverse 1975
Verrucosisporites morulae Klaus 1960

JACKSONWALD SYNCLINE SECTIONS

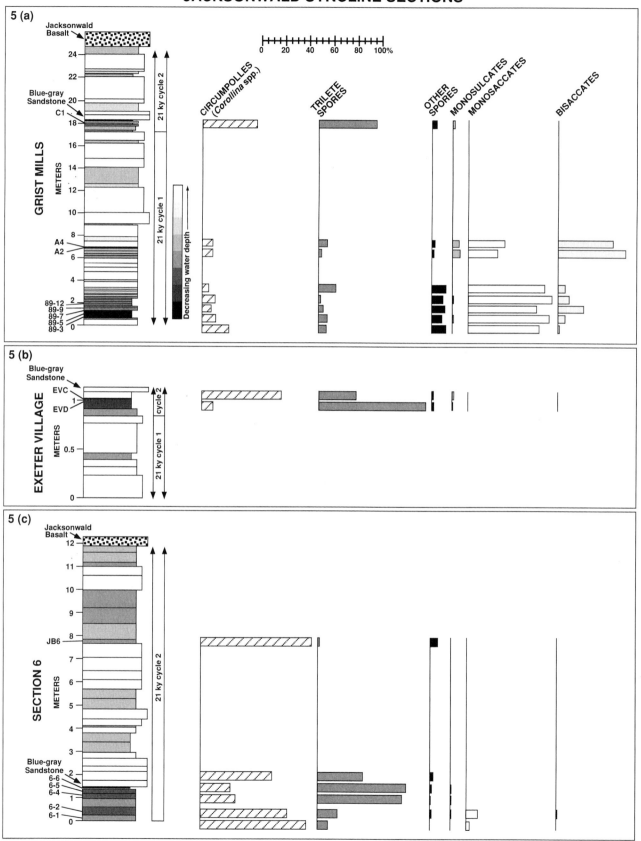

Figure 5. Triassic/Jurassic boundary sections from the Jacksonwald Syncline of the Newark basin. A blue-gray, plant-bearing sandstone present in all three sections serves as a basis for correlations. Relative abundances of pollen and spore morphotypes are plotted opposite their stratigraphic positions. 21-k.y. Milankovitch cycles constrain the duration of the palynological turnover. (a) Grist Mills section: Sample C1 contains 50% spores and is underlain by diverse assemblages typical of the Late Triassic. (b) Exeter Village section: Spore-dominated floras are replaced by Jurassic assemblages between samples EVD and EVC. EVD consists of 89% trilete spores; EVC contains 67% *Corollina* and lacks characteristic Late Triassic species. (c) Section 6: Spore-dominated floras first appear between samples 6-2 and 6-4. Sample JB6 is a typical Jurassic assemblage containing 95% *Corollina*. Samples 6-1 and 6-2 contain 89% and 73% *Corollina*, respectively, but unlike JB6 these samples retain monosaccate and bisaccate species characteristic of the Late Triassic.

◀

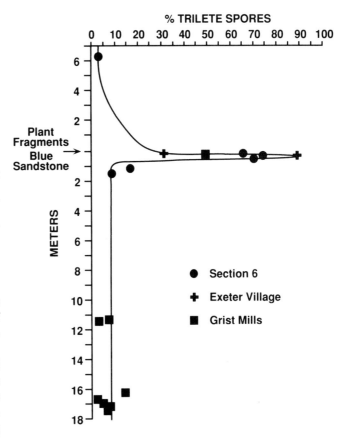

Figure 6. Percentage of trilete spores from all productive localities in Figure 5. Measured sections are correlated to the base of a distinctive blue-gray sandstone. Spore-dominated palynofloras occupy a narrow stratigraphic range less than 0.5 m thick.

abrupt disappearances of Rhaetian bivalves and Late Triassic foraminifera. Bice et al. (1992) suggest that the presence of three shocked quartz layers fits the comet shower model proposed by Hut et al. (1987).

Aspects of the Newark Supergroup palynofloral record are consistent with a multiple-impact scenario. The presence of a geologically brief spore-spike above the last appearances of Late Triassic palynomorph species is analogous to Cretaceous/Tertiary boundary fern spikes (Tschudy et al., 1984; Tschudy and Tschudy, 1986; Nichols et al., 1986; Fleming, 1990) hypothesized to represent a recolonization of ferns following catastrophic destruction of the Cretaceous flora.

The presence of short-lived "transitional" assemblages, in which *Corollina* is dominant but rare Late Triassic species persist (samples 6-1 and 6-2, Fig. 5c), indicates possible disruption of the flora prior to the Triassic/Jurassic boundary turnover. It is tempting to suggest a relationship between these palynofloras and one of the lower shocked quartz horizons of Bice et al. (1992) and to correlate the spore-spike with the uppermost shocked quartz layer and the extinctions of Triassic bivalves and foraminifera. Such correlations are premature, however, and require better estimates of sedimentation rates in the Tuscany section and evidence for shocked quartz in the Newark basin sections. To date, a comprehensive search for shocked quartz in the Newark Supergroup has not been completed, but we are currently conducting this crucial test of the validity of the impact hypothesis.

Enhanced temporal resolution and accurate stratigraphic correlations are also essential to future comparisons of Triassic/Jurassic boundary sections. Periodic sedimentary cycles and good palynofloral preservation within the Newark basin allow temporal calibration of Late Triassic palynofloral zones. Preliminary results are shown in Figure 2 and compared to published chronostratigraphic time scales. Recently acquired cores of the entire Triassic Newark basin section will permit refinement of the temporal data and better resolution of

the boundaries between palynofloral zones. It is hoped that the combination of palynological and tetrapod data from the Newark Supergroup will eventually enable correlation between our continuously calibrated Late Triassic time scale and global sections with ammonite control.

ACKNOWLEDGMENTS

We thank S. Silvestri and R. Litwin for access to their unpublished data. We also thank Superior Oil Company (now Mobil) for the funds to process the Horner #1 well samples and R. Jones for accomplishing the bulk of the Horner well processing. We are grateful to A. Traverse for sharing his laboratory during the initial phases of this study and providing useful discussion. B. Coakley, A. Traverse, and an anonymous reviewer read the manuscript and suggested changes that significantly improved it. Their time and effort is greatly appreciated. This research was supported by a grant from the National Science Foundation (EAR 89 16726).

REFERENCES CITED

Benton, M. J., 1986, More than one event in the late Triassic mass extinction: Nature, v. 321, p. 857–861.

Berger, A., and Pestiaux, P., 1984, Accuracy and stability of the Quaternary terrestrial insolation, *in* Berger, A. L., Imbrie, J., Hays, J., Kukla, G., and Saltzman, B., eds., Milankovitch and climate: Dordrecht, Reidel, p. 83–111.

Berger, A., Loutre, M. F., and Laskar, J., 1992, Stability of the astronomical frequencies over the Earth's history for paleoclimate studies: Science, v. 225, p. 560–566.

Bice, D. M., Newton, C. R., McCauley, S., Reiners, P. W., and McRoberts, C. A., 1992, Shocked quartz at the Triassic-Jurassic boundary in Italy: Science, v. 255, p. 443–446.

Cornet, B., 1977, The palynostratigraphy and age of the Newark Supergroup [Ph.D. thesis]: University Park, The Pennsylvania State University, 505 p.

Cornet, B., and Olsen, P. E., 1985, A summary of the biostratigraphy of the Newark Supergroup of eastern North America with comments on early Mesozoic provinciality, *in* Weber, R., ed., III Congreso Latinoamericano de Paleontologia Mexico, Simposio Sobre Floras del Triasico Tardio, su Fitogeografia y Paleoecologia: Memoria: Mexico City, Universidad National Autonoma de Mexico, Instituto de Geologia, p. 67–81.

Dunning, G. R., and Hodych, J. P., 1990, U/Pb zircon and baddeleyite ages for the Palisades and Gettysburg sills of the northeastern United States: Implications for the age of the Triassic/Jurassic boundary: Geology, v. 18, p. 795–798.

Fleming, R. F., 1990, Nonmarine Cretaceous-Tertiary boundary, southwestern United States: Geological Society of America, Abstracts with Programs, v. 22: A278.

Fowell, S. J., and Olsen, P. E., 1993, Time-calibration of Triassic/Jurassic microfloral turnover, eastern North America: Tectonophysics, v. 222, p. 361–369.

Hallam, A., 1981, The end-Triassic bivalve extinction event: Palaeogeography, Palaeoclimatology, Palaeoecology, v. 35, p. 1–44.

Harland, B. W., Armstrong, R. L., Cox, A. V., Craig, L. E., Smith, A. G., and Smith, D. G., 1989, A geologic time scale: Cambridge, Cambridge University Press, 263 p.

Hays, J. D., Imbrie, J., and Shackleton, N. J., 1976, Variations in the Earth's orbit: Pacemaker of the ice ages: Science, v. 194, p. 1121–1132.

Hodych, J. P., and Dunning, G. R., 1992, Did the Manicouagan impact trigger end-of-Triassic mass extinction?: Geology, v. 20, p. 51–54.

Hubert, J. F., and Mertz, K. A., 1980, Eolian dune field of Late Triassic age, Fundy Basin, Nova Scotia: Geology, v. 8, p. 516–519.

Hut, P., and seven others, 1987, Comet showers as a cause of mass extinctions: Nature, v. 329, p. 118–126.

Johnson, A.L.A., and Simms, M. J., 1989, The timing and cause of late Triassic marine invertebrate extinctions: Evidence from scallops and crinoids, *in* Donovan, S. K., ed., Mass extinctions: New York, Columbia University Press, p. 174–194.

Kerp, H., 1991, Some recently published (numerical) time scales compared: Albertiana, v. 9, p. 19–21.

Kutzbach, J. E., and Gallimore, R. G., 1989, Pangaean climates: Megamonsoons of the megacontinent: Journal of Geophysical Research, v. 94, p. 3341–3357.

Nichols, D. J., Jarzen, D. M., Orth, C. J., and Oliver, P. Q., 1986, Palynological and iridium anomalies at Cretaceous/Tertiary boundary, south-central Saskatchewan: Science, v. 231, p. 714–717.

Olsen, P. E., 1986, A 40-million-year lake record of early Mesozoic orbital climatic forcing: Science, v. 234, p. 842–848.

Olsen, P. E., 1991, Tectonic, climatic, and biotic modulation of lacustrine ecosystems—examples from Newark Supergroup of eastern North America, *in* Katz, B., ed., Lacustrine basin exploration: Case studies and modern analogs: American Association of Petroleum Geologists Memoir 50, p. 209–224.

Olsen, P. E., Shubin, N. H., and Anders, M. H., 1987, New Early Jurassic tetrapod assemblages constrain Triassic-Jurassic tetrapod extinction event: Science, v. 237, p. 1025–1029.

Olsen, P. E., Schlische, R. W., and Gore, J. W., eds., 1989, Tectonic, depositional, and paleoecological history of Early Mesozoic rift basins, eastern North America (International Geological Congress field trip guidebook T351): Washington, D.C., American Geophysical Union, 174 p.

Olsen, P. E., Fowell, S. J., and Cornet, B., 1990, The Triassic/Jurassic boundary in continental rocks of eastern North America; A progress report, *in* Sharpton, V. L., and Ward, P. D., eds., Global catastrophes in Earth history: Geological Society of America Special Paper 247, p. 585–593.

Palmer, A. R. (compiler), 1983, The decade of North American geology, 1983 geologic time scale: Geology, v. 11, p. 503–504.

Ratcliffe, N. M., 1988, Reinterpretation of the relationship of the western extension of the Palisades sill to the lava flows at Ladentown, New York, based on new core data, *in* Froelich, A. J., and Robinson, G. R., Jr., eds, Studies of the Early Mesozoic basins of the eastern United States: U.S. Geological Survey Bulletin 1776, p. 113–135.

Sepkoski, J. J., Jr., 1984, A kinetic model of Phanerozoic taxonomic diversity. III: Post-Paleozoic families and mass extinctions: Paleobiology, v. 10, p. 246–267.

Shaw, A. B., 1964, Time in stratigraphy. New York, McGraw Hill, 365 p.

Short, D. A., Mengel, J. G. Crowley, T. J., Hyde, W. T., and North, G. R., 1991, Filtering of Milankovitch cycles by earth's geography: Quaternary Research, v. 35, p. 157–173.

Silvestri, S. M., 1991, Ichnofauna of the last 7 million years of the Triassic from the Jacksonwald Syncline, Newark Basin, Pennsylvania [Master's thesis]: Newark, New Jersey, Rutgers University, 94 p.

Silvestri, S. M., and Szajna, M. J., 1993, Biostratigraphy of vertebrate footprints in the Late Triassic section of the Newark basin: Reassessment of stratigraphic ranges, *in* Lucas, S. G., and Morales, M., eds., The nonmarine Triassic: New Mexico Museum of Natural History and Science Bulletin 3, p. 439–445.

Smoot, J. P., and Olsen, P. E., 1985, Massive mudstones in basin analysis and paleoclimatic interpretation of the Newark Supergroup, *in* Robinson, G. R., Jr., and Froelich, A. J., eds., Proceedings, Second U.S. Geological Survey Workshop on the Early Mesozoic Basins of the Eastern United States: U.S. Geological Survey Circular 946, p. 29–33.

Smoot, J. P., and Olsen, P. E., 1988, Massive mudstones in basin analysis and paleoclimatic interpretation of the Newark Supergroup, in Manspeizer, W., ed., Triassic-Jurassic rifting, continental breakup and the origin of the Atlantic Ocean and passive margins: New York, Elsevier, p. 249–274.

Sutter, J. F., 1988, Innovative approaches to dating igneous events in the early Mesozoic basins of the eastern United States, *in* Froelich, A. J., and Robinson, G. R., Jr., eds., Studies of the Early Mesozoic basins of the eastern United States: U.S. Geological Survey Bulletin 1776, p. 194–200.

Tschudy, R. H., and Tschudy, B. D., 1986, Extinction and survival of plant life following the Cretaceous/Tertiary boundary event, Western Interior, North America: Geology, v. 14, p. 667–670.

Tschudy, R. H., Pillmore, C. L., Orth, C. J., Gilmore, J. S., and Knight, J. D., 1984, Disruption of the terrestrial plant ecosystem at the Cretaceous-Tertiary boundary, western interior: Science, v. 225, p. 1030–1032.

Webb, J. A., 1981, A radiometric time scale of the Triassic: Journal of the Geological Society of Australia, v. 28, . 107–121.

Witte, W. K., Kent, D. V., ad Olsen, P. E., 1991, Magnetostratigraphy and paleomagnetic poles from Late Triassic–earliest Jurassic strata of the Newark basin: Geological Society of America Bulletin, v. 103, p. 1648–1662.

Manuscript Accepted by the Society May 14, 1993

Geological Society of America
Special Paper 288
1994

The carbon and oxygen isotope record during the evolution of Pangea: Carboniferous to Triassic

Ethan L. Grossman
Department of Geology, Texas A&M University, College Station, Texas 77843

ABSTRACT

Stable isotopes can be used to monitor global and paleoceanographic changes associated with supercontinent formation and breakup. Substantial amounts of isotopic data have been produced for the time interval represented by the evolution of Pangea, but data free of diagenetic effects are uncommon. Thick nonluminescent brachiopod shells and marine cements of original minerology and chemistry are the materials most likely to retain their original isotopic composition. Altered marine cements can be used to infer an original marine signature. Whole rock samples are the least reliable for isotopic study, providing only an approximation of marine $\delta^{13}C$ values and diagenetically altered $\delta^{18}O$ values. These different techniques have different shortcomings but tend to complement each other.

The isotopic record for Pangea is too sparse for detailed interpretation, but several robust features are evident. Carbon isotopic values of brachiopod shells and former marine cements from Eurasia (Paleotethyan) and Arctic Canada increase by about 2‰ during the mid Carboniferous. This increase is not seen in samples from the central and south-central United States (Panthalassan) and in part reflects changes in ocean circulation with the closing of the equatorial seaway as Gondwana collided with Laurussia. The Paleotethyan-Panthalassan $\delta^{13}C$ difference appears to extend into the Permian. Permian $\delta^{13}C$ values are high but decrease by roughly 3‰ at or near the Permian-Triassic boundary. This decline in $\delta^{13}C$ is attributed to a decrease in the inventory of buried organic carbon. $\delta^{13}C$ values remain low in the Triassic (<4‰) compared to Permian values (generally >4‰).

Oxygen isotopic values for the Carboniferous are generally between –3‰ and –1‰, whereas Permian values are between –3‰ and +1‰. The high $\delta^{18}O$ values for the Permian are either for latitudes with excess evaporation or for middle to high latitudes with cooler temperatures. No reliable $\delta^{18}O$ data are available for the Permian-Triassic boundary.

INTRODUCTION

Oxygen and carbon isotope studies are unique because they provide quantitative data on global change and paleotemperature. Numerical models of geochemical cycles (Berner, 1987; Kump, 1989) and paleoclimate (Crowley and North, 1991) require such data to understand the past and predict the future. Oxygen isotopic compositions reflect changes in temperature, salinity, and continental ice volume (Epstein et al., 1953; Shackleton and Opdyke, 1973; Williams, 1984). Carbon isotopic compositions record changes in dissolved O_2 content, circulation, productivity, and the global carbon budget (Shackleton, 1977a; Scholle and Arthur, 1980). To apply stable isotopes to the study of Pangean paleoenvironments and global

Grossman, E. L., 1994, The carbon and oxygen isotope record during the evolution of Pangea: Carboniferous to Triassic, *in* Klein, G. D., ed., Pangea: Paleoclimate, Tectonics, and Sedimentation During Accretion, Zenith, and Breakup of a Supercontinent: Boulder, Colorado, Geological Society of America Special Paper 288.

change requires the solution of three problems: (1) finding isotopically unaltered marine carbonate; (2) differentiating local, regional, and global causes for isotopic variability; and (3) isolating the main environmental factor controlling isotopic variability (e.g., salinity versus temperature) (Grossman, 1992). With careful sample selection, sensible use of geologic information, and collection of data with wide geographic coverage, these problems can be overcome.

STABLE ISOTOPES AS ENVIRONMENTAL INDICATORS

Oxygen isotopes

$^{18}O/^{16}O$ ratios are reported in δ-notation as the per mil (‰) difference relative to a standard:

$$\delta^{18}O\ (‰) = \frac{(^{18}O/^{16}O)\text{sample} - (^{18}O/^{16}O)\text{standard}}{(^{18}O/^{16}O)\text{standard}} \times 1,000$$

For carbonates the standard is usually a belemnite from the Pee Dee formation in South Carolina (PDB). For waters, silicates, and sometimes carbonates, oxygen isotope data are reported versus Standard Mean Ocean Water (SMOW; Friedman and O'Neil, 1977).

The $\delta^{18}O$ values of carbonates are dependent upon the $\delta^{18}O$ of the ambient water and the fractionation of oxygen isotopes between the carbonate mineral and the water. ^{18}O is preferentially enriched in carbonate minerals relative to water at earth-surface temperatures, and the degree of enrichment is temperature dependent—hence, oxygen isotope paleothermometry. Epstein et al. (1953) developed a paleotemperature equation for calcium carbonate based mostly on mollusks, which was later confirmed with abiogenic calcite precipitates by O'Neil et al. (1969). In this chapter I use a quadratic representation of the calcite-water fractionation relation of O'Neil et al. (1969) as reported in Hays and Grossman (1991):

$$T\ (°C) = 15.7 - 4.36\ (\delta^{18}O_{calcite} - \delta_{w,SMOW}) + 0.12\ (\delta^{18}O_{calcite} - \delta_{w,SMOW})^2,$$

where T = temperature in °C, $\delta^{18}O_{calcite}$ is the $\delta^{18}O$ of calcite versus PDB, and $\delta_{w,SMOW}$ is the $\delta^{18}O$ of the ambient water versus SMOW.

Aragonite grown at 25°C is enriched in ^{18}O by 0.6‰ compared with calcite grown under the same conditions (Tarutani et al., 1969). The paleotemperature equation for aragonite (Grossman and Ku, 1986, as modified by Hudson and Anderson, 1989) is based on naturally occurring aragonitic foraminifera and mollusks that grew at temperatures of 4°C to 20°C:

$$T\ (°C) = 19.7 - 4.34\ (\delta^{18}O_{aragonite} - \delta_{w,SMOW}).$$

This aragonite paleotemperature equation cannot be applied to samples roasted at high temperature (>450°C) to remove organic matter because roasting can convert aragonite to calcite and decrease $\delta^{18}O$ values.

For calcite and aragonite the temperature dependence of oxygen isotope fractionation is –0.2‰ to –0.3‰ per °C. This

temperature dependence increases slightly with decreasing temperature. Because the precision of the measurement is usually ±0.1‰ or better, paleotemperatures can be measured with a precision of ±0.5°C. In practice, the error associated with isotopic analyses of carbonates is small compared with the uncertainty in the estimation of the $\delta^{18}O$ of ancient waters and the uncertainty added by diagenesis.

Biogenic carbonate can be precipitated out of isotopic equilibrium with the ambient water. This apparent disequilibrium due to physiological processes is termed "vital effect" and usually results in lower $\delta^{18}O$ values (Wefer and Berger, 1991). Although vital effect has been shown to influence the $\delta^{18}O$ values of taxa in essentially all phyla, it is uncommon or small (<1‰) in certain taxa such as mollusks and brachiopods (Epstein et al., 1953; Lowenstam, 1961; Grossman and Ku, 1986).

Determining the oxygen isotopic composition of the water in which carbonate was precipitated (δ_w) is one of the most difficult and important tasks in isotopic studies. This determination involves consideration of local variations in δ_w due to salinity variations as well as global changes in the δ_w of ancient oceans. Modern open-ocean waters range in salinity from 33 ppt to 37 ppt and in $\delta_{w,SMOW}$ from –0.5‰ to 1.1‰ (GEOSECS, 1987). This δ_w variation is mainly due to evaporation and mixing with ^{18}O-depleted meltwater or river runoff. Depending on the source of runoff, $\delta^{18}O$ can decrease by 0.1‰ to 0.6‰ per ppt salinity decrease (Craig and Gordon, 1965). Evaporation can increase $\delta^{18}O$ by 0.3‰ to 0.4‰ per ppt salinity increase (Railsback et al., 1989). Where $\delta^{18}O$ data are available from shallow through bathyal depths of deposition, temperature-salinity profiles can be estimated by the model of Railsback et al. (1989), which makes use of the fact that water density increases with depth in the ocean. This model is especially useful where calcite $\delta^{18}O$ decreases with depth, as in times with warm, saline bottom waters.

Most of the marine geologic record prior to Jurassic comes from epicontinental seas and continental shelves where it is possible for salinities to be less than 33 ppt or more than 37 ppt. Where freshwater is subject to extensive evaporation, as in swamps such as the Florida Everglades, the $\delta^{18}O$ of freshwater entering the ocean can be greater than that of the local seawater (Lloyd, 1964). To minimize the effects of variable salinity on isotopic data, sample selection can be restricted to sediments showing high taxonomic diversity and containing stenohaline fauna such as crinoids and most brachiopods (Dodd and Stanton, 1990). The ability of stenohaline taxa to tolerate salinity changes in the Paleozoic is largely unknown, but it is likely to have been much less than that of presumably euryhaline taxa.

On time scales of 10^3 to 10^6 years, the average δ_w of seawater varies as a function of continental ice buildup. Glacial ice is depleted in ^{18}O; typical $\delta^{18}O$ values of Greenland and Antarctic ice are –29‰ and –33‰, respectively (Johnsen et al., 1972). The greater the ice volume, the higher the $\delta^{18}O$ of seawater and consequently the $\delta^{18}O$ of carbonates precipi tated in that seawater. Because both sea level and seawater $\delta^{18}O$ are functions of ice volume, the effect of ice volume on seawater $\delta^{18}O$ can be calculated from Pleistocene ice volume (either from continental evidence or sea-level change) and the average $\delta^{18}O$ of Pleistocene ice. This approach yields a 0.1‰ increase in δ_w for a 10-m drop in sea level (Shackleton, 1977b). Using another approach—the elevation and $\delta^{18}O$ of Pleistocene corals from Barbados—Fairbanks and Matthews (1978) obtained a similar value: an increase of 0.11‰ in δ_w per 10-m decrease in sea level. This value, $d\delta_w/d[\text{sea level}]$, is itself probably a function of ice volume. On a highly glaciated Earth, high latitudinal temperature gradients will produce polar ice caps of lower $\delta^{18}O$ (resulting in a higher $d\delta_w/d[\text{ice volume}]$ and $d\delta_w/d[\text{sea level}]$) than would occur on an Earth with minor glaciation (Mix and Ruddiman, 1984). For Pangean marine sediments, the *glacial effect* on δ_w can be evaluated by comparing the ^{18}O stratigraphy of a section with its record of transgression and regression (Adlis et al., 1988; Grossman et al., 1991).

On time scales of 10^7 to 10^8 years, isotopic exchange between seawater and crustal rock in processes like weathering and mid-ocean ridge hydrothermal alteration can be important (Muehlenbachs, 1986; Gregory, 1991). Generally, high temperature exchange at mid-ocean ridges causes ^{18}O enrichment in water and ^{18}O depletion in rocks. Low temperature hydrothermal systems (<300 ±50°C) and weathering reactions tend to lower the $\delta^{18}O$ of water and increase the $\delta^{18}O$ of rocks. Low $\delta^{18}O$ values for Paleozoic and Precambrian sedimentary rocks have been interpreted as indicating that δ_w has increased through geologic time (Perry, 1967, and Veizer et al., 1986, among others). Results from studies of ophiolites, seawater-associated ore deposits, meteoric cements, and fluid inclusions in halite show no evidence for a large change in δ_w (Muehlenbachs, 1986; Gregory, 1991; Hays and Grossman, 1991; Knauth and Roberts, 1991). However, the data from ores, ophiolites, meteoric cements, and fluid inclusions are too variable to resolve 1‰ to 2‰ changes in seawater $\delta^{18}O$. Several attempts have been made to model the relative importance of low temperature and high temperature exchange mechanisms in an effort to constrain the potential variability of δ_w with time. The models of Chase and Perry (1972) and Walker and Lohmann (1989) suggest that the $\delta^{18}O$ of seawater could have varied through time, whereas the models of Muehlenbachs and Clayton (1976) and Holland (1984) suggest that the high and low temperature processes tend to buffer seawater at a δ_w value near 0‰. Because of the uncertainties in the overall temperature and rates of oxygen isotope exchange between the various reservoirs, the question of long-term change in the average $\delta^{18}O$ of seawater remains open.

Carbon isotopes

The two most important factors controlling the $^{13}C/^{12}C$ ratio of carbonates (reported as $\delta^{13}C$ versus PDB) are mineralogy and the $\delta^{13}C$ of dissolved bicarbonate (HCO_3^-). In reporting environmental data, researchers refer to the $\delta^{13}C$ of dissolved inorganic carbon (DIC = aqueous CO_2 + HCO_3^- + CO_3^{2-}). This is because the $\delta^{13}C$ of HCO_3^- cannot be measured directly but $\delta^{13}C_{DIC}$ can. At oceanic pH's the calculated $\delta^{13}C$ of HCO_3^- is only 0.2‰ to 0.3‰ greater than the $\delta^{13}C$ of DIC (Grossman and Ku, 1986). Calcite-HCO_3^- and aragonite-HCO_3^- fractionation are 1.0 ±0.1‰ (±2 × standard error) and 2.7 ±0.2‰, respectively, and are independent of temperature over the range 10°C to 40°C (Romanek et al., 1992). Calcite precipitated in water with a $\delta^{13}C_{DIC}$ of 2.0‰, a typical value for the modern surface ocean, should have $\delta^{13}C$ values of roughly 3.3‰ (i.e., 2.0 + 0.3 + 1.0‰), and aragonite should have values of roughly 5.0‰ (i.e., 2.0 + 0.3 + 2.7‰).

Local environmental $\delta^{13}C_{DIC}$ depends on photosynthesis and respiration rates. Photosynthesis in the surface ocean preferentially removes light (^{13}C-depleted) carbon as organic matter, enriching the remaining DIC in ^{13}C. Below the photic zone, respiration dominates, releasing light carbon (Berger and Vincent, 1986). These processes cause middle- and low-latitude surface waters to have $\delta^{13}C$ values generally between 1.2 and 2.2‰ and intermediate to bottom waters to have values generally between –0.5 and 1.0‰ (Kroopnick, 1985; GEOSECS, 1987). In reefal environments, diurnal variation in photosynthesis and respiration cause day-night differences in $\delta^{13}C$ of 0.6‰ to 1.5‰ depending on location (Weber and Woodhead, 1971); in surface waters of the tropical Pacific Ocean, day-night differences are 0.2‰ or less (Tilbrook, 1982). Although $\delta^{13}C$ is often used as an indicator for productivity, the relationship between $\delta^{13}C$ and primary productivity is complex. Increased productivity will preferentially remove light carbon from the water and thus increase $\delta^{13}C_{DIC}$. However, productivity is limited by nutrients, and when nutrients are brought to the surface through upwelling, light carbon is brought up as well. Furthermore, if respiration rates are high in the surface ocean, high primary productivity will not have a major effect on $\delta^{13}C_{DIC}$.

The size of the organic carbon reservoir (biomass and sedimentary organic carbon) controls the $\delta^{13}C_{DIC}$ values of the global ocean. A net increase in the burial of organic carbon will enlarge the organic carbon reservoir and increase the $\delta^{13}C$ of seawater and consequently of marine carbonates (Garrels and Lerman, 1984; Berger and Vincent, 1986; Kump, 1991). Alternatively, increased weathering rates—as might accompany increased tectonism—may result in a net decrease in the organic carbon reservoir and lower the global ocean $\delta^{13}C$ value. Because of the relatively small ^{13}C fractionation between calcium carbonate and DIC, the cycling of calcium carbonate has a very minor role in controlling the $\delta^{13}C$ of ocean DIC and marine carbonates.

Vital effect and microhabitat effect can influence the $\delta^{13}C$ of biogenic carbonates (Wefer and Berger, 1991; Grossman, 1987; McCorkle et al., 1990). Vital effect causes lower-than-expected $\delta^{13}C$ values as well as lower $\delta^{18}O$ values, as mentioned earlier. Generally, carbon isotope disequilibrium is more common and less systematic than ^{18}O disequilibrium (see McConnaughey [1989a, b] and Wefer and Berger [1991] for discussions on the causes and patterns of vital effect). Microhabitat effect refers to the modification of the expected isotopic composition because the microenvironment in which an organism lives differs from the open environment. For example, infaunal bivalves and foraminifera have lower δ^{13}C values than expected because the sediment pore waters in which they live have lower $\delta^{13}C_{DIC}$ values than the bottom water above the sediment (Krantz et al., 1987; Grossman, 1987). Some environmental and taxonomic considerations in the interpretation of isotopic data are summarized in Table 1.

INFLUENCE OF DIAGENESIS ON ISOTOPIC COMPOSITION

The effect of diagenesis depends on the temperature, $\delta^{13}C_{DIC}$, and δ_w of the diagenetic fluids and on the isotopic composition of the sample. The effect of seafloor diagenesis on the δ^{18}O of carbonate can be complex. The skeletal carbonate of planktonic organisms may increase in δ^{18}O during early diagenesis because bottom waters are colder than surface waters. However, with burial of the sediment, temperatures increase, and alteration may cause δ^{18}O to remain unchanged or decrease. Carbon isotopic compositions generally decrease with diagenesis because diagenetic fluids usually have been modified by respiration. An exception is methanogenic environments, where DIC δ^{13}C values may exceed 10‰ (Claypool and Kaplan, 1974). Meteoric environments are zones of active carbonate diagenesis because freshwaters are often undersaturated with respect to carbonate minerals. The least stable carbonate components, aragonite and magnesian calcite, will dissolve and provide Ca_2^+ and CO_3^{2-} for secondary (low Mg) calcite precipitation. Such diagenesis tends to lower the δ^{18}O of the resulting carbonate because meteoric water is usually depleted in ^{18}O relative to seawater (Yurtsever and Gat, 1981). However, there are exceptions. For example, Meyers and Lohmann's (1985) zone 1 meteoric cements in Mississippian limestones from southern New Mexico have the same δ^{13}C values as and higher δ^{18}O values than marine cements.

The effect of diagenesis on δ^{13}C depends on the ability of carbonate minerals to buffer the contribution of light carbon from the oxidation of organic matter in soils and subsurface sediment. Where carbonate minerals are common, as in carbonate sediments and rocks, the carbon in diagenetic carbonate will be derived mostly from the dissolution of less stable carbonate minerals and δ^{13}C will be high (>0‰) (Meyers and Lohmann, 1985). Where carbonate minerals are less common, as in clastic sediments, diagenetic carbonates will probably have a greater proportion of carbon derived from the oxidation of organic matter and δ^{13}C will be low (<0‰). Because of the

TABLE 1. PROTOCOL FOR INTERPRETING ISOTOPIC DATA AND EVALUATING LEVEL OF CONFIDENCE IN PRESERVATION OF ORIGINAL MINERAL CHEMISTRY

Environmental and Taxonomic Considerations

A. What is the paleodepth of deposition? With increased paleodepth, δ^{13}C will likely decrease and (if ocean bottom waters are cold, such as expected during glaciated times) δ^{18}O will likely increase.

B. If carbonate is biogenic, is it from a planktonic or benthic organism? Planktonic fauna and flora will record conditions in the surface ocean even if the fossils are recovered from deep water deposits.

C. If benthic, what is the growth habit? Infaunal or semi-infaunal organisms likely to be subject to microhabitat effects.

D. If carbonate is biogenic, is it from an organism that exhibits vital effect? Corals and echinoderms are more prone to vital effect than mollusks and brachiopods.

Preservation of Marine Cements (Carpenter et al., 1991)

A. Primary checks

1. Is original mineralogy preserved?
2. Are cements clear and texturally preserved?
3. Are minor and trace element contents of cement typical for marine cement from that depositional environment?
4. Are the cements nonluminescent? (Early diagenetic marine cements could be luminescent if precipitated in anoxic pore waters.)
5. Are microdolomite inclusions absent?
6. Do cements have the expected $^{87}Sr/^{86}Sr$ ratios for marine carbonate of that age?

Preservation of Brachiopods (Grossman et al., 1993)

A. Primary checks

1. Is microstructure preserved in analyzed shells?
2. Are shells or shell areas analyzed nonluminescent? If yes:
   a. Are nonluminescent areas low in Fe and luminescent areas high in Fe?
   b. Does matrix luminesce?
   c. Does the outer rim luminesce?
   d. Do altered sedimentary components like crinoids luminesce?
3. Do shells have the expected $^{87}Sr/^{86}Sr$ ratios for marine carbonate of that age?

B. Secondary checks

1. Are fossils all well preserved?
   a. What is the proportion of accepted shells?
   b. Is there any silica replacement of shells?

C. Tertiary checks

1. Is there no correlation between δ^{13}C and δ^{18}O values of nonluminescent calcite ($p<0.05$)? (Correlation could be environmentally derived also.)
2. Is the range in isotopic composition reasonable for the environment and paleolatitude?
3. Are species effects in isotopic composition retained?
   a. Are diagenetically susceptible species depleted in ^{13}C relative to diagenetically resistant species?
   b. Are diagenetically susceptible species depleted in ^{18}O relative to diagenetically resistant species?
4. Are species effects in trace element composition retained?

large $\delta^{13}C$ difference between carbonates and organic matter (25‰ to 30‰), even a small input of carbon (5%) from organic matter oxidation can alter the marine $\delta^{13}C$ signal of a pure limestone by more than 1‰. In general, the alteration of the original isotopic signal will be greater in diagenetic systems more open to fluid flow (Marshall, 1992).

SELECTION OF SAMPLE MATERIALS

Carbon and oxygen isotopic records of Earth history can be derived from carbonates (e.g., Veizer and Hoefs, 1976), organic matter (e.g., Galimov et al., 1975; Dean et al., 1986), phosphate minerals (e.g., Luz et al., 1984; Shemesh et al., 1988), and cherts (e.g., Perry, 1967; Knauth and Epstein, 1976). The isotopic record for carbonate components—whole rock, marine cements, brachiopods—is the most comprehensive and is the focus of this review.

Several research groups have used whole-rock samples for isotopic records (Keith and Weber, 1964; Veizer and Hoefs, 1976; Magaritz et al., 1983). The ease of sampling and analyzing this material permits the development of detailed isotopic records with minimum effort. In addition, the nonspecific nature of the material means that the record will not be limited by sample availability. More recent studies have concentrated on fine-grained carbonate sediments and have included petrographic screening of samples (e.g., Magaritz and Holser, 1990). Because of the high inorganic carbon content of limestones, the $\delta^{13}C$ of whole-rock samples is rock buffered and somewhat resistant to alteration, but the $\delta^{18}O$ of the samples has undoubtedly been modified by lithification and diagenesis. In biologically active intervals like soil zones, organic carbon cycling is rapid enough that even the $\delta^{13}C$ of a carbonate sediment or rock is altered by diagenesis. Thus care must be taken to avoid exposure surfaces, which tend to show negative $\delta^{13}C$ excursions (Allan and Matthews, 1982). Care must also be taken to avoid intervals with low carbonate or high sand content. Fine-grained clastic sediments tend to be enriched in organic carbon (Gehman, 1962) which, upon oxidation, supplies ^{13}C-depleted carbon for secondary carbonate precipitation. Intervals of high sand content are more likely to be open to fluid flow and experience greater fluxes of oxygen (as H_2O) and carbon (as DIC).

An additional disadvantage of whole-rock samples is the lack of control on the source of carbonate. The source of fine-grained carbonate may be biogenic or abiogenic, calcite or aragonite. Weber (1967) showed that the $\delta^{13}C$ of modern carbonate sediments varied by as much as 2‰ depending on environment and size fraction. Fine-grained sediments from the lagoons of Bermuda and Eniwetok Atoll tended to be enriched in ^{13}C compared with fine-grained sediments from reefs. This difference occurred because of a greater proportion of ara-

gonite in lagoonal sediments and because the aragonite associated with the reefs tended to be derived from coral skeletons, which are depleted in ^{13}C as a result of vital effect (Weber, 1967; Weber and Schmalz, 1968). Oxygen isotopic compositions also varied with environment because of differences in sediment source but to a smaller extent.

Skeletal carbonate is commonly used for isotopic studies of Earth history. The fossils selected must be resistant to diagenesis and should exhibit no vital effects or microhabitat effects. If vital effect is unavoidable, it should be constant and calibrated with analyses of other species. Chemically preserved carbonate from mollusks, corals, and echinoderms is rare in samples older than Cretaceous age because of the poor preservation potential of aragonite and magnesian calcite. Low Mg calcite brachiopod shells, on the other hand, commonly retain what appears to be original chemistry. The dense and compact microstructure of the shells of certain brachiopods isolates crystals from diagenetic fluids and further enhances their preservation potential (Compston, 1960; Grossman et al., 1991).

Based on analyses of modern brachiopods, Lowenstam (1961) and Lepzelter et al. (1983) proposed that brachiopods tend to precipitate their shell at or near oxygen isotopic equilibrium with the ambient water. Carpenter (1991), however, concluded that modern brachiopod calcite is generally not precipitated in ^{18}O equilibrium with ambient seawater. He found that the thin, outer prismatic (primary) layer of Holocene brachiopods is substantially depleted in ^{13}C and ^{18}O relative to expected equilibrium and the isotopic compositions of the thicker, secondary layer. Fortunately, isotopic studies of ancient specimens rely on the secondary and tertiary shell layers; the thin primary layer is rarely preserved. Carpenter also found that $\delta^{18}O$ values of secondary shell on average deviate by −1.5‰ to +0.5‰ from his calculated equilibrium values. Considering the environmental variability of nearshore localities and the difficulty in determining the ambient temperature and δ_w of growth of Holocene brachiopods without direct measurements, much of the disagreement between brachiopod and equilibrium $\delta^{18}O$ may reflect the uncertainty in the determination of ambient conditions rather than vital effects. The data of Carpenter do show 1‰ variations in $\delta^{18}O$ and $\delta^{13}C$ between co-occurring species that could be caused by vital effects in certain species. Isotopic studies of brachiopods in ancient sedimentary rocks would clearly benefit from isotopic studies of live brachiopods grown under measured conditions.

Ancient brachiopods exhibit species-dependent isotope effects, especially with $\delta^{13}C$. Veizer et al. (1986) noted $\delta^{13}C$ differences between different genera of Middle Devonian brachiopods. Popp et al. (1986a) observed that $\delta^{13}C$ values for Carboniferous *Martinia* were 1‰ to 2‰ higher than coeval specimens of *Gigantoproductus*. And Grossman et al. (1993)

demonstrated that the δ^{13}C values of Late Pennsylvanian *Composita* were 1.0 ±0.4‰ higher (p <0.04) than coeval specimens of *Crurithyris* and *Neospirifer* from Kansas, New Mexico, and Texas (Fig. 1). Grossman et al. (1991) also observed a 0.6‰ ^{18}O enrichment in *Eridmatus* relative to co-occurring *Crurithyris*. Except for ^{13}C in *Composita* and ^{18}O in *Eridmatus*, however, the δ^{13}C and δ^{18}O of *Composita*, *Crurithyris*, *Neospirifer*, and *Eridmatus* from central North America are similar, averaging within ±0.3‰ of each other (Grossman et al., 1991, 1993).

The causes of the observed species effects could be microhabitat or vital effects. Grossman et al. (1991) suggested that the ^{13}C enrichment in *Composita* relative to *Crurithyris* was caused by the semi-infaunal habitat of *Crurithyris* as indicated by its morphology. However, *Composita* is unique among the species analyzed by Grossman et al. (1991) in that the Mg, Na, and S contents of the shell are very low (Grossman et al., 1991, 1992). If trace element contents in *Composita* exhibit vital effect, perhaps stable isotope contents do also. Differential diagenesis can also cause apparent species effects. Species with low preservation potential may be preferentially depleted in ^{13}C and ^{18}O and appear to exhibit vital effect. Grossman et al. (1983) attributed low δ^{18}O values in New Mexican *Crurithyris* relative to co-occurring *Composita* and *Neospirifer* to partial alteration of the less-resistant *Crurithyris* (Fig. 1). Fortunately, petrographic evidence for preservation potential (to be discussed later) enables identification of diagenetically controlled species effects. Because of the uncertainty introduced by vital, microhabitat, and diagenetic effects, it is helpful to replicate isotope stratigraphies using different species and to isotopically analyze sediment matrix or altered components to understand how diagenesis affects the isotopic signal.

Marine cements, if preserved, provide an isotopic record free of direct influence by organisms and a good check on brachiopod data (Lohmann and Walker, 1989). But because these cements were originally aragonite or magnesian calcite, they are rarely preserved. One exception is the aragonite marine ce-

ments of the Pennsylvanian Holder Formation in New Mexico (Dickson et al., 1991). Isotopic trends in altered marine cements can be used to infer their original isotopic composition. δ^{13}C–δ^{18}O trends caused by diagenesis can be traced back to a precursor composition if different samples experienced somewhat different diagenetic conditions. Figure 2 shows Given and Lohmann's (1985) classic example from the Permian Reef Complex. Marine cements from samples of varying paleodepth (A, B, C, D) yield four isotopic trends, each reflecting different diagenetic environments and different degrees of isotopic modifications. These trends intersect at δ^{13}C = 5.3‰ and δ^{18}O = –2.5‰, the apparent precursor isotopic composition. The method assumes that these values represent the original isotopic compositions of the marine cement and not those of a transitional diagenetic phase.

The stratigraphic resolution of an isotopic record varies depending on the materials analyzed. Marine cements are often syndepositional with carbonate sediments (James and Choquette, 1983) but can also be precipitated millions of years later (Saller and Koepnick, 1990). Fossils provide better stratigraphic resolution than cements, but slow sedimentation, resedimentation, and sediment mixing can juxtapose shells or sediment thousands of years different in age (Powell et al., 1989). These problems, of course, are not unique to isotopic studies and occur with any study of the rock record.

METHODS FOR IDENTIFYING DIAGENETICALLY ALTERED CARBONATE

Historical geochemistry relies on our ability to identify preserved shell, but it is only possible to identify altered shell; thus we rely on negative evidence for shell preservation: the absence of evidence of diagenesis. Petrographic studies show that even aragonitic shell, which is expected to revert to calcite when altered, can be altered and contain diagenetic aragonite (Bathurst, 1975; Scherer, 1977). Researchers in the past have used isotopic compositions simultaneously as diagenetic and

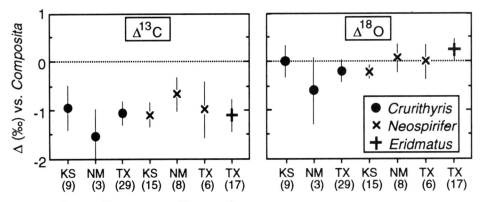

Figure 1. δ^{13}C and δ^{18}O difference (Δ^{13}C and Δ^{18}O respectively) between *Crurithyris, Neospirifer,* and *Eridmatus* and co-occurring *Composita* from the same interval in shales from Kansas (KS), New Mexico (NM), and Texas (TX). Error bars represent ±2 times the standard errors of the mean. Numbers in parentheses represent number of intervals which were compared (from Grossman et al., 1993).

Permian Reef Complex (McKittrick Canyon)

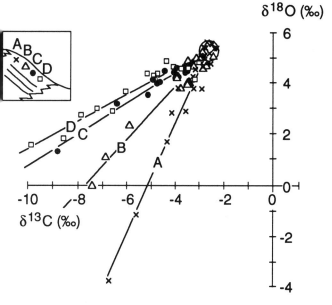

Figure 2. Covariant trends generated from four samples from the Permian reef complex at McKittrick Canyon, New Mexico, U.S.A. The circle has a radius of 0.5‰ about the intersection of the four trends. Inset shows a schematic cross section with the relative positions of the four samples on the reef complex (modified from Given and Lohmann, 1985).

paleoenvironmental indicators. Low $\delta^{18}O$ or $\delta^{13}C$ values were interpreted as caused by diagenesis, and only the highest values were used to interpret paleoenvironments. Implicit is the assumption that diagenesis always causes ^{18}O and ^{13}C depletions, but fluids from evaporative or methanogenic environments can be enriched in heavy isotopes (Stiller et al., 1985; Claypool and Kaplan, 1974). More importantly, the highest $\delta^{13}C$ and $\delta^{18}O$ values may be less than primary marine values, especially if only a few analyses have been performed. Independent methods are needed to cull diagenetically altered specimens before isotopic measurements are made.

Textural evidence for diagenesis

Textural alteration of carbonate minerals usually indicates chemical and isotopic alteration. Alteration features include loss of microstructure, micritization, partial silicification, and cementation in microfractures and pores. The effects of diagenesis on the isotopic composition of carbonate components depend on the original isotopic composition of the component (^{18}O- and ^{13}C-depleted corals and echinoderms versus mollusks and brachiopods), the diagenetic fluids (e.g., meteoric versus marine), and the ambient temperature. Marshall (1992) gives a thorough discussion of the impact of diagenesis on isotopic composition.

Workers who rely on fine-grained, whole-rock samples will use field, hand sample, and thin-section observations to avoid pedogenic features, sparry cements, and vein material (Magaritz and Holser, 1990). Workers who use brachiopod shells for isotopic studies examine hand specimens for borings and fractures and thin-sections for loss of microstructure.

The microstructure of articulate brachiopod shells typically consists of a thin prismatic outer layer (primary layer) and a thicker fibrous layer underlying it (secondary layer) (Williams and Rowell, 1965; MacKinnon, 1974). Many spiriferoid and pentameroid brachiopods also contain a thick prismatic layer (tertiary layer) underlying the secondary layer. Shells may be punctate, with punctae (pores) oriented normal to the shell exterior; pseudopunctate, with calcite rods enclosed in normal shell; and impunctate. In our experience, impunctate shells tend to be more resistant to diagenesis than punctate or pseudopunctate shells. Also, prismatic shell from the tertiary layer (when present) is more resistant to diagenesis than fibrous calcite of the secondary layer (Grossman et al., 1993; more later). Shell thickness is as important as shell microstructure; thick shells tend to be better preserved. In Pennsylvanian brachiopods from the North American craton, destruction of shell microstructure appears as micritized outer rims and fractures.

Trace element evidence

Calcite and aragonite contain varying amounts of Mg, Na, Sr, Fe, Mn, and S (Morse and MacKenzie, 1990). The elemental composition of carbonates is controlled by the structure of the lattice and the composition of the fluids. Marine carbonates are high in Na, Mg, Sr, and S and low in Fe and Mn compared to meteoric carbonates, reflecting compositional differences between marine and meteoric waters (Brand and Veizer, 1980). Trace element contents can be evaluated quantitatively by cathodoluminescence (CL; Meyers, 1974; Frank et al., 1982) or quantitatively either by wet analysis (dissolution of carbonate and analysis of ions in solution) or electron microprobe. CL is activated by Mn and quenched by Fe. Both elements become enriched in shells with diagenesis. In using CL as a diagenetic indicator, it is assumed that fossil brachiopod shells were precipitated with less than the minimum amount of Mn to cause luminescence. The value is often considered to be less than 300 ppm (Frank et al., 1982) but may be as low as 10 to 20 ppm (ten Have and Heijnen, 1985; Mason, 1987; Machel et al., 1991). Mn contents of modern articulate brachiopod shells were found to be low (<180 ppm) by Lepzelter et al. (1983, in Delaney et al., 1989) and H-S. Mii, E. Grossman, and T. Yancey (work in preparation). However, Dittmar and Vogel (1968) reported high Mn contents—mostly between 120 and 1,530 ppm—for *Waltonia, Waldheimia,* and *Gryhus* [sic], and Morrison and Brand (1986) gave a range for modern brachiopods of roughly 4 to 460 ppm. With such high Mn contents, modern brachiopod shells could exhibit CL. Preliminary petrographic study of 23 modern brachiopod shells of four different species showed them to be nonluminescent (Mii and others, work in preparation).

Studies of fossil brachiopods attest to the utility of CL as an indicator of diagenesis (Grossman et al., 1991, 1993; Popp et al., 1986a, b). Figure 3 shows that shell material exhibiting CL yields variable and generally lower $\delta^{13}C$ and $\delta^{18}O$ values, whereas nonluminescent (NL) shell provides consistent data more in line with the expected isotopic compositions.

Numerous studies have used quantitative trace element analyses to identify altered brachiopod shells (see, for example, Brand and Veizer, 1981; Morrison et al., 1985; Veizer et al., 1986; Popp et al., 1986a). Trace element contents are generally measured by atomic absorption spectrophotometry (AA), inductively coupled plasma spectrophotometer (ICP), or electron microprobe (EM). AA and ICP measure the concentrations of elements from dissolved samples at high sensitivity (ppm level

and below). EM can analyze 10 to 20 μm spots on thin-sections but at lower sensitivity (75 to 350 ppm depending upon the element). The trace element–isotopic composition trends can be extrapolated to the expected original trace element concentration of the brachiopod. As seen in the Permian data of Veizer et al. (1986), this approach constrains "original" isotopic composition to within roughly ±2‰ (Fig. 4). Popp (1986) refined the application of trace elements in brachiopods by separately sampling nonluminescent and luminescent portions of shells as well as whole shells. He found that the average Mn and Fe contents increase with CL and that whole shells are usually enriched in Mn relative to NL shell (Popp et al., 1986a). In addition, Popp et al. (1986a) demonstrated species effects in the trace element composition of NL brachiopod shell. The

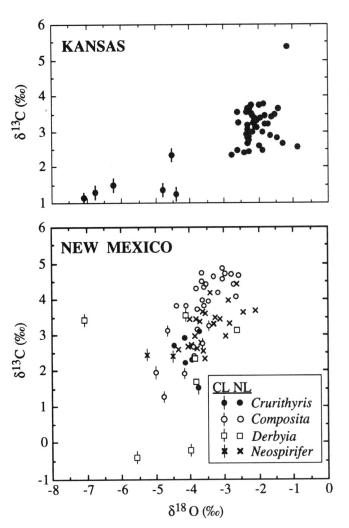

Figure 3. Scatter diagram of isotopic composition of luminescent (CL) versus nonluminescent (NL) shells from specimens of late Pennsylvanian brachiopods from Kansas and New Mexico shales (from Grossman et al., 1993).

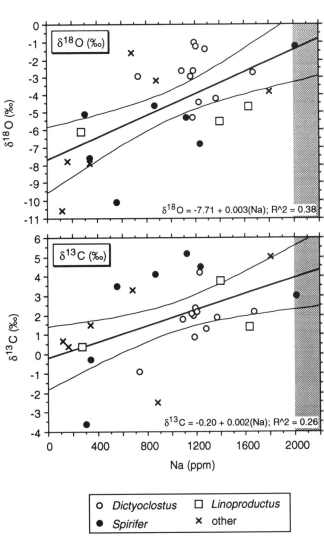

Figure 4. Scatter diagrams of isotopic composition versus Na content for Permian brachiopods from Canada, Alaska, and Utah. Stippled area represent typical Na contents of Recent brachiopods. The lines and equations are for least squares fit (the independent variable, Na content, is assumed to have no error). Also shown are the 95% confidence bands for the mean (modified from Veizer et al., 1986).

productid *Gigantoprodutus* had much higher Mg and Sr contents than the spiriferids *Martinia* and *Choristites*. Modern and Carboniferous brachiopods show a species effect in Na content as well (Morrison and Brand, 1986; Grossman et al., 1991, 1992). These results suggest that the sensitivity of trace element contents as indicators of diagenesis in brachiopod shells can be improved if species effects are considered. The results of Popp et al. also demonstrate that NL shell is better preserved chemically than whole shell.

To provide a better indication of trace element variation within brachiopods, Adlis et al. (1988) and Grossman et al. (1991, 1992) performed electron microprobe analyses of trace element contents across shells. They found that CL areas were enriched in Fe and Mn relative to NL areas. Species enriched in Na and S in NL shell tended to be depleted in those elements in CL shell. Furthermore, Adlis et al. (1988) found that NL *Crurithyris* shell yielded relatively constant S and Fe contents with no gradients from the shell interior to exterior. Where luminescent character changed sharply, trace element contents did also. Presumably, isotopic composition varies in the same manner.

Nonluminescence and low Mn and Fe contents are not foolproof indicators that brachiopod shells are chemically preserved. Diagenetic fluids of high Eh and pH will have low Mn and Fe concentrations; therefore cements precipitated in these fluids will be Mn- and Fe-poor. Rush and Chafetz (1990) observed that both $\delta^{13}C$ and $\delta^{18}O$ of Devonian NL brachiopod shell decreased upsection toward diagenetic values as an exposure surface was approached, suggesting that the brachiopod shell was altered in Mn-poor fluids. A similar trend was observed by Plocher et al. (1992) for brachiopods from the Devonian Coralville Formation. Thus, "marine" trace element compositions increase the probability that a shell is isotopically preserved, but exceptions do occur and caution is recommended.

Because microstructural preservation and nonluminescence are not foolproof indicators of preservation, a number of other tests (and common sense) should be used to establish the credibility of isotopic data (Table 1). For example, what proportion of shells appears preserved? Is there silica replacement? Do texturally altered components luminesce? Is there a correlation between $\delta^{13}C$ and $\delta^{18}O$ (which may indicate diagenesis)? Are diagenetically susceptible species depleted in ^{13}C and ^{18}O relative to resistant ones? Are species effects on isotopic and trace element composition preserved? These tests are listed in Table 1 and provide a means for standardizing the evaluation of data. In the isotope profile of Rush and Chafetz (1990), the ^{13}C-depleted interval below the exposure surface corresponds to an interval where the proportion of NL brachiopods decreased and the frequency of recrystallized fabrics and silicification increased; thus the data from this interval should be treated with caution. It is also possible that the observed isotopic shifts in NL brachiopods associated with exposure surfaces (Rush and Chafetz, 1990; Plocher et al., 1992) are caused by environmental change such as greater freshwater in-

fluence with regression. However, for the purpose of producing an isotopic record of the Pangean *ocean*, such unreliable intervals should be avoided.

In summary, microstructural evaluation and trace element analysis provide methods for culling samples of major diagenetic artifacts. Cathodoluminescent screening can refine the data set, generally producing more consistent and less variable results. Consideration of species effects allows easier recognition of diagenetic artifacts. Trace element and cathodoluminescence screening, however, are not foolproof and should be combined with other more subtle tests for preservation.

THE ISOTOPIC RECORD FOR PANGEA

Because the geologic record is discontinuous both geographically and temporally, the global isotopic record is unavoidably a composite of suitable sites and materials. This endeavor is still in its infancy, and many suitable sites have yet to be investigated. The following discussion will focus on data from NL brachiopods and marine cements when possible. With the exception of the Late Carboniferous data from New Mexico (Dickson et al., 1991), results for marine cements are based on altered components. Because of rock buffering (discussed earlier), these data are more reliable for $\delta^{13}C$ than for $\delta^{18}O$. NL brachiopod shells can be a reliable source of $\delta^{18}O$ and $\delta^{13}C$ data; no brachiopod data are available for the Permian-Triassic boundary, however, so only whole-rock $\delta^{13}C$ results will be discussed.

Carboniferous

Isotopic data for the Carboniferous are shown in Figure 5 and Table 2. The samples represent mostly North America (Kansas, Missouri, New Mexico, Texas, Arctic Canada) and Eurasia (Great Britain, Belgium, Russia, Spain) (Fig. 6). The isotopic compositions of nonluminescent brachiopods are from Popp (1986), Grossman et al. (1991, 1993), and Banner et al. (1988). Marine cement data, represented by boxes that span the time interval in which they were likely to have formed, are from Davies (1977), Dickson et al. (1991), and Meyers and Lohmann (1985). The isotopic values for Upper Carboniferous marine cement from New Mexico are from a laser microprobe analysis of aragonite cement (dashed outline in Fig. 5; Dickson et al., 1991). The result from Meyers and Lohmann (1985) represents the convergence of data for marine cements, crinoids, and meteoric cements. The Davies (1977) data are for former magnesian calcite cements. Because no convergent trend was observed, only the relatively invariant $\delta^{13}C$ values are shown.

The development of major continental glaciers in the Carboniferous (Veevers and Powell, 1987) should be detectable as a $\delta^{18}O$ increase caused by the glacial effect (see previous discussion). No significant difference in $\delta^{18}O$ values is seen between the relatively ice-free lower Carboniferous

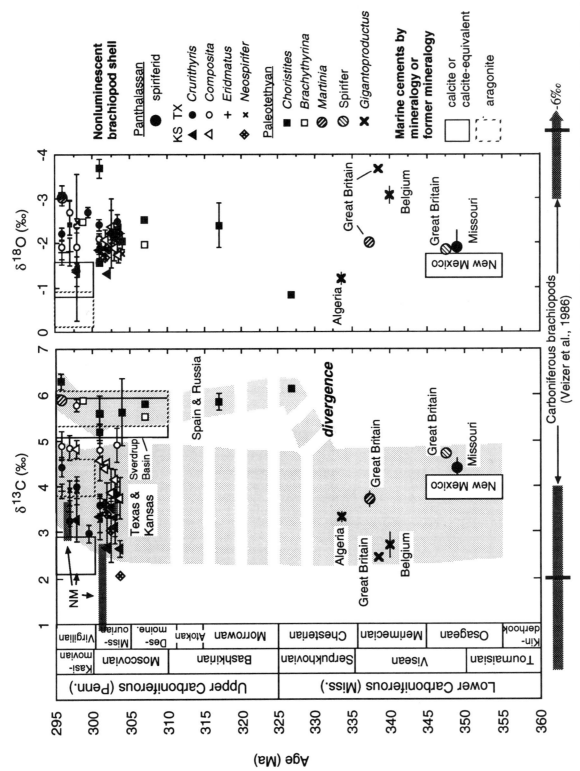

Figure 5. Summary of the carbon and oxygen isotopic data for nonluminescent brachiopod shell of Carboniferous age. Data for Spain, Russia, Algeria, Great Britain, and Belgium are from Popp (1986; "luminescent character group 1"). Missouri data are for spiriferid brachiopods (Banner et al., 1988; J. Banner, personal communication, 1992). Data for Texas and Kansas are from Grossman et al. (1991, 1993). Sources of marine cement data are Graber (1989; Upper Carboniferous, New Mexico; stippled area), Dickson et al. (1991; Upper Carboniferous, New Mexico; dashed box = aragonite, solid box = calcite-equivalent), Davies (1977; Sverdrup Basin, Canadian Arctic), and Meyers and Lohmann (1985; Lower Carboniferous, New Mexico). Range in values for Carboniferous brachiopods from Veizer et al. (1986) based on trace element–isotope trends in whole brachiopods. Data and their sources are shown in Table 2. Time scale from Haq and van Eysinga (1987. $\delta^{18}O$ plotted increasing to the left (from Grossman et al., 1993).

and the glaciated Upper Carboniferous (Fig. 5). $\delta^{18}O$ values for most Carboniferous samples fall between –3‰ and –1‰ and show no obvious stratigraphic or regional trends. However, the data for the Lower Carboniferous are sparse. New Mexico NL brachiopods have slightly lower $\delta^{18}O$ values (–4‰ to –3‰; Fig. 7) than contemporary brachiopods from Kansas and Texas, possibly because of a shallower, more restricted depositional environment (Grossman et al., 1993). The value for Carboniferous $\delta^{18}O$ estimated by Veizer et al. (1986; –4.5 ±1.5‰, Fig. 5) using trace element–$\delta^{18}O$ trends in whole brachiopods mostly from Canada is lower than values in NL brachiopods and marine cements from other areas. The highest $\delta^{18}O$ value observed (–0.5‰) is for the least altered sample of Late Pennsylvanian aragonite cement from New Mexico (Dickson et al., 1991). Allowing for the 0.7‰ enrichment of aragonite relative to calcite (Grossman and Ku, 1986), the calcite-equivalent $\delta^{18}O$ value (–1.2‰) is just within the range of NL brachiopod data.

To understand the significance of the isotope data, it is useful to calculate paleotemperatures using estimated δ_w values. Assuming the ice volume of the glaciated Late Carboniferous was similar to today's, a reasonable estimate of $\delta_{w,SMOW}$ is 0‰. Using this value, the $\delta^{18}O$ range of –3‰ to –1‰ translates to a temperature range of 20°C to 30°C (Hays and Grossman, 1991). Using the estimated $\delta_{w,SMOW}$ for an ice-free Earth, –1.0‰ (Savin, 1977), the temperature range is 16°C to 25°C. These temperature ranges are reasonable for the tropical and subtropical surface waters from which most of the samples were deposited (Fig. 6) and suggest that the δ_w value may be close to the modern value. Without the ability to better constrain paleotemperature or δ_w, however, determination of these variables remains conjectural.

The carbon isotopic record for the Carboniferous is characterized by a mid-Carboniferous increase in the $\delta^{13}C$ values of brachiopods and cements in the Paleotethyan region (Spain and Russia) and Arctic Canada (Fig. 5). Values for brachiopods from these areas are less than 5‰ in the lower Carboniferous and greater than 5‰ in the upper Carboniferous. Popp et al. (1986a) suggested that this $\delta^{13}C$ shift was due to a global increase in the burial of organic carbon, but subsequent data have shown that the event was not global. As seen in Figure 5, brachiopods from the United States (Panthalassan) show no increase in $\delta^{13}C$—values generally remain between 3‰ and 5‰. Preserved aragonite marine cement of late Pennsylvanian age from New Mexico also has a low $\delta^{13}C$ value (4.2‰; Dickson et al., 1991), especially considering that aragonite will be 1.7‰ enriched relative to calcite (Romanek et al., 1992). Likewise, late Pennsylvanian former marine cements from New Mexico have $\delta^{13}C$ values that average 2‰ to 3‰ (Graber, 1989). Grossman et al. (1993) suggest that the $\delta^{13}C$ difference that arises between eastern Panthalassan and Paleotethyan carbonates reflects a change in ocean circulation associated with the closing of the equatorial seaway with the formation of Pangea (see Fig. 6).

Magaritz and Holser (1990) observed $\delta^{13}C$ fluctuations of more than 6‰ in the whole-rock record of the Carboniferous Horquilla Limestone in New Mexico (Fig. 7), which they attributed to storage of organic carbon on continental shelves during high sea level. Magaritz and Holser also presented a ^{13}C stratigraphy for a Nevada section that, like the New Mexico stratigraphy, showed a negative anomaly at the Morrowan-Atokan boundary (Fig. 7). Unlike the New Mexico anomaly, however, the Nevada $\delta^{13}C$ values quickly return to more typical marine values (3‰). NL brachiopod data do not show evidence of the negative $\delta^{13}C$ excursions of Magaritz and Holser, nor do they show such low $\delta^{13}C$ values. Graber (1989), in her study of the Upper Horquilla Limestone, used $\delta^{13}C$–$\delta^{18}O$ trends to argue that micrite $\delta^{13}C$ values like those used by Magaritz and Holser (1990) can be overprinted by diagenesis. Furthermore, she found that carbon isotopic compositions in the matrix calcite of a single hand sample could vary by 3‰. These observations suggest a diagenetic origin for the whole-rock ^{13}C excursions reported by Magaritz and Holser (1990).

Permian

The Permian yields some of the highest $\delta^{18}O$ values of the Paleozoic (Fig. 8). Popp (1986) obtained values between –1‰ and +1‰ for nonluminescent brachiopods from Timor and Russia and values between –4‰ and –2‰ for NL brachiopods from Yugoslavia. Data for the brachiopod *Neospirifer* from Compston (1960) are also shown in Figure 8. Although these specimens were not examined using cathodoluminescence, the valves sampled have the thick prismatic layers that our studies show to be resistant to diagenesis (Grossman et al., 1991, 1993). Like the brachiopods from Russia and Timor, the Australian *Neospirifer* are enriched in ^{18}O (–1‰ to +1‰). Veizer et al.'s (1986) estimate for the $\delta^{18}O$ of Permian brachiopods is -2.5 ±1.5‰ (Fig. 8). The samples were predominantly from northern Canada and had relatively low and variable $\delta^{18}O$ values ranging from –10.6‰ to –1.0‰. Because of this variability, the trace element–isotope trends can only constrain "original" $\delta^{18}O$ to roughly ±2‰ (95‰ confidence bands assuming that values for Na content have no error; Fig. 4). The cement data of Given and Lohmann (1985) range between –3‰ and –1‰.

The high $\delta^{18}O$ values for the samples from Timor and Australia can be explained by cooler temperatures at middle and high latitudes (Fig. 9; Hudson and Anderson, 1989). These higher $\delta^{18}O$ values (–1‰ to +1‰) yield temperatures of 11°C to 20°C if $\delta_{w,SMOW}$ equals 0‰ and temperatures of 7°C to 16°C if $\delta_{w,SMOW}$ equals –1‰. An exception to this interpretation is the low $\delta^{18}O$ values of the mid-latitude Afghanistan samples (Fig. 9). The high $\delta^{18}O$ values for brachiopods from Russia can be explained by Russia's placement in the latitudes of excess evaporation where evaporative enrichment of δ_w is possible. Low-latitude samples from New Mexico and Yugoslavia had $\delta^{18}O$ values between –4‰ and –1‰, similar to the values for low-latitude localities in the Carboniferous.

TABLE 2. COMPILATION OF ISOTOPIC DATA FOR CARBONIFEROUS AND PERMIAN BRACHIOPODS, MARINE CEMENTS, LIMESTONES, AND DOLOSTONES

Reference	Age	Location	Formation	Sample	Type/Genus	$\delta^{13}C$	2xSE*	$\delta^{18}O$	2xSE*	N	Note
Permian (data for Fig. 5)											
Popp, 1986	Kazanian	Russia		NL brachiopod	*Licharewia*	3.35	0.49	0.67	0.61	6	
	Kungurian	Timor		NL brachiopod	*Martinia*	5.96	0.17	-0.09	0.35	5	
				NL brachiopod	Other spiriferids	5.50	0.17	-0.60	0.11	5	
		Afghanistan		NL brachiopod	Rhynchonellids	5.58	0.10	-0.68	0.13	5	
	Sakmarian-Artinskian			NL brachiopod	*Neospirifer*	4.44		-2.72		1	
				NL brachiopod	*Choristites*	5.23		-2.33		1	
Compston, 1960	Sakmarian-Artinskian	Yugoslavia	Clastic Trogkofel Fm	NL brachiopod	*Martinia*	6.30		-3.35		1	
	"prob." Kungarian	Carn. Basin, W. Australia	Coolkilya greywacke	Brachiopod	*Neospirifer*	5.10		-1.20		1	
	Artinskian	Carn. Basin, W. Australia	Nalbia greywacke	Brachiopod	*Neospirifer*	4.38	1.28	-0.37	0.17	4/3	1
	Artinskian	Carn. Basin, W. Australia	Wandagee Fm	Brachiopod	*Neospirifer*	2.90		-0.50		1	
	Late Sakmarian	Carn. Basin, W. Australia	Callytharra Fm	Brachiopod	*Neospirifer*	4.54	0.47	0.04	0.48	7/5	1
	Late Sak.-Tatarian	Fitz. Basin, W. Australia	Liveringa Gp	Brachiopod	*Neospirifer*	5.20	0.20	-0.20		3/1	1
	Lower Artinskian	Fitz. Basin, W. Australia	Noonkanbah Fm	Brachiopod	*Neospirifer*	4.48	0.46	-0.52	0.71	7	
Beauchamp et al., 1987	Asselian-Sakmarian	Sverdrup Basin, Canada		Marine cement		6.13	0.29	-2.50		3	
Veizer et al., 1966	Permian	N. America, esp. Canada	Many	Brachiopods	Many	4.00	1.50	-2.50	1.50	29	2
Given and Lohmann, 1985	Guadalupian	New Mexico, U.S.A.	Youngest upper Capitan	Marine cement	Former arag.	5.80		-0.70		≈27	3
			Upper Capitan Fm	Marine cement	Former arag.	5.30		-2.50		>70	3
			Lower Capitan Fm	Marine cement	Former arag.	5.20		-2.80		≈26	3
Scholle et al., 1991	Guadalupian	East Greenland	Wegener Halvo Fm	Marine cement	Fibrous	5.53	0.17			30	
Graber, 1989	Wolfcampian	New Mexico, U.S.A.	Horquilla Ls	Marine cement		2.77	0.36	-6.75	0.34	8	
	Wolfcampian	New Mexico, U.S.A.	Horquilla Ls	Marine cement		3.80	0.30	-7.69	0.39	9	
Other Permian Data											
Scholle et al., 1991	Guadalupian	East Greenland	Wegener Halvo Fm	Brachiopods	Not given	5.27	0.47	-4.96	0.79	10	
Gruszczynski et al., 1989	Artinskian-?Kazanian	West Spitsbergen	Kapp Starostin	Brachiopods	Productacean	≈-3 to +8		≈-12 to -2			
Magaritz and Stemmerik, 1989	Late Permian	East Greenland	Karstryggen and Wegener Halvo Fms	WR calcite							
Rao and Green, 1982	Early Permian	Tasmania	Darlington Ls	Brachiopod	Not given	5.37	0.29	-2.63	0.69	10	
Rao, 1988	Lower Permian	Tasmania	Berriedale Ls	Brachiopod	Not given	4.39	0.35	-3.47	1.01	11	
Carboniferous (data for Fig. 3)											
Graber, 1989	Virgilian	New Mexico, U.S.A.	Horquilla Ls	Marine cement	Isopachous	3.24	0.43	(-6.44)	(-0.41)	10	
	Missourian	New Mexico, U.S.A.	Horquilla Ls	Marine cement	Isopachous	1.81	0.93	(-5.92)	(-1.64)	3	
Grossman et al., 1993	Missourian-Virgilian	Kansas, U.S.A.	Kansas City-Shawnee Gp	NL brachiopod	*Crurithyris*	3.18	0.17	-2.04	0.13	41	
			Kansas City-Shawnee Gp	NL brachiopod	*Composita*	4.34	0.19	-1.78	0.14	57	
			Kansas City-Shawnee Gp	NL brachiopod	*Neospirifer*	3.46	0.19	-1.85	0.12	41	
	Missourian-Virgilian	New Mexico, U.S.A.	Madera Gp	NL brachiopod	*Crurithyris*	2.64	0.32	-4.10	0.25	5	
			Madera Gp	NL brachiopod	*Composita*	4.14	0.26	-3.42	0.26	25	
			Madera Gp	NL brachiopod	*Neospirifer*	3.29	0.22	-3.43	0.22	25	
Grossman et al., 1991	Missourian-Virgilian	Texas, U.S.A.	Canyon, Cisco Gps	NL brachiopod	*Crurithyris*	3.27	0.14	-2.53	0.07	195	
			Canyon, Cisco Gps	NL brachiopod	*Composita*	4.87	0.13	-2.18	0.11	93	
			Canyon, Cisco Gps	NL brachiopod	*Neospirifer*	3.90	0.20	-2.25	0.18	21	
Davies, 1977	Mid Perm/lower Perm	Ellesmere Is.		Marine cement	Former HMC	5.50	0.42			14	4
				Marine cement	Former arag.	5.70	0.38			13	4

TABLE 2. COMPILATION OF ISOTOPIC DATA FOR CARBONIFEROUS AND PERMIAN BRACHIOPODS, MARINE CEMENTS, LIMESTONES, AND DOLOSTONES (continued)

Reference	Age	Location	Formation	Sample	Type/Genus	$\delta^{13}C$	2xSE*	$\delta^{18}O$	2xSE*	N	Note
Carboniferous (data for Fig. 3) (continued)											
Dickson et al., 1991	Virgilian	New Mexico, U.S.A.	Holder Fm	Marine cement	Aragonite	4.20	0.40	-0.50	0.40	1	5
Popp, 1986	Kasimovian	Spain		NL brachiopod	*Choristites*	6.27	0.17	-3.06	0.22	9	
		Spain		NL brachiopod	*Martinia*	5.89		-3.08		1	
	Early Kasimovian	Spain	Barruelo Fm	NL brachiopod	*Brachythyrina*	5.88		-2.47		1	
	Late Moscovian	Spain	Sierra Corsia Fm	NL brachiopod	*Choristites*	5.17	0.18	-1.56	0.06	3	
	Late Moscovian	Russia		NL brachiopod	*Choristites*	5.57	0.40	-3.66	0.21	9	
	Moscovian	Spain	Louis Ciruera and Eslalada Fms	NL brachiopod	*Choristites*	5.60	0.73	-2.03	0.18	4	
	Early Moscovian	Spain	Perapertu Fm	NL brachiopod	*Choristites*	5.78		-2.51		1	
		Spain	Perapertu Fm	NL brachiopod	*Brachythyrina*	5.52		-1.96		2	
	Bashkirian	Spain	Valdeteja and another fm	NL brachiopod	*Choristites*	5.84	0.18	-2.38	0.46	3	
	Late Serpukhovian	Spain	Resoba Ls	NL brachiopod	*Choristites*	6.13		-0.83		1	
	Serpukhovian	Algeria		NL brachiopod	*Gigantoproductus*	3.32	0.10	-1.19	0.12	5	
	Late Visean	Great Britain	Monsaldale Fm	NL brachiopod	*Martinia*	3.68	0.16	-1.96	0.07	6	
			Monsaldale Fm	NL brachiopod	*Gigantoproductus*	1.97		-3.67		1	
	Visean	Belgium		NL brachiopod	*Gigantoproductus*	2.66	0.27	-3.07	0.19	14	
	Visean	Great Britain		NL brachiopod	Spirifer	4.63		-1.84		1	
Meyers and Lohmann, 1985	Osagean or younger	New Mexico, U.S.A.	Dalton beds	Marine cement		4.0		-1.5			6
Banner et al., 1988	Osagean	Missouri, U.S.A.	Burlington-Keokuk	NL brachiopod	Spiriferids?	4.40	0.23	-1.90	0.37	7	
Other Carboniferous Data											
Graber, 1989	Missourian-Virgilian	SW New Mexico, U.S.A.	Horquilla Ls	Matrix	Not given	0.42	1.48	-5.88	0.48	11	
Morrison et al., 1985	Upper Penn	Western PA, U.S.A.	Glenshaw Fm	Brachiopods	Not given	2.00	2.00	-4.50	1.50	37	2
Veizer et al., 1986	Carboniferous	North America, esp. Canada	Many	Brachiopods	Many	2.00		-6.40		≈48	7
Magaritz and Holser, 1990	Penn	SW New Mexico, U.S.A.	Horquilla Ls	Matrix	Not given	2.00		-2.56		26	8
	Lower Penn	Southern Nevada, U.S.A.	Bird Spring Group	Matrix	Not given	2.23	0.43	-4.63	0.35	4	
Brand, 1987	Lower Penn	Eastern Kentucky, U.S.A.	Breathitt Fm	Brachiopods	Not given	3.3	0.31	-2.00	0.46	3	
Brand, 1982	Osagean	Southern Nevada, U.S.A.	Lake Valley Fm	Brachiopods	Not given			-5.10	0.35	1	9
Brand, 1981	Lower Penn	Eastern Kentucky, U.S.A.	Kendrick Sh	Brachiopods	Not given	1.70		-2.90		4	
Wiggins, 1986	Lower Penn	Central Texas, U.S.A.	Marble Falls Ls	Micrite	Reef foreslope	0.43	2.47	-2.44	0.52	3	
Lowenstam, 1961	Chesterian	Oklahoma, U.S.A.	Goddard Sh	Brachiopods	*Chonetes*	2.80		-2.30	0.68	1	
Brand and Veizer, 1981	Osagean	Iowa, U.S.A.	Burlington Ls	Brachiopods	*Dictyoclostus*	3.88	0.47	-3.65	0.78	4	
	Osagean	Missouri, U.S.A.	Burlington Ls	Brachiopods	*Dictyoclostus*						10

*2xSE = 2 x standard error.

Notes:
1. N/N = $N(\delta^{18}O)/N(\delta^{13}C)$
2. Estimated based on trace element trends.
3. Estimated based on isotopic trends.
4. Estimated from figure.
5. Analytical precision shown instead of 2xSE.
6. Estimated based on isotopic trends; error unknown.
7. Approximate median values shown.
8. Approximate.
9. "Least-altered fossils." ^{18}O only.
10. ^{18}O only.

Late Middle Carboniferous (306 Ma)

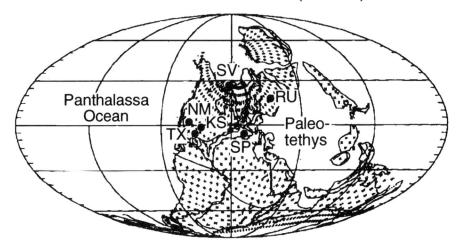

Early Carboniferous (342 Ma)

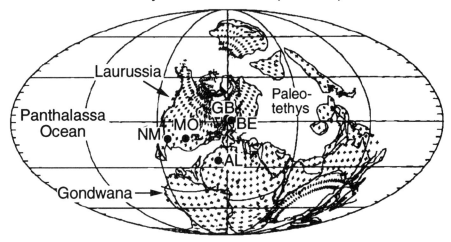

Figure 6. Locations of samples shown in Figure 5. AL = Algeria, BE = Belgium, GB = Great Britain, KS = Kansas, MO = Missouri, NM = New Mexico, RU = Russia, SP = Spain, SV = Sverdrup Basin, and TX = Texas. Paleogeographic maps from C. Scotese (personal communication, 1992).

The Panthalassa-Paleotethys difference in $\delta^{13}C$ of the late Carboniferous is carried into the Permian. Wolfcampian cements from New Mexico are low (2‰ to 4‰), whereas those from the Sverdrup Basin are high (≈6‰). Above the Sakmarian, regional differences in $\delta^{13}C$ values are indistinct, with values for Panthalassan and Paleotethyan brachiopods and cements generally falling between 4 and 6‰. Gruszczynski et al. (1989) observed a distinct maximum of ≈7‰ in the $\delta^{13}C$ of Upper Permian productacean brachiopod shells from West Spitsbergen (Fig. 8). The $\delta^{13}C$ shifts correlate with a $\delta^{18}O$ increase from −7‰ to −3‰, then a decrease to less than −10‰. Such large $\delta^{18}O$ shifts suggest diagenetic overprinting of the

isotopic compositions. Veizer et al. (1986) estimated a $\delta^{13}C$ for Permian brachiopods of 4.0 ±1.5‰, within the range of samples from Australia, Russia, and Afghanistan. Overall, there is little isotopic data for nonluminescent brachiopods of Permian age and almost no data for the lowermost Permian and the Upper Permian.

Permian-Triassic boundary and the Triassic

The Permian-Triassic boundary event (P-Tr) represents one of the Earth's major biological reorganizations. Stable isotopes allow an evaluation of how the Earth's systems responded to, or perhaps caused, such an event. All the isotopic data for

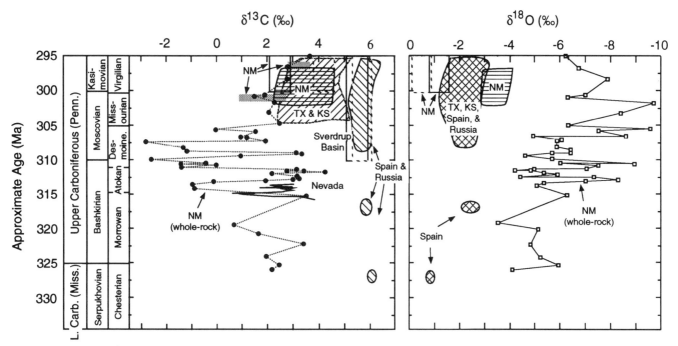

Figure 7. Comparison of isotopic data from whole-rock samples from Big Hatchet Peak, New Mexico, and Arrow Canyon, Nevada (Magaritz and Holser, 1990), with data from nonluminescent brachiopods and marine cements. Stratigraphic placement of the Arrow Canyon data is based on Langenheim et al. (1984). The data for New Mexico brachiopods are from Grossman et al. (1993). Brachiopod data from Kansas, Texas, Spain, and Russia (see Fig. 5) are shown as fields. Marine cement data from New Mexico and Sverdrup Basin (rectangles and stippled areas) are from Figure 5. $\delta^{18}O$ plotted increasing to the left.

the Permian-Triassic boundary are based on whole-rock analyses. Gruszczynski et al. (1989) reported on isotopic variation in brachiopods from the Permian Kapp Starostin Formation in West Spitsbergen, which was thought to include latest Permian rocks; however, recent stratigraphic studies suggest that the upper part of the Kapp Starostin Formation may be Ufimian to Kazanian in age (Nakrem et al., 1992; H. A. Nakrem, personal communication, 1992). This finding emphasizes the importance of good stratigraphic control in developing a global isotope stratigraphy. Because the original $\delta^{18}O$ values of limestones and dolostones are easily altered by diagenesis, only the carbon isotopic data for the P-Tr boundary provide reliable paleoenvironmental information.

The isotopic record of the P-Tr boundary has been the subject of many studies (for instance, Chen et al., 1984, 1991; Xu et al., 1986; Holser and Magaritz, 1987; Baud et al., 1989). The scarcity of marine sections for this interval has limited development of a global record. The best sections are found around the margin of the Paleotethyan Seaway in present-day Austria, Yugoslavia, Iran, Armenia, Pakistan, India, and south China (Fig. 9). The biostratigraphy of the P-Tr boundary has not been completely resolved, but most sections appear to be marked by a paraconformity with sediment missing from the latest Permian (Dorashamian or late Changhsingian) or earliest Triassic (Lower Griesbachian). This includes sections in

Yugoslavia, Turkey, Iran (Emarat), and Pakistan (Fig. 10; Baud et al., 1989). Recent studies argue for a continuous record of the P-Tr boundary at sections in the Carnic Alps (Gartnerkofel), China (Meishan), and Iran (KAB-1) (Fig. 10; Broglio Loriga and Cassinis, 1992; Sweet, 1992). On the other hand, Ding (1992) contends that the Upper Changhsingian in South China "is the youngest Permian recognized anywhere in the world."

Typically, late Permian $\delta^{13}C$ values of 3‰ to 4‰ decrease approaching and through the boundary to values of −1‰ to +1‰. The $\delta^{13}C$ shift at the P-Tr boundary appears rapid when viewed at the scale of Figure 10. However, as pointed out by Magaritz et al. (1988), the shift can occur over several meters. Detailed determination of the rate and timing of the shift is limited by the stratigraphic information available. In many sections the stratigraphic age of the sediments is not well constrained, and in some sections the placement of the P-Tr boundary is in question. A second problem is the amount of time represented by the hiatus in the sections. Stable isotope studies may resolve these stratigraphic problems by providing a global datum for the P-Tr boundary—the $\delta^{13}C$ shift—and by providing a means of determining sedimentation rate across the boundary based on the rate of $\delta^{13}C$ change. Such an application requires controls on sample quality to eliminate diagenetic effects.

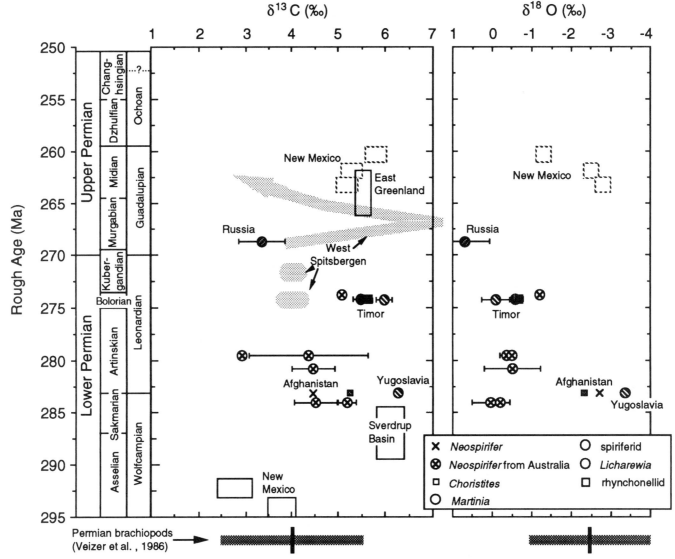

Figure 8. Summary of the carbon and oxygen isotopic data for brachiopods and marine cements of Permian age. Stratigraphic placement is rough. Data for *Neospirifer* from Australia (Compston, 1960) and brachiopods from West Spitsbergen (Gruszczynski et al., 1989; Veizer et al., 1986) are for whole brachiopods. The stratigraphic placement of the West Spitsbergen data is uncertain, and the δ¹⁸O data are not shown because almost all are less than the lower limit of the figure (–4‰; the preservation of these samples is in question). The ranges of Veizer et al. are estimates based on trace element–isotope trends of samples from the entire Permian (Fig. 4). All other brachiopod data are for nonluminescent shell (Popp, 1986). Data and their sources are shown in Table 2. All error bars are 2 × standard error except for Guadalupian cement data (Given and Lohmann, 1985). Permian time scale from C. Ross, A. Baud, and M. Menning (work in preparation). See Figure 5 for key to cement data. δ¹⁸O plotted increasing to the left.

Some sections, such as the Cürük Dag section in Turkey (Fig. 10), have pedogenic calcrete at the boundary. Oxidation of organic matter in the soil zone will cause this calcrete to be depleted in ¹³C (Allan and Matthews, 1982). Because most sections contain a hiatus at the P-Tr boundary, there is ample opportunity for a lowering of the δ¹³C of carbonate directly below the boundary, causing the "global" P-Tr δ¹³C shift to ap-

pear to begin below the boundary. Demonstrating this effect is the fact that many sections show a decrease in δ¹³C approaching the boundary regardless of whether the uppermost Permian sediments are Dzhulfian or Dorashamian in age (Fig. 10).

Except for the China sections, the δ¹³C of marine deposits above the P-Tr boundary generally increases upsection from minima below 1‰ to values between 1 and 2‰ (Fig. 10; Baud

Latest Permian (255 Ma)

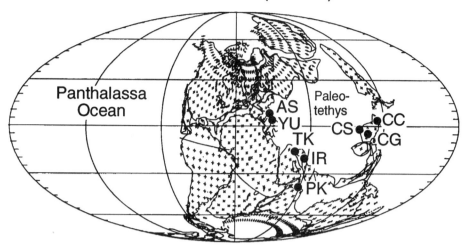

Late Early Permian (277 Ma)

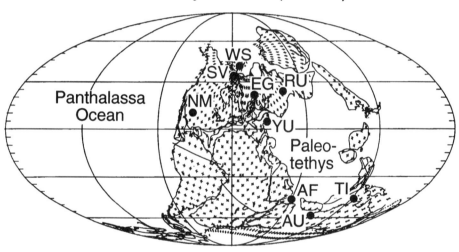

Figure 9. Location of samples shown in Figure 8 and 10. Map abbreviations: AF = Afghanistan, AS = Austria, AU = Australia, CC = Changxing (China), CG = Guizhou (China), CS = Shaanxi (China), EG = East Greenland, IR = Iran, NM = New Mexico, PK = Pakistan, RU = Russia, SV = Sverdrup Basin, TI = Timor, TK = Turkey, WS = West Spitzbergen, and YU = Yugoslavia. Paleogeographic maps from C. Scotese (personal communication, 1992).

et al., 1989; Holser et al., 1989). The China sections do not show the recovery of $\delta^{13}C$ values to 1 to 2‰ but instead remain below 1‰ (Xu et al., 1986; Baud et al., 1989; Chen et al., 1991). Of course, the Griesbachian interval represented by the China sections may include only the earliest interval (Fig. 10).

Carbon isotopic values of other Triassic carbonates do not recover to the >4‰ values common in Permian carbonates. $\delta^{13}C$ values of about 0.3‰ to 3.3‰ are observed in "original" marine limestone of Early to Middle Triassic age from the upper Yangtze area of China (Wu et al., 1989). Middle Triassic fibrous cements from northern Italy have $\delta^{13}C$ values of

1‰ to 2‰ (Frisia-Bruni et al., 1989), and aragonitic corals and sponges have $\delta^{13}C$ values of 3‰ to 4‰ (Scherer, 1977), which is equivalent to calcite $\delta^{13}C$ values of 1.3‰ to 2.3‰ assuming the aragonite was precipitated in carbon isotopic equilibrium (Romanek et al., 1992). Late Triassic marine cements and bivalves (original high Mg calcite and low Mg calcite, respectively) from the Steinplatte complex in Austria have average $\delta^{13}C$ values of 2.9‰ and 2.8‰, respectively (Mazzullo et al., 1990). Finally, Late Triassic nannofossil bulk sediments from ODP Leg 122 off northwest Australia average 2.1 ±0.53‰ (N = 9; Bralower et al., 1991). That no Triassic sam-

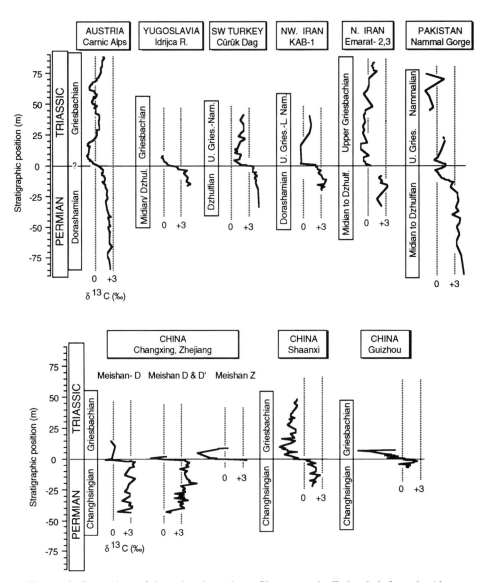

Figure 10. Comparison of the carbon isotopic profiles across the Tethys belt from the Alps to China. Data are shown as a function of stratigraphic position with no attempt at stratigraphic correlation except for the P-Tr boundary. Modified from Baud et al. (1989) with additional profiles from Holser et al. (1989; Carnic Alps, Austria) and Chen et al. (1991; Zhejiang [Meishan D & D' and Z], Shaanxi, and Guizhou, China).

ples, not even aragonitic shell, have $\delta^{13}C$ values as high as those for the Permian is evidence that the P-Tr ^{13}C shift is environmental and not diagenetic.

The P-Tr ^{13}C shift is generally attributed to a global increase in the oxidation of organic carbon and a subsequent decrease in the size of the organic carbon reservoir. This event apparently occurred in conjunction with a drop in sea level and exposure of shallow shelves (Holser et al., 1989). The magnitude of the shift varies because the $\delta^{13}C$ minima vary from near 0‰ in sections in Armenia, Iran, and Turkey to <–8‰ in sections from China (Fig. 10; Baud et al., 1989; Chen et al., 1991). The lowest $\delta^{13}C$ values in the China sec-

tions occur in mudstones and are likely diagenetic in origin. In general the P-Tr shift appears to be roughly 3‰. Better resolution of the timing and magnitude of the ^{13}C shift at the P-Tr boundary will require analyses of well-preserved brachiopod shells and marine cements.

CONCLUSIONS

The Carboniferous, Permian, and Triassic periods are represented by a piecemeal isotopic record based on different materials with varying susceptibilities to diagenesis and degrees of diagenetic alteration. Careful sample screening and characterization can minimize or eliminate diagenetic effects. The best materials for analyses are aragonite or high Mg marine cements and nonluminescent brachiopod shells. Trace element–isotope and convergent $\delta^{13}C$–$\delta^{18}O$ trends also can be used to estimate original isotopic composition.

Several important isotopic phenomena are observed. Analyses of well-preserved brachiopod shells, as indicated by low Mn and Fe contents and the absence of cathodoluminescence, suggest that Paleotethyan brachiopods increased in $\delta^{13}C$ by about 2‰ in the mid-Carboniferous, whereas Panthalassan brachiopods from the North American craton showed no change in $\delta^{13}C$. Marine cements show the same trend. These data suggest a change in ocean circulation, with eastern Laurussia becoming increasingly isolated from western Laurussia as a result of collision with Gondwana. Limited data suggest that the Paleotethyan-Panthalassan ^{13}C divergence extends into the Permian. The $\delta^{13}C$ of Permian carbonates remains high until the Permian-Triassic boundary. At the P-Tr boundary, the $\delta^{13}C$ of whole-rock limestone declines by roughly 3‰. This shift is generally attributed to a decrease in the amount of carbon stored as sedimentary organic matter. Carbon isotopic data for the Triassic are limited but suggest that $\delta^{13}C$ values remained lower than Permian values.

The oxygen isotopic record is more scant than the carbon isotopic record because of the unreliability of whole-rock data. Reliable brachiopods and former marine cements yield $\delta^{18}O$ values of mostly –3‰ to –1‰ for the Carboniferous and –3‰ to +1‰ for the Permian. The high $\delta^{18}O$ values (–1‰ to 1‰) for some Permian localities can be explained by placement in latitudes with cool temperatures (>40° latitude) or excess evaporation (20° to 35° latitude).

Because temporal trends in the late Paleozoic–early Mesozoic isotopic record are based on composite records of samples from different continental margin locations of different age, care must be taken to ensure that *regional* differences are not interpreted as *global* change. Defining global trends requires analyses of chemically preserved brachiopods and marine cents with good geographic coverage for a particular time interval.

Stable isotopes can testify to the paleoceanographic and paleoclimatic changes associated with the formation and breakup of Pangea. In future studies, oxygen isotopes may be used to monitor the waxing and waning of Late Paleozoic glaciers and changes in the latitudinal temperature gradient. Carbon isotopes may be used to refine the timing and nature of the P-Tr boundary and—combined with geochemical models—to relate the ^{13}C event to changes in the O_2 and CO_2 content of the paleoatmosphere.

ACKNOWLEDGMENTS

I gratefully acknowledge years of fruitful collaboration with Tom Yancey and the contributions of our students: David Adlis, Zhang Chuanlun ("John"), and Mii Horng-Sheng ("Orson"). The manuscript was improved by the reviews of Tom Anderson, Bill Holser, George Klein, Peter Scholle, and Tom Yancey. I thank the National Science Foundation for supporting this research (EAR-8720886, EAR-9005030) and for providing support for contributors to a Geochemical Society Symposium on this subject at the 1990 Geological Society of America Meeting (EAR-9018378).

REFERENCES CITED

Adlis, D. S., Grossman, E. L., Yancey, T. E., and McLerran, D. R., 1988, Isotope stratigraphy and paleodepth changes of Pennsylvanian cyclical sedimentary deposits: Palaios, v. 3, p. 487–506.

Allan, J. R., and Matthews, R. K., 1982, Isotopic signatures associated with early meteoric diagenesis: Sedimentology, v. 29, p. 797–818.

Banner, J. L., Hanson, G. N., and Meyers, W. J., 1988, Water-rock interaction history of regionally extensive dolomites of the Burlington-Keokuk Formation (Mississippian): Isotopic evidence, *in* Shukla, V., and Baker, P. A., eds., Sedimentology and geochemistry of dolostones: Society of Economic Paleontologists and Mineralogists Special Publication 43, p. 97–113.

Bathurst, R.G.C., 1975, Carbonate sediments and their diagenesis: Amsterdam, Elsevier, 658 p.

Baud, A., Magaritz, M., and Holser, W. T., 1989, Permian-Triassic of the Tethys: Carbon isotope studies: Geologische Rundschau, v. 78, p. 649–677.

Beauchamp, B., Oldershaw, A. E., and Krouse, H. R., 1987, Upper Carboniferous to upper Permian ^{13}C-enriched primary carbonates in the Sverdrup Basin, Canadian Arctic: Comparisons to coeval western North American ocean margins: Chemical Geology (Isotope Geoscience Section), v. 65, p. 391–413.

Berger, W. H., and Vincent, E., 1986, Deep-sea carbonates: Reading the carbon-isotope signal: Geologische Rundschau, v. 75, p. 249–269.

Berner, R. A., 1987, Models for carbon and sulfur cycles and atmospheric oxygen: Application to Paleozoic geologic history: American Journal of Science, v. 287, p. 177–196.

Bralower, T. J., Bown, P. R., and Siesser, W. G., 1991, Significance of the Upper Triassic nannofossils from the Southern Hemisphere (ODP Leg 122, Wombat Plateau, N.W. Australia): Marine Micropaleontology, v. 17, p. 119–154.

Brand, U., 1981, Mineralogy and chemistry of the lower Pennsylvanian Kendrick fauna, eastern Kentucky. 2: Stable isotopes: Chemical Geology, v. 32, p. 16–28.

Brand, U., 1982, The oxygen and carbon isotope composition of Carboniferous fossil components: Sea water effects: Sedimentology, v. 29, p. 139–147.

Brand, U., 1987, Depositional analysis of the Breathitt formation's marine horizons, Kentucky, U.S.A.: Trace elements and stable isotopes: Chemical Geology (Isotope Geoscience Section), v. 65, p. 117–136.

Brand, U., and Veizer, J., 1980, Chemical diagenesis of a multicomponent carbonate system. 1: Trace elements: Journal of Sedimentary Petrology, v. 50, p. 1219–1236.

Brand, U., and Veizer, J., 1981, Chemical diagenesis of a multicomponent carbonate system. 2: Stable isotopes: Journal of Sedimentary Petrology, v. 51, p. 987–997.

Broglio Loriga, C., and Cassinis, G., 1992, The Permo-Triassic boundary in the Southern Alps (Italy) and in adjacent Periadriatic regions, *in* Sweet, W. C., Yang, Z., Dickins, J. M., and Yin, H., eds., Permo-Triassic events in the eastern Tethys: Cambridge, Cambridge University Press, p. 78–97.

Carpenter, S. J., 1991, Isotopic and minor element chemistry of Devonian-Carboniferous abiotic marine calcite [Ph.D. thesis]: Ann Arbor, University of Michigan, 314 p.

Carpenter, S. J., Lohmann, K. C., Holden, P., Walter, L. M., Huston, T. J., and Halliday, A.N., 1991, $\delta^{18}O$ values, $^{87}Sr/^{86}Sr$ ratios of Late

Devonian abiotic marine calcite: Implications for the composition of ancient seawater: Geochimica et Cosmochimica Acta, v. 55, p. 1991–2010.

Chase, C. G., and Perry, E. C., Jr., 1972, The oceans: Growth and oxygen isotope evolution: Science, v. 177, p. 992–994.

Chen, J., Shao, M., Huo, W., and Yao, Y., 1984, Carbon isotope of carbonate strata at Permian-Triassic boundary in Changxing, Zhejiang: Scientia Geologica Sinica, no. 1, p. 88–93.

Chen, J., Chu, X., Shao, M., and Zhong, H., 1991, Carbon isotope study of the Permian-Triassic boundary sequences in China: Chemical Geology (Isotope Geoscience Section), v. 89, p. 239–251.

Claypool, G. E., and Kaplan, I. R., 1974, The origin and distribution of methane in marine sediments, in Kaplan, I. R., ed., Natural gases in marine sediments: New York, Plenum, p. 99–139.

Compston, W., 1960, The carbon isotopic composition of certain marine invertebrates and coals from the Australian Permian: Geochimica et Cosmochimica Acta, v. 18, p. 1–22.

Craig, H., and Gordon, L. I., 1965, Deuterium and oxygen 18 variation in the ocean and the marine atmosphere, in Torgiorgi, E., ed., Second Conference on Stable Isotopes in Oceanographic Studies and Paleotemperatures: Pisa, Consiglio Nazionale delle Richerche, p. 9–130.

Crowley, T. J., and North, G. R., 1991, Paleoclimatology: New York, Oxford University Press, 339 p.

Davies, G. R., 1977, Former magnesian calcite and aragonite submarine cements in upper Paleozoic reefs of the Canadian Arctic: A summary: Geology, v. 5, p. 11–15.

Dean, W. E., Arthur, M. A., and Claypool, G. E., 1986, Depletion of ^{13}C in Cretaceous marine organic matter: Source, diagenetic, or environmental signal?, in Meyers, P. A., and Mitterer, R. M., eds., Deep ocean black shales: Organic geochemistry and paleoceanographic setting: Marine Geology, v. 70, p. 119–157.

Delaney, M. L., Popp, B. N., Lepzelter, C. G., and Anderson, T. F., 1989, Lithium-to-calcium ratios in modern, Cenozoic, and Paleozoic articulate brachiopod shells: Paleoceanography, v. 4, p. 681–691.

Dickson, J.A.D., Smalley, P. C., and Kirkland, B. L., 1991, Carbon and oxygen isotopes in Pennsylvanian biogenic and abiogenic aragonite (Otero County, New Mexico): A laser microprobe study: Geochimica et Cosmochimica Acta, v. 55, p. 2607–2613.

Ding, M., 1992, Conodont sequences in the Upper Permian and Lower Triassic of South China and the nature of conodont faunal changes at the systemic boundary, in Sweet, W. C., Yang, Z., Dickins, J. M., and Yin, H., eds., Permo-Triassic events in the eastern Tethys: Cambridge Cambridge University Press, p. 109–119.

Dittmar, H., and Vogel, H., 1968, Die spurenelemente mangan und vanadium in brachiopoden-schalen in abhangigkeit vom biotop: Chemical Geology, v. 3, p. 95–110.

Dodd, J. R., and Stanton, R. J., 1990, Paleoecology, concepts and applications (2nd edition): New York, John Wiley and Sons, 502 p.

Epstein, S., Buchsbaum, R., Lowenstam, H. A., and Urey, H. C., 1953, Revised carbonate-water isotopic temperature scale: Geological Society of America Bulletin, v. 64, p. 1315–1325.

Fairbanks, R. G., and Matthews, R. K., 1978, The marine oxygen isotope record in Pleistocene coral, Barbados, West Indies: Quaternary Research, v. 10, p. 181–196.

Frank, J. R., Carpenter, A. B., and Oglesby, T. W., 1982, Cathodoluminescence and composition of calcite cement in the Taum Sauk Limestone (upper Cambrian), southeast Missouri: Journal of Sedimentary Petrology, v. 52, p. 631–638.

Friedman, I., and O'Neil, J. R., 1977, Data of geochemistry. Chapter KK: Compilation of stable isotope fractionation factors of geochemical interest: U.S. Geological Survey Professional Paper 440-KK, 12 p.

Frisia-Bruni, S., Jadoul, F., and Weissert, H., 1989, Evinosponges in the Triassic Esino Limestone (Southern Alps): Documentation of early lithification and late diagenetic overprint: Sedimentology, v. 36, p. 685–699.

Galimov, E. M., Migdisov, A. A., and Ronov, A. B., 1975, Variation in the isotopic composition of carbonate and organic carbon in sedimentary rocks during Earth's history: Geochemistry International, v. 12, p. 1–19.

Garrels, R. M., and Lerman, A., 1984, Coupling of the sedimentary sulfur and carbon cycles—an improved model: American Journal of Science, v. 284, p. 989–1007.

Gehman, H. M., Jr., 1962, Organic matter in limestone: Geochimica et Cosmochimica Acta, v. 26, p. 885–897.

GEOSECS, 1987, GEOSECS Atlantic, Pacific, and Indian Ocean expeditions. Vol. 7: Shorebased data and graphics: Washington, D.C., National Science Foundation, 200 p.

Given, R. K., and Lohmann, K. C., 1985, Derivation of the original isotopic composition of Permian marine cements: Journal of Sedimentary Petrology, v. 55, p. 430–439.

Graber, E. R., 1989, Sedimentology, diagenesis, and secular δ^{13}C variations in the upper Horquilla limestone (Pennsylvanian/Permian) of New Mexico [Ph.D. thesis]: Ann Arbor, University of Michigan, 276 p.

Gregory, R. T., 1991, Oxygen isotope history of seawater revisited: Timescales for boundary event changes in the oxygen isotope composition of seawater, in Taylor, H. P., Jr., O'Neil, J. R., and Kaplan, I. R., eds., Stable isotope geochemistry: A tribute to Samuel Epstein: San Antonio, Texas, The Geochemical Society Special Publication 3, p. 65–76.

Grossman, E. L., 1987, Stable isotopes in modern benthic foraminifera: A study of vital effect: Journal of Foraminiferal Research, v. 16, p. 48–61.

Grossman, E. L., 1992, Isotope studies of Paleozoic paleoceanography—Opportunities and pitfalls: Palaios, v. 7, p. 241–243.

Grossman, E. L., and Ku, T-L., 1986, Oxygen and carbon isotope fractionation in biogenic aragonite: Temperature effects: Chemical Geology (Isotope Geoscience Section), v. 59, p. 59–74.

Grossman, E. L., Zhang, C., and Yancey, T. E., 1991, Stable-isotope stratigraphy of brachiopods from Pennsylvanian shales in Texas: Geological Society of America Bulletin, v. 103, p. 953–965.

Grossman, E. L., Mii, H-S., Zhang, C., and Yancey, T. E., 1992, Trace element variations in Pennsylvanian brachiopods from North America—A microprobe study: Geological Society of America Abstracts with Programs, v. 24, p. A37.

Grossman, E. L., Mii, H-S., and Yancey, T. E., 1993, Stable isotopes in late Pennsylvanian brachiopods from the United States: Implications for Carboniferous paleoceanography: Geological Society of America Bulletin, v. 105, p. 1284–1296.

Gruszczynski, M., Halas, S., Hoffman, A., and Malkowski, K., 1989, A brachiopod calcite record of the oceanic carbon and oxygen isotope shifts at the Permian/Triassic transition: Nature, v. 337, p. 64–68.

Haq, B. U., and van Eysinga, F.W.B., 1987, Geological time table (4th edition): Amsterdam, Elsevier.

Hays, P. D., and Grossman, E. L., 1991, Oxygen isotopes in meteoric calcite cements as indicators of continental climate: Geology, v. 19, p. 441–444.

Holland, H. D., 1984, The chemical evolution of the atmosphere and oceans, Princeton, New Jersey, Princeton University Press, 582 p.

Holser, W. T., and Magaritz, M., 1987, Events near the Permian-Triassic boundary: Modern Geology, v. 11, p. 155–180.

Holser, W. T., Schönlaub, H-P., and others, 1989, A unique geochemical record at the Permian/Triassic boundary: Nature, v. 337, p. 39–44.

Hudson, J. D., and Anderson, T. F., 1989, Ocean temperatures and isotopic compositions through time: Transactions of the Royal Society of Edinburgh: Earth Science, v. 80, p. 183–192.

James, N. P., and Choquette, P. W., 1983, Diagenesis 6. Limestones—The sea floor diagenetic environment: Geoscience Canada, v. 10, p. 162–179.

Johnsen, S. J., Dansgaard, W., Clausen, H. B., and Langway, C. C., 1972, Oxygen isotope profiles through the Antarctic and Greenland ice sheets: Nature, v. 235, p. 429–434.

Keith, M. L., and Weber, J. N., 1964, Carbon and oxygen isotopic composition of selected limestone and fossils: Geochimica et Cosmochimica Acta, v. 28, p. 1787–1816.

Knauth, L. P., and Epstein, S., 1976, Hydrogen and oxygen isotope ratios in nodular and bedded cherts: Geochimica et Cosmochimica Acta, v. 40, p. 1095–1108.

Knauth, L. P., and Roberts, S. K., 1991, The hydrogen and oxygen isotope history of the Silurian-Permian hydrosphere as determined by direct measurement of fossil water, *in* Taylor, H. P., Jr., O'Neil, J. R., and Kaplan, I. R., eds., Stable isotope geochemistry: A tribute to Samuel Epstein, San Antonio, Texas, The Geochemical Society Special Publication 3, p. 91–104.

Krantz, D. E., Williams, D. F., and Jones, D. S., 1987, Ecological and paleoenvironmental information using stable isotope profiles from living and fossil molluscs: Palaeogeography, Palaeoclimatology, Palaeoecology, v. 58, p. 249–266.

Kroopnick, P. M., 1985, The distribution of ^{13}C of ΣCO_2 in the world oceans: Deep-Sea Research, v. 32, p. 57–84.

Kump, L. R., 1989, Alternative modeling approaches to the geochemical cycles of carbon, sulfur, and strontium isotopes: American Journal of Science, v. 289, p. 390–410.

Kump, L. R., 1991, Interpreting carbon-isotope excursions: Strangelove oceans: Geology, v. 19, p. 299–302.

Langenheim, R. L., Jr., Webster, G. D., and Weibel, C. P., 1984, Atokan rocks of the Bird Spring Group, Arrow Canyon, Clark County, Nevada, *in* Sutherland, P. K., and Manger, W. L., eds., The Atokan Series (Pennsylvanian) and its boundaries—A symposium: Oklahoma Geological Survey Bulletin 136, p. 133–156.

Lepzelter, C. G., Anderson, T. F., and Sandberg, P. A., 1983, Stable isotope variation in modern articulate brachiopods [abs.]: American Association of Petroleum Geologists Bulletin, v. 67, p. 500–501.

Lloyd, R. M., 1964, Variations in the oxygen and carbon isotope ratios of Florida Bay mollusks and their environmental significance: Journal of Geology, v. 72, p. 84–111.

Lohmann, K. C., and Walker, J.C.G., 1989, The ^{18}O record of Phanerozoic abiotic marine calcite cements: Geophysical Research Letters, v. 16, p. 319–322.

Lowenstam, H. A., 1961, Mineralogy, O^{18}/O^{16} ratios, and strontium and magnesium contents of recent and fossil brachiopods and their bearing on the history of the oceans: Journal of Geology, v. 69, p. 241–260.

Luz, B., Kolodny, Y., and Kovach, J., 1984, Oxygen isotope variations in phosphate of biogenic apatites. III: Conodonts: Earth and Planetary Science Letters, v. 69, p. 255–262.

Machel, H. G., Mason, R. A., Mariano, A. N., and Mucci, A., 1991, Causes and emission of luminescence in calcite and dolomite, *in* Barker, C. E., and Kopp, O. C., eds., Luminescence microscopy and spectroscopy: Qualitative and quantitative applications: Tulsa, Oklahoma, Society for Sedimentary Geology, p. 9–25.

MacKinnon, D. I., 1974, The shell structure of Spiriferide brachiopoda: Bulletin of the British Museum (Natural History), Geology, v. 25, 261 p.

Magaritz, M., and Holser, W. T., 1990, Carbon isotope shifts in Pennsylvanian seas: American Journal of Science, v. 290, p. 977–994.

Magaritz, M., and Stemmerik, L., 1989, Oscillation of carbon and oxygen isotope compositions of carbonate rocks between evaporative and open marine environments, Upper Permian of East Greenland: Earth and Planetary Science Letters, v. 93, p. 233–240.

Magaritz, M., Anderson, R. Y., Holser, W. T., Saltzman, E. S., and Garber, J., 1983, Isotope shifts in the Late Permian of the Delaware Basin, Texas, precisely timed by varved sediments: Earth and Planetary Science Letters, v. 66, p. 111–124.

Magaritz, M., Bär, R., Baud, A., and Holser, W. T., 1988, The carbon-isotope shift at the Permian/Triassic boundary in the southern Alps is gradual: Nature, v. 331, p. 337–339.

Marshall, J. D., 1992, Climatic and oceanographic isotopic signals from the carbonate rock record and their preservation: Geological Magazine, v. 129, p. 143–160.

Mason, R. A., 1987, Ion microprobe analysis of trace elements in calcite with an application to the cathodoluminescence zonation of limestone cements from the Lower Carboniferous of South Wales, U.K.: Chemical Geology, v. 64, p. 209–224.

Mazzullo, S. J., Bischoff, W. D., and Lobitzer, H., 1990, Diagenesis of radiaxial fibrous calcites in a subunconformity, shallow-burial setting: Upper Triassic and Liassic, Northern Calcareous Alps, Austria: Sedimentology, v. 37, p. 407–425.

McConnaughey, T., 1989a, ^{13}C and ^{18}O isotopic disequilibrium in biological carbonates. I: Patterns: Geochimica et Cosmochimica Acta, v. 53, p. 151–162.

McConnaughey, T., 1989b, ^{13}C and ^{18}O isotopic disequilibrium in biological carbonates. II: *In vitro* simulation of kinetic isotope effects: Geochimica et Cosmochimica Acta, v. 53, p. 163–171.

McCorkle, D. C., Keigwin, L. D., Corliss, B. H., and Emerson, S. R., 1990, The influence of microhabitats on the carbon isotopic composition of deep-sea benthic foraminifera: Paleoceanography, v. 5, p. 161–185.

Meyers, W. J., 1974, Carbonate cement stratigraphy of the Lake Valley formation (Mississippian), Sacramento Mountains, New Mexico: Journal of Sedimentary Petrology, v. 44, p. 837–861.

Meyers, W. J., and Lohmann, K. C., 1985, Isotope geochemistry of regionally extensive calcite cement zones and marine components in Mississippian limestones, New Mexico, in Schneidermann, N., and Harris, P. M., eds., Carbonate cements: Society of Economic Paleontologists and Mineralogists Special Publication 36, p. 223–239.

Mix, A. C., and Ruddiman, W. F., 1984, Oxygen-isotope analyses and Pleistocene ice volumes: Quaternary Research, v. 21, p. 1–20.

Morse, J. W., and MacKenzie, F. T., 1990, Geochemistry of sedimentary carbonates: Amsterdam, Elsevier, 707 p.

Morrison, J. O., and Brand, U., 1986, Paleoscene #5. Geochemistry of recent marine invertebrates: Geoscience Canada, v. 13, p. 237–254.

Morrison, J. O., Brand, U., and Rollins, H. B., 1985, Paleoenvironmental and chemical analysis of the Pennsylvanian Brush Creek Fossil allochems, Pennsylvania, U.S.A.: 10th International Congress on Carboniferous Stratigraphy and Geology, v. 2, p. 271–280.

Muehlenbachs, K., 1986, Alteration of the oceanic crust and the ^{18}O history of seawater, *in* Valley, J. W., Taylor, H. P., Jr., and O'Neil, R. R., eds., Stable isotopes in high temperature geological processes, Reviews in mineralogy, v. 16, p. 425–444.

Muehlenbachs, K., and Clayton, R. N., 1976, Oxygen isotope composition of the oceanic crust and its bearing on seawater: Journal of Geophysical Research, v. 81, p. 4365–4369.

Nakrem, H. A., Nilsson, I., and Mangerud, G., 1992, Permian biostratigraphy of Svalbard (Arctic Norway)—A review: International Geology Review, v. 34, p. 933–959.

O'Neil, J. R., Clayton, R. N., and Mayeda, T. K., 1969, Oxygen isotope fractionation in divalent metal carbonates: Journal of Chemical Physics, v. 51, p. 5547–5558.

Perry, E. C., Jr., 1967, The oxygen isotope chemistry of ancient cherts: Earth and Planetary Science Letters, v. 3 p. 62–66.

Plocher, O. W., Ludvigson, G. A., Witzke, B. J., González, L. A., and Day, J. E., 1992, Stable isotopic systematics of the Coralville T-R cycle, *in* Day, J., and Bunker, B. J., eds., The stratigraphy, paleontology, depositional and diagenetic history of the Middle-Upper Devonian Cedar Valley Group of Central and Eastern Iowa: Iowa Department of Natural Resources Guidebook Series 16, p. 27–34.

Popp, B. A., 1986, The record of carbon, oxygen, sulfur, and strontium isotopes and trace elements in late Paleozoic brachiopods [Ph.D. thesis]: Urbana, University of Illinois, 199 p.

Popp, B. N., Anderson, T. F., and Sandberg, P. A., 1986a, Brachiopods as indicators of original isotopic compositions in some Paleozoic limestones: Geological Society of America Bulletin, v. 97, p. 1262–1269.

Popp, B. N., Anderson, T. F., and Sandberg, P. A., 1986b, Textural, elemental, and isotopic variations among constituents in Middle Devonian limestones, North America: Journal of Sedimentary Petrology, v. 56, p. 715–727.

Powell, E. N., Staff, G. M., Davies, D. J., and Callender, W. R., 1989, Macrobenthic death assemblages in modern marine environments: Formation, interpretation, and application: Reviews in Aquatic Sciences, v. 1, p. 555–589.

Railsback, L. B., Anderson, T. F., Ackerly, S.C., and Cisne, J. L., 1989, Paleoceanographic modeling of temperature-salinity profiles from stable isotope data: Paleoceanography, v. 4, p. 585–591.

Rao, C. P., 1988, Oxygen and carbon isotope composition of cold-water Berriedale Limestone (Lower Permian), Tasmania, Australia: Sedimentary Geology, v. 60, p. 221–231.

Rao, C. P., and Green, D. C., 1982, Oxygen and carbon isotopes of Early Permian cold-water carbonates, Tasmania, Australia: Journal of Sedimentary Petrology, v. 52, p. 1111–1125.

Romanek, C. S., Grossman, E. L., and Morse, J. W., 1992, Carbon isotopic fractionation in synthetic aragonite and calcite: Effects of temperature and precipitation rate: Geochimica et Cosmochimica Acta, v. 56, p. 419–430.

Rush, P. F., and Chafetz, H. S., 1990, Fabric-retentive, non-luminescent brachiopods as indicators of original $\delta^{13}C$ and $\delta^{18}O$ composition: A test: Journal of Sedimentary Petrology, v. 60, p. 968–981.

Saller, A. H., and Koepnick, R. B., 1990, Eocene to early Miocene growth of Enewetak Atoll: Insight from strontium-isotope data: Geological Society of America Bulletin, v. 102, p. 381–390.

Savin, S. M., 1977, The history of the Earth's surface temperature during the past 100 million years: Annual Review of Earth and Planetary Sciences, v. 5, p. 319–355.

Scherer, M., 1977, Preservation, alteration and multiple cementation of aragonitic skeletons from the Cassian Beds (U. Triassic, Southern Alps): Petrographic and geochemical evidence: Neues Jahrbuch für Geologie und Paläontologie Abhandlungen, v. 154, p. 213–262.

Scholle, P. A., and Arthur, M. A., 1980, Carbon isotope fluctuations in Cretaceous pelagic limestones: Potential stratigraphic and petroleum exploration tool: American Association of Petroleum Geologists Bulletin, v. 64, p. 67–87.

Scholle, P. A., Stemmerik, L., and Ulmer, D.S., 1991, Diagenetic history and hydrocarbon potential of Upper Permian carbonate buildups, Wegener Halvo Area, Jameson Land Basin, East Greenland: American Association of Petroleum Geologists Bulletin, v. 75, p. 701–725.

Shackleton, N. J., 1977a, Carbon-13 in *Uvigerina:* Tropical rainforest history and the equatorial Pacific carbonate dissolution cycles, *in* Andersen, N. R., and Malahoff, A., eds., The fate of fossil fuel CO_2 in the oceans: New York, Plenum, p. 401–428.

Shackleton, N. J., 1977b, The oxygen isotope stratigraphic record of the Late Pleistocene: Philosophical Transactions of the Royal Society of London B, v. 280, p. 169–182.

Shackleton, N. J., and Opdyke, N. D., 1973, Oxygen isotope and palaeomagnetic stratigraphy of equatorial Pacific core V28-238: Oxygen isotope temperatures and ice volumes on a 10^5 year and 10^6 year scale: Quaternary Research, v. 3, p. 39–55.

Shemesh, A., Kolodny, Y., and Luz, B., 1988, Isotope geochemistry of oxygen and carbon in phosphate and carbonate of phosphorite francolite: Geochimica et Cosmochimica Acta, v. 52, p. 2565–2572.

Stiller, M., Rounick, J. S., and Shasha, S., 1985, Extreme carbon-isotope enrichments in evaporating brines: Nature, v. 316, p. 434–435.

Sweet, W. C., 1992, A conodont-based high-resolution biostratigraphy for the Permo-Triassic boundary interval, *in* Sweet, W. C., Yang, Z., Dickins, J. M., and Yin, H., eds., Permo-Triassic events in the eastern Tethys: Cambridge, Cambridge University Press, p. 120–133.

Tarutani, T., Clayton, R. N., and Mayeda, T. K., 1969, The effect of polymorphism and magnesium substitution on oxygen isotope fractionation between calcium carbonate and water: Geochimica et Cosmochimica Acta, v. 33, p. 987–996.

ten Have, H., and Heijnen, W., 1985, Cathodoluminescence activation and zonation in carbonate rocks: An experimental approach: Geologie en Mijnbouw, v. 64, p. 297–310.

Tilbrook, B. D., 1982, Variations in the stable carbon isotopic composition of tropical Pacific surface waters [M.S. thesis]: Honolulu, University of Hawaii, 98 p.

Veevers, J. J., and Powell, C. M., 1987, Late Paleozoic glacial episodes in Gondwanaland reflected in transgressive-regressive depositional sequences in Euramerica: Geological Society of America Bulletin, v. 98, p. 475–487.

Veizer, J., and Hoefs, J., 1976, The nature of O^{18}/O^{16} and C^{13}/C^{12} secular trends in sedimentary carbonate rocks: Geochimica et Cosmochimica Acta, v. 40, p. 1387–1395.

Veizer, J., Fritz, P., and Jones, B., 1986, Geochemistry of brachiopods: Oxygen and carbon isotopic records of Paleozoic oceans: Geochimica et Cosmochimica Acta, v. 50, p. 1679–1696.

Walker, J.C.G., and Lohmann, K. C., 1989, Why the oxygen isotopic composition of sea water changes with time: Geophysical Research Letters, v. 16, p. 323–326.

Weber, J. N., 1967, Factors affecting the carbon and oxygen isotopic composition of marine carbonate sediments. Part 1: Bermuda: American Journal of Science, v. 265, p. 586–608.

Weber, J. N., and Schmalz, R. F., 1968, Factors affecting the carbon and oxygen isotopic composition of marine carbonate sediments. Part III: Eniwetok Atoll: Journal of Sedimentary Petrology, v. 38, p. 1270–1279.

Weber, J. N., and Woodhead, P.M.J., 1971, Diurnal variations in the isotopic composition of dissolved inorganic carbon in seawater from coral reef environments: Geochimica et Cosmochimica Acta, v. 35, p. 891–902.

Wefer, G., and Berger, W. H., 1991, Isotope paleontology: Growth and composition of extant calcareous species: Marine Geology, v. 100, p. 207–248.

Wiggins, W. D., 1986, Geochemical signatures in carbonate matrix and their relation to deposition and diagenesis, Pennsylvanian Marble Falls Limestone, Central Texas: Journal of Sedimentary Petrology, v. 56, p. 771–783.

Williams, A., and Rowell, A. J., 1965, Morphology, *in* Moore, R. C., ed., Treatise on invertebrate paleontology. Part H: Brachiopoda, v. 1: Boulder, Colorado, The Geological Society of America, Inc., and Lawrence, Kansas, University of Kansas Press, p. 57–155.

Williams, D. F., 1984, Correlation of Pleistocene marine sediments of the Gulf of Mexico and other basins using oxygen isotope stratigraphy, *in* Healy-Williams, N., Principles of Pleistocene stratigraphy applied to the Gulf of Mexico: Boston, International Human Resources Development Corporation, p. 65–118.

Wu, Y., Zhu, Z., Mang, J., Yuan, J., and Wang, Z., 1989, Lithofacies-paleogeography and environmental control of sedimentary deposits of the Early and Middle Triassic in the Upper Yangtze area [Chinese, English abstract]: Chongqing, Chongqing Publishing House, 221 p.

Xu, D., Yan, Z., Zhang, Q., and Sun, Y., 1986, Three main mass extinctions—Significant indicators of major natural divisions of geological history in the Phanerozoic: Modern Geology, v. 10, p. 365–375.

Yurtsever, Y., and Gat, J. R., 1981, Atmospheric waters, *in* Gat, J. R., and Gonfiantini, R., eds., Stable isotope hydrology: Vienna, International Atomic Energy Agency, p. 103–142.

MANUSCRIPT ACCEPTED BY THE SOCIETY MAY 14, 1993

Geological Society of America
Special Paper 288
1994

Permian climatic cooling in the Canadian Arctic

Benoit Beauchamp
Institute of Sedimentary and Petroleum Geology, Geological Survey of Canada, 3303 33rd Street NW,
Calgary, Alberta, T2L 2A7, Canada

ABSTRACT

The biotic succession of the Sverdrup Basin, Canadian Arctic, records a significant Permian climatic cooling trend. Highly diversified, tropicallike associations dominated by calcareous alga and foraminifer (Chloroforam) prevailed during the Asselian and Sakmarian, whereas poorly diversified, temperatelike associations, dominated by bryozoan, echinoderm, and brachiopod, characterized the Artinskian (Bryonoderm-extended) to Kazanian (Bryonoderm) interval. Polarlike, siliceous sponge–dominated biota (Hyalosponge) prevailed during the latest Permian. The climatic gradient suggested by this trend, and by other climatic indicators (ooid, oncoid, evaporite, reef, submarine cement, dropstone, red bed, caliche, coal), is far greater than that expected from the 10 to 15° of northerly migration inferred for Pangea during the Permian. The cooling trend, the causes of which are unknown, is evidence for a dramatic climatic deterioration in northern Pangea at the end of the Paleozoic.

INTRODUCTION

Little has been published on the late Paleozoic climates of northern Pangea. This contrasts sharply with the vast knowledge available for southern and central Pangea, where trends, events, and various climatic perturbations have been documented. A certain vision of Pangean climates has emerged from the many studies of glacial deposits in Australia, coal-bearing strata in Pennsylvania, evaporites in western Europe, or carbonate reefs around the Tethys. However, recently published data from the Sverdrup Basin and other Arctic regions may change the way Pangean climates should be envisioned. Among other things, this newly acquired data provides evidence for a dramatic climatic cooling during Permian time, cooling that appears to have affected most of northern Pangea.

During Late Carboniferous time, the Sverdrup Basin lay at a paleolatitude of about 25°N; tropical carbonates and algal reefs were widely developed. The same region is now centered around 80°N; it is a polar desert. One would think that the 55° of northerly migration, which translates into a 6,000-km leap spanning the Carboniferous to mid-Tertiary interval, would have produced evidence of a progressive cooling of the climates. Instead, cooling occurred in a stepwise fashion through

three separate episodes: one from the Late Carboniferous to the Late Permian, one from the Early Triassic to the Early Cretaceous, and one from the Late Cretaceous until now (this chapter; Embry, 1992a). Each episode culminated in very cold conditions, only to be followed by much warmer conditions at the dawn of the next episode. This chapter documents the Late Carboniferous to Late Permian cooling episode. Evidence for the cooling trend comes from the observation of marine (benthic associations, ooids, oncoids, reefs, carbonate mineralogy, dropstones, evaporites, and so on) and nonmarine (red beds, caliches, coals, paleosols, and so on) indicators, whose presence or absence tells us a great deal about past climatic conditions.

GEOLOGIC SETTING

The Sverdrup Basin is a 1,000-km-long and 400-km-wide depocenter located in the Canadian Arctic Archipelago (Fig. 1). The basin contains up to 12 km of Lower Carboniferous to mid-Tertiary clastics, carbonates, evaporites, and minor volcanics. The Sverdrup Basin is a successor rift basin that formed through faulting and collapse of highly deformed Precambrian to Devonian rocks belonging to the Franklinian Mobile Belt (Trettin, 1989). The latter had previously been

Beauchamp, B., 1994, Permian climatic cooling in the Canadian Arctic, *in* Klein, G. D., ed., Pangea: Paleoclimate, Tectonics, and Sedimentation During Accretion, Zenith, and Breakup of a Supercontinent: Boulder, Colorado, Geological Society of America Special Paper 288.

subjected to at least five orogenic phases, the last of which is the Ellesmerian Orogeny in latest Devonian–earliest Carboniferous time. Rocks of the Sverdrup Basin were deformed and uplifted in mid-Tertiary time (Eurekan Orogeny).

Rifting and fault-controlled subsidence in the Sverdrup Basin lasted from the Viséan to the Kungurian (Fig. 2). Later, a regime of passive subsidence was established and prevailed until the earliest Cretaceous, when fault-controlled subsidence resumed as a result of the opening of the Arctic Ocean (Stephenson et al., 1987). The transition from rifting to passive subsidence was accompanied by a brief, yet significant, episode of tectonism called the Melvillian Disturbance, characterized by variably high uplifts at the basin margin (Thorsteinsson, 1974; Thorsteinsson and Tozer, 1970; Beauchamp et al., 1989a). The Melvillian Disturbance coincided with a plate reorganization of regional magnitude, as indicated by contemporaneous tectonism throughout the circum-Arctic regions (Beauchamp, 1992a).

The upper Paleozoic succession of the Sverdrup Basin, which is up to 5 km thick, is characterized by eight long-term sequences bounded by major unconformities at the basin margin, passing basinward into correlative conformities (Fig. 2). Each sequence displays a complex spectrum of facies ranging from basin marginal fluvial and nearshore sandstones, to shelf carbonates and clastics, to slope and basinal shales, cherts, and evaporites (Beauchamp et al., 1989b). Hundreds of reefs are known to occur in the Bashkirian to Artinskian succession, forming variably large structures on the shelf and at the shelf-margin (Davies et al., 1989; Beauchamp, 1992b). Reefs have not yet been observed in the younger Permian and Mesozoic succession.

Early in the history of the Sverdrup Basin, its paleogeography was typical of an active rift with a series of smaller basins and depressions (half grabens) bounded by extensional structures (Harrison et al., 1988). Recurring rifting phases rapidly led to the creation of a northeasterly trending trough surrounded by a shallow platform, a platform that was carbonate dominated in Late Carboniferous and Early Permian time and clastic dominated in Late Permian and Mesozoic time (Beauchamp et al., 1989b; Embry, 1991). Major sources of clastic sediments lay east and south of the Sverdrup Basin; a secondary supply of terrigenous material was provided by a northern landmass called Crockerland, which was later rifted away following creation of the Arctic Ocean (Embry, 1992b). On a circum-Arctic paleogeographic map, the Sverdrup Basin forms a narrow sigmoidal seaway that was part of a several-thousand-kilometer-long rift system linking northern Alaska with North Greenland, Svalbard, and the Barents Sea (Fig. 3).

MARINE BENTHIC ASSOCIATIONS AS CLIMATIC INDICATORS

Marine benthic associations are an important tool for monitoring climatic changes. Because biotic associations living on low-latitude warm-water shelves differ greatly from bi-

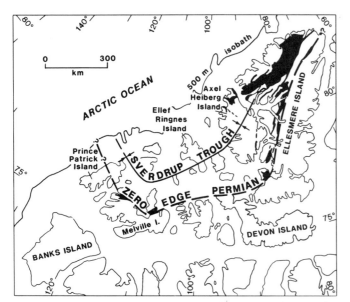

Figure 1. Map of the Canadian Arctic Archipelago showing Permian subcrop limit (zero edge) of the Sverdrup Basin, axis of Sverdrup Trough, and distribution of Carboniferous and Permian outcrops (dark areas).

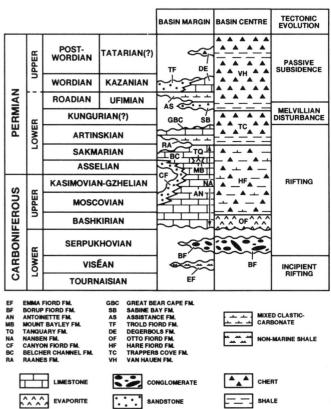

Figure 2. Carboniferous and Permian stratigraphic sequences of Sverdrup Basin. Diagram shows unconformities at basin margin and correlative conformities at basin center. Phases of tectonic evolution are also shown.

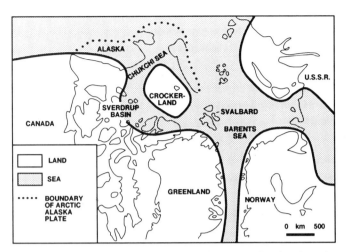

Figure 3. Late Paleozoic circum-Arctic paleogeography showing relations between the Sverdrup Basin, northern Alaska (rotated), Svalbard, and the Barents Sea. The Sverdrup Basin received clastic sediments from a northern landmass called Crockerland (Embry, 1992b). Crockerland was rifted away following the opening of the Arctic Ocean in Cretaceous time.

otic associations living on high-latitude cold-water shelves, the replacement of some associations by others may be the result of a change in ambient temperatures, reflecting some shifts in the prevailing climate. This principle works reasonably well with both modern and ancient sediments, even though modern biotic associations differ much from their ancient counterparts, especially their late Paleozoic counterparts.

Modern associations

Many authors have described the basic differences between modern carbonate sediments forming at low latitudes and those forming at high latitudes (Lees and Buller, 1972; Lees, 1975; Nelson, 1988a). Low-latitude carbonates, also called tropical carbonates, comprise a variety of bioclasts, peloids, ooids, and aggregate grains. High-latitude carbonates, also called temperate carbonates, comprise mostly bioclasts, with very few or no peloids (Fig. 4). Aggregate grains and ooids do not form on high-latitude shelves.

The composition of low-latitude bioclasts differs greatly from that of high-latitude bioclasts, reflecting basic differences in the benthic associations (Fig. 4). Low-latitude bioclasts comprise a wide variety of organisms dominated by green algae and hermatypic corals but also associated with a variety of molluscs, red algae, and benthic foraminifers. Lees and Buller (1972) and Lees (1975) coined the name Chlorozoan for this tropical association (Chloro = green algae; zoan = corals). A variety of this association that lacks the corals and occurs in salinity-restricted environments is called Chloralgal. High-latitude, or temperate, bioclasts are less diversified and devoid of green algae and hermatypic corals. Temperate associations comprise abundant bryozoans, molluscs, and benthic foraminifers and less abundant sponge

spicules, brachiopods, echinoderms, ahermatypic corals, serpulids, and barnacles. This association is known as the Foramol association (foram = foraminifers; mol = molluscs); some prefer the term *Bryomol* because of the dominance of bryozoans over benthic foraminifers in many parts of the world (Nelson, 1988b). A third association is found on shelves of Arctic and Antarctic regions (Henrich et al., 1992; Van Waggoner et al., 1989; Murchey et al., 1988; Piepenburg, 1988; Domack, 1988; Bullivant and Dearborn, 1967). This very high latitude, or polar, association comprises abundant siliceous sponge spicules with elements of the Foramol association; it is herein referred to as the Hyalosponge association (Fig. 4).

Basic mineralogical differences occur between tropical, temperate, and polar bioclastic sediments (Nelson, 1988a). Tropical sediments of the Chlorozoan and Chloralgal associations are dominated by aragonite and high magnesian calcite, which reflects the composition of the main organisms and early diagenetic submarine cements (Fig. 4). Temperate sediments of the Foramol (or Bryomol) association comprises minor amounts of aragonite, variable proportions of high-Mg calcite, and significant volumes of low-Mg calcite, reflecting the mineralogical contribution of both bioclasts and cements. Variably large amounts of authigenic glauconite are commonly associated with temperate carbonates, reflecting the slower sedimentation rates that characterize cooler water settings. Polar sediments of the Hyalosponge association are dominated by biogenic silica with minor amounts of low-Mg calcite, glauconite, and various manganese and iron oxides (Henrich et al., 1992; Van Wagoner et al., 1989; Piepenburg, 1988; Domack, 1988; Bullivant and Dearborn, 1967).

According to Lees (1975), it is temperate and, to a lesser extent, salinity that are the main controls on the worldwide distribution of the Chlorozoan (Chloralgal) and Foramol associations. The boundary between both associations lies near the 15 to 18°C annual isotherm (Fig. 4), which parallels the tropics in most parts of the world, except in areas affected by Coriolis-driven cold-water currents. The 10°C and 5°C isotherms also coincide with significant impoverishment in the Foramol association, which led some workers to break temperate carbonates into a temperate-warm and a temperate-cold category (Fig. 4; Brookfield, 1988). Polar Hyalosponge sediments invariably lie beyond the 5°C isotherm, usually in areas with a permanent or semipermanent ice cover (Henrich et al., 1992; Van Wagoner et al., 1989; Piepenburg, 1988; Domack, 1988; Bullivant and Dearborn, 1967). The temperature-controlled latitudinal gradient between the Chlorozoan, Foramol, and Hyalosponge associations parallels a gradient of decreasing salinity from the tropics to the pole. Whereas salinities in excess of 37 per mil are commonly measured in the tropics, salinities are measured as low as 30 per mil on high-latitude shelves and even lower on polar shelves where seawater mixes with meltwater from adjacent ice sheets.

Because temperature is the main factor controlling the compositional changes observed from the equator to the pole

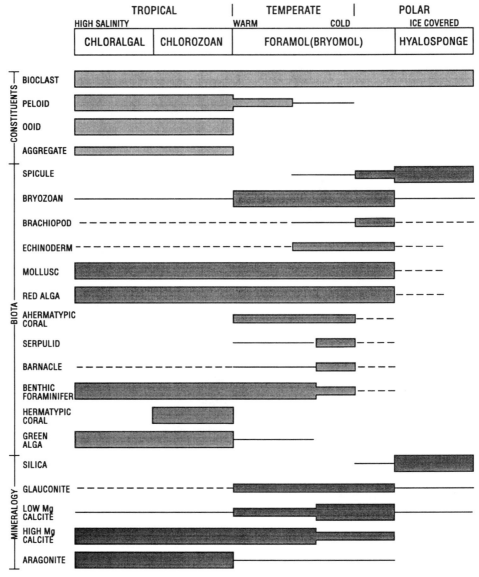

Figure 4. Chart showing constituents, biota, and mineralogy of modern shallow-water carbonate sediments. Note major differences between tropical, temperate, and polar carbonates. From various sources, including Lees and Buller (1972), Lees (1975), and Nelson (1988a, b).

in bioclastic sediments, similar changes can be observed with increasing water depth (Brookfield, 1988). At low latitudes, the 15°C, 10°C, and 5°C isotherms—or the inferred temperature barriers between tropical, temperate-warm, and temperate-cold carbonate associations—lie at increasing water depth beneath the sea surface. In consequence, tropicallike carbonates (Chlorozoan) are restricted to shallow-water environments, whereas temperatelike (Foramol) carbonates occur in deeper-water environments (Fig. 5). As these barriers shallow up with increasing latitude, one observes a progressive replacement of shallow-water-like biotic and mineralogic associations by deeper-water-like associations from the equator to

the poles. In other words, low-latitude deep-water associations are similar to high-latitude shallow water associations (Fig. 5). This relationship is analogous to that of terrestrial plants: The most-diversified floras (rain forests) are restricted to low-latitude/low-altitude areas, whereas the least-diversified floras (tundra-alpine) occur both in low-latitude/high-altitude areas and in high-latitude/low-latitude areas.

Late Paleozoic associations

Carboniferous and Permian low-latitude carbonates are quite different than their high-latitude counterparts (Fig. 6). Tropicallike shelf carbonates comprise a wide variety of bio

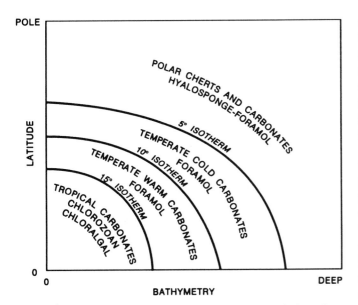

Figure 5. Distribution of modern benthic carbonate associations along latitudinal and bathymetric gradient. Deep-water carbonates forming at low latitudes are similar to shallow-water carbonates forming at high latitudes.

clasts, peloids, ooids, and oncoids. Temperate carbonates are composed of mostly bioclasts; ooids and oncoids are rare or absent.

Tropicallike shelf carbonates are characterized by a highly diversified biota dominated by phylloid and dasycladacean algae, small benthic and epibiotic foraminifers, and fusulinaceans to form an association herein named the Chloroforam association (Fig. 6). In the Tethyan regions (Wahlman, 1985; Flügel, 1982), these organisms combine with abundant calcisponges (inozoans and sphinctozoans) to form an even more diversified association referred to as the Chlorosponge association. Temperatelike and some polarlike shelf carbonates comprise a much impoverished biota dominated by bryozoans, echinoderms, and brachiopods (Rao, 1981, 1988), herein called the Bryonoderm association. Most other elements of the Chlorosponge or Chloroforam association are extremely rare or absent in the Bryonoderm association. Exceptionally, solitary and colonial rugose corals as well as small benthic foraminifers and fusulinaceans can be present and sometimes abundant, forming a slightly more diversified association referred to as the Bryonoderm-extended association (Fig. 6).

Mineralogically, upper Paleozoic tropicallike shelf carbonates differ from their temperatelike counterparts by the dominance of aragonite and high-Mg calcite over low-Mg calcite (Fig. 6). That aragonite was the main carbonate phase of a variety of organisms (phylloid and dasycladacean algae, *Palaeoaplysina*, calcisponges) and ooids is indicated by the dissolved nature of these organisms and some unusually well preserved skeletal fabrics (Sandberg, 1975). Early submarine botryoidal aragonite cements, now inverted to calcite, have

also been widely documented from Upper Carboniferous to Upper Permian reefs worldwide. Temperate carbonates characteristically lack aragonite-secreting organisms, ooids, and cements; the composition of these carbonates was likely dominated by low-Mg calcite. Many carbonates of the Bryonoderm association also comprise a significant proportion of glauconite as well as biogenic silica derived from the breakdown of siliceous sponge spicules.

Based on the distribution of modern benthic associations, the Chlorosponge to Bryonoderm environmental gradient depicted in Fig. 6 must parallel a gradient of decreasing temperature. This environmental gradient should thus be observed with both increasing paleolatitude and paleobathymetry (Fig. 7). Good examples demonstrating the paleolatitudinal trend can be found in Lower Permian shallow-water carbonates. For instance, Tethyan carbonates, which formed around the paleoequator, are characteristic of the Chlorosponge association (Walhman, 1985; Flügel, 1982). Contemporaneous shallow-water carbonates of the circum-Arctic regions that lay at tropical latitudes display the Chloroforam association (Beauchamp et al., 1989c). At the same time, Bryonoderm carbonates formed next to continental glaciers at very high latitudes in Australia and Tasmania (Rao, 1981). Likewise, multiple examples are known for demonstrating the paleobathymetric trend. In several basins of the world (Sverdrup, Delaware, Carnic Alps, Ural Mountains, and so on), shallow-water Chloroforam (or Chlorosponge) shelf carbonates pass basinward, firstly into deeper-water Bryonoderm-extended carbonates, then into Bryonoderm carbonates, and ultimately into deepwater spiculitic carbonates and cherts (Flügel, 1981, 1982; Chuvashov, 1983; Beauchamp, 1987).

The deepest-water facies in many sedimentary basins is characterized by the Hyalosponge assemblage. Using the modern latitudinal/bathymetric analogue, one would expect spiculitic chert to have also formed on shallow shelves at very high latitudes during the Carboniferous and Permian. However, shallow-water chert is not a major component of Permian polar deposits of Australia and Tasmania (Rao, 1981), suggesting that a very cold environment is not the only factor favoring the growth of siliceous sponges. Perhaps it is the combination of very low temperatures with the scarcity of light that favors the Hyalosponge association. Accordingly, spiculitic cherts occurring in the axial regions of ancient sedimentary basins often formed well below the photic zone. Similarly, modern shallow-water siliceous sediments of the Hyalosponge association accumulate beneath permanent or semipermanent ice sheets that prevent light from reaching the seafloor. Alternately, it may be the seasonal melting of such permanent ice sheets and the lowering of salinity that is responsible for the eradication of most elements of the Foramol assemblage. According to Henrich et al. (1992), the occurrence of high-latitude spicule-rich siliceous sediments is believed to reflect a strong seasonality in food supply, resulting from short, ice-free, nutrient-rich summers alternating with

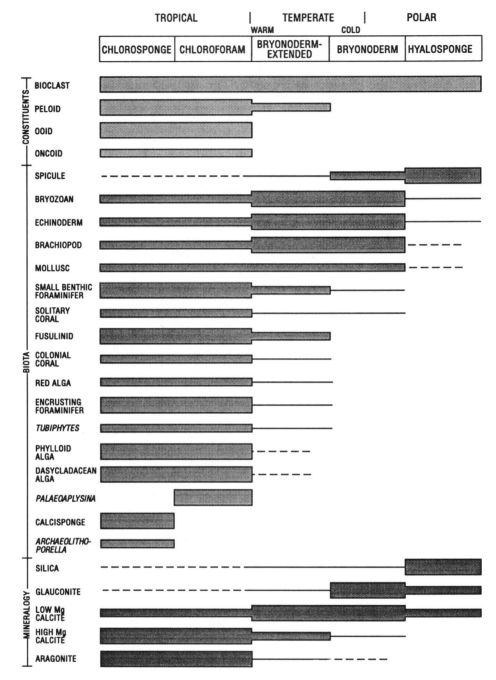

Figure 6. Chart showing constituents, biota, and mineralogy of late Paleozoic shallow water carbonate sediments. Note major differences between tropical, temperate, and polar carbonates.

long, ice-covered, nutrient-depleted winters. In any event, one can safely postulate—using the modern comparison—that late Paleozoic Hyalosponge sediments must have accumulated on shallow shelves at very high latitudes (Figs. 6 and 7), provided that the right environmental conditions (semipermanent ice sheet?, absence of light?, brackish sea?, nutrient seasonality?) were present.

BENTHIC ASSOCIATIONS AND OTHER CLIMATIC INDICATORS IN THE SVERDRUP BASIN

Four of the five late Paleozoic benthic associations are recognized in the Sverdrup Basin: Chloroforam, Bryonoderm-extended, Bryonoderm, and Hyalosponge (Fig. 8). From the Serpukhovian (late Early Carboniferous) to the Sakmarian

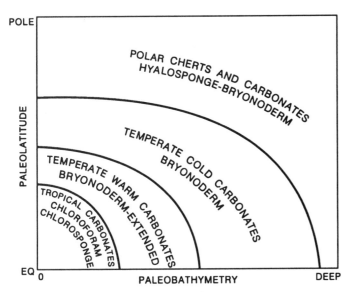

Figure 7. Distribution of late Paleozoic benthic carbonate associations along paleolatitudinal and paleobathymetric gradient. Deep-water carbonates forming at low latitudes are similar to shallow-water carbonates forming at high latitudes.

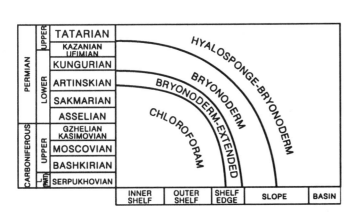

Figure 8. Spatial and temporal distribution of late Paleozoic benthic carbonate associations in Sverdrup Basin.

(Early Permian), these four assemblages were distributed along a gradient of increasing bathymetry with Choloroforam carbonates forming above and below wave base in the shallowest portion of the inner and outer shelf, Bryonoderm-extended carbonates forming below wave base on the outer shelf and at the shelf edge, Bryonoderm carbonates forming in much deeper water on the upper and middle slope, and Hyalosponge carbonates and chert forming below the photic zone in the lower reaches of the slope and in the deep basin. Over time, however, the deeper-water associations progressively replaced the shallow-water associations (Fig. 8). By Artinskian time, the Chloroforam association no longer existed, and the shallowest portions of the shelf were occupied

by the Bryonoderm-extended association. From the Kungurian to the Kazanian, the Bryonoderm association occupied the shallowest niches of the shelf, only to be replaced by the Hyalosponge association in post-Kazanian time (Tatarian?).

As mentioned above, and further emphasized in the next sections, this ecological turnover is observed in the shallowest deposits of various stratigraphic sequences. These deposits lie at the very margin of the Sverdrup Basin and form the uppermost part of transgressive-regressive low-order sequences, the boundaries of which are widespread subaerial unconformities. Accordingly, these deposits always show textural evidence of very shallow water deposition (e.g., cross-bedded grainstones) in addition to often interfingering with nonmarine fluvial deposits and displaying evidence of subaerial exposure and pedogenesis. This demonstrates beyond doubt that the late Paleozoic ecological turnover in the Sverdrup Basin cannot be explained by a progressive deepening of the basin. Instead, it can only be explained by a steady deterioration of the climate in late Paleozoic time. Using modern analogy, one can suggest that a tropicallike climate prevailed in the Sverdrup Basin for more than 60 m.y., that is, from the Serpukhovian to the Sakmarian. The climates then rapidly shifted to a temperate-warm setting during the Artinskian, to a temperate-cold setting during the Kungurian-Kazanian, and to a polarlike setting during the post-Kazanian (Tatarian?). Other climatic indicators appear to corroborate this hypothesis, as shown in the following sections.

Serpukhovian-Sakmarian

Sequences and formations. The Serpukhovian to Sakmarian succession of the Sverdrup Basin comprises three broad sequences bounded by major unconformities and passing basinward into their correlative conformities (Fig. 2). The first sequence is Serpukhovian and comprises up to 400 m of red sandstones and conglomerates of the Borup Fiord Formation. These rocks are mostly nonmarine and were deposited in a series of half-grabens during an early rift phase of the basin. The second sequence encompasses the 20-m.y.-long Bashkirian to Gzhelian interval (Beauchamp et al., 1989b). It is a broad transgressive-regressive sequence that comprises up to 1.5 km of marginal sandstones and conglomerates (Canyon Fiord Formation); platform carbonates (Nansen and Antoinette formations); slope-to-basinal shales, argillaceous limestones, and cherts (Hare Fiord Formation); and evaporites (Otto Fiord Formation). The third sequence contains up to 1 km of rocks that were deposited during the 15-m.y.-long Asselian and Sakmarian interval (Morin et al., 1991). Most formations of the second sequence are also part of the third sequence (Fig. 2); additional formations include Belcher Channel and Tanquary (platform carbonates) and Mount Bayley (platform evaporites).

Chloroforam association. The shallowest carbonate facies in the Bashkirian to Sakmarian platformal succession are grainstones and packstones forming the regressive part of in-traformational shelf cycles. These facies display a typical Chloroforam association (Fig. 9). Green algae are ubiquitous and comprise several groups (Mamet et al., 1987): phylloid (*Ivanovia, Eugonophyllum, Neoanchicodium*), dasycladaceans (*Epimastopora, Epimastoporella, Macroporella, Paraepimastopora, Clavaporella, Diplopora, Gyroporella*), and tubular (*Beresella, Dvinella, Donezella, Anthracoporella, Anthracoporellopsis*). Foraminifers are abundant and are represented by several groups that fall into three broad categories (Pinard, 1990): fusulinids (e.g., *Fusulina, Fusulinella, Pseudofusulina, Pseudofusulinella, Schwagerina*), encrusting foraminifers (e.g., *Apterrinella, Hedraites, Trepeilopsis, Volvotextularia, Tuberitina, Ammovertella*), and small benthic foraminifers (Palaeotextulariidae, Bradyinidae, Lasiodiscidae, Biseriamminidae, Pseudoendothyriidae, Tetrataxidae, Syzraniidae,

Geinitzinidae, Hemigordiopsidae, Pseudovidalinidae, Archaediscidae, Endothyrinidae, Eostaffellidae).

These organisms are associated with a variety of other forms that include several families of bryozoans, echinoderms, brachiopods, pelecypods, gastropods, solitary and colonial rugose corals, red algae (*Stacheia, Fourstonella, Stacheoides, Stacheoidella, Epistachoides, Aoujgalia, Ungdarella, Komia, Archaeolitophyllum, Cuneiphycus*; Mamet et al., 1987), and incertae sedis (*Tubiphytes, Palaeoaplysina*). This typical Chloroforam association differs from the Chlorosponge association of the Tethyan regions by the presence of *Palaeoaplysina* and by the absence of reef-building inozoan and spinctozoan calcisponges and *Archaeolithoporella*, an incertae sedis (Flügel, 1981, 1982).

Nonskeletal grains. Bashkirian to Sakmarian Chloroforam carbonates are also associated with a variety of nonskeletal grains, such as peloids, oncoids, and ooids (Fig. 10). Oncoidal encrustations comprise different types of green algae, such as *Bevocastria, Ortonella, Nansenella,* and *Ellesmerella* (Mamet et al., 1987). Most ooids comprise a partially to completely dissolved cortex that shows a tangential fabric, indicating an aragonitic origin (Fig. 10). Tangential ooids are abundant throughout the upper Moscovian to Asselian succession; they are less common in the Bashkirian to lower Moscovian and in the Sakmarian. Radial calcitic ooids and bimineralic ooids are rare in Bashkirian to Sakmarian strata.

Reefs. Hundreds of Bashkirian to Sakmarian carbonate buildups, ranging from a few meters to hundreds of meters in thickness, have been discovered in the Sverdrup Basin. Reefs fall into three broad categories (Beauchamp, 1992b): algal reefs, mixed reefs, and bryozoan reefs. Algal reefs formed on shallow parts of the inner and outer shelf; bryozoan reefs grew in a deeper-water slope setting. Mixed reefs formed at intermediate depth at the shelf margin; they are bryozoan reefs that evolved upward into algal reefs (Beauchamp et al., 1991). Algal reefs comprise various associations of phylloid algae, tubular algae, red algae, *Palaeoaplysina*, and *Tubiphytes*, associated with some encrusting and benthic foraminifers and other organisms (Beauchamp et al., 1989c).

Mineralogy. The mineralogy of Bashkirian to Sakmarian shelf carbonates was dominated by aragonite and high-Mg calcite. Many of the organisms of the Chloroforam association secreted an aragonitic skeleton, as shown by their invariably dissolved texture (Figs. 9 and 10). These organisms include phylloid algae, dasycladacean algae, molluscs (pelecypods, gastropods), staffellid and pseudoendothyrid foraminifers, *Archaeolithophyllum,* and *Palaeoaplysina*. As seen above, most ooids display a completely to partially dissolved texture, also indicative of an aragonite precursor. Aragonite was also the original mineralogy of botryoids and fans of submarine cements that line the walls of large cavities in shelf-edge reefs (Davies and Nassichuk, 1990). High levels of strontium have been detected in these cements, confirming the aragonitic precursor (Davies, 1977).

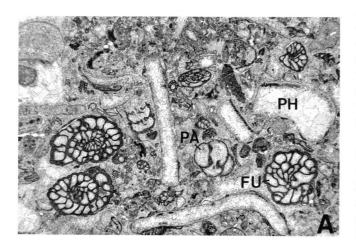
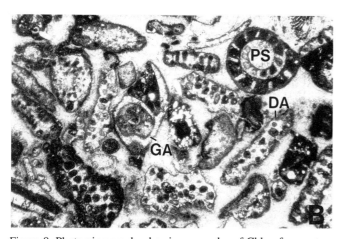

Figure 9. Photomicrographs showing examples of Chloroforam association in Sakmarian carbonates of Sverdrup Basin. A, grainstone comprising phylloid algae (PH), Fusulinaceans (FU), and palaeotextularid foraminifers (PA). Width of area shown in photograph is 5 mm. B, grainstone comprising partially dissolved epimastoporid dasycladacean algae (DA), with pseudoendothyrid foraminifers (PS) and gastropods (GA). Width of area shown in photograph is 4 mm.

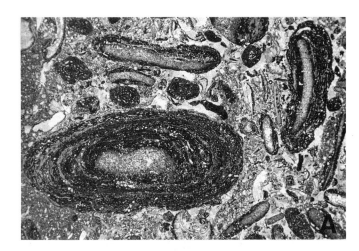

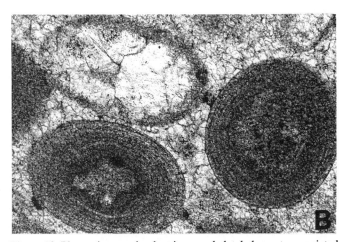

Figure 10. Photomicrographs showing nonskeletal elements associated with Sakmarian Chloroforam carbonates of Sverdrup Basin. A, oncoids comprising multilayered alternations of various green and blue-green algae. Width of area shown in photograph is 5 cm. B, ooids displaying tangential cortex indicative of a primary aragonite mineralogy. Dissolved ooid in upper part of photograph also had an aragonite precursor. Width of area shown in photograph is 1.5 mm.

High-Mg calcite was the mineralogy of nonbotryoidal submarine cements in reefs and other carbonates, as shown by a variety of petrographic and geochemical techniques (Davies and Nassichuk, 1990). These cements are an important constituent of Bashkirian to Sakmarian shelf carbonates, displaying a variety of fibrous fabrics filling both inter- and intraparticle pore spaces. Many of the organisms of the Chloroforam association grew a high-Mg calcite skeleton; these probably include echinoderms, bryozoans, rugose corals, and most families of foraminifers.

Evaporites. Evaporites formed in various parts of the Sverdrup Basin during the Bashkirian to Sakmarian interval; these include Bashkirian evaporites of the Otto Fiord Formation—up to 400 m of subaqueous gypsum, anhydrite, and halite that accumulated over large areas of the basin (Nassichuk and Davies, 1980); Moscovian evaporites of the Canyon Fiord Formation—up to 100 m of gypsum and anhydrite that formed in fault-bounded depressions at the southern and northern margin of the basin (Thériault, 1991); Asselian and Sakmarian evaporites of the Antoinette and Mount Bayley formations—up to 600 m of subaqueous gypsum and anhydrite that grew in one large subbasin on west-central Ellesmere Island (Wallace and Beauchamp, 1990).

Red beds and caliches. Alluvial fan and stream conglomerates and sandstones that filled Serpukhovian to Moscovian half-grabens are characteristically red-weathering (Borup Fiord and Canyon Fiord formations). Fluvial overbank shales and siltstones lying at the basin margin (Canyon Fiord Formation) also display various hues of red. Caliches are extensively developed in both the half-graben fill and the basin marginal overbank sediments. Caliches display a wide variety of fabrics ranging from nodular to laminar, reflecting the maturity of the caliche profile as well as the nature of the substrate (Thériault, 1991).

Summary and interpretation. The widespread development of a Chloroforam biota suggests that a warm tropicallike climate prevailed in the Sverdrup Basin from the Serpukhovian to the Sakmarian. Other climatic indicators corroborate this hypothesis: abundant ooids and oncoids, widespread occurrences of algal reefs, and an original aragonite and Mg calcite mineralogy for numerous fossils and submarine cements. Furthermore, the contemporaneous development of marine evaporites, nonmarine red beds, and widespread caliches indicates an arid to semiarid setting for that 60-m.y.-long interval.

Artinskian

Sequence and formations. The Artinskian succession (Fig. 2), which is up to 1 km thick, is characterized by one broad sequence bounded at its base and top by major unconformities that can be traced basinward into their correlative conformities (Beauchamp et al., 1989b; Scott et al., 1991). Deposition of the Artinskian sequence lasted between 5 and 10 m.y. The basal part of the sequence comprises a greenish-weathering, deepening-upward succession of shales and mixed clastics-carbonates (Raanes Formation) that recorded one of the most widespread transgression in the basin history. The overlying regressive package is a shallowing-upward succession of bioclastic shelf limestones that culminates in very coarse grainstones (Great Bear Cape Formation). The widespread unconformity at the top of this sequence coincided with the cessation of rifting in the Sverdrup Basin and marks the onset of the Melvillian Disturbance. Both the Raanes and Great Bear Cape formations pass basinward into a succession of black siliceous shale and spiculitic chert (Trappers Cove Formation) that represented slope-to-basinal sedimentation.

Bryonoderm-extended association. The shallowest carbonates in the Artinskian platformal succession are bioclastic grainstones that are commonly cross-bedded. These carbonates contain a typical Bryonoderm-extended association (Fig. 11). Bryozoans, echinoderms, and brachiopods are the main biotic components, associated with relatively minor amounts of solitary and colonial rugose corals, schwagerinid fusulinaceans, and rare small benthic foraminifers represented by only a few groups (Palaeotextulariidae, Bradyinidae, Lasiodiscidae, Tetrataxidae, and Geinitzinidae). Other organisms include very few stacheinlike red algae, *Tubiphytes,* gastropods, and pelecypods.

Non-skeletal grains. Except for one poorly developed occurrence, ooids are absent from Artinskian strata in the Sverdrup Basin; the same can be said about oncoids. Peloidlike micritized grains of unknown origin locally occur.

Reefs. A number of bryozoan Artinskian reefs are known in the Sverdrup Basin. The largest reefs (150 m thick) formed at the shelf edge and on the upper part of the slope; smaller patch reefs formed on the shelf. These buildups are Waulsortian-like mud mounds composed of fenestellid and ramose bryozoans associated with stromatactoid cavities that are interpreted as the remnants of soft-bodied sponges (Beauchamp, 1989).

Mineralogy. The mineralogy of Artinskian sediments was probably dominantly low-Mg calcite with varying proportions of high-Mg calcite. Except for rare gastropods and pelecypods, there are no aragonite-secreting organisms in Artinskian strata. These rocks also contain no ooids or botryoidal cements that can be interpreted as primary aragonite precipitates. Submarine cements do occur, especially in large reef cavities (Beauchamp, 1989). These cements display the same fibrous and radiaxial fabrics as Sakmarian and older cents interpreted as high-Mg calcite (Fig. 12). Some Artinskian grainstones are cemented by early diagenetic bladed calcite, a probable low-Mg submarine phase, based on its texture and habit.

Evaporites. There are no known Artinskian evaporite deposits in the Sverdrup Basin. However, pseudomorphs after gypsum have been observed at at least one locality on Ellesmere Island, where lacustrine strata are preserved. These lacustrine deposits formed in a small depression that was isolated from the main Sverdrup Basin during the early part of the Artinskian. Lacustrine beds contain varying proportions of finely crystalline dolostone and silty dolostone that display varvelike and stromatolitic laminations. Swallow taillike pseudomorphs after gypsum were found in a number of dolostone beds.

Red beds and caliches. Red-weathering strata are relatively common throughout the Artinskian succession. Variably thick seams of red shales lie on top of intraformatial erosional surfaces, especially in the Great Bear Cape Formation. Some of the most marginal sections display fluvial overbank shales and siltstones that are deep red in coloration. A variety of caliche profiles formed in these overbank strata. Caliches are also widely developed on top of the subaerially exposed Great Bear Cape Formation, forming horizons that reach 5 to 10 m in thickness.

Summary and interpretation. The disappearance of Chloroforam-type assemblages and their replacement by a

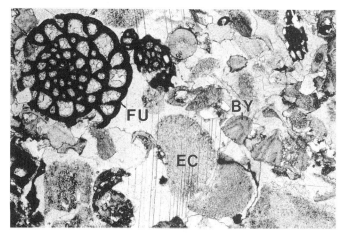

Figure 11. Photomicrograph showing Bryonoderm-extended grainstone typical of shallowest Artinskian carbonates. Note Fusulinaceans (FU), echinoderms (EC), bryozoan (BY) and brachiopod spine. Width of area shown in photograph is 5 mm.

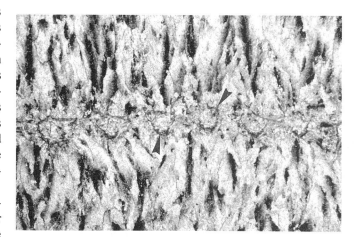

Figure 12. Photomicrograph (crossed Nicols) showing radiaxial calcite cement growing outward from a bryozoan substrate (arrows). Such cements probably originated as high-Mg calcite cement. From Artinskian reef, southwestern Ellesmere Island. Width of area shown in photograph is 5 mm.

Bryonoderm-extended association suggests that a temperate-warm climate prevailed in the Sverdrup Basin during the 5- to 10-m.y.-long Artinskian interval. This is further indicated by the lack of ooids and oncoids, the replacement of numerous algal buildups by fewer bryozoan buildups, the eradication of nearly all aragonite-secreting organisms, and the absence of aragonite submarine cements. That the climate remained at least seasonally arid is indicated by the red coloration of overbank strata and paleosol profiles, the development of caliches, and the presence of pseudomorphs after gypsum associated with lacustrine dolostones.

Artinskian carbonate shelf deposits of the Sverdrup Basin

bear striking similarities with Tertiary temperate shelf sediments of Southern Australia, which probably constitute the best-studied example of ancient temperate carbonates (James and Bone, 1992, 1991, 1989; Bone et al., 1992; James and van der Borch, 1991). Except for the basic faunal difference (Bryonoderm versus Foramol), the Artinskian Arctic examples and the Tertiary Australian examples appear stunningly similar in terms of stacking patterns, sedimentary textures and structures, prevailing climatic conditions, hydraulic regimes, associated lacustrine dolostones, early and late diagenetic products, and many more features (N. P. James, personal communication, 1992).

Kungurian-Kazanian

Sequences and formations. The 10-m.y.-long Kungurian to Kazanian succession of the Sverdrup Basin comprises two sequences that are bounded by significant unconformities that pass basinward into their correlative conformities (Fig. 2). The first sequence comprises a 300-m-thick low stand succession of spiculitic chert that was deposited while the Great Bear Cape shelf was exposed, during an interval correlated with the Kungurian (Beauchamp, 1994). The shelf was then flooded by a major transgression that was followed by the progradation of a regressive package of essentially unfossiliferous, clean quartzose sandstones of late Kungurian–early Ufimian (Roadian) age (Sabine Bay Formation). Deposition of the Sabine Bay Formation, which is up to 300 m thick, was contemporaneous with the Melvillian Disturbance (Beauchamp et al., 1989b).

The second sequence comprises a deepening-upward package of marine calcareous sandstone and fossiliferous sandy limestone (Assistance Formation) that records a major transgression and the onset of passive subsidence in the basin. The Assistance Formation of Ufimian (Roadian) age is up to 300 m thick; it is overlain by a shallowing-upward, regressive succession of fossiliferous glauconitic sandstones (Trold Fiord Formation) and correlative bioclastic carbonates (Degerböls Formation) that prograded basinward in Kazanian (Wordian) time (Fig. 2) and culminated in a widespread regional unconformity (Beauchamp, 1994). The maximum recorded thicknesses of the Trold Fiord and Degerböls formations are 500 m and 300 m, respectively. The Sabine Bay, Assistance, Trold Fiord, and Degerböls formations pass basinward into black siliceous shale and spiculitic chert of the Van Hauen Formation (Fig. 2)

Bryonoderm association. Fossils in the shallowest portions of the Assistance, Trold Fiord, and Degerböls formations are typical of a Bryonoderm association (Fig. 13). In most cases, bryozoans, echinoderms, and brachiopods are the only organisms present. Rare additional fossils may locally include horn corals, gastropods, and pelecypods and a few varieties of small benthic foraminifers belonging to various uniserial groups (frondicularid, pachyphloid, geinitzinid, and nodosarid). Sponge spicules can be locally abundant.

Mineralogy. Except for extremely rare gastropods and pelecypods, Kungurian to Kazanian strata contain no arago-

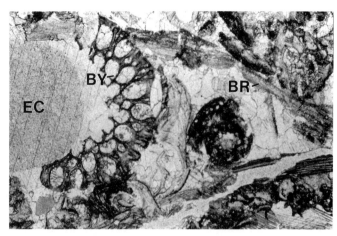

Figure 13. Photomicrograph showing example of bryonoderm grainstones from Upper Permian (Kazanian) Degerböls Formation, southwestern Ellesmere Island. Note echinoderms (EC), bryozoans (BY), and brachiopods (BR). Width of area shown in photograph is 2 mm.

nite-secreting organisms. There is no botroyoidal, fibrous, or radiaxial cement indicative of an aragonite or high-Mg calcite precursor. There is no indication of early diagenetic submarine carbonate cementation, as the bulk of the interparticle porosity is occluded by late diagenetic sparry calcite of either meteoric or burial origin. Some of the porosity is, however, cemented by glauconite and, to a lesser extent, phosphate. Glauconite grains and peloidlike concretions range from common in the Assistance and Degerböls formations to abundant in the Trold Fiord Formation. The overall mineralogy of Ufimian and Kazanian Bryonoderm sediments was dominated by more or less equal proportions of low-Mg calcite and glauconite, with minor amounts of high-Mg calcite.

Coal. Fluvial overbank strata in the Sabine Bay and Assistance formations are composed of black coaly seams that are up to 1 m thick. Root casts and other plant imprints are common. No red-weathering horizons exist in the Sabine Bay Formation, contrasting sharply with the underlying Artinskian and older succession. Likewise, there is no evidence for caliche development in the Sabine Bay–Assistance interval.

Siderite concretions and ooids. Red-weathering horizons reappear in the Trold Fiord succession, coinciding with the disappearance of black coaly horizons. Red horizons are associated with siderite concretions and siderite ooids of uncertain origin; they appear to have formed on top of various erosion surfaces and may be related to some paleosol development. Caliches are absent in this part of the succession.

Dropstones. Pebble- and cobble-sized clasts, interpreted as dropstones, were found locally in Kazanian strata (Fig. 14). These rock fragments, up to 30 cm in diameter, are contained in fine-grained glauconitic and fossiliferous sandstones of the Trold Fiord Formation. These clasts commonly depress primary laminae, indicating that they were dropped from above.

Figure 14. Cobble-sized dropstone in brachiopood-rich glauconitic sandstone, Upper Permian ((Kazanian) Trold Fiord Formation, southwestern Ellesmere Island.

Summary and interpretation. The widespread occurrence of Bryonoderm sediments in Kungurian to Kazanian strata, even in the shallowest nearshore facies, suggests that a temperate-cold climate prevailed in the Sverdrup Basin during that time interval. Additional evidence supporting this hypothesis includes absence of nonskeletal carbonate grains, absence of reefs, near complete absence of aragonitic biota, absence of submarine cement, abundance of glauconite, and presence of dropstones. The presence of coaly seams and absence of red coloration and caliches in fluvial overbank strata of the Sabine Bay and Assistance formations suggest a humid climate for that part of the succession. Sedimentation of the Trold Fiord and Degerböls formations coincided with a return to a more-arid climate, as shown by the disappearance of coal seams and the reappearance of red-weathering units. The latter are no longer associated with caliches, but rather with siderite concretions and ooids, which may be another indication of a temperate-cold setting.

Post-Kazanian

Sequence and formations. In the Sverdrup Basin, up to 500 m of undated chert associated with minor carbonates, shales, and siltstones occur between dated Kazanian and Griesbachian (Triassic) strata (Fig. 2). The age of these rocks has not been substantiated by paleontological evidence, but they are likely to represent the latest Permian interval (Tatarian in Russia; Dzhulfian-Changhsingian in the Tethys; Ochoan in the Western United States; Beauchamp, 1994). This assumption is reasonable considering the stratigraphic position of these rocks in conjunction with sedimentologic evidence indicating continuous deposition across the Permian-Triassic boundary in slope to basinal areas.

The post-Kazanian succession, which was deposited over an interval of time ranging from between 5 to 15 Ma, is one

broad sequence characterized by two distinct packages (Fig. 15). The basal package is a low stand succession that was deposited in the slope-to-basinal environments while the adjacent Wordian shelf was subaerially exposed and subjected to erosion. Up to 400 m of spiculitic chert (Van Hauen Formation) were deposited in that manner, suggesting that relative sea level remained low for a very long period of time. Deposition of this low stand package appears contemporaneous to a well-documented global eustatic low that led to the widespread exposition and erosion of Late Permian shelves and the accumulation of basinal evaporites in many basins (e.g., Delaware, Zechstein). The upper package of the post-Kazanian succession is a 150-m-thick shallowing-upward succession of siliceous shales passing upward into spiculitic chert, with minor bioclastic carbonates and glauconitic sandstones (Van Hauen Formation). These rocks form a regressive package that prograded basinward following a moderate transgression that flooded both the previously deposited low stand succession and the adjacent Kazanian shelf (Fig. 15). At the basin margin, these rocks are separated from overlying Triassic strata by an unconformity that passes into a correlative conformity in the more distal areas.

Hyalosponge assemblage. The shallowest-water facies in the post-Kazanian sequence are dominated by spiculitic chert (Fig. 16), locally interstratified with rare lenses of Bryonoderm carbonates and glauconitic sandstones. These cherts are much different than the deep-water cherts that occur widely throughout the upper Paleozoic slope to basinal succession of the Sverdrup Basin. Several lines of evidence point to much shallower shelf setting for the uppermost Permian chert (Table 1); these include (1) paleogeographic position, (2) white to pale gray coloration, (3) thick to very thick and massive beds, (4) extreme bioturbation, (5) medium- to coarse-grain quartzose sand admixture, (6) high glauconite content, (7) low organic matter content, (8) cross-beddings, (9) interstratification with glauconite sandstone and Bryonoderm carbonates, and (10) presence of foraminifers. Clearly, these cherts were deposited in a relatively shallow shelf setting.

Post-Kazanian shallow-water cherts comprise a Hyalosponge association overwhelmingly dominated by monotaxon spicules, which often constitute the only biotic remnant (Fig. 17). Rare elements of the Bryonoderm association can be found locally: These include bryozoans, echinoderms, brachiopods, and rare but significant uniserial foraminifers belonging to the frondicularids, pachyphloids, geinitzinids, and nodosarids. Beds of the Hyalosponge association are locally interstratified with lenses of Bryonoderm carbonates.

Mineralogy. Post-Kazanian strata are dominantly composed of siliceous minerals (mostly chalcedony), displaying various habits ranging from microcrystalline mesh to spherulites and splays. Siliceous minerals occlude both intra- and interparticle pore spaces. Most spicules were dissolved early and refilled rapidly by diagenetic siliceous phases. Some spicules show an outstanding state of preservation, with their

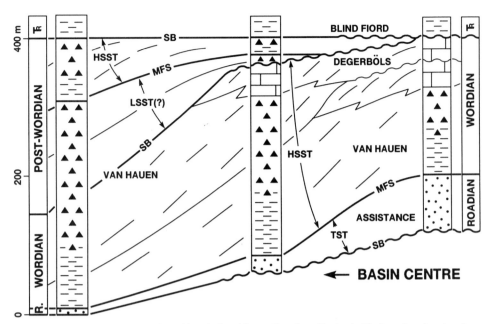

Figure 15. Upper Permian stratigraphic relationships at Sverdrup Basin shelf edge, showing development of a post-Wordian (post-Kazanian) sequence consisting of a low stand systems track (LSST), capped by a maximum flooding surface (MFS), and overlain by a high stand systems track (HSST). TST, transgressive systems track; SB, sequence boundary.

internal canal still preserved and with little modification to their original siliceous texture. Glauconite is locally an important component of the post-Kazanian Hyalosponge sediments. Glauconite occurs both as grains (peloids and irregular globules) and intra- and interparticle cements.

Summary and interpretation. The widespread occurrence of shallow-water Hyalosponge chert in strata of post-Kazanian age suggests environmental conditions similar to those prevailing on some modern polar shelves that are characterized by a permanent or semipermanent ice cover. This is further suggested by the rare occurrences of Bryonoderm carbonates and glauconitic sandstones interstratified with the chert. The entire post-Kazanian sequence contains very little terrigenous clastic material. This suggests that the climates remained relatively arid in latest Permian time.

The uppermost Permian spiculitic chert is compositionally, texturally, and sedimentologically remarkably similar to the recently documented spiculitic mats that floor the Canadian continental polar margin and the Vesterisbanken Seamount in the central Greenland Sea (Van Wagoner et al., 1989; Henrich et al., 1992). In both areas, relatively shallow shelves (<200 m) are floored with variably thick mats dominated by siliceous sponge spicules associated with minor elements of the Foramol association, mostly bryozoans. Some sponges form small mounds and thickets in association with bryozoans. Henrich et al. (1992) consider this siliceous facies, herein referred to as the Hyalosponge association, to represent the end member of the Foramol facies. It is believed to reflect cold and aphotic environmental conditions characterized by a strong seasonality in nutrient supply and by a low clastic influx. Such conditions characteristically prevail on very high latitude shelves beneath a permanent or semipermanent ice cover.

Similar conditions may also develop in areas of upwelling. The mid-Permian Phosphoria Formation contains abundant siliceous sponge spicules that accumulated at the equatorial western margin of Pangea in areas believed to have been affected by intense cold-water upwelling (Wardlaw and Collinson, 1986). Controversy exists regarding the water depth at which these spiculites were deposited, and bathymetric interpretations range from deep to relatively shallow. Spiculites of the Phosphoria Formation pass laterally into bioclastic Bryonoderm carbonates. The Roadian to Wordian (Ufimian to Kazanian) Phosphoria Formation thus appears, at least compositionally, similar to the uppermost Permian chert of the Sverdrup Basin. Could this chert have formed in a manner similar to that of the Phosphoria Formation; in other words, could it have accumulated in areas of cold-water upwelling in an otherwise relatively warm region?

This mechanism is plausible but for several reasons is hard to envision. First, the post-Kazanian chert of the Sverdrup Basin contains no significant amounts of phosphates, except for a few thin layers that are sparsely distributed. Second, this chert can be traced from the Sverdrup Basin to the Barents Sea, a depositional area that is more than 2,500 km long and in places more than 1,000 km wide (Fig. 3). Third, spiculitic chert occurs in more or less equal proportions on both the

Figure 16. Uppermost Permian chert in Sverdrup Basin, Ellesmere Island. A, thickly bedded to massive white spiculitic chert. B, cross-bedded spiculitic chert.

TABLE 1. DIFFERENCES BETWEEN UPPER PALEOZOIC DEEP WATER CHERT AND SHALLOW WATER CHERT IN SVERDRUP BASIN

	Deep Water Chert	Shallow Water Chert
Paleogeographic position	Basin axial	Basin marginal
Color	Black to dark gray	White to pale gray
Bedding thickness	Thin to medium	Thick to very thick
Bioturbation	Absent to rare	Pervasive
Grain size of quartz admixture	Silt to fine sand	Medium to coarse sand
Glauconite	Absent to rare	Common to abundant
Organic matter	Common to abundant	Absent to rare
Cross-bedding	Absent	Present
Associated facies	Black siliceous shale and siltstone	Glauconite sandstone **Bryonoderm** carbonate
Foraminifer	Absent	Present
Interpreted environment	Slope to basin	Shelf

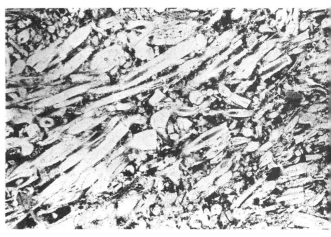

Figure 17. Photomicrograph showing typical Hyalosponge assemblage from uppermost Permian chert of Sverdrup Basin. Note abundant sponge spicules, some with their internal canal still preserved. Width of area shown in photograph is 3 mm.

northern and southern margins of the Sverdrup Basin; upwelling usually affects one side of a sedimentary basin only (southbound currents in the Northern Hemisphere create upwelling on western continental margins; northbound currents induce upwelling on eastern continental margins). Fourth, no tropical or temperate climatic indicators can be found in the chert, not even in the most-cratonward exposures; the Phosphoria Formation, in contrast, grades laterally into continental red beds (Wardlaw and Collinson, 1986). Fifth, various lines of evidence stated before clearly indicate that the climates shifted from tropical conditions to temperate-cold conditions from the Early to Late Permian; cold climatic conditions had therefore been prevailing for tens of millions of years prior to latest Permian chert deposition. Finally, no evidence exists to suggest that major upwelling affected the Sverdrup Basin–Barents Sea area from the Asselian to the Kazanian, and there is no indication that this area was paleogeographically different in post-Kazanian time.

In the absence of any evidence supporting a Phosphoria-like upwelling mechanism for the accumulation of the latest Permian chert in the Sverdrup Basin, one has to look at the possibility that an extensive permanent or semipermanent ice cover might have created the environmental conditions necessary for the accumulation of siliceous chert. Admittedly, evidence for the existence of this ice cover is meager. Nevertheless, the following are real: (1) the cooling trend from an Asselian-Sakmarian tropical climate, first to an Artinskian temperate-warm climate and then to a Kungurian to Kazanian temperate-cold climate, suggests that the next logical step should be an even colder climate, namely a polar climate; (2) evidence for some ice exists in the Kazanian succession (dropstones): More ice should logically be expected in the post-Kazanian; (3) the only modern analogues for relatively shallow water accumulations of siliceous sponge spicules occur beneath permanent or semipermanent ice covers in the Arctic and Antarctic.

LATE PALEOZOIC CLIMATIC EVOLUTION OF SVERDRUP BASIN AND NORTHERN PANGEA

The analysis of marine and nonmarine climatic indicators reveals that a dramatic cooling took place in Permian time in the Sverdrup Basin (Fig. 18). For more than 60 million years (Serpukhovian to Sakmarian), a tropicallike, semiarid climate prevailed in the Sverdrup Basin. The climate then deteriorated rapidly in the Permian as it shifted to a temperate-warm setting in Artinskian time, to a temperate-cold setting in Kungurian to Kazanian time, and to a polarlike setting in latest Permian time (post-Kazanian). Relatively arid conditions prevailed throughout most of the Permian, except for a brief interval in Ufimian time when humid conditions were established.

The late Paleozoic climatic evolution of the Sverdrup Basin is inconsistent with any of the inferred paleolatitudal reconstructions for this area. Even though nearly all proposed reconstructions indicate that Pangea migrated in a northerly direction from the Early Carboniferous to the Late Permian, none of them place the Sverdrup Basin far enough to the north in Late Permian time to account, in modern terms, for the observed climatic indicators. The most recent reconstructions of Scotese (personal communication, 1991) place the Sverdrup Basin at a latitude of 25°N in Late Carboniferous time (Moscovian), 35°N in Early Permian (Asselian-Sakmarian) time, and 40°N in Late Permian (Kazanian) time (Fig. 18). These estimates agree reasonably well with paleomagnetic data measured in Lower Triassic shale of the Sverdrup Basin, indicating a paleolatitude of about 35°N (A. F. Embry, personal communication, 1992). Most other reconstructions match fairly closely that of Scotese for that part of the world (Irving, 1977; Smith et al., 1981). The Early to Late Permian climatic gradient interpreted from the analysis of Permian strata is thus far greater than that expected from the inferred paleolatitudinal shift of 10 to 15°.

Evidence for a dramatic cooling and climatic deterioration in Permian time is not restricted to the Sverdrup Basin. Evi-

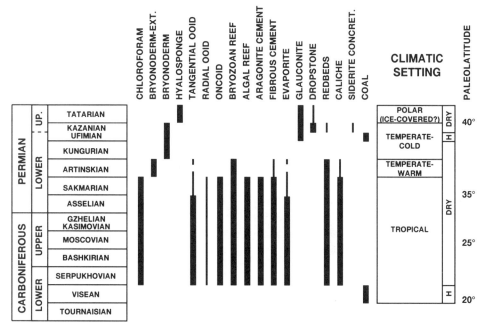

Figure 18. Summary chart showing distribution of shallow-water benthic associations and other climatic indicators (black boxes) in upper Paleozoic succession of Sverdrup Basin. Based on these indicators, the climatic setting of the area is interpreted to have evolved from a tropical setting from the Viséan to the Sakmarian, to a temperate-warm setting during the Artinskian, to a temperate-cold setting during the Kungurian-Kazanian, and to a polarlike setting with a permanent or semipermanent ice cover during the latest Permian (Tatarian?) time. Relatively dry conditions prevailed throughout most of the late Paleozoic, except for two brief humid (H) episodes in the Viséan and late Kungurian–early Ufimian. The Late Carboniferous to Late Permian climatic gradient is far greater than that inferred from paleolatitude data (C. Scotese, personal communication, 1992), indicating that northern Pangea was subjected to a dramatic cooling in Permian time.

dence for such a cooling exists throughout the circum-Arctic regions, from Northern Alaska to the Timan-Petchora Basin, including North Greenland, Svalbard, Bjørnøya, and the Barents Sea (Stemmerik and Worsley, 1989). In these regions, shallow-water carbonates typically display a Chloroforam biota in the Asselian and Sakmarian, a Bryonoderm-extended biota in the Artinskian, a Bryonoderm biota in the Kungurian to Kazanian, and a Hyalosponge biota in the uppermost part of the Permian succession. This trend parallels the well-documented progressive contraction of fusulinids, phylloid, and dasycladacean algae and other tropicallike organisms around the paleoequator during Permian time. During latest Permian time, Chloroforam- and Chlorosponge-type biota were restricted to a narrow belt in the Tethyan regions. It may be significant that a great number of dropstones have been documented from Upper Permian deposits of the Kolyma Block in Siberia (Ustritsky, 1973).

Whereas a significant Permian cooling appears to have affected the entire Northern Hemisphere, no solid evidence can be produced for an equivalent climatic deterioration in the Southern Hemisphere. Some authors have even suggested that Gondwana climates evolved toward warmer conditions from the Early to the Late Permian. This is based on the replacement of Asselian and Sakmarian tillites and other continental glacial deposits by younger Permian, coal-bearing continental deposits in various parts of Gondwana (Frakes, 1979). Some believe, however, that glaciogenic deposits can be found in strata as young as Late Permian in other regions of Gondwana. Most workers will agree that post-Sakmarian glacial deposits are not nearly as abundant as Sakmarian and older glacial deposits, in spite of the fact that large areas of Gondwana lay south of 60°S in Late Permian time (Veevers and Powell, 1987). Perhaps one should envision a scenario whereby the Permian cooling was, to some large extent, restricted to the Northern Hemisphere.

The causes of the Permian cooling are unknown. Many interactive factors can cause long-term climatic changes; these include continental drift, deflection of surficial oceanic currents, deflection of deep oceanic currents, deflection of atmospheric currents, fluctuation in atmospheric greenhouse gases, fluctuation in non-Milankovitch astronomical parameters, and fluctuation in polar ice cover. Many recent studies have demonstrated how simple fluctuations in the global atmospheric and oceanic circulation system can drastically change the climatic setting of large regions of the Earth, without necessarily affecting others (e.g., Younger Dryas event, Lehman and Keigwin, 1992.

Perhaps it was an irreversible change in the global pattern of oceanic and/or atmospheric circulation that caused the Permian cooling in the Northern Hemisphere. Such a change could have been brought about by the opening of narrow seaways or the uplift of large plateaus (Ruddiman and Kutzbach, 1991). Perhaps it was the northward migration of Pangea and its impingement upon the polar regions that led to a major re-

organization of the Earth's circulation pattern. Could the northern tip of Pangea have deflected circumpolar cold currents southward along its northwestern margin? Such currents could have dramatically cooled the Barents Sea–Sverdrup Basin region, and their effect could have been felt all along the western margin of North America. Perhaps it was the same currents that created extensive upwelling in the Western United States from the Artinskian onward and led to deposition of the Phosphoria Formation. But can we realistically envision such currents to be effective enough to bring a semipermanent ice cover at a latitude of 40°N and create conditions similar to those currently prevailing beyond 65°N? Or, could this ice be indicative of extreme seasonality between very cold, ice-forming winters and milder, ice-free summers, with siliceous sponges being the only organisms that could thrive in such an extreme and quickly changing environment? These ideas may not be entirely unrealistic considering that modern pack ice forms at latitudes as low as 43°N along Canada's east coast, an area cooled by the southward-flowing Labrador and East Greenland currents.

It may be significant that the major climatic changes in the Sverdrup Basin coincide with long-term sequence boundaries (Fig. 2), boundaries believed to reflect some shifts in the Earth's tectonic system (e.g., Hubbard, 1988). Long-lasting changes in the global circulation pattern could thus be linked to global tectonism. Mountain building in one part of the world could have caused a climatic shift in another part of the world, and the shift need not have been global in magnitude. The return to much warmer climatic conditions in earliest Triassic time in the Sverdrup Basin–Barents Sea area, coupled with a rapid shift back to far more equable climates across Pangea, suggests that a major tectono-climatic reorganization of global magnitude coincided with the Paleozoic-Mesozoic boundary. No wonder that more than 90% of all living species did not make it past that boundary.

CONCLUSIONS

The biotic succession of the Sverdrup Basin records an important Permian climatic cooling trend. Highly diversified, tropicallike associations dominated by calcareous alga, foraminifer, ooid, and oncoid (Chloroforam) prevailed in the Asselian and Sakmarian, whereas poorly diversified, temperatelike associations, dominated by bryozoan, echinoderm, and brachiopod, characterized the Artinskian (Bryonoderm-extended) to Kazanian (Bryonoderm) interval. Polarlike, siliceous sponge–dominated biota (Hyalosponge) prevailed in the latest Permian. The climatic gradient suggested by this trend, and by other climatic indicators, is far greater than that expected from the 10 to 15° of northerly migration inferred for Pangea during the Permian. The cooling trend, the causes of which are unknown, is evidence for a dramatic climatic deterioration in northern Pangea at the end of the Paleozoic, deterioration that may have played a role in the most significant mass extinction in the Earth's history.

ACKNOWLEDGMENTS

The author wishes to thank Robert N. Ginsburg, Noel P. James, Pierre Thériault, and Richard L. Hay for their constructive criticisms of an earlier version of the manuscript.

REFERENCES CITED

Beauchamp, B., 1987, Stratigraphy and facies analysis of the Upper Carboniferous to Lower Permian Canyon Fiord, Belcher Channel and Nansen formations, southwestern Ellesmere Island [Ph.D. thesis]: Calgary, Alberta, University of Calgary, 370 p.

Beauchamp, B., 1989, Lower Permian (Artinskian) sponge-bryozoan buildups, southwestern Ellesmere Island, Canadian Arctic Archipelago, in Geldsetzer, H.H.J., James, N. P., and Tebbutt, G. E., eds., Reefs, Canada and adjacent areas: Canadian Society of Petroleum Geologists Memoir 13, p. 575–584.

Beauchamp, B., 1992a, Mid-Permian tectonic event in Arctic North America: International Conference on Arctic Margins (ICAM), Anchorage, Alaska, 2–4 September, 1992: ICAM Abstracts, p. 7.

Beauchamp, B., 1992b. Upper Paleozoic reefs of Sverdrup Basin, Canadian Arctic: An aid to Barents Sea exploration, in Vorren, T. O., and six others, eds., Arctic geology and petroleum potential: Amsterdam, Elsevier, Norwegian Petroleum Society Special Publication 2, p. 217–241.

Beauchamp, B., 1994, Permian history of Arctic North America, in Scholle, P.A., ed., Permian of the Northern Hemisphere: Springer Verlag (in press).

Beauchamp, B., Harrison, J. C., and Henderson, C. M., 1989a, Upper Paleozoic stratigraphy and basin analysis of the Sverdrup Basin, Canadian Arctic Archipelago. Part 2: Transgressive-regressive sequences, in Current Research, Part G, Geological Survey of Canada Paper 89-1G, p.115–124.

Beauchamp, B., Harrison, J. C., and Henderson, C. M., 1989b, Upper Paleozoic stratigraphy and basin analysis of the Sverdrup Basin, Canadian Arctic Archipelago. Part 1: Time frame and tectonic evolution, in Current Research, Part G, Geological Survey of Canada Paper 89-1G, p.105–113.

Beauchamp, B., Davies, G. R., and Nassichuk, W. W., 1989c, Upper Carboniferous to Lower Permian *Palaeoaplysina*-phylloid algal buildups, Canadian Arctic Archipelago, in Geldsetzer, H.H.J., James, N. P., and Tebbut, G. E., eds., Reefs, Canada and adjacent areas: Canadian Society of Petroleum Geologists Memoir 13, p. 590–599.

Beauchamp, B., Olchowy, B., and Henderson, C. M., 1991, A newly-recognized Lower Permian reef tract, west-central Ellesmere Island, Canadian Arctic, in Current Research, Part D, Geological Survey of Canada Paper 91-1D, p. 23–32.

Bone, Y., James, N. P., and Kyser, T. K., 1992, Synsedimentary detrital dolomite in Quaternary cool-water carbonate sediments, Lacepede shelf, South Australia: Geology, v. 20, p. 109–112.

Brookfield, M. E., 1988, A mid-Ordovician temperate carbonate shelf—The Black River and Trenton Limestone Groups of southern Ontario, Canada: Sedimentary Geology, v. 60, p. 137–154.

Bullivant, J. S., and Dearborn, J. H., 1967, The fauna of the Ross Sea, Part 5: Wellington, New Zealand Department of Scientific Industrial Research Bulletin, v. 176, 76 p.

Chuvashov, B. I., 1983, Permian reefs of the Urals: Facies, v. 8, p. 191–212.

Davies, G. R., 1977, Former magnesian calcite and aragonite submarine cements in upper Paleozoic reefs of the Canadian Arctic: A summary: Geology, v. 5, p. 11–15.

Davies, G. R., and Nassichuk, W. W., 1990, Submarine cements and fabrics in Carboniferous to Lower Permian, reefal, shelf-margin and slope carbonates, Northwestern Ellesmere Island, Canadian Arctic Archipelago: Geo-

logical Survey of Canada Bulletin 399, 77 p.

Davies, G. R., Richards, B. C., Beauchamp, B., and Nassichuk, W. W., 1989, Carboniferous and Permian reefs of Canada and adjacent areas, in Geldsetzer, H.H.J., James, N. P., and Tebbutt, G. E., Reefs, Canada and Adjacent Areas: Canadian Society of Petroleum Geologists Memoir 13, p. 565–574.

Domack, E. W., 1988, Biogenic facies in the Antarctic glacimarine environment: Basis for a polar glacimarine summary: Palaeogeography, Palaeoclimatology, Palaeoecology, v. 63, p. 357–372.

Embry, A. F., 1991, Mesozoic history of the Arctic Islands, in Trettin, H. P., ed., Geology of the Innuitian Orogen and Arctic Platform of Canada and Greenland: Geological Survey of Canada, Geology of Canada, no. 3, p.369–434.

Embry, A. F., 1992a, Triassic and Jurassic paleoclimatic trends in the Canadian Arctic Archipelago: Geological Society of America Abstracts with Programs, v. 23, p. A28.

Embry, A. F., 1992b Crockerland—The Northwest source area for the Sverdrup Basin, Canadian Arctic Islands, in Vorren, T. O., and six others, eds., Arctic geology and petroleum potential: Amsterdam, Elsevier, Norwegian Petroleum Society Special Publication 2, p. 205–216.

Flügel, E., 1981, Lower Permian *Tubiphytes/Archaeolithoporella* buildups in the Southern Alps (Austria and Italy), in Toomey, D. F., ed., European fossil reef models: Society of Economic Paleontologists and Mineralogists Special Publication 30, p. 143–160.

Flügel, E., 1982, Microfacies analysis of limestones: Berlin, Heidelberg, New York, Springer-Verlag, 633 p.

Frakes, L. A., 1979, Climates throughout geologic times: Amsterdam, Elsevier, 310 p.

Harrison, J. C., Riediger, C. L., and Brent, T., 1988, Late Paleozoic extension and associated sedimentation at the southern margin of the Sverdrup Basin, in Geological Association of Canada–Mineralogical Association of Canada Joint Annual Meeting, St. John's, Newfoundland: Program with Abstracts, v. 13, p. A53.

Henrich, R., and seven others, 1992, Facies belts and communities of Arctic Vesterisbanken Seamount (Central Greenland Sea): Facies, v. 27, p. 71–104.

Hubbard, R. J., 1988, Age and significance of sequence boundaries on Jurassic and Early Cretaceous rifted continental margins: American Association of Petroleum Geologists Bulletin, v. 72, p. 49–72.

Irving, E., 1977, Drift of the major continental blocks since the Devonian: Nature, v. 270, p. 304–309.

James, N. P., and Bone, Y., 1989, Petrogenesis of Cenozoic, temperate water calcarenites, South Australia: A model for meteoric/shallow burial diagenesis of shallow water calcite cements: Journal of Sedimentary Petrology, v. 59, p. 191–203.

James, N. P., and Bone, Y., 1991, Origin of a cool-water, Oligo-Miocene deep shelf limestone, Eucla Platform, southern Australia: Sedimentology, v.38, p. 323–341.

James, N. P., and Bone, Y., 1992, Synsedimentary cemented calcarenite layers in Oligo-Miocene cool-water shelf limestones, Eucla Platform, southern Australia: Journal of Sedimentary Petrology, v. 62, p. 860–872.

James, N. P., and van der Borch, C. C., 1991, Carbonate shelf edge off southern Australia: A prograding open-platform margin: Geology, v. 19, p.1005–1008.

Lees, A., 1975, Possible influence of salinity and temperature on modern shelf carbonate sedimentation, Marine Geology, v. 19, p. 159–198.

Lees, A., and Buller, A. T., 1972, Modern temperate-water and warm-water shelf carbonate sediments contrasted: Marine Geology, v. 13, p. M67–M73.

Lehman, S. J., and Keigwin, L. D., 1992, Sudden changes in North Atlantic circulation during the last deglaciation: Nature, v. 17, p. 357–360.

Mamet, B., Roux, A., and Nassichuk, W. W., 1987, Algues et stratigraphie du Paléozoïque supérieur de l'Arctique canadien: Geological Survey of Canada Bulletin 242, 143 p.

Morin, J., Beauchamp, B., and Desrochers, A., 1991, Lower Permian cyclic shelf sedimentation, west-central Ellesmere Island, Canadian Arctic: Preliminary results and interpretations, *in* Current Research, Part B, Geological Survey of Canada Paper 91-1B, p. 71–80.

Murchey, B. L., Jones, D. L., Holdsworth, B. K., and Wardlaw, B. R., 1988, Distribution patterns of facies, radiolarians, and conodonts in the Mississippian to Jurassic siliceous rocks of the northern Brooks Range, Alaska, *in* Gryc, G., ed., Geology and exploration of the National Petroleum Reserve in Alaska, 1974 to 1982: U.S. Geological Survey Professional Paper 1399, p. 697–724.

Nassichuk, W. W., and Davies, G. R., 1980, Stratigraphy and sedimentation of the Otto Fiord Formation: Geological Survey of Canada Bulletin 268, 87p.

Nelson, C. S., 1988a, An introductory perspective on non-tropical shelf carbonates: Sedimentary Geology, v. 60, p. 3–14.

Nelson, C. S., 1988b, Non-tropical carbonate deposits on the modern New Zealand shelf: Sedimentary Geology, v. 60, p. 71–94.

Piepenburg, D., 1988, Zur zusammensetzung der bodenfauna in der westlichen Fram Strasse: Berichte zur Polarforschung, v. 52, p. 1–117, Bremerhaven.

Pinard, S., 1990, Taxonomie des petits foraminifères du Carbonifère-Permien inférieur du Bassin de Sverdrup, Arctique canadien [Ph.D. thesis]: Montreal, Université de Montréal, 782 p.

Rao, C. P., 1981, Criteria for recognition of cold-water carbonate sedimentation: Berriedale Limestone (Lower Permian), Tasmania, Australia: Journal of Sedimentary Petrology, v. 51, p. 491–506.

Rao, C. P., 1988, Paleoclimate of some Permo-Triassic carbonates of Malaysia: Sedimentary Geology, v. 60, p. 163–172.

Ruddiman, W. F., and Kutzbach, J. E., 1991, Late Cenozoic plateau uplift and climate change: Transactions of the Royal Society of Edinburgh: Earth Sciences, v. 81, p. 301–314.

Sandberg, P. A., 1975, New interpretation of Great Salt Lake ooids and of ancient non-skeletal carbonate mineralogy: Sedimentology, v. 22, p. 497–537.

Scott, E., Henderson, C. M., and Beauchamp, B., 1991, Field investigations of Artinskian (Lower Permian) strata, west-central Ellesmere Island, *in* Current Research, Part D, Geological Survey of Canada Paper 91-1D, p. 81–92.

Smith, A. G., Henley, A. M., and Briden, J. C., 1981, Phanerozoic paleocontinental world maps: Cambridge, Cambridge University Press, 102 p.

Stemmerik, L., and Worsley, D., 1989, Late Palaeozoic sequence correlations, North Greenland, Svalbard and the Barents Shelf, *in* Collinson, J. D., ed., Correlation in hydrocarbon exploration, (meeting of the Norwegian

Petroleum Society, Bergen, Norway, 1985): (London, Graham and Trotman), p. 99–111.

Stephenson, R. A., Embry, A. F., Nakiboglu, S. M., and Hastoglu, M. A., 1987, Rift-initiated Permian to Early Cretaceous subsidence of the Sverdrup Basin, *in* Beaumont, C., and Tankard, A. J., eds., Sedimentary basins and basin-forming mechanisms: Canadian Society of Petroleum Geologists Memoir 12, p. 213–231.

Thériault, P., 1991, Syn-rift sedimentation in the Upper Carboniferous Canyon Fiord Formation, SW Ellesmere Island, Canadian Arctic [M.Sc. thesis]: Ottawa, Canada, University of Ottawa, 250 p.

Thorsteinsson, R., 1974, Carboniferous and Permian stratigraphy of Axel Heiberg Island and western Ellesmere Island, Canadian Arctic Archipelago: Geological Survey of Canada Bulletin 224, 115 p.

Thorsteinsson, R., and Tozer, E. T., 1970, Geology of the Arctic Archipelago, *in* Geology and economic minerals of Canada, 5th ed.: Geological Survey of Canada Economic Report 1, p. 548–590.

Trettin, H. P., 1989, The Arctic Islands, *in* Bally, A. W., and Palmer, A. R., eds., The geology of North America. Vol. A: An overview: Boulder, Colorado, Geological Society of America, p. 349–370.

Ustritsky, V. I., 1973, Permian climate, *in* Logan, A., and Hills, L. V., eds., The Permian and Triassic systems and their mutual boundaries: Canadian Society of Petroleum Geologists, Memoir 2, p. 733–744.

Van Wagoner, N. A., Mudie, P. J., Cole, F. E., and Daborn, G., 1989, Siliceous sponge communities, biological zonation, and Recent sea-level change on the Arctic margin: Ice Island results: Canadian Journal of Earth Sciences, v. 26, p. 2341–2355.

Veevers, J. J., and Powell, C. M., 1987, Late Paleozoic glacial episodes in Gondwanaland reflected in transgressive-regressive depositional sequences in Euramerica: Geological Society of America Bulletin, v. 98, p. 475–487.

Wahlman, G. P., 1985, Lower Permian (Wolfcampian) *Archaeolithoporella-Tubiphytes*-sponge boundstones from the subsurface of West Texas, *in* Toomey, D. F., and Nitecki, M. H., eds.: Paleoalgology; Contemporary Research and Applications, Springer-Verlag, Berlin, p. 208–215.

Wallace, C. A., and Beauchamp, B., 1990, Field investigation of the Mount Bayley Formation, a Lower Permian evaporite in the Canadian Arctic, in Current Research, Part D, Geological Survey of Canada Paper 90-1D, p. 139–146.

Wardlaw, B. R., and Collinson, J. W., 1986, Paleontology and deposition of the Phosphoria Formation: University of Wyoming, Contributions to Geology, v. 24, p. 107–142.

MANUSCRIPT ACCEPTED BY THE SOCIETY MAY 14, 1993

Geological Society of America
Special Paper 288
1994

Pangean shelf carbonates: Controls and paleoclimatic significance of Permian and Triassic reefs

Erik Flügel
Institut für Paläontologie, Friedrich-Alexander Universität Erlangen-Nürnberg, D91054 Erlangen, Loewenichstrasse 28, Federal Republic of Germany

ABSTRACT

Late Paleozoic to Liassic reefs and shelf carbonates, forming at the time of accretion and dispersal of Pangea, are specific because of the frequency of reef types other than framework reefs, the importance of microbial contribution, an increase of bioerosional control, the probable invention of algal/coral symbiosis, and the occurrence of major evolutionary crises of reef biota partly connected with extinction events.

The data base is biased with regard to time intervals and geographic regions. The use of reef distribution in paleoclimatic reconstructions is strongly dependent on paleomaps available. The current three-step processes model describing the evolution of Mesozoic reefs must be modified.

Important constituents of Pangean shelf and reef biota include algae, sponges, and corals exhibiting distinct changes in taxonomic composition, diversity, skeletal mineralogy, and the contribution to reef-building. Reef evolution is characterized by the development of various reef types with different time ranges during accretion and dispersal times of Pangea. Changes in the composition of reef biota with regard to taxa and guild membership are evident during the Permian and Triassic. Reef gaps might have existed during the Early Triassic and perhaps also during the lowermost Early Jurassic. Crucial questions concerning reef evolution in the time of Pangea concern the mode of biotic changes; the lack of Paleozoic holdovers in Triassic reef biotopes and the Scythian reef gap; the coincidence of the late Triassic reef crises with other major modifications of paleogeography, paleoceanography, and climate during the Carnian; and the meaning of the apparently synchronous end-Triassic reef extinction.

Both biological and nonbiological processes depending on paleoclimate and paleolatitudes and connected with sea-level changes of different orders should have been active in the control of the evolution of reefs. The latitudinal distributional patterns of Late Paleozoic reefs, however, might not necessarily reflect low-latitudinal warm-water regions as would be derived from recent distributional patterns. Control of reef development, especially by water temperature and light, may have been different for the various types of reef mounds and reefs originating during Pangean times as compared with Holocene coral reefs. Comparisons of distribution patterns of ancient reefs and global circulation models could help in understanding climatic shifts (as indicated by apparently different paleolatitudinal maxima of Carboniferous to Triassic reefs), in testing long-lasting factors that might have limited reef distribution (e.g., storm tracks, high precipitation areas) as well as in interpreting biogeographical patterns on the shelves around Pangea.

Flügel, E., 1994, Pangean shelf carbonates: Controls and paleoclimatic significance of Permian and Triassic reefs, *in* Klein, G. D., ed., Pangea: Paleoclimate, Tectonics, and Sedimentation During Accretion, Zenith, and Breakup of a Supercontinent: Boulder, Colorado, Geological Society of America Special Paper 288.

Prerequistites for the use of Permian and Triassic reefs in the interpretation and reconstruction of the Pangean paleoclimate are the improvement of the paleontological data base; the critical evaluation of climate sensitivity, especially of Late Paleozoic reef organisms; carbonate grain associations; and the transformation of reef-derived data into proxy data that can be used in quantitative modeling

SPECIFICS OF PANGEAN SHELF CARBONATES

Introduction

The assemblage of Lesser Pangea at the end of Early Carboniferous, the accretion of Greater Pangea during the Permian, and the dispersal of Pangea starting during the Triassic resulted in changes in landmass distributions, climate, and ocean current dynamics, which in turn controlled the expansion and reduction of biogenic carbonate production, the dispersal and distributional patterns of shelf biota, and the development of reefs.

The absence or existence of reefs that could grow up to sea level on platform margins had a profound effect on the facies evolution of Pangean carbonate platforms. The investigation of reefs, therefore, should be a major target in Project Pangea because of the importance of reefs as paleoenvironmental and paleolatitudinal indicators. It is crucial, however, to consider that Pangean shelf carbonates were formed in times of significant evolutionary changes of biota and ecosystems related with several maxima in marine extinctions (late Stephanian, late Permian, late Triassic, Liassic; Sepkoski, 1986; Flessa, 1990) and of paleolatitudinal and paleoclimatic changes connected with temporal variations in marine precipitates, skeletal mineralogy of shelf and reef organisms, and diagenetic patterns (Sandberg, 1983; Tucker and Wright, 1990).

The setting of Pangean reefs was unusual as compared with the distribution of modern reefs because most Pennsylvanian and many Permian buildups formed in and around the margins of intracratonic basins. Starting with the breakup of Pangea, the growth of Permian and Triassic reefs took place along the margins of or in basins adjacent to the east-west–trending Tethyan sea at the western end of the Panthalassia ocean. In most paleocontinental reconstructions, the Permian and partly also the Triassic Tethys is shown as a wedge-shaped oceanic area between the Laurasian and Gondwanian continents (Smith et al., 1981; Scotese and McKerrow, 1990) that might have included a seaway along the northern margin of Gondwana from Sicily to Timor during the Permian (Blendinger et al., 1992), but more recent paleomaps (Scotese and Golonka, 1992) for the Permian and Early Triassic show a quite different configuration with semiclosed oceanic basins. The Triassic evolution of the Tethys is still a matter of debate (Bernoulli and Lemoine, 1980). Initial rifting is assumed to have taken place during the Middle Triassic and an even stronger rifting during the late Triassic, especially in the Eastern Mediterranean (Argyriadis et al., 1980), resulting in the formation of horsts and platforms triggering the growth of reefs.

Most paleontological and microfacies data concerning Pangean reef carbonates are known from the northwestern part of Tethys, which shows a differentiation into a northern and a southern zone (Tollman and Kristan-Tollmann, 1985; Ciarapica et al., 1987), at times possibly separated by swells that might also have been sites for reefs. Different terms have been proposed referring to parts or to the entirety of the western Tethys (*Tethys, Mesogean Sea, Paleotethys, Neotethys*), and various definitions of these terms are in use (Hsü and Bernoulli, 1978; Jenkyns, 1980; H. W. Flügel, 1981; Nakazawa, 1985; Tollmann and Kristan-Tollmann, 1985). For instance, *Paleotethys* refers to an Early Paleozoic ocean situated in Central and Southern Europe (Stille, 1951), to a seaway enabling the distribution of Late Paleozoic fusulinids along the southern margins of Eurasia (Kahler, 1939), to the northern part of the Triassic Tethys (Hsü and Bernoulli, 1978), or to the northern trough of the Tethys (Stöcklin, 1974; Sengör et al., 1988), separated from a southern trough (Neotethys) by swells. Tollmann and Kristan-Tollmann (1985, p. 6) emphasized the identity of all of these and other terms and claimed that all these terms are synonyma of the term *Tethys,* comprising "the Permian and Triassic and later development of a northern and southern trough with accompanying shelves and also a median platform".

Other important Permian and especially Triassic reef sites are located on microcontinental fragments, represented by exotic terranes in western North America (Stanley, 1982, 1988; Reid, 1985), Southeast Asia (e.g., Primorie Mountains; Boiko et al., 1991), and Japan (Sano et al., 1990). The motion of terranes should produce a number of marginal seas favoring reef growth. Determination of the paleopositions of terranes on global and regional scales (Wilson et al., 1991) is crucial to the discussion of reef evolution in terms of controls by oceanic currents and water temperature. Reefs should assist also in the discussion of different scenarios describing departure, path, and arrival of terranes (e.g., western North American terranes derived from the southern Tethys region and traveling across the Pacific or transported along the western margins of the Americas at greater or lesser distances offshore).

What is special about Pangean reefs?

Several points separate late Carboniferous to Liassic reef from other Phanerozoic reefs.

The reef types. Ancient reef types may be defined according to the geometry and the amount of organic framework, according to the processes involved in the development of the reef structures, and according to the principal biota contributing to the formation of the buildups.

Following the classification of James and Macintyre (1985), Pangean reefs correspond to reef mounds and mud mounds as well as reefs. Most of the Carboniferous and many Permian and Middle to early Late Triassic reefs are reef mounds. Both types—reef mounds and reefs—occurred during the Late Triassic and Jurassic.

Regarding processes, Permian and Triassic reefs comprise a broad spectrum of carbonate buildups that are by no means restricted to framework reefs but include also "biodetrital reefs" and "hydromechanical reefs" as distinguished by Gerhard (1991). Figure 1 gives the classification of some Permian and Triassic reefs that have been studied by the Erlangen Reef Research Group during the last fifteen years. Organic framework may be poorly developed or even lacking, as exempli-

fied by the Rhaetian Steinplatte "reef" of Austria (Stanton and Flügel, 1989) or by the Norian Lime Peak reef in the Yukon Territories (Reid, 1985; Reid and Ginsburg, 1986). "Biodetrital reefs" characterized by more than 50% bioclastic sediment and with only a thin veneer of framework are common Triassic reef types (cf. Flügel, 1981). Another specific Permian and Triassic reef type is characterized by a framework formed by low-growing organisms, predominantly algal and microbial crusts, and high amount of synsedimentary carbonate cement (algal/cement reefs, Flügel, 1989; serpulid/cement reefs, Braga and Lopez-Lopez, 1989). The late Permian stromatolite reefs (Paul, 1980, 1991; Smith, 1981) correspond to a specific and time-dependent reef type.

Using differences at group level in taxonomic composi-

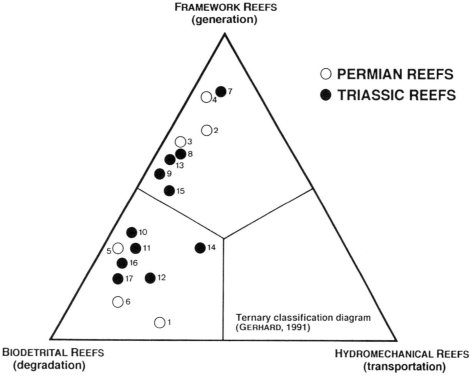

Figure 1. Ternary classification diagram (Gerhard, 1991) of major Permian and Triassic reef types, based on investigations by the "Erlangen Reef Research Group." 1—Ringmauer, Carnic Alps (Austria/Italy), dasycladacean reef mound, early Permian (Asselian). 2—Trogkofel, Carnic Alps (Austria/Italy), algal/cement reef mound, early Permian (Sakmarian). 3—Straza near Bled (Slovenia), algal/cement reef mound, early Upper Permian (Murghabian). 4—Pietra di Salomone, Sosio valley (Western Sicily), calcisponge reef, early Upper Permian (Murghabian/Midinian). 5—Skyros Island, Agean (Greece), calcisponge reef mound, late Permian (Dzhulfian). 6—Tudya, Sichuan (southern China), calcisponge reef mound, late Permian (Chiangsiangian). 7—Seiser Alm, Dolomites (Italy), upper-slope reef mounds, Middle Triassic (Ladinian). 8—Cahorros de Monachil, Granada (southern Spain), algal/cement reef, Middle Triassic (Ladinian). 9—Hydra Island (Greece), calcisponge/coral reef mound, late Triassic (Carnian). 10—Gosaukamm (Austria), calcisponge/coral reef, late Triassic (Norian). 11—Kalbling, Gesäuse Mountains (Austria), calcisponge/coral reef, late Triassic (Norian). 12—Hohe Wand near Neustadt (Austria), calcisponge/coral reef, late Triassic (Norian). 13—Panormide Mountains (Sicily), calcisponge/coral reefs, late Triassic (Norian/Rhaetian). 14—Gaissau near Hallein (Austria), coral reef mound, late Triassic (Rhaetian). 15—Adnet near Hallein (Austria), coral reef mound, late Triassic (Rhaetian). 16—Rötelwand near Hallein (Austria), calcisponge/coral reef mound, late Triassic (Rhaetian). 17—Steinplatte near Waidring (Austria/Germany), coral "reef" mound, late Triassic (Rhaetian).

tion, predominance of reef-builders, and the roles of organisms in reef-building, Carboniferous to Liassic reefs can be attributed to about 12 types (Fig. 2; Fig. 5), most of which are restricted to particular time intervals but which also include the first modern reef type ("coral reefs," late Triassic and Liassic).

A conspicuous microbial/algal contribution in the formation of organic frameworks. Micritic biogenic crusts of various composition are important constituents of Permian, Triassic, and some Liassic reefs (Table 1). Often interpreted as algal products, many of these crusts probably are of microbial origin. Examples with strong microbial contribution are known from late Permian reefs (Guo and Riding, 1992) and from Anisian and Ladinian reefs as well as Liassic reefs (Brandner et al., 1991; Senowbari-Daryan et al., 1993). Middle Triassic and Middle Liassic examples show that these crusts underwent rapid submarine lithification. Both the Triassic and Liassic crusts seem to reflect condensed sedimen-

tation in open-marine depositional up-slope, slope, or deeper-shelf environments. Some of these microbial biostromes may be used as flooding markers in sequence stratigraphy (Dromart, 1992).

Only minor bioerosional control? The style of bioerosion seen in modern reefs is believed to have occurred at least as early as the Tertiary (Vogel, 1993). Bioclastic carbonate sands that might have been produced by the bioerosional degradation of reef organisms seem to be more common in late Triassic reefs carbonates than in Middle Triassic or Permian reefs. This change would indicate quite a different control of reef destruction as compared with Holocene reefs.

The invention of coral/algal symbiosis? Modern shallow-water reefs are characterized by symbiotic algae within corals and other organisms triggering a strong light-enhanced calcification, one of the major factors in the development of organic reef frameworks. Algal symbiosis might have started

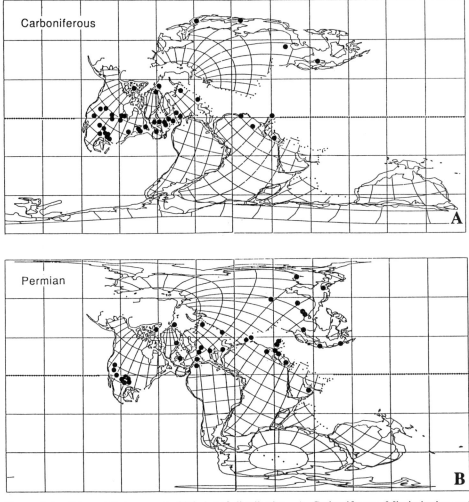

Figure 2 (on this and facing page). Global reef distribution. A, Carboniferous. Mississippian and Pennsylvanian reefs are not specifically distinguished. Base map (Smith et al., 1981): Early Pennsylvanian. B, Permian. Base map: Late Permian, Tatarian. C, Triassic. Base map: Late Triassic, Rhaetian. D, Jurassic. Base map: Late Jurassic (Tithonian). From Flügel and Flügel-Kahler, 1992.

in scleractinian corals in the late Triassic (Stanley, 1981), being a major prerequisite in the development of modern-type reefs. The proof of zooxanthellate and azooxanthellate corals in the fossil record is still difficult and controversial (Coates and Jackson, 1987; Cowen, 1988; Stanley and Cairns, 1988; Talent, 1988), but the recognition of algal symbiosis is fundamental for the understanding of the development of Pangean and other Phanerozoic reefs. Only indirect indications are available just now, such as morphological criteria or shifts in the stable isotope ratios in carbon and oxygen (Swart, 1983).

Dramatic reef crises. There were at least two spectacular crises in the evolution of reef ecosystems: one the global "reef gap" in the Early Triassic and the other the nearly total absence or the complete lack of lowermost Liassic reefs. The reorganization of Triassic reef biotopes started about 10 m.y. after the disappearance of the last Late Permian reefs; the reorganization of the Early Liassic reefs began about 7 m.y. years after the probably synchronous disappearance of latest Triassic reefs in the western Tethys and at the eastern end of the Tethys.

Objectives of this section

This section summarizes the present state of knowledge concerning late Paleozoic to Liassic reefs. A discussion of the quality of the data base is followed by an overview of the shelf and reef biota and of the development of reefs in time. The last sections deal with the paleoclimatic inferences of Pangean reefs and with the pertinent questions that should be targets for activities in the Pangea Project.

QUALITY AND CONSTRAINTS OF THE DATA BASE

Biased information

The information available is biased with regard to the age of the reefs studied, the geographical position of the reefs, and the intensity of paleontological studies.

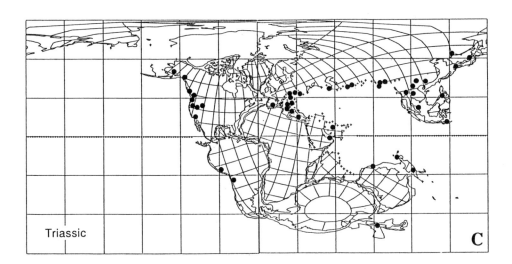

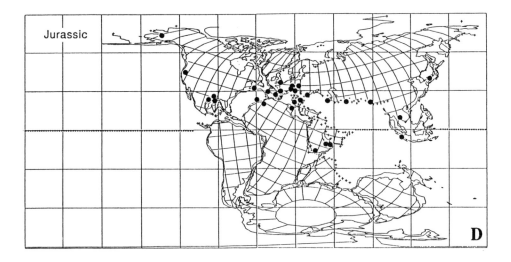

TABLE 1. BIOGENIC CRUST CONSTITUENTS OF THE BINDER GUILD IN PERMIAN AND TRIASSIC REEFS*

Norian and Rhaetian
Spongiostromate "algae," sphinctozoan sponges *(Uvanella, Annae-coelia)*, sclerosponges ("Tabulozoans"), various microproblematica *(Radiomura, Bacinella, Lithocodium)*, and foraminifera.

Norian and Rhaetian

Carnian
Chambered and bubblelike crusts (algae and/or sponges), sphincto-zoan sponges, porostromate "algae," *"Tubiphytes,"* microproblematica.

Ladinian
Various laminar crusts including micrite crusts, micrite/sparite crusts, cement-rich festooned crusts, microproblematica.

Anisian
Sphinctozoan sponges *(Celyphia)*, porostromate "algae," bryozoans.

Late Permian
Archaeolithoporella, Tubiphyes, Stromatolitic algae.

Early Permian
Algae, foraminifera, sphinctozoan sponges, bryozoans, microproblem-atica.

*Crusts from different time intervals differ significantly according to their composition and the relative importance of the taxa involved and in the position of the encrusting associations within platform-reef-slope transects.

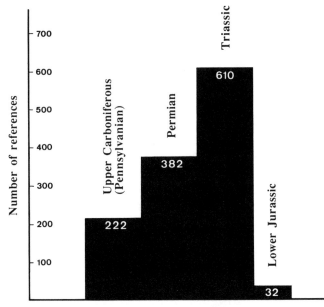

Figure 3. Number of references dealing with Pennsylvanian to Liassic reefs. The information is biased with regard to Triassic reefs. The lower number of references about Liassic reefs reflects the global scarcity of Early Jurassic reefs. Data base: Flügel and Flügel-Kahler, 1992.

Despite the tremendous number of papers describing reefs and reef biota from the Pennsylvanian to Liassic, the information is strongly biased with regard to Permian and Triassic reefs (Fig. 3), which have been studied more thoroughly during the last 20 years than Pennsylvanian and Liassic reefs. More than 75% of the Triassic references are concerned with Late Triassic reefs. Much more information is needed about Middle Triassic reefs, especially about Anisian reefs (which have been described in only about 20 papers [cf. Senowbari-Daryan et al., 1993]). The scarcity of papers dealing with Liassic reefs is due to the fact that exposures of Early Jurassic reefs are limited geographically.

Unevenness of the paleontological study of reef organisms is another reason for the present insufficient data base. Problems include difficulties in the classification and systematics as well as the scarcity of modern descriptions of reef organisms as corals, chaetetid sponges, or porostromate algae, for example.

A punctuated fossil record may be a further cause of inconsistencies of the models describing reef evolution during the Late Paleozoic, when strong eustatic sea-level changes produced unconformities of worldwide extent and considerable duration (Ross and Ross, 1985b; 1987a).

Difficulties with paleogeographical maps

Differences in the position and configuration of landmasses as well as the time slice selected for the paleogeographic maps (Ziegler et al., 1981; Hallam, 1984, 1985; Ross and Ross, 1985a, 1987a, 1988, 1990; Scotese and McKerrow, 1990; Lottes and Rowley, 1990; Nie Shangyou et al., 1990; Scotese and Golonka, 1992) will strongly influence the discussion of paleoclimatic and paleooceanographic controls of reefs and shelf carbonates.

A discussion of Pangean reefs as paleoclimatic indicators needs well-founded data about paleolatitudes of the shelves and specific location of the reefs on the shelves or at shelf margins. The few maps available, however, display only very generalized patterns (shelves: Ziegler et al., 1984; Ross and Ross, 1988; reefs: Stanley, 1988; Flügel and Flügel-Kahler, 1992) or they show only parts of the Pangean shelf (e.g., Brandner, 1984; Witzke, 1990). Most of maps are compiled at the system and/or stage level. A strong need exists for more detailed maps regarding the apparent course of the coast lines (Thiede, 1983) and the positions of exotic terranes (e.g., Wilson et al., 1991).

Models

The evolution of Permian to Jurassic reefs is explained by a "three-step process" (Stanley, 1988). This model argues that mass extinctions had a strong control on reef evolution. Following the Permian/Triassic extinction, the first step took place after the Scythian nonreef interval during the Anisian and Ladinian, when survivors of Permian reefs established Permian-type reef communities that flourished until the lower Late Triassic. The second step includes a reorganization of the reef ecosystem during the Carnian, connected with a small-scale extinction and followed by a turnover of reef biota. The long-lived Norian reef ecosystem culminated in the latest Triassic in framework reefs formed by corals living probably in symbiosis with zooxanthellate algae. The third step, following the end-Triassic extinction and a gap in coral reefs during the lowermost Liassic, began in the Pliensbachian and continued with coral-algal–dominated framework reefs into the Middle Jurassic.

This model assumes the existence of Permian holdovers in the Middle Triassic and Carnian, a faunal changeover of reef organisms between Carnian and Norian time, the existence of hermatypic corals and of ecologic reefs in the Rhaetian, and the differentiation of corals between constructional zooxanthellate and nonconstructional azooxanthellate and nonconstructional azooxanthellate types starting with the Middle Liassic. Some of these assumptions are not tenable any more (there are no Permian holdovers) and must be reviewed in the light of new data (ecological reefs, algal/coral symbiosis) or must be modified concerning the time of changes in biota and reef types (Carnian and Norian turnovers).

SHELF AND REEF BIOTA

Major groups of organisms

Calcareous algae, foraminifera, and mollusks were the main contributors to biogenic carbonate production of Late Paleozoic, Triassic, and Liassic shelf carbonates. Additional important carbonate-producing organisms during the Permian were corals, bryozoans, brachiopods, and echinoderms. During the Permian and Triassic, organisms of uncertain systematic position (microproblematica) contributed significantly to shelf as well as reef carbonates (Flügel, 1981; Kano, 1992). Principal late Paleozoic reef organisms were calcareous algae, bryozoans, echinoderms, and calcisponges. Triassic reefs are characterized by sponges, scleractinian corals, and algae (Fig. 4).

Taxonomic composition and frequency of calcareous algae in shelf carbonates changed during the Permian and Triassic. Major taxonomic changes on group level took place near the Lower/Middle Permian time interval, in the late Permian, and during the Carnian. Several changes on genus and species level are evident in the early Permian (Flügel, 1990), during the Middle Triassic, and within the Norian/Rhaetian time interval.

Calcisponges (Senowbari-Daryan, 1990, 1991; Riedel and Senowbari-Daryan, 1991) are relatively well studied, but major problems exist concerning the systematics and the phylogeny of this polyphyletic group (Reitner, 1992). Strong evidence exists for a change in the biotopes of sphinctozoan calcisponges during the late Lower Permian from predominantly shelf environments to reef environments in low-energy, down-slope settings. Both sphinctozoan and inozoan calcareous sponges acted as primary or secondary framework-builders and reef dwellers but also as sediment-stabilizing encrusters.

Corals did not become important reef-builders until the Late Triassic (Riedel, 1991), perhaps triggered by the evolution of algal symbiosis controlling the energy budget, skeletal growth, and distribution of modern corals. The origin of scleractinian corals and their relationships with Paleozoic rugose corals as well as the zooxanthellate nature of Triassic corals is still a matter of debate (e.g., Marcoux et al., 1982; Beauvais, 1980, 1982; Roniewicz, 1989).

Microproblematica in Permian and Triassic reefs are another problem, as exemplified by *"Tubiphytes."* This name was applied to conspicuous enigmatic organisms occurring in Carboniferous to Cretaceous shelf and reef carbonates. Recent SEM and thin-section investigations of Permian samples (Senowbari-Daryan and Flügel, 1994) show that the name refers to organisms of distinctly different morphology and structure and probably also of different systematic position. These organisms occur within different guilds and were adapted to different environments with regard to water depth.

Skeletal mineralogy

Railsback and Anderson (1987) reported a change in the dominating skeletal mineralogy of benthic organisms at the Permian-Triassic boundary. Permian calcite-secreting organisms (e.g., many brachiopods; rugose and tabulate corals) were replaced by aragonite-secreting groups (e.g., mollusks, scleractinian corals). The authors explained these changes by a unique combination of geochemical conditions (sulfate concentrations, elevated temperatures, and possibly elevated Mg/Ca ratios) that could have triggered the course of the biological evolution.

The patterns of skeletal mineralogical changes, however, seem to be very complicated, as shown by thalamid calcareous sponges (Senowbari-Daryan, 1991) that exhibit aragonitic basal skeletons in the Permian and Triassic but also high-magnesium calcite skeletons restricted to the time interval Middle and Late Triassic. Reitner (1992) recognized a temporal and causal correlation between changes of Phanerozoic aragonite-dominated and calcite-dominated shallow-water carbonates (Sandberg, 1983) and evolutionary phases of coralline sponges. He postulated that changes of the Mg/Ca ratio of seawater could have influenced the development of aragonitic basal skeletons of coralline sponges during the Late Paleozoic and Triassic icehouse time.

Reef construction

The organic framework of modern reefs is formed predominantly by corals and coralline algae acting as constructors and binders. By contrast, the constructor guild is relatively insignificant in Late Paleozoic reefs (Fagerstrom, 1991) in comparison to baffler and binder guilds. The constructors probably

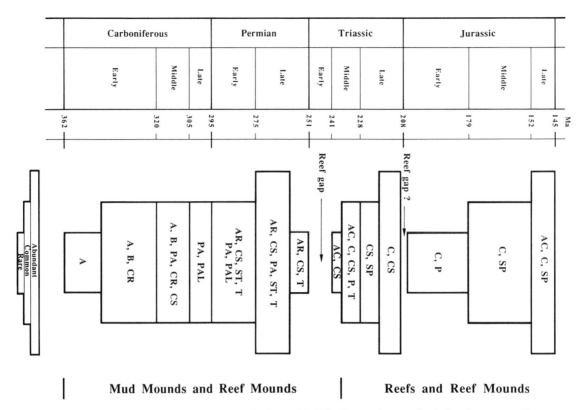

Figure 4. Temporal distribution of principal "reef-building" organisms and relative frequency of Carboniferous to Jurassic reefs. A—algae; AC—algal and microbial crusts; AR—*Archaeo-lithoporella*; B—bryozoa; C—corals; CR—crinoids; CS—"Calcisponges"; P—pelecypods; PA—phylloid algae; PAL—*Palaeoaplysina*; SP—"siliceous sponges"; ST—stromatolites; T—*Tubiphytes*. No reefs are known from the early Triassic and probably also from the lowermost Jurassic. Reefs are rare (or poorly studied) in the lower part of the Early Carboniferous, in the uppermost Late Permian, and in the Liassic.

became more important during the Late Triassic and the Liassic. But the existence of an organic framework formed by constructors should not be derived merely from the size, presumed growth rates, and/or assumed location of coral thickets at a "reef crest" (Stanley, 1988, p. 178) but should also consider the whole composition of the reef community and the existence of encrusters as well as the frequency of vertically stacked reef builders (Stanton and Flügel, 1987), as shown in the re-study of the classical Late Triassic Steinplatte "reef" of the Alps (Stanton and Flügel, 1989).

Cryptic reef habitats

Cavities in and between reef-builders as well spaces under and between reef boulders provide a larger surface area for colonization in many recent reefs than the surface area of the outer reef surface. The life of these cavity-dwelling cryptic organisms is controlled by lower light levels, reduced access to food resources, and specific kinds of water movement and internal sedimentation. Current information indicates an increasing competition between surface-dwelling and cavity-

dwelling reef organisms (Kobluk, 1988) from the Paleozoic to the Mesozoic, but much more data are needed in order to understand the role of these coelobites (especially those represented as "biogenic crusts") in the formation and early diagenesis of Late Paleozoic as well as Triassic reef mounds and reefs.

REEF EVOLUTION

Overview

Late Paleozoic to Liassic reef types shown in Figure 5 can be differentiated into three groups based on their time range and their occurrence during times of accretion or dispersal of Pangea:

1. Short-lived reefs (with a maximum range up to about 12 m.y.) include Early Permian dasycladacean reefs, Late Permian stromatolite reefs, bivalve reefs (Middle Triassic pelecypod reefs and Liassic *Lithiotis* reefs, all ranging approximately 5 m.y.), Late Permian bryozoan reefs and Carnian

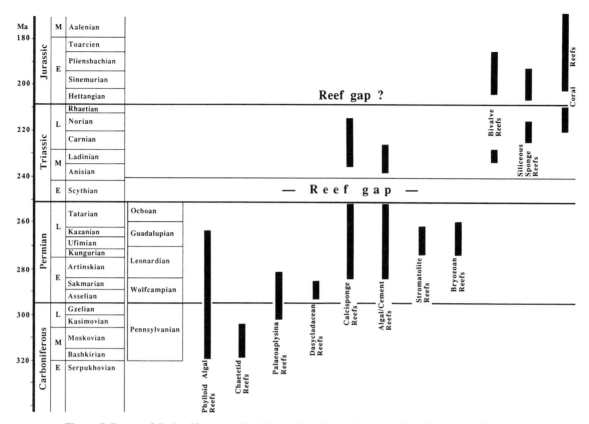

Figure 5. Range of Carboniferous to Early Jurassic major reef types, defined by the principal "reef-builders." The role of organisms in the formation of reefs varied highly over time, depending on their importance as frame-builders, bafflers, or binders. Reef types included in the figure are framework reefs (e.g., chaetetid reefs, calcisponge reefs, algal/cement reefs, some coral reefs) as well as reef mounds (e.g., phylloid algal reefs, *Palaeoaplysina* reefs, and siliceous sponge reefs).

Norian siliceous sponges reefs (existing for a time of about 8 m.y.), Middle Carboniferous chaetetid reefs, and Middle and Late Triassic algal/cement reefs as well as Late Triassic and Early Liassic coral reefs (ranging for about 10 m.y.).

2. Medium-lived reefs (with a time range between 20 and 30 m.y.) are represented by Triassic calcisponge reefs (existing about 20 m.y.), Late Carboniferous to Early Permian *Palaeoaplysina* reefs (25 m.y.), and Permian calcisponge reefs and algal/cement reefs (ranging approximately 30 m.y.).

3. Phylloid algae reefs are the most long-lived reefs (ranging for about 50 m.y.), but they are common and frequent for only about 20 m.y. during the Pennsylvanian and lower Early Permian.

Most of the medium- and long-lasting reef types are restricted to the accretion phase of Pangea. The dispersal phase starting during the Triassic is characterized by the dominance of rather short-lived reef types.

The types of Late Paleozoic reefs as well as the composition of reef biota exhibit distinct changes during the Sakmarian or Artinskian. Most of the Late Permian and "Middle Permian"

("Kazanian," "Guadalupian") reefs predominantly corresponds to calcisponge and algal/cement reefs (e.g., Wu, 1991).

Following the end-Permian extinction and a reef gap lasting probably more than 10 m.y., a revival took place during the Middle Anisian characterized by small reef mounds with sphinctozoans, bryozoans, blue-green algae, and rare corals formed in downslope environments (Fois and Gaetani, 1984; Senowbari-Daryan et al., 1993). One of the prerequisites for the reestablishment of reef biotopes during the Anisian and Ladinian might have been rifting (Argyriadis et al., 1980), resulting in the destruction of the extended Scythian platforms and causing horst structures. Anisian reefs are very rare (Southern Alps, Poland, Carpathians, Hungary, Southern China) as compared with more widely distributed but only partly studied Ladinian reefs. Anisian, Ladinian, and lower Upper Triassic reef biota show similarities with regard to biotic gross composition ("calcisponges," "algal crusts," *"Tubiphytes"*) but differ distinctly from Norian and Rhaetian reef communities. These differences are apparent at generic and specific levels of reef-building and reef-dwelling organisms as well as in the number of communities and in diversity patterns (Flügel,

1982; Stanton and Flügel, 1987; Senowbari-Daryan, 1990, 1991; Riedel, 1991). This biotic changeover took place between the middle Carnian (Julian substage) and the lower Norian (Lacian substage). Norian and Rhaetian reefs are known from the Alps across Asia to the Pacific (e.g., Wombat Plateau, Australia [Röhl et al., 1991; Sarti et al., 1992]) and farther to the Cordilleran region of North America from Alaska to Mexico. Tethyan reefs differ in terms of size, geometry, and paleogeographical setting from the North American buildups, but a Tethyan influence of Pacific and North American Norian and Rhaetian reefs is evident in molluscs, sponges, and corals (Senowbari-Daryan and Stanley, 1988; Boiko et al., 1991).

Liassic reefs have been studied to a much smaller extent than Late Triassic reefs. Most reefs described from the Early Jurassic are of Sinemurian and Pliensbachian age. The best information on Liassic reefs comes from the High and Central Atlas of Morocco (DuDresnay, 1977; Park, 1983; Beauvais, 1986), which exhibit the existence of different reef types (e.g., coral reefs, coral-algal reefs, sponge mounds, bivalve mud mounds), some of which are known also from the Triassic. Other Liassic reefs are located in southern Spain (Turnsek et al., 1975), Portugal (Dromart, 1992), the Southern Alps, and British Columbia (Poulton, 1988). Bivalve reefs (*Lithiotis* reefs) are most widely distributed all over the Tethyan region (Geyer, 1977) but have been described also from Oregon (Nauss and Smith, 1988). Many Liassic reefs, except some of the Moroccan reefs, seem to correspond to reef mounds rather than to large reef complexes.

Crucial questions

Mode of biotic changes: Turnovers, holdovers, extinction, and recovery. Distinct changes of the reef biota during time expressed by turnovers in the taxonomic composition and diversity of reef organisms and by significant reef gaps in earth history require answers concerning the possible controls. Some of these changes seem to be coeval with times of general extinction events, and it has therefore been argued that reefs and other faunas are responding to the same history of environmental stress (Sheehan, 1985; Raup and Boyajian, 1988). This interpretation was questioned by Fagerstrom (1987), who showed that the boundaries between the major temporal units of reef communities do not always coincide with mass extinction events of the world biota but rather reflect evolutionary events of the major reef-building higher taxa or even only a gradational and slow displacement of old reef communities by new ones. The end-Permian reef crisis is regarded as a first-order extinction characterized by high extinction rates of higher taxa of the predominant members of the reef guilds; the end-Triassic reef crisis, in contrast, is interpreted as a second-order extinction characterized by high extinction rates of lower taxa of important members of the reef guilds.

Figure 6 shows extinction/origination percentage rates of sphinctozoan sponges and scleractinian corals from different Triassic reef guilds. Both "calcisponges" and corals appear during the Middle Triassic, about 10 m.y. after the extinction of calcisponge reefs and algal/cement reefs near the end of the uppermost Permian. Corals and sphinctozoans underwent changeovers in taxonomic composition during the Late Triassic and were severely affected by the end-Triassic biotic crisis.

End-Permian crisis: No holdovers. Uppermost Permian reefs of Dzhulfian and Dorashamian age are only known from South China (Fan et al., 1990) and the Aegean region (Flügel and Reinhardt, 1989; Baud et al., 1991b). The high diversity of these reefs is not in accordance with the long-lasting decrease in the diversity of shelf organisms during the Late Permian (cf. Erwin, 1993).

The general assumption until now has been that some holdovers of Permian reef organisms were responsible for the rebuilding of reef guilds in the Middle Triassic (Flügel, 1982; Flügel and Stanley, 1984; Fagerstrom, 1987; Stanley, 1988). This interpretation is now rejected, for the following reasons:

1. There are no Permian Lazarus taxa in Triassic reef-building communities, as shown by thorough systematic investigations of sphinctozoan sponges (Senowbari-Daryan, 1990), algae, and microproblematica (Senowbari-Daryan and Flügel, 1994). Apparent Paleozoic holdovers are probably simulated by difficulties in taxonomic discrimination. This is exemplified by *Tubiphytes* Maslov, a most common constituent of Late Paleozoic reefs. SEM studies show distinct differences between Permian and Mesozoic "Tubiphytes," demanding a taxonomic separation. The same most probably is true also for some Permian sphinctozoan genera that have been reported to range up to the Late Triassic. These genera are known only from the Ladinian and the Norian but not from the Anisian and Carnian. These temporal distribution patterns as well as the striking morphological simplicity of most of the genera (*"Amblysiphonella," "Colospongia"*) point to homeomorphy rather than to an extremely wide stratigraphic range (Senowbari-Daryan et al., 1993). Also the calcisponges reported from Upper Scythian deposits of the Alps (Flügel and Stanley, 1984) should not be taken as proof of Permian holdovers because poor preservation prevents an undisputable taxonomic determination.

2. Recent studies of uppermost Permian reefs (Flügel and Reinhardt, 1989) and of Anisian buildups in the Southern Alps (Senowbari-Daryan et al., 1993) indicate that similarities in guild structures are restricted only to the more frequent occurrence of members of the binder guild. The composition of the binder guild, however, is distinctly different in Late Permian and in Triassic reefs (see Table 1).

The absence of true Paleozoic holdovers in Triassic reefs is in agreement with the interpretation of scleractinian corals as descendants not of Permian rugose corals but of soft-bodied actinarians pioneering skeletonizing at the beginning of the Triassic (Oliver, 1980). On the other hand, Permian-type organisms are known from shelf environments of the Early

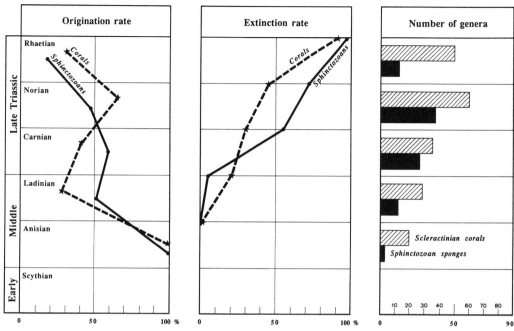

Figure 6. Origination and extinction rates of Triassic sphinctozoan "calcisponges" and scleractinian corals. Data: Senowbari-Daryan (1990, and personal communication 1992, sphinctozoans); Riedel (1991, corals).

riassic (e.g, mollusks (Erwin, 1993) and bryozoans; Schäfer nd Fois, 1986) and from the Permian/Triassic interval in vari- us parts of the Tethys ("mixed fauna"; Pakistani-Japanese esearch Group, 1985; Yin, 1985; Erwin, 1993).

The refuges upon which Permian reef organisms or the ncestors of the Triassic corals and calcisponges survived the nd-Permian crisis are unknown. Tropical volcanic islands of ie ancient Pacific region now represented by exotic terranes ccreted along the Pacific continental margins might have cted as refuges (Stanley, 1988, 1992), but the youngest ermian coral faunas were not found in exotic terranes but in elf carbonates from the South China microcontinent (Fedo- wski, 1989).

The reef gap in the Early Triassic: A major target for rther research. The few localities known where Early Trias- c reef carbonates might exist are as follows:

1. Subsurface of the eastern part of the northern Cauca- an Range, Russia (Nazarevich et al., 1986; Soronina, 1988): ower Scythian (Induan) biohermal algal limestones with ibiphytes. Samples, provided by Dr. Vitaly Kuznetsov, oscow, indicate lagoonal carbonates rather than reef facies.

2. Gorni Karabach, Azerbaidzhan (Alizade and Babaev, 991): Early Triassic biostromes with corals and algal bio- rms. The coral buildups yielding plerophyllid rugose corals e probably Permian in age, but the algal buildups may be in- ed of Early Triassic age.

3. Aghdarband, northeastern Iran (Baud et al., 1991a): Upper Scythian carbonate mounds with algae and encrusting foraminifera.

4. Southern Guizhou, southern China (Enos et al., 1989; Wei and Enos, 1991): Scythian (?) thrombolitic mounds, over- lain by Anisian *Tubiphytes* reef limestones. Samples provided by D. Lehrmann and P. Enos, University of Kansas, exhibit algal structures pointing to the existence of reef mounds. The age of the limestones, however, is not yet fully understood.

Using the paleomap of the Induan stage published by Ziegler et al. (1981) all these regions would occur near a paleo- latitude of 30°N within an area where the production of shal- low-marine carbonate is reliable, accepting the results of modeling Early Triassic circulation patterns (Hay et al., 1982; Ziegler et al., 1984).

The late Triassic crisis: The Carnian event. Distinct changes in the taxonomic composition, diversity, and commu- nities of Carnian to Norian reef biota are reflected by sphinc- tozoans and corals (Fig. 6) and also by other reef organisms (foraminifera, biogenic crusts, microproblematica, algae). This faunal turnover probably started during the Julian and contin- ued during the late Carnian (Tuvalian) and early Norian (Lacian; see Riedel, 1990). Carnian and Norian scleractinian corals are different with regard to both predominant taxa and septal microstructures (Roniewicz and Morykowa, 1989) and the prevailing growth forms of colonies (Riedel, 1991). These changes during the Carnian affected nonmarine and terrestrial organisms, too (Benton, 1986, 1991; Simms and Ruffel, 1989, 1990). The changes of reef biota are generally explained in terms of a Carnian mass extinction followed immediately by a major reorganization between Carnian and Norian time. Changes in paleoclimate as well as in the size of the shelf areas connected with a Carnian-Norian transgression to regression pattern are postulated to be the major controls (Hallam, 1981, 1985; Stanley, 1988).

The end-Triassic crisis: Sea-level control? Compared with Norian reef biota, the "Upper Rhaetian reefs" of the Northern Alps exhibit a continued biotic change caused by still-increasing extinction rates combined with low origination rates of sphinctozoan sponges and of corals (Fig. 6). At the western end of the Tethys, the end-Triassic reef crisis is documented by the abrupt and probably synchronous disappearance of reefs in the Alps and western Carpathian Mountains (Hallam and Goodfellow, 1990; Riedel, 1991). Depending on the primary topographical relief and controlled by the location on carbonate ramps, shelves, or near the shelf-margins, some of these reefs were subaerially exposed during the Rhaetian prior to an Early Liassic deepening that finally caused the drowning of Triassic reefs (Hallam, 1990; Böhm, 1992). The proposed demise of reefs due to cooling of the surface water temperatures (Fabricius et al., 1970) does not seem reliable because of the insignificance of the oxygen isotope data (Hallam and Goodfellow, 1990). Salinity reduction may have been another, regionally important factor in end-Triassic biotic changes (Hallam, 1981; Hallam and El-Shaarawy, 1982).

CONTROLS

The evolution of reefs is controlled by biological as well as by nonbiological processes. Temporal changes in the types, biotic composition, and latitudinal distribution of reefs can be caused by biologically mediated controls—for example, evolutionary factors (origination and extinction rates, different evolution rates of reef guilds), the invention of algal/coral symbiosis (Talent, 1988), or different access to nutrients (Hallock and Schlager, 1986). In addition, the position of tectonic plates migrating into or out of tropical seas has a major impact. Initial rifting is an important control in the setting of reefs, as shown by the development of Triassic reefs. Growth and demise of reefs should be strongly controlled by sea-level fluctuations as well as by oceanographic and atmospheric circulations patterns, which in turn control climate evolution.

Biological processes

Organic evolution represents a control factor of shelf carbonates' producing unique patterns (Schlager and Philip, 1990). This should be kept in mind when using modern reefs as models for ancient reefs. Carboniferous to Early Jurassic reefs were different from recent reefs. Biologically mediated differences concern:

• the organisms involved in reef-building and reef destruction (increase of destructing organisms during the late Triassic?)
• the role of symbiotic organisms in the growth and calcification of reef-building organisms (algal/coral symbiosis starting during the late Triassic?)
• the ability of sessile organisms to act as constructors, bafflers, or binders (increase of the constructor guild during the Late Permian and late Triassic?)
• the role of microbes and crust-building associations in the formation of a framework (decrease of the reef-building role from Carnian to Liassic?)

Some of these points have been used to explain major differences between Early and Late Permian reefs (differences in guild structure) and between Anisian to Carnian and Norian/Rhaetian reefs (differences in guild structures and the role of microbes, invention of algal/coral symbiosis). Differences in the input of nutrients are regarded as a major control in the biotic turnover near the Carnian/Norian boundary (Riedel, 1990).

Sea-level fluctuations

Growth of recent coral reefs is dependent on light, water depth, and water temperature. Rise and fall of sea level will influence and stop reef growth. Reefs are therefore regarded as excellent indicators of relative sea-level fluctuations, despite the paradox of Holocene reef growth rates being apparently several orders of magnitude higher than the rates of sea-level rises (Schlager, 1981; Kühlmann, 1989). Reefs should tolerate rapid sea-level rises, but they do not because organic growth may be slowed down by such various factors as temperature and salinity changes, decrease of growth rates with water depths, oxygen deficiency, and flooding of platforms connected with the flow of hypersaline or nutrient-poor waters from lagoons to the reefs and an influx of terrigenous material.

Lowering of sea level affects reef environments not only by subaerial exposure of reefs and shedding of reef material into slope and basin environments (Reijmer and Everaars, 1991) but also by a reduction of the size of shelf areas connected with significant habitat reductions (Hallam, 1991). Major regressions might lead to an increased input of terrestrial carbon to the shelves, as indicated by isotope studies of the Permian/Triassic boundary interval (Holser et al., 1986; Holser and Margaritz, 1987, 1992; Baud et al., 1989; Holser et al., 1991; Wignall and Hallam, 1992). This increase could in turn have been responsible for retarding the reorganization of reef biotopes during the early Triassic.

During glacially influenced times (Veevers and Powell, 1987), the development of Pangean reefs should have been significantly influenced by short-term high-frequency pulses of sea-level rises equivalent to about the lower limit of maximum reef growth (in modern reefs 30 to 70 m, depending on geographical setting and light extinction coefficient).

The degree of the eustatic control of buildup formation depends on the paleobathymetrical and topographical position of the reefs and will be different in periods of highstand or lowstand of sea level, as revealed by the Middle Triassic Latemar platform of the Dolomites, where marginal boundstones do not record the exposure horizons common in the platform deposits exhibiting cyclic sea-level fluctuations (Goldhammer and Harris, 1989; Goldhammer et al., 1990). The eustatic control will be different also during icehouse and greenhouse times (Wright, 1992).

Recognition of cyclicity within subtidal reef carbonates that have not been subaerially exposed may be difficult but should be possible considering quantitative guild data (Grötsch, 1991). To do so, a better understanding of reef guilds is necessary (Flügel and Krainer, 1992).

Rising sea level might be reflected by vertical changes in the composition of reef biota (catch-up, keep-up, and give-up stages; Kendall and Schlager, 1981) as shown by end-Triassic reef development near the western end of the Tethys (Stanton and Flügel, 1989) but also near the eastern end of the Tethys (Röhl et al., 1991). Microbial reefs may be used as markers of flooding events (Drormart, 1992).

A control of reef development by transgressive/regressive cycles is evident for buildups formed on stable cratonic shelves and influenced by waxing and waning of ice shields (e.g., Late Paleozoic; Heckel, 1986; Ross and Ross, 1988; Krainer, 1992) but is difficult to apply to reefs formed on shelves near continental margins where differential subsidence was a major factor (e.g., Triassic of the western Tethys; Biddle, 1984; Brandner, 1984). The timing of major changes in the evolution of Triassic reefs at the western end of the Tethys is difficult to correlate with global and regional sea-level curves (Haq et al., 1987, 1988; Embry, 1988; Mork et al., 1989), except for the end-Rhaetian time, where a causal correlation between the worldwide sea-level fall and the disappearance of Late Triassic reefs has been proved for the western and in the eastern part (Wombat Plateau) of the Tethys (Röhl et al., 1991).

Paleolatitudes and paleoclimate

Recent shallow-marine carbonates and reefs occur between latitudes of about 30°N and 30°S, but the boundary may be displaced poleward 5 to10 degrees by western boundary currents.

The distribution of ancient reefs is commonly used to infer paleolatitudes and, in addition, to speculate about carbonate deposition in warm-water regions (e.g., Frakes et al., 1992). This approach should be viewed with caution in the study of Pangean carbonates.

During the Late Carboniferous and Early Permian the sites of carbonate sedimentation on marine shelves changed and cold-water and temperate carbonates characterized by foramol and bryomol grain associations became important sediments in addition to the widely distributed warm-water carbonates characterized by bahamian-type carbonate grains (Ross and Ross, 1990; Rao, 1981; Rao and Green, 1982; Nelson, 1988).

The composition of carbonate grain associations is a valuable tool to distinguish warm- and cold-water depositional sites, but it should be considered that foramol and bryomol carbonate grain associations of Late Paleozoic shelf carbonates are less studied than presumed warm-water carbonates and reefs. Controversial opinions exist concerning the role of water temperature in the distribution of fusulinids and smaller foraminifera that are important constituents of Carboniferous and Permian shelf carbonates (Stehli, 1971; Ross and Ross, 1985a). Fusulinids show a wide paleolatitudinal distribution. In the transgressive phases of Pennsylvanian and Early Permian T/R depositional cycles, they are related to rises in sea level and warm water (Ross and Ross, 1987a, 1987b, 1988), but they occur also in epicontinental shelf-edge environments, on shelves around oceanic seamounts as well as on exotic terranes passing through low and high latitudes (Ross, 1979; Ishii et al., 1985).

The increase in geographic distribution of reef communities and in diversity from Early to Late Permian might suggest a rise of water temperature during that time (Ross and Ross, 1988; Dickins, 1984, 1985). But this assumption implies that water temperature was of equal importance to sponge reefs and corals reefs and to reefs growing in different positions and water depths. The study of Triassic reefs, however, indicates that water temperature might have been just one factor controlling the latitudinal distribution of the reefs (Riedel, 1990).

Ziegler et al. (1984) have stressed the fact that light penetration, rather than water temperature, appears to be the latitudinally limiting factor of marine shallow-water carbonates in general and reefs in particular. Limiting factors are light reflection, cool water temperatures, clastic input, and upwelling. Reefs should preferentially develop within low-latitude areas with year-round high solar angles away from zones of upwelling and clastic influx. Cloudy regions, such as those along the intratropical convergence zone, should reduce solar radiation, resulting in a relative decrease of carbonate deposits and reefs along the equator. The significant role of light as the dominant control on reef growth is emphasized by the computer model of Bosscher and Schlager (1992).

Distributional patterns of ancient reefs are of interest in the discussion of paleoclimate simulation models, as shown by Moore et al. (1992) in reconstructing the paleoclimate of the Late Jurassic. The distribution of Permian and Triassic reefs has not been used yet in a similar way to test those time slices that have been objects of modeling studies up to now (Robinson, 1973; Parrish and Curtis, 1982; Hay et al., 1982; Scotese and Summerhayes, 1986; Kutzbach and Gallimore, 1989; Parrish et al., 1982; Parrish and Peterson, 1988; Dubiel et al., 1991). The reef distribution, however, should be of specific interest in order to test simulated storm tracks (Marsaglia and Klein, 1983) as well as simulated precipitation patterns.

A shift in paleolatitudes of reefs during time might indicate climatic shifting. Figure 7 shows the change of the paleolatitudinal position of Carboniferous to Jurassic reefs based on the distribution of reefs on the paleomap by Smith et al. (1981). Besides the striking asymmetrical concentration of reefs in the Northern Hemisphere, the figure points to a distinct shift of the paleolatitudinal reef distribution to the north from Carboniferous to Triassic.

Simulation models of oceanic paleocirculation can assist in the discussion of conceptual models proposed in order to explain faunal relationships. Several authors (e.g., Ross and Ross, 1990; Kristan-Tollmann and Tollmann, 1981, 1982, 1983; Tollmann and Kristan-Tollmann, 1982-1983, 1985; Stanley, 1988) have published maps showing inferred Permian and Triassic paleocurrent patterns (Fig. 8). These maps are based on the application of actualistic principles of ocean surface current and trade wind patterns to the changing configura-

tion of Pangean landmasses as well as on paleontological dat indicating differences in the degree of provinciality and diver sity or striking similarities and dissimilarities in distribution patterns of marine organisms (e.g., Yancey, 1979; Lys, 198 Ross and Ross, 1985a, 1988, 1990; Kristan-Tollmann an Tollmann, 1982; Kristan-Tollmann, 1988, 1990). Kristan Tollmann and Tollmann (1982) regarded the strong overa similarity of Triassic shelf biota of the Tethys, Panthalassi and western North America as a strong argument for a wes ward larval transport and biota migration, perhaps facilitate by displaced terranes used as stepping stones. Both larv transport and suspect terranes are connected with problems the first with the question of long-lasting larval transpo (Valentine, 1986), the latter with the paleolatitudinal positio and departure-arrival history of the terranes.

Apparent differences in the taxonomic composition and d versity of Triassic reef biota from the southern and northern bo

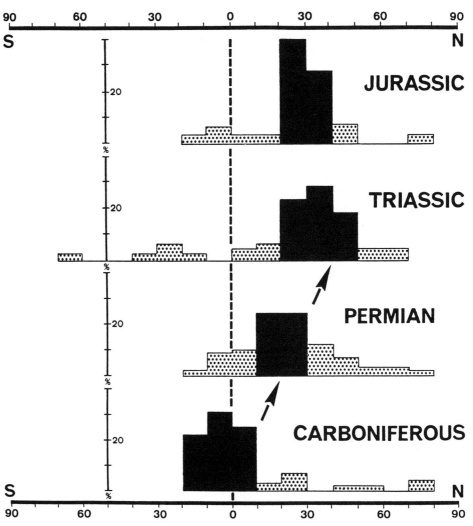

Figure 7. Paleolatitudinal distribution of Carboniferous to Jurassic reefs. Note the concentration of the reefs in the Northern Hemisphere and the shift of the frequency maxima from the Carboniferous to the Triassic. Data base: Flügel and Flügel-Kahler, 1992.

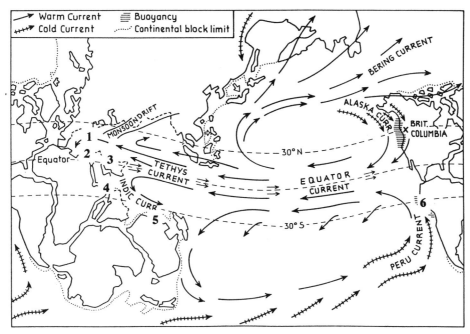

Figure 8. Triassic paleogeography and generalized paleocurrent patterns of the Tethys and the Panthalassia ocean (after Tollmann and Kristan-Tollmann, 1985). Approximate location of some Late Triassic reefs: 1—Northern Alps; 2—Sicily; 3—southern Turkey; 4—Oman; 5—Wombat Plateau off northwest Australia; 6—Wrangellia, western North America (approximate departure position, after Wilson et al., 1991).

er of the Tethys (e.g., Oman, Sicily, and southern Anatolia ersus the Northern Alps) might point to a strong control of oceanic surface-water circulation patterns similar to that in recent reefs. The ocean model published by Kutzbach et al. (1990) postulates a relatively strong western boundary current along the ast coast of Pangea, carrying warm water in high latitudes. This would be in agreement with the occurrence of Permian and Triassic reefs near paleolatitudes of 35° to 40°S (Oman).

Extraterrestrial causes?

As compared with the end-Cretaceous bioevent, extraterrestrial causes are rather rarely postulated for the explanation f major changes of Permian and Triassic ecosystems. Geochemical data used as evidence for an impact at the Permoriassic Boundary could not be verified (Erwin, 1993).

ALEOCLIMATIC INFERENCES

The primary interdisciplinary focus of Project Pangea is aleoclimatology (Klein, 1992). Reefs and reef organisms are enerally regarded as good paleoclimatic indicators, reflecting e existence of shallow warm-water and well-lighted shelves within low latitudes north and south of the equator.

Prerequisites for such an interpretation are:

• a critical discussion of taxonomic uniformitarianism (Dodd and Stanton, 1990) and an improvement of the qualitative and quantitative data base (cf. Weidlich et al., 1993)

• an evaluation of climate sensitivity, particularly of Late Paleozoic reef organisms, some of which might have lived in higher paleolatitudes and perhaps even in cold-water regions (e.g., *Palaeoaplysina*)

• the study of linear growth of framebuilders (measurements of increments) in order to test seasonality

• the study of narrower stratigraphic intervals and the documentation and comparison of reefs from different paleolatitudes

• a transformation of reef-derived data into proxy data (Crowley and North, 1991) that relate paleontological and paleoecological data as well as distributional patterns of ancient reefs into environmental variables, allowing the inclusion of reefs in modeling processes.

The time slices (Westphalian, Kazanian, and Carnian) selected during the first Pangea Workshop in Lawrence, Kansas, for a detailed study of the Pangean world offer excellent possibilities for testing the value of ancient reefs as paleoclimatic indicators, comparing reefs formed in a time of extreme climatic change, and getting a better understanding of reef evolution.

ACKNOWLEDGMENTS

Projects focusing on the evolution of Late Paleozoic and Mesozoic reefs are supported by grants from the German Research Foundation (Deutsche Forschungsgemeinschaft) within the frame of the Priority Program "Global and Regional Controls on Biogenic Sedimentation." Constructive reviews by G. M. Friedman, R. N. Ginsburg, and G. D. Klein are gratefully acknowledged.

REFERENCES CITED

Alizade, A. A., and Babaev, R. G., 1991, Mesozoic reefs of Aserbaijan: Abstract, 7th International Cnidaria Symposium, Münster: Münster, n.p., 1 p.

Argyriadis, I., de Graciansky, P. C., Marcoux, J., and Ricou, L. E., 1980, The opening of the Mesozoic Tethys between Eurasia and Arabia-Africa, *in* Aubouin, J., et al., eds., Geologie des chaines alpines issues de la Tethys [Geology of the Alpine chains born of the Tethys]: Paris, Bureau de Recherches Geologiques et Minieres, Memoires, no. 115, p. 119–214.

Baud, A., Magaritz, M., and Holser, W. T., 1989, Permian-Triassic of the Tethys: Carbon isotope studies: Geologische Rundschau, v. 78, p. 649–677.

Baud, A., Brandner, R., and Donofrio, D. A., 1991a, The Sefid Kuh Limestone—A late Triassic carbonate ramp (Aghdarband, NE-Iran): Abhandlungen der Geologischen Bundesanstalt Wien, v. 38, p. 111–123.

Baud, A., Jenny, C., Papanikolaou, D., Sideris, C., and Stampfli, G., 1991b, New observations on Permian stratigraphy in Greece and geodynamic interpretation: Bulletin of the Geological Society of Greece, v. 25, p. 187–206.

Beauvais, L., 1980, Donnes actuelles sur la paleobiogeographie des Madréporaires mesozoiques: Comptes Rendus Societé Biogéographie Paris, v. 57, p. 51–64.

Beauvais, L., 1982, Paléobiogéographie des Madréporaires du Trias: Bulletin de Societé géologique de France, sér. 7, v. 24, p. 963–970.

Beauvais, L., 1986, Monographie des Madréporaires du Jurassique inférieur du Maroc: Palaeontographica A, v. 194, p. 1–68.

Benton, M. J., 1986, More than one event in the late Triassic mass extinction: Nature, v. 321, p. 857–861.

Benton, M. J., 1991, What really happened in the late Triassic?: Historical Biology, v. 5, p. 263–278.

Bernoulli, D., and Lemoine, M., 1980, Birth and early evolution of the Tethys: The overall situation, *in* Aubouin, J., et al., Geologie des chaines alpines issues de la Tethys: Paris, Bureau de Recherches Geologiques et Minieres, Memoires, no. 115, p. 168–179.

Biddle, K. T., 1984, Triassic sea level change and the Ladinian-Carnian stage boundary: Nature, v. 308, p. 631–633.

Blendinger, W., Furnish, W. M., and Glenister, B. F., 1992, Permian cephalopod limestones, Oman Mountains: Evidence for a Permian seaway along the northern margin of Gondwana: Palaeogeography, Palaeoclimatology, Palaeoecology, v. 93, p. 13–20.

Böhm, F., 1992, Mikrofazies und Ablagerungsmilieu des Lias und Dogger der Nordöstlichen Kalkalpen: Erlanger geologische Abhandlungen, v. 121, p. 57–217.

Boiko, E. V., Belyaeva, G. V., and Zhuravleva, L. T., 1991, Phanerozoic Sphinctozoa of the territory of the USSR: Moscow, Nauka, 185 p.

Bosscher, H., and Schlager, W., 1992, Computer simulation of reef growth: Sedimentology, v. 39, p. 503–512.

Braga, J. C., and Lopez-Lopez, J. R., 1989, Serpulid bioconstructions at the Triassic-Liassic boundary in Southern Spain: Facies, v. 21, p. 1–10.

Brandner, R., 1984, Meeresspiegelschwankungen und Tektonik in der Trias der NW-Tethys: Jahrbuch der Geologischen Bundesanstalt Wien, v. 126, p. 435–475.

Brandner, R., Flügel, E. and Senowbari-Daryan, B., 1991, Microfacies of ca[r]bonate slope boulders: Indicator of the source area (Middle Triass[ic] Mahlknecht cliff, western Dolomites): Facies, v. 25, p. 279–296.

Ciarapica, G., Cirilli, S., d'Argenio, B., Marsella, E., Passeri, L., and Zaninet[ti,] L., 1987, Late Triassic open and euxinic basins in Italy: Rendiconti Società Geologica Italiana, v. 9, p. 157–166.

Coates, A. J., and Jackson, J.B.C., 1987, Clonal growth, algal symbiosis a[nd] reef formation by corals: Paleobiology, v. 13, p. 363–378.

Cowen, R., 1988, The role of algal symbiosis in reefs through time: Palaic[s,] v. 3, p. 221–227.

Crowley, T. C., and North, G. R., 1991, Paleoclimatology: New York, Oxfo[rd] University Press.

Dickins, J. M., 1984, Evolution and climate in the Upper Palaeozoic, *in* Brenchley, P., ed., Fossils and climate: New York, John Wiley and Sor[s,] p. 317–327.

Dickins, J. M., 1985, Palaeobiofacies and palaeobiography of Gondwanala[nd] from Permian to Triassic, *in* Nakazawa, K., and Dickins, J. M., eds., T[he] Tethys: Tokyo, Tokai University Press, p. 83–92.

Dodd, J. R., and Stanton, R. J., 1990, Paleoecology, concepts and applicatio[ns] (second edition): New York, John Wiley and Sons, 502 p.

Dromart, G., 1992, Jurassic deep-water microbial biostromes as floodi[ng] markers in carbonate sequence stratigraphy: Palaeogeography, Palae[o]climatology, Palaeoecology, v. 91, p. 219–229.

Dubiel, R. F., Parrish, J. T., Parrish, J. M., and Good, S. C., 1991, T[he] Pangaean Megamonsoon—Evidence from the Upper Triassic Chinle Fo[r]mation, Colorado Plateau: Palaios, v. 6, p. 347–370.

DuDresnay, R., 1977, Le milieu récifal fossile du Jurassique inférieur (Lia[s]) dans le domaine des Chaines atlasiques du Maroc: Bulletin Bureau d[e] Rechereches Mines Memoir, v. 89, p. 296–312.

Embry, A. P., 1988, Triassic sea-level changes: Evidence from the Canadi[an] Arctic Archipelago, *in* Wilgus, C. K., Hastings, B. S., Kenda[ll,] C.G.St.C., Posamentier, H. W., Ross, C. A., and Van Wagoner, J. [C.,] eds., Sea-level changes: An integrated approach: Society of Econom[ic] Paleontologists and Mineralogists Special Publication 42, p. 249–259.

Enos, P., Wei Jianjang, and Yan Yangji, 1989, Platform margin collapse a[nd] slope retreat, mid-Triassic, Guizhou, China [abs.]: 10th Internation[al] Association of Sedimentologists Regional Meeting, Budapest: Budape[st,] n.p., 1 p.

Erwin, D. H., 1993, The great Paleozoic crisis: Life and death in the Permia[n:] New York, Columbia University Press, 327 p.

Fabricius, F. H., Friedrichsen, V., and Jacobshagen, V., 1970, Paläoten[m]peraturen und Paläoklima in Obertrias und Lias der Alpen: Geologisc[he] Rundschau, v. 59, p. 805–828.

Fagerstrom, J. A., 1987, The evolution of reef communities: New York, Jo[hn] Wiley and Sons, 600 p.

Fagerstrom, J. A., 1991, Reef-building guilds and a checklist for determini[ng] guild membership: Coral Reefs, v. 10, p. 47–52.

Fan, Jiasong, Rigby, J. K., and Qi, Jingwen, 1990, The Permian reefs of Sou[th] China and comparisons with the Permian Reef Complex of the Gua[d]alupe Mountains, west Texas and New Mexico: Brigham Young Un[i]versity Geological Studies, v. 36, p. 15–55.

Federowski, J., 1989, Extinction of Rugosa and Tabulata near the Pe[r]mian/Triassic boundary: Acta Palaeontologica Polonica, v. 34, p. 47–7[0.]

Flessa, K. W., 1990, The "facts" of mass extinction, *in* Sharpton, V. L., a[nd] Ward, P. D., Global catastrophes in earth history; an interdisciplina[ry] conference on impacts, volcanism, and mass mortality: Geological S[o]ciety of America Special Paper 247, p. 1–8.

Flügel, E., 1981, Paleoecology and facies of Upper Triassic reefs in t[he] Northern Calcareous Alps: Society of Economic Paleontologists a[nd] Mineralogists Special Publication, 30, p. 291–359.

Flügel, E., 1982, Evolution of Triassic reefs: Current concepts and problem[s:] Facies, v. 6, p. 297–328.

Flügel, E., 1989, "Algen/Zement"-Riffe: Archiv für Lagerstättenforschun[g,] Geologische Bundesanstalt Wien, v. 10, 125–131.

Flügel, E., 1990, "Einschnitte" in der Entwicklung permischer Kalkalgen: Mitteilungen des Naturwissenschaftlichen Vereins Steiermark, v. 120, p. 99–124.

Flügel, E., and Flügel-Kahler, E., 1992, Phanerozoic reef evolution: Basic questions and data base: Facies, v. 26, p. 167–278.

Flügel, E., and Krainer, K., 1992, Allogenic and autogenic controls of reef mound formation: Late Carboniferous auloporid coral buildups from the Carnic Alps, Italy: Neues Jahrbuch für Geologie und Paläontologie, Abhandlungen, v. 185, p. 39–62.

Flügel, E., and Reinhardt, J., 1989, Uppermost Permian reefs in Skyros (Greece) and Sichuan (China): Implications for the late Permian extinction event: Palaios, v. 4, p. 502–518.

Flügel, E., and Stanley, G. D., 1984, Reorganization, development and evolution of post-Permian reefs and reef organisms: Palaeontographica Americana, v. 54, p. 177–186.

Flügel, H. W., 1981, Die paläozoische Tethys: Fakten, Fiktionen, Fragen: Mitteilungen der Österreichischen Geologischen Gesellschaft, v. 74/75, p. 83–100.

Fois, E., and Gaetani, M., 1984, The recovery of reef-building communities and the role of cnidarians in carbonate sequences of the Middle Triassic (Anisian) in the Italian Dolomites: Palaeontographica Americana, v. 54, p. 191–200.

Frakes, L. A., Frakes, J. E., and Syktus, J. I., 1992, Climate modes of the Phanerozoic: Cambridge, Cambridge University Press, 274 p.

Gerhard, L. C., 1991, Reef modeling: Progress in simulation of carbonate environments: Bulletin Kansas Geological Survey, v. 233, p. 345–358.

Geyer, O. F., 1977, Die *Lithiotis*-Kalke im Bereich der unterjurassischen Tethys: Neues Jahrbuch für Geologie und Paläontologie, Abhandlungen, v. 153, p. 304–340.

Goldhammer, R. K., and Harris, M. T., 1989, Eustatic controls on the stratigraphy and geometry of the Latemar buildup (Middle Triassic), the Dolomites of Northern Italy, *in* Crevello, P. D., Wilson, J. L., Sarg, J. F., and Read, J. F., Controls on carbonate platform and basin development: Society of Economic Paleontologists and Mineralogists Special Publication 44, p. 339–352.

Goldhammer, R. K., Dunn, P. A., and Hardie, L. A., 1990, Depositional cycles, composite sea-level changes, cycle stacking patterns, and the hierarchy of stratigraphic forcing: Examples from Alpine Triassic platform carbonates: Geological Society of America Bulletin, v. 102, p. 535–562.

Grieve, R.A.F., 1987, Terrestrial impact structures: Annual Review of Earth and Planetary Sciences, v. 15, p. 245–270.

Grötsch, J., 1991, Die Evolution von Karbonatplattformen des offenen Ozeans in der mittleren Kreide (NW-Jugoslawien, NW-Pazifik, NW-Griechenland): Möglichkeiten zur Rekonstruktion von Meeresspiegeländerungen verschiedener Grössenordnung [Ph.D. thesis]: Erlangen, Universität Erlangen-Nürnberg, Institut für Paläontologie, 229 p.

Guo, Li, and Riding, R., 1992, Microbial carbonates in uppermost Permian reefs, Sichuan Basin, southern China: Some similarities with Recent travertines: Sedimentology, v. 39, p. 37–54.

Hallam, A., 1981, The end-Triassic bivalve extinction event: Paleogeography, Paleoclimatology, Paleoecology, v. 35, p. 1–44.

Hallam, A., 1984, Distribution of fossil marine invertebrates in relation to climate, *in* Brenchley, P., Fossils and climate: New York, John Wiley & Sons, p. 107–125.

Hallam, A., 1985, A review of Mesozoic climates: Journal of the Geological Society London, v. 142, p. 433–445.

Hallam, A., 1990, The end-Triassic mass extinction event: Geological Society of America Special Paper 247, p. 577–583.

Hallam, A., 1991, Why was there a delayed radiation after the end-Paleozoic extinctions?: Historical Biology, v. 5, p. 257–262.

Hallam, A., and El-Shaarawy, Z., 1982, Salinity reduction of the end-Triassic sea from the Alpine region into northwestern Europe: Lethaia, v. 15, p. 169–178.

Hallam, A., and Goodfellow, W. D., 1990, Facies and geochemical evidence

bearing on the end-Triassic disappearance of the Alpine reef ecosystem: Historical Biology, v. 4, p. 131–138.

Hallock, P., and Schlager, W., 1986, Nutrient excess and the demise of coral reefs and carbonate platforms: Palaios, v. 1, p. 389–398.

Haq, B. U., Hardenbol, J., and Vail, P., 1987, Chronology of fluctuating sea-levels since the Triassic (250 million years ago to present): Science, v. 235, p. 1156–1166.

Haq, B. U., Hardenbol, J., and Vail, P., 1988, Mesozoic and Cenozoic chronostratigraphy and cycles of sea-level change: Society of Economic Paleontologists and Mineralogists Special Publication 42, p. 71–108.

Hay, W. W., Behensky, J. F., Barron, E. J., Sloan, J. L., II, 1982. Late Triassic-Liassic paleoclimatology of the proto-central north Atlantic rift system: Palaeogeography, Palaeoclimatology, Palaeoecology, v. 40, p. 13–30.

Heckel, P. H., 1986, Sea-level curve for Pennsylvanian eustatic marine transgressive-regressive depositional cycles along midcontinent outcrop belt, North America: Geology, v. 14, p. 330–334.

Hodych, J. P., and Dinning, G. R., 1992, Did the Manicouagan impact trigger end-of-Triassic mass extinction?: Geology, v. 20, p. 51–54.

Holser, W. T., and Magaritz, M., 1987, Events near the Permian-Triassic boundary: Modern Geology, v. 11, p. 155–180.

Holser, W. T., and Margaritz, M., 1992, Cretaceous/Tertiary and Permian/Triassic boundary events compared: Geochimica et Cosmichimica Acta, v. 56, p. 3397–3309.

Holser, W. T., Magaritz, M., and Clark, D. L., 1986, Carbon-isotope stratigraphic correlations in the late Permian: American Journal of Science, v. 286, p. 390–402.

Holser, W. T., Schönlaub, H. P., Boeckelmann, K., and Magaritz, M., 1991, The Permian-Triassic of the Gartnerkofel-1 Core (Carnic Alps, Austria): Synthesis and conclusions: Abhandlungen der Geologischen Bundesanstalt Wien, v. 45, p. 231–232.

Hsü, J., and Bernoulli, D., 1978, Genesis of the Tethys and the Mediterranean: Initial report of the Deep Sea Drilling Project, v. 42, p. 943–949.

Ishii, K., Okimura, Y., and Ichikawa, K., 1985, Notes on Tethys biogeography with reference to Middle Permian Fusulinaceans, *in* Nakazawa, K., and Dickins, J. M., eds., The Tethys: Tokyo, Tokai University Press, p. 139–155.

James, N. P., and Macintyre, I. G., 1985, Carbonate depositional environments, modern and ancient. 1: Reefs. Zonation, depositional facies, diagenesis: Colorado School of Mines Quarterly, v. 80, p. 1–70.

Jenkyns, H., 1980, Tethys: Past and present: Proceedings of the Geological Association, v. 91, p. 107–118.

Kano, A., 1992, Paleoecology of palaeoaplysinid bioherms of the Lower Permian in central Spitzbergen, *in* K., Nakamura, ed., Investigations on the Upper Carboniferous–Upper Permian succession of West Spitsbergen 1989–1991: Sapporo, Hokkaido University, p. 119–125.

Kendall, C.G.St.C., and Schlager, W., 1981, Carbonates and relative changes in sea level: Marine Geology, v. 44, p. 181–212.

Klein, G. deV., 1992, Project Pangea: Goals and development; tectonic-climatic discrimination of cyclic deposition: Global Sedimentary Geology Program, Project Pangea Workshop, Lawrence, Kansas, Program: Lawrence, Kansas, n.p., p. 7.

Kobluk, D. R., 1988, Pre-Cenozoic fossil record of cryptobionts and their presence in early reefs and mounds: Palaios, v. 3, p. 243–250.

Krainer, K., 1992, Fazies, Sedimentationsprozesse und Paläogeographie im Karbon der Ost- und Südalpen: Jahrbuch der Geologischen Bundesanstalt Wien, v. 135, p. 99–193.

Kristan-Tollmann, E., 1988, Unexpected microfaunal communities within the Triassic Tethys, in Audley-Charles, M. G., and Hallam, A., eds., Gondwana and Tethys: Geological Society Special Publication 37, p. 213–223.

Kristan-Tollmann, E., 1990, Tethysweite Verbreitung triadischer und liassischer Ostracoden: Geologica et Palaeontologica, v. 24, p. 173–183.

Kristan-Tollmann, E., and Tollmann, A., 1981, Die Stellung der Tethys in der Trias und die Herkunft ihrer Fauna: Mitteilungen der Österreichischen

Geologischen Gesellschaft, v. 74/75, p. 129–135.

Kristan-Tollmann, E., and Tollmann, A., 1982, Die Entwicklung der Tethystrias und Herkunft ihrer Fauna: Geologische Rundschau, v. 71, p. 987–1019.

Kristan-Tollmann, E., and Tollmann, A., 1983, Tethys-Faunenelemente in der Trias der USA: Mitteilungen der Österreichischen Geologischen Gesellschaft, v. 76, p. 213–272.

Kühlmann, D.H.H., 1989, Ecological adaption and a compensatory theory of coral assemblages in the maintenance of reef growth: Memoir of the Association of Australasian Paleontologists 8, p. 433–438.

Kutzbach, J. E., and Gallimore, R. G., 1989, Pangaean climates: Megamonsoons of the megacontinent: Journal of Geophysical Research, v. 94, p. 3341–3357.

Kutzbach, J. E., Guetter, P. J., and Washington, W. M., 1990, Simulated circulation of an idealized ocean for Pangean time: Paleooceanography, v. 5, p. 299–317.

Lottes, A. L., and Rowley, D. B., 1990, Reconstruction of the Laurasian and Gondwana segments of Permian Pangaea, in McKerrow, W. S., and Scotese, C. R., eds., Palaeozoic palaeogeography and biogeography: Geological Society Memoir 12, p. 383–395.

Lys, M., 1987, Comparaison de biocoenoses du Permien supérieur des domaines mésogéen (en Méditerranée centrale et orientale) et téthysien: Intéret paléogéographique: Annales Societé Géologique du Nord, v. 105, p. 259–267.

Marcoux, J., Mascle, G., and Cuid, J.-P., 1982, Existence des marqueurs biosédimentaires et structuraux téthysiens issus de la marge gondwanienne à la bordure ouest-américaine: Implications paléogéographiques et paléobiologiques: Bulletin de Societè Géologique de France, sér. 7, v. 24, p. 971–980.

Marsaglia, K. M., and Klein, G. D., 1983, The paleogeography of Paleozoic and Mesozoic storm depositional systems: Journal of Geology, v. 91, p. 117–142.

Moore, G. T., Hayashida, D. N., Ross, C. A., and Jacobson, S. R., 1992, Paleoclimate of the Kimmeridgian/Tithonian (Late Jurassic) world. I: Results using a general circulation model: Palaeogeography, Palaeoclimatology, Palaeoecology, v. 93, p. 113–150.

Mork, A., Embry, A. F., and Weitschat, W., 1989, Triassic transgressive-regressive cycles in the Sverdrup Basin, Svalbard and the Barents Shelf, in Collinson, J. D., ed., Correlation in hydrocarbon exploration: London, United Kingdom, Graham & Trotman, p. 113–130.

Nakazawa, K., 1985, The Permian and Triassic systems in the Tethys—Their paleogeography, in Nakazawa, K., and Dickins, J. M., eds., The Tethys: Tokyo, Tokai University Press, p. 93–111.

Nauss, A. L., and Smith, P. L., 1988, Lithiotis (Bivalvia) bioherms, Lower Jurassic, Oregon, in Geldsetzer, H.H.J., James, N. P., and Tebbutt, G. E., eds., Reefs, Canada and adjacent areas: Memoir of the Canadian Society of Petroleum Geologists 13, p. 738–740.

Nazarevich, B. N., Nazarevich, I. A., and Shrydko, N. I., 1986, Usloviya formirovaya osobennosti razmesheniya nizhnetriasovik iskopaenikh organgogogennikh postrok vostochnogo Predkavkazya, in Sokolov, B. S., ed., Fanerzoiskie rify i korally SSSR; Moscow, Akademia nauk SSSR, Otdel. geol. geofiz. geochim. i gornikh nauk, p. 161–166.

Nelson, C. S., 1988, An introductionary perspective on non-tropical shelf carbonates: Sedimentary Geology, v. 60, p. 3–14.

Nie Shangyou, Rowley, D. B., and Ziegler, A. M., 1990, Constraints on the locations of Asian microcontinents in Palaeo-Tethys during the Late Palaeozoic, in McKerrow, W. S., and Scotese, C. R., eds., Palaeozoic palaeogeography and biogeography: Geological Society Memoir 12, p. 397–409.

Oliver, W. A., 1980, The relationship of the scleractinian corals to the rugose corals: Paleobiology, v. 6, p. 146–160.

Pakistani-Japanese Research Group, 1985, Stratigraphy and correlation of the marine Permian–Lower Triassic in the Shurgar Range and the Salt Range, Pakistan, in Nakazawa, K., and Dickins, J. M., eds., The Tethys:

Her paleogeography and paleobiogeography from the Paleozoic to Mesozoic: Tokyo, Tokai University Press, p. 221–312.

Park, L. K., 1983, Lower Jurassic carbonate buildups and associated facies, Central and Western Morocco: Society of Economic Paleontologists and Mineralogists Core Workshop, v. 4, p. 327–365.

Parrish, J. T., and Peterson, F., 1988, Wind directions predicted from global circulation models and wind directions determined from eolian sandstones of the western United States—A comparison: Sedimentary Geology, v. 56, p. 261–282.

Parrish, J. T., Ziegler, A. M., and Scotese, C. R., 1982, Rainfall patterns and the distribution of coals and evaporites in the Mesozoic and Cenozoic: Palaeogeography, Palaeoclimatology, Palaeoecology, v. 40, p. 67–101.

Paul, J., 1980, Upper Permian stromatolite reefs: Contributions to Sedimentology, v. 9, p. 253–268.

Paul, J., 1991, Zechstein carbonates—Marine episodes of a hypersaline sea: Zentralblatt für Geologie und Paläontologie, Teil I, v. 1991, p. 1029–1045.

Poulton, T. P., 1988, A Lower Jurassic coral reef, Telkwa Range, British Columbia, in Geldsetzer, H.H.J., James, N. P., and Tebbutt, G. E., eds., Reefs, Canada and adjacent areas: Memoir of the Canadian Society of Petroleum Geologists 13, p. 754–757.

Railsback, L. B., and Anderson, T. F., 1987, Control of Triassic seawater chemistry and temperature on the evolution of post-Paleozoic aragonite-secreting faunas: Geology, v. 15, p. 1002–1005.

Rao, C. P., 1981, Criteria for recognition of cold-water carbonate sedimentation: Berriedale limestone (Lower Permian), Tasmania, Australia: Journal of Sedimentary Petrology, v. 51, p. 491–506.

Rao, C. P., and Green, D. C., 1982, Oxygen and carbon isotopes of Early Permian cold-water carbonates, Tasmania, Australia: Journal of Sedimentary Petrology, v. 52, p. 1111–1125.

Raup, D. M., and Boyaijan, G. E., 1988, Patterns of generic extinction in the fossil record: Paleobiology, v. 14, p. 109–125.

Reid, R. P., 1985, The facies and evolution of an Upper Triassic reef complex in Northern Canada [Ph.D. thesis]: Coral Grables, Florida, University of Miami, 343 p.

Reid, R. P., and Ginsburg, R. N., 1986, The role of framework in Upper Triassic patch reefs in the Yukon (Canada): Palaios, v. 1, p. 590–600.

Reijmer, J.J.G., and Everaars, J.S.L., 1991, Carbonate platform facies reflected in carbonate basin facies (Triassic, Northern Calcareous Alps, Austria): Facies, v. 25, p. 253–278.

Reitner, J., 1992, "Coralline Spongien": Der Versuch einer phylogenetisch-taxonomischen Analyse: Berliner Geowissenschaftliche Abhandlungen, Reihe E, v. 1, 352 p.

Riedel, P., 1990, Riffbiotope im Karn und Nor (Obertrias) der Tethys: Entwicklung, Einschnitte und Diversitätsmuster [Ph.D. thesis]: Erlangen, Universität Erlangen-Nürnberg, 145 p.

Riedel, P., 1991, Korallen in der Trias der Tethys: Stratigraphische Reichweiten, Diversitätsmuster, Entwicklungstrends und Bedeutung als Rifforganismen Mitteilungen der Gesellschaft der Geologie- und Bergbaustudenten in Österreich, v. 37, p. 97–118.

Riedel, P., and Senowbari-Daryan, B., 1991, Pharetronids in Triassic reefs, in Reitner, J., and Keupp, H., eds., Fossil and Recent sponges: Berlin, Springer Verlag, p. 465–476.

Robinson, P. L., 1973, Palaeoclimatology and continental drift, in Tarling, D. H., and Runcorn, S. K., eds., Implications of continental drift to the earth sciences, I: London, Academic Press, p. 449–476.

Röhl, U., Dumont, T., von Rad, U., Martini, R., and Zaninetti, L., 1991, Upper Triassic Tethyan carbonates off Northwest Australia (Wombat Plateau, ODP Leg 122): Facics, v. 25, p. 211–252.

Roniewicz, E., 1989, Triassic scleractinian corals of the Zlambach beds, Northern Calcareous Alps, Austria: Denkschriften der Österreichischen Akademie der Wissenschaften Wien, v. 126, 152 p.

Roniewicz, E., and Morykowa, E., 1989, Triassic Scleractinia and the Triassic/Liassic boundary: Memoir of the Association of the Australasian Paleontologists 8, p. 347–354.

Ross, C. A., 1979, Evolution of Fusulinacea (Protozoa) in Late Paleozoic space and time, *in* Gray, J., and Boucot, A. J., eds., Historical biogeography, plate tectonics and the changing environment: Corvallis, Oregon State University, p. 215–226.

Ross, C. A., and Ross, J.R.P., 1985a, Carboniferous and Early Permian biogeography: Geology, v. 13, p. 27–30.

Ross, C. A., and Ross, J.R.P., 1985b, Late Paleozoic depositional sequences are synchronous and worldwide: Geology, v. 13, p. 194–197.

Ross, C. A., and Ross, J.R.P., 1987a, Late Paleozoic sea levels and depositional sequences: Cushman Foundation for Foraminiferal Research Special Publication 24, p. 137–149.

Ross, C. A., and Ross, J.R.P., 1987b, Biostratigraphic zonation of late Paleozoic depositional sequences: Cushman Foundation for Foraminiferal Research Special Publication 24, p. 151–168.

Ross, C. A., and Ross, J.R.P., 1988, Late Paleozoic transgressive-regressive deposition: Society of Economic Paleontologists and Mineralogists Special Publication 42, p. 227–247.

Ross, J.R.P., and Ross, C. A., 1990, Late Palaeozoic bryozoan biogeography, *in* McKerrow, W. S., and Scotese, C. R., eds., Palaeozoic palaeogeography and biogeography: Geological Society Memoir 12, p. 353–362.

Sandberg, P. A., 1983, An oscillating trend in Phanerozoic non-skeletal carbonate mineralogy: Nature, v. 305, p. 19–22.

Sano, H., Horibo, K., and Mumamoto, Y., 1990, Tubiphytes-Archaeolithoporella-Girvanella reef facies in Permian buildup, Mino terrane, central Japan: Sedimentary Geology, v. 68, p. 293–306.

Sarti, M., Russo, A., and Bosellini, F. R., 1992, Rhaetian strata, Wombat Plateau: Analysis of fossil communities as a key to paleoenvironmental change, *in* von Rad, U., Haq, B. U., et al., eds., Proceedings of the Ocean Drilling Program, Scientific Results, v. 122, p. 181–195.

Schäfer, P., and Fois, E., 1986, Triassic bryozoa and the evolutionary crisis of Paleozoic Stenolaemata, *in* Walliser, O., ed., Global bio-events: Lecture Notes in Earth Sciences, v. 8, p. 251–255.

Schlager, W., 1981, The paradox of drowned reefs and carbonate platforms: Geological Society of America Bulletin, v. 92, p. 197–211.

Schlager, W., and Philip, J., 1990, Cretaceous carbonate platforms, *in* Ginsburg, R. N., and Beaudoin, B., eds., Cretaceous resources, events and rhythms: Amsterdam, Kluwer Academic Publishers, p. 173–195.

Scotese, C. R., and Golonka, J., 1992, PALEOMAP paleogeographic atlas: Department of Geology, University of Texas at Arlington, PALEOMAP Progress Report v. 20, p. xxx.

Scotese, C. R., and McKerrow, W. S., 1990, Revised world maps and introduction, *in* McKerrow, W. S., and Scotese, C. R., eds., Palaeozoic palaeogeography and biogeography: Geological Society Memoir 12, p. 1–21.

Sengör, A. M., Altiner, D., Cin, A., Ustaömer, T., and Hsü, K. J., 1988, Origin and assembly of the tethyside orogenic collage at the expense of Gondwana Land, *in* Audley-Charles, M. G., and Hallam, A., Gondwana and Tethys: Geological Society Special Publication 37, p. 119–181.

Senowbari-Daryan, B., 1990, Die systematische Stellung der thalamiden Schwämme und ihre Bedeutung in der Erdgeschichte: Münchener Geowissenschaftliche Abhandlungen, Reihe A, Geologie und Paläontologie, v. 21, 326 p.

Senowbari-Daryan, B., 1991, "Sphinctozoa": An overview, *in* Reitner, J., and Keupp, H., eds., Fossil and Recent sponges: Berlin, Springer Verlag, p. 224–241.

Senowbari-Daryan, B., and Flügel, E., 1994, *Tubiphytes* Maslov, an enigmatic fossil: Classification, fossil record and significance through time. Part I: Discussion of Late Paleozoic material: Bolletino Società di Paleontologia Italia Special Volume 1 (in press).

Senowbari-Daryan, B., and Stanley, G. D., 1988, Triassic sponges (Sphinctozoa) from Hells Canyon, Oregon: Journal of Paleontology, v. 62, p. 419–423.

Senowbari-Daryan, B., Zühlke, R., Bechstädt, T., and Flügel, E., 1993, Anisian (Middle Triassic) buildups of the Northern Dolomites (Italy): The recovery of reef communities after the Permian/Triassic crisis:

Facies, v. 28, p. 181–256.

Sepkowski, J. J., 1986, Phanerozoic overview of mass extinctions, *in* Raup, D. M., and Jablonski, D., eds., Patterns and processes in the history of life: Dahlem Konferenzen, Life Sciences Research Report, v. 36, (Berlin, Springer Verlag), p. 277–295.

Sheehan, P. M., 1985, Reefs are not so different—They follow the evolutionary pattern of level communities: Geology, v. 13, p. 46–49.

Simms, M. J., and Ruffel, A. H., 1989, Synchroneity of climatic change and extinctions in the Late Triassic: Geology, v. 17, p. 265–268.

Simms, M. J., and Ruffel, A. H., 1990, Climatic and biotic change in the late Triassic: Journal of the Geological Society London, v. 147, p. 321–327.

Smith, A. G., Hurley, A. M., and Briden, J. C., 1981, Phanerozoic paleocontinental world maps: Cambridge, Cambridge University Press, 102 p.

Smith, D. B., 1981, The Magnesian Limestone (Upper Permian) reef complex of northeastern England: Society of Economic Paleontologists and Mineralogists Special Publication 30, p. 161–186.

Soronina, I. E., 1988, *in* Letavin, A. E., ed., Mezozoisko-kainozoiskie kompleksy Predkavkazya (stroni i korrelyatsia): Moscow, Akademie nauk. SSSR, Min. neft. prom., Inst. geol. razrabotki gornykh iskopaenikh Moskva.

Stanley, G. D., 1981, Early history of scleractinian corals and its geological consequences: Geology, v. 9, p. 507–511.

Stanley, G. D., 1982, Triassic carbonate development and reefbuilding in western North America: Geologische Rundschau, v. 71, p. 1071–1075.

Stanley, G. D., 1988, The history of early Mesozoic reef communities: A three-step process: Palaios, v. 3, p. 170–183.

Stanley, G. D., 1992, Exotic terranes, late Paleozoic to early Mesozoic fossils and circum-Pacific events: Abstracts and Programs, Fifth North American Paleontological Convention, Paleontological Society Special Publication 6, p. 277.

Stanley, G. D., and Cairns, S. D., 1988, Constructional azooxanthellate coral communities: An overview with implications for the fossil record: Palaios, v. 3, p. 233–242.

Stanton, R. J., and Flügel, E., 1987, Palecology of Upper Triassic reefs in the Northern Calcareous Alps: Reef communities: Facies, v. 16, p. 157–186.

Stanton, R. J., and Flügel, E., 1989, Problems with reef models: The Late Triassic Steinplatte "reef" (Northern Alps, Salzburg/Tyrol, Austria): Facies, v. 20, p. 1–138.

Stehli, F. G., 1971, Tethyan and boreal Permian faunas and their significance, *in* Dutro, J. T., ed., Paleozoic perspectives: A paleontological tribute to G. Arthur Cooper: Smithsonian Contributions to Paleontology, v. 3, p. 337–345.

Stille, H., 1951, Das mitteleuropäische variszische Grundgebirge im Bilde des gesamteuropäischen: Beihefte Geologisches Jahrbuch, v. 2, 138 p.

Stöcklin, J., 1974, Possible Ancient continental margins in Iran, *in* Burk, C., and Drake, C., eds., The geology of continental margins: Heidelberg, Springer, p. 974–987.

Swart, P. K., 1983, Carbon and oxygen isotope fractionation in scleractinian corals: A review: Earth Science Reviews, v. 19, p. 51–80.

Talent, J. A., 1988, Organic reef-building: Episodes of extinction and symbiosis?: Senckenbergiana Lethaea, v. 69, p. 315–368.

Thiede, J., 1983, Paleogeography and paleobathymetry: Quantitative reconstructions of ocean basins, *in* Brosche, A., and Sündermann, B., eds., Tidal friction and earth's rotation, v. 2: Berlin, Springer, p. 229–239.

Tollmann, A., and Kristan-Tollmann, E., 1985, Paleogeography of the European Tethys from Paleozoic to Mesozoic and the Triassic relations of the eastern part of Tethys and Panthalassia, *in* Nakazawa, K., and Dickins, J. M., The Tethys: Tokyo, Tokai University Press, p. 3–22.

Tucker, M. E., and Wright, V. P., 1990, Carbonate sedimentology: Oxford, Blackwell Scientific Publications, 482 p.

Turnsek, D., Seyfried, H., and Geyer, O. F., 1975, Geologische und paläontologische Untersuchungen an einem Korallenvorkommen im Subbetischen Unterjura von Murcia (Südspanien): Razprave Academia Scientia et Artium Slovenica, Classis IV, v. 26, p. 120–149.

266 E. Flügel

Valentine, J. W., 1986, The Permian-Triassic extinction event and invertebrate developmental modes: Bulletin of Marine Sciences, v. 39, p. 607–615.

Veevers, J. J., and Powell, C. McA., 1987, Late Paleozoic glacial episodes in Gondwanaland reflected in transgressive-regressive depositional sequences in Euramerica: Geological Society of America Bulletin, v. 98, p. 475–487.

Vogel, K., 1993, Bioeroders in fossil reefs: Facies, v. 28, p. 109–114.

Wei Jiayong, and Enos, P., 1991, Triassic evolution of the southern margin of the Yangtze Platform, China: Abstracts, International Dolomieu Conference on Carbonate Platforms and Dolomitization, Ortisei/St. Ulrich: Ortisei, Dolomieu Conference, p. 287–288.

Weidlich, O., Bernecker, M., and Flügel, E., 1993, Combined quantitative analysis and microfacies studies of ancient reefs: An integrated approach to Upper Permian and Upper Triassic reef carbonates (Sultanate of Oman): Facies, v. 28, p. 115–144.

Wignall, P. B., and Hallam, A., 1992, Anoxia as a cause of the Permian/Triassic mass extinction: Facies evidence from northern Italy and the western United States: Palaeogeography, Palaeoclimatology, Palaeoecology, v. 93, p. 21–46.

Wilson, K. M., Hay, W. W., and Wold, C. N., 1991, Mesozoic evolution of exotic terranes and marginal seas, western North America: Marine Geology, v. 102, p. 311–361.

Witzke, B. J., 1990, Palaeoclimatic constraints for Palaeozoic palaeolatitudes of Laurentia and Euramerica, in McKerrow, W. S., and Scotese, C. R.,

eds., Palaeozoic palaeogeography and biogeography: Geological Society Memoir 12, p. 57–73.

Wright, V. P., 1992, Speculations on the controls on cyclic peritidal carbonates: Ice-house versus greenhouse eustatic controls: Sedimentary Geology, v. 76, p. 1–5.

Wu, Ya Sheng, 1991, Organisms and communities of Permian reef of Xiangbo, China: Beijing, International Academic Publishers, 192 p.

Yancey, T. E., 1979, Permian positions of the Northern Hemisphere continents as determined from marine biotic provinces, in Gray, J., and Boucot, A. J., eds., Historical biogeography, plate tectonics and the beginning of changing environments: Proceedings, 37th Annual Biology Colloquium and selected papers: Corvallis, Oregon State University Press, p. 239–247.

Yin, H. F., 1985, On the transitional beds and the Permian-Triassic boundary in South China: Newsletter on Stratigraphy, v. 15, p. 13–27.

Ziegler, A. M., and seven others, 1981, Paleozoic biogeography and climatology, in Niklas, K. J., ed., Paleobotany, paleoecology and evolution: Chicago, Prager Scientific, p. 231–266.

Ziegler, A. M., Hulver, M. L., Lottes, A. L., and Schmachtenberg, W. F., 1984, Uniformitarianism and paleoclimates: Inferences from the distribution of carbonate rocks, in Brenchley, P. J., ed., Fossils and climate: New York, John Wiley & Sons, p. 3–25.

MANUSCRIPT ACCEPTED BY THE SOCIETY MAY 14, 1993

Geological Society of America
Special Paper 288
1994

Stratal hierarchy and sequence stratigraphy—Middle Pennsylvanian, southwestern Kansas, U.S.A.

John C. Youle*
Department of Geology, University of Kansas, Lawrence, Kansas 66045
W. Lynn Watney
Kansas Geological Survey, 1930 Constant, Campus West, Lawrence, Kansas 66047
Lance L. Lambert*
Department of Geology, University of Iowa, Iowa City, Iowa 52242

ABSTRACT

Sequence-stratigraphic methods are used to interpret the stratal architecture and depositional history of Middle Pennsylvanian cyclothems that onlap the Central Kansas uplift from the Hugoton embayment of the Anadarko basin. Thirteen fourth-order (0.1 to 1.0 m.y.) depositional sequences are recognized between the "V" shale of the Cherokee Group (Desmoinesian) and the base of the "Gray group" (upper Atokan). Depositional sequence boundaries, recognized in core as subaerial exposure surfaces developed on subtidal rocks, were correlated by wireline logs from the lower-shelf to updip depositional limits. They were used to interpret the complex history of sea-level change in the midcontinent.

In lower-shelf settings individual sequences are 3 to 9 m thick, consisting of a basal "hot" black shale (1.25 to 3 m thick) that grades upward into a dense limestone (1.75 to 4.5 m thick). The lower-shelf black shales thin and bifurcate shelfward as they grade into limestones and gray shales. Lower-shelf limestones thicken toward the mid-shelf and grade into bioclastic and phylloid-algal wackestones and packstones. Sequences reach maximum thickness in the mid-shelf (35 m), where they consist of multiple shoaling-upward parasequences. Mid-shelf sequences thin landward as successively older parasequences toplap beneath the overlying sequence boundary. These sequences are thus sigmoidal in shape, downlapping onto the lower-shelf and toplapping onto the proximal shelf. Mid-shelf limestones thin shelfward and grade into thin, karsted, subtidal and peritidal carbonates. Farther landward, limestones grade into thin siliciclastics, amalgamated soil profiles, or locally estuarine valley-fill siliclastics.

Changes in the geometries, lithologies, and stacking patterns of "Gray" and lower Cherokee Group sequences record the influence of a third-order relative sea-level cycle (1 to 10 m.y.). This larger-order cycle is treated as a *composite sequence* and is subdivided into three sequence sets. Lower "Gray group" sequences make up

*Present address: Youle, 231454 Golden Road, Linwood, Kansas 6502; Lambert, 1008 Arbor Hills Apartments, 250 Heimer Road, San Antonio, Texas 78232.

Youle, J. C., Watney, W. L., and Lambert, L. L., 1994, Stratal hierarchy and sequence stratigraphy—Middle Pennsylvanian, southwestern Kansas, U.S.A., *in* Klein, G. D., ed., Pangea: Paleoclimate, Tectonics, and Sedimentation During Accretion, Zenith, and Breakup of a Supercontinent: Boulder, Colorado, Geological Society of America Special Paper 288.

the transgressive sequence set. These sequences are dominated by lower-shelf lithofacies. Younger sequences overstep older ones as they onlap pre–"Gray group" rocks. Sequences in the transgressive sequence set double in thickness from lower-shelf to mid-shelf positions, although intrasequence stratal relationships are indistinct. Upper "Gray group" sequences of the early highstand sequence-set exhibit a wide range of lithofacies, display well-defined internal stratal packages, and thicken 500% from the lower-shelf into the mid-shelf. The late-highstand sequence-set makes up the Lower Cherokee Group. These sequences lack lower-shelf lithofacies, and half of them onlap subjacent sequences.

INTRODUCTION

The goals of this investigation are: (1) to describe lithologies and geometries of Middle Pennsylvanian cyclothems in sequence stratigraphic terms and (2) to interpret the relative sea-level history of the study area as revealed by the distribution of facies, stacking patterns, and geometries of these depositional sequences through time.

Sequence stratigraphic analysis, when constrained by biostratigraphy, can provide a high-resolution temporal framework for comparing sediment accommodation histories between basins. By combining data from the study area with similar data from other areas, construction of a high-resolution eustatic sea-level curve for the Middle Pennsylvanian may become possible. Sequence stratigraphic–biostratigraphic frameworks coupled with sea-level curves will provide for more precise interbasinal correlations and improve resolution of paleogeographic and paleoclimatic reconstructions.

Pennsylvanian strata have traditionally been referred to as cyclothems—lithostratigraphic units consisting of predictable facies successions bounded by unconformities (Wanless and Weller, 1932; Moore, 1936; Heckel, 1977). Cyclothems are typically widespread and relatively uniform across cratonic shelves. They can be correlated regionally and interbasinally, based on a combination of lithostratigraphic and biostratigraphic evidence (e.g., Boardman and Heckel, 1989).

Cyclic successions in southwestern Kansas exhibit considerable variations in thickness, lateral extent, and lithofacies over short distances, and cannot be accurately described using traditional cyclothem terminology. However, sequence stratigraphic methods provide precise description of the complex multicyclic nature of Middle Pennsylvanian strata in the Hugoton embayment and lead to greater understanding of facies distribution patterns in cyclothemic successions.

Sequence stratigraphy: Methods versus scale

The depositional sequence is the fundamental unit of sequence stratigraphy. It is defined as a genetically related succession of strata bounded by unconformity surfaces or their correlative conformities (Mitchum, 1977). *Sequence boundaries* are identified by an abrupt basinward shift in facies or a change in parasequence stacking patterns (Van Wagoner et al.,

1990). Van Wagoner (1985) defines a *parasequence* as ". . . a relatively conformable succession of genetically related beds . . . bounded by marine-flooding surfaces and their correlative surfaces." Within each sequence, vertically adjacent parasequences that display similar stacking patterns may be grouped into systems tracts. Parasequences within system tracts were deposited in stratigraphically distinct but genetically linked depositional environments (deltas, for example). They may be formed by either autocyclic or allocyclic means.

Sequence sets are groups of sequences that stack into similar progradational, aggradational, or retrogradational motifs and are analogous to systems tracts within a single depositional sequence (Mitchum and Van Wagoner, 1991). A *composite sequence* consists of lowstand, transgressive, and highstand sequence sets (Mitchum and Van Wagoner, 1991).

Although sequence stratigraphers agree that the depositional sequence is the "fundamental unit of sequence stratigraphy" (Vail et al., 1991), they disagree on the relative importance of scalar properties. Vail et al. (1991) refer to the depositional sequence as a third-order cycle that ranges from 0.5 to 3 m.y. in duration. However, other workers (e.g., Mitchum and Van Wagoner, 1991; Posamentier et al., 1992) treat depositional sequence as scale independent. In a broad preliminary study, Watney et al. (1989) successfully applied sequence analysis to younger Pennsylvanian cyclothems. We use scale-independent methods here because cyclothems possess all components of a depositional sequence. The relative merits of methodological versus scalar emphasis in sequence stratigraphic analysis will be addressed in a forthcoming paper.

General Geology

This study describes the facies and geometries of the "Gray group" (Youle, 1991). In the study area, the "Gray group" lies unconformably upon the Kearny Formation (Morrowan?; Thompson, 1944) and, with the overlying Cherokee Group (Desmoinesian), forms a continuous succession of strata that onlap either the Kearny Formation or the pre-Pennsylvanian unconformity surface as they onlap the Central Kansas uplift (Fig. 1).

Six recurring lithofacies were identified. Seven depositional sequences were identified in a 26-m core from the

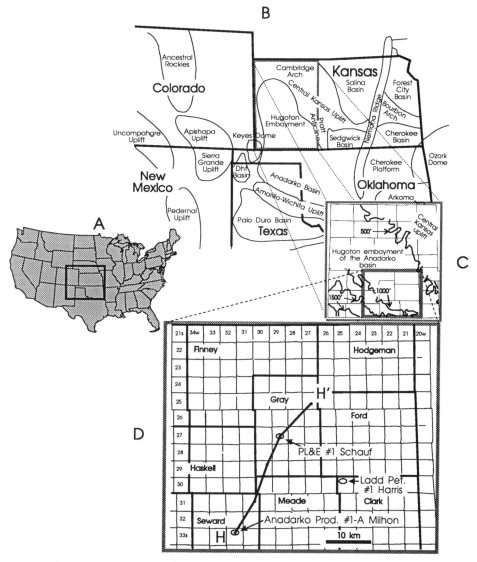

Figure 1. A, Map of continental United States showing location of B. B, Pennsylvanian features of the Midcontinent (modified from Moore, 1979). C, Isopach of Lansing to Mississippian (500-ft [152-m] contour interval; modified from Merriam, 1963). D, Study area including key wells and cross section.

Pendleton Land and Exploration Inc. #1 Schauf core (16-T27S-R26W; Gray County, Kansas). Sequence boundaries were identified by well-developed subaerial exposure surfaces upon subtidal or lower shoreface rocks. The Shauf core provided the primary petrographic and biostratigraphic database tied to the well's gamma-ray and neutron-density wireline logs. Regional cross sections were constructed and sequence boundaries were traced over an area of about 14,000 km², from the interior of the Hugoton embayment to the flanks of the Central Kansas uplift (Fig. 1). Eight other cores that include small intervals of the "Gray group" were also incorporated into the correlation grid. This correlation grid provided a framework that estab-

lished facies relationships and geometries that were used to interpret the depositional history of the "Gray group" and lower Cherokee Group in southwestern Kansas.

Fusulinid and conodont data indicate that sequences *i* through *l* were deposited during the late Atokan and that sequences *f* through *h* accumulated in the early Desmoinesian (Fig. 2). This is significantly later than the Morrowan to early Atokan age widely accepted for these strata. The Atokan-Desmoinesian boundary lies within the "Gray group" as it does in the lower type Des Moines Supergroup (Lambert, 1992). Primitive species of *Beedeina* belonging to the *B. insolita* assemblage first occur at the base of sequence *h*, mark-

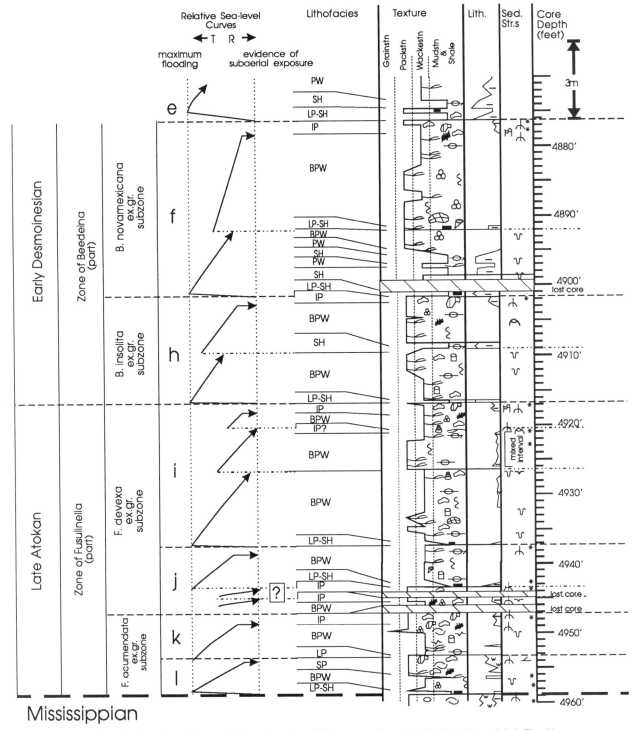

Figure 2. Core description and biostratigraphy of "Gray group" rocks in the Pendleton Ld. & Ex. #1 Schauf, Sec. 16, T27S, R29W, Gray County, Kansas. See Figure 4 for key. Fusulinid zones from Clopine (1992) and Meyers (1988).

ing the earliest Desmoinesian by fusulinid faunas. The base of sequence *h* also contains the earliest occurrence of *Neognathodus caudatus,* a conodont datum proposed by Lambert and Heckel (1991) to define the Atokan/Desmoinesian boundary. The overlying sequence *g* laps out downdip from the Pendleton #1 Schauf core.

Figure 2 includes a fusulinid zonation of the #1 Schauf core, and each sequence present is assigned to a fusulinid subzone. Although fusulinid subzones are informal biostratigraphic subdivisions, each of these is widely recognized—under different names by various specialists. Here, the late Atokan subzones follow the nomenclature of Clopine (1992) and the early Desmoinesian ones follow Meyers (1988). The subzones impart a distinctive biostratigraphic designation to the sequences. As a result, these sequences can be precisely correlated with contemporaneous strata deposited under similar paleoenvironmental conditions (e.g., the lower type Des Moines Supergroup). They can also be confidently correlated into regions where dissimilar

paleoenvironmental regimes resulted in strikingly different stratigraphic character (e.g., type Derry carbonates in New Mex ico—see Clopine, 1992). That is because the independent sequence stratigraphic and biostratigraphic constraints operate in tandem to circumscribe more accurate lithostratigraphic correlations than either method alone could attain.

LITHOFACIES AND THEIR INTERPRETATION

Lithofacies in the Schauf core are presented in Figure 2. The order in which the lithofacies are described coincides with the vertical succession of facies, from bottom to top, in a simplified depositional sequence (Fig. 3).

Mississippian-Pennsylvanian contact

Throughout most of the midcontinent, post-Mississippian regression is marked by widespread subaerial exposure, valley incision, and erosion (e.g., Rascoe and Adler, 1983). A sharp

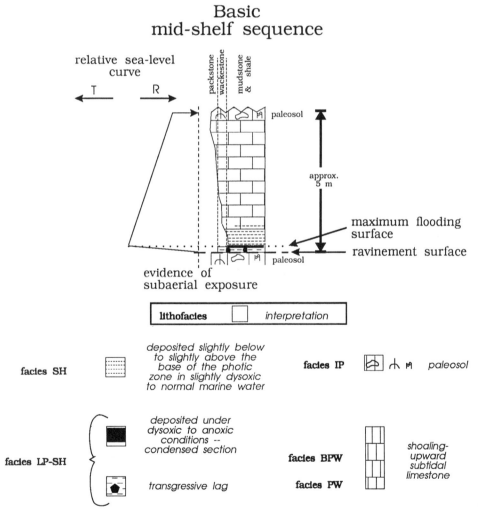

Figure 3. Simplified mid-shelf sequence (without parasequences) showing interpretation of lithofacies recognized in the #1 Schauf core. See Figure 4 for key.

contact divides Mississippian strata from overlying black, silty, argillaceous, lithoclastic packstone and wackestone of Pennsylvanian age. The top 1.2 m of Mississippian strata consist of green silty peloidal packstone with root molds and caliche nodules interpreted to represent subaerial exposure. The lithoclasts at the base of the Pennsylvanian were derived from underlying Mississippian strata.

Dark-gray to black lithoclastic packstone and shale facies (LP-SH)

Description. The contact below facies LP-SH is always sharp and the contact above is always gradational with overlying facies. Facies LP-SH overlies light-colored intraclastic packstones and wackestones (facies IP) in most occurrences. However, it overlies light-colored bioclastic packstones and wackestones (facies BPW) at the top of sequence *j* and within sequence *f* (Fig. 2). There it is overlain by either gray shales and argillaceous wackestones (facies SH) or dark colored bioclastic wackestones (facies PW).

A 7.5-cm-thick zone at the base of facies LP-SH contains poorly sorted, angular to subangular lithoclasts (up to 30 mm in diameter) in a dark-gray to black micritic matrix. The lithoclasts consist of bioclastic wackestones and packstones and abraded caliche nodules that closely resemble facies of underlying units. Fusulinids and echinoderm fragments are also locally common. The dark-gray to black matrix contains abundant unoxidized organic-rich material. Basal lithoclastic wackestones grade upward into a black to dark-gray shale (up to 30 cm thick) that locally contains concentrated phosphate nodules. There is little evidence of bioturbation. Silt occurs within the matrix only where facies LP-SH overlies Mississippian strata.

Wireline-log cross sections indicate that facies LP-SH grades laterally down depositional dip into radioactive "hot" black shales (up to 3 m thick) with elevated gamma radiation in the deeper portions of the Hugoton embayment.

Interpretation. Lithoclastic packstones at the base of facies LP-SH are interpreted to have been deposited upon a ravinement surface during transgression. The poor sorting, angularity, and lithoclasts derived from underlying units suggest that these deposits originated from local sources and were deposited without significant transport. The sharp contact below the facies may result from planation of underlying units.

The presence of unoxidized organic-rich matrix and the paucity of burrows indicate that this facies represents dysoxic to anoxic conditions. The black shale is interpreted to have been deposited during ocean-water stratification at times of rising (Calvert et al., 1987; Wetzel, 1991) or maximum water depths (Heckel, 1977, 1986). In the shalier upper part of the facies, phosphate nodules suggest slow depositional rates. The basinward thickening of black shales in this unit and their absence shelfward also suggest deposition in deepening water.

Limy shale to argillaceous wackestone facies (SH)

Description. Facies SH consists of dark to medium gray calcareous shale with local argillaceous carbonate interbeds. The facies is moderately to completely bioturbated. The dominant allochems are whole, unabraded brachiopods and disarticulated echinoderms. Wireline-logs indicate that facies SH grades basinward into black shales up to 3 m thick.

Interpretation. Facies SH is interpreted to have been deposited below wave base near the bottom of the photic zone under open-marine conditions. Abundant fine-grained material and unabraded fossils suggest low-energy deposition. Boardman et al. (1984) interpreted similar facies to represent deposition slightly below the photic zone under normal-marine to slightly dysoxic conditions.

Dark-colored peloidal wackestone facies (PW)

Description. Facies PW is burrow mottled and ranges from dark-gray to gray to brown. Dominant allochems include peloids, echinoderm fragments, brachiopods, and fusulinids. Other foraminifera, phylloid algae, and intraclasts are less common. Allochems are generally whole and unabraded. Burrowing is moderate to extensive. Facies PW lies gradationally above facies SH and below overlying carbonates. It is interbedded with facies SH at the base of sequence *f* (Fig. 2). Locally it contains abundant solution-seam stylolites.

Interpretation. Unabraded fossils, phylloid algae, and moderate to extensive burrowing suggest facies PW was deposited below wave base but within the photic zone under normal marine to slightly dysoxic conditions.

Medium-gray to tan bioclastic packstone and wackestone facies (BPW)

Description. Facies PBW grades from medium-gray or light-colored wackestones into light-gray to tan packestones. Facies BPW lies gradationally above PW, SH, or LP-SH and grades upward into light-colored intraclastic packstone to wackestone (facies IP). Locally, the unit may be interbedded with facies LP-SH, PW, IP, and SH.

Dominant allochems in the packestones include tubular and encrusting forams, fusulinids, peloids, and phylloid algae. The allochems are commonly abraded. Brachiopods, crinoids, fusulinids, and solitary corals are locally common throughout this facies but are most abundant in the wackestones, where allochems remain unabraded. Chaetetids, bryozoans, and ostracodes are present in places. Bioturbation is pervasive throughout the facies.

Phylloid algae, mollusks, coated grains, and intraclasts become common toward the top of facies BPW. Locally, root traces extend downward from overlying facies IP into the top of this facies. Solution-seam and suture-seam stylolites are common and in places are abundant. Dark-gray clay is a common residue in the stylolites and may account for the high gamma ray counts within portions of this facies.

Interpretation. The commonly broken but relatively unabraded allochems in the medium- to dark-gray wackestones indicate occasional reworking of sediment by waves and bioturbation. The appearance of coated grains, intraclasts, and abraded bioclastic material near the top of this facies indicates more rigorous and consistent reworking of the sediment by waves and suggests shoaling. The relative decrease in abundance of corals, brachiopods, crinoids, and fusulinids and commensurate increase in abundance of phylloid algae and mollusks up through the section also suggest an upward decrease in water depth (e.g., Boardman et al., 1984). Facies BPW is interpreted to represent a shoaling-upward carbonate deposited from below to slightly above wave base, under normal marine conditions.

Tan to cream silty bioclastic and lithoclastic packstone facies (SP)

Description. Facies SP is present only at the top of sequence *1* (Fig. 2), where it is thinly interbedded with facies BPW. Facies SP contains heavily abraded allochems and lithoclasts in a silty packstone to siltstone matrix and locally displays low-angle cross-bedding.

Interpretation. The abraded allochems and low-angle cross-bedding indicate deposition in a high-energy environment, probably above normal wave base. Some of the silt in the matrix may have been derived from erosion of the silt-rich Mississippian Ste. Genevieve Limestone that subcrops beneath the "Gray group" in the area. Interbeds of facies BPW suggest that deposition occurred in a lower-shoreface environment near wave base.

Light-colored intraclastic packstone to wackestone facies (IP)

Description. Facies IP is a light-green to light-gray intraclastic packstone to wackestone. However, at the top of sequence *f* it displays color gradation from green and light-gray at the top into red and tan near the base. Biotic constituents include phylloid algae, brachiopods, foraminifera, mollusks, and fusulinids and are the same constituents that are present in the top of the underlying facies. Autoclastic brecciation, root molds, rhizocretions, and cream to dark-brown caliche crusts are common throughout the facies. Alveolar textures, rhizocretions, and circumgranular cracking are common features seen in thin section. Intraclasts are ovoid to polygonal in shape and range from several centimeters to less than 1 mm in diameter. The matrix is a green to light-gray, locally silty, micrite that displays, in places, a clotted peloidal texture. Facies IP lies gradationally above underlying facies (generally facies BPW)

and is sharply overlain by the succeeding facies (generally facies LP-SH).

Interpretation. The common rhizocretions, autoclastic brecciation, root traces, caliche nodules, circumgranular cracking, and alveolar textures indicate that this facies has been altered by subaerial exposure. The intraclasts are interpreted to represent peds created during the soil-forming process. The commonly green to light-gray coloration may be a function of postexposure transgression and gleying of the tops of soil profiles (Joeckel, 1991). The color gradation from red up into green at the top of sequence *f* is common in soils that have experienced transgressive gleying (Joeckel, 1991).

DISCUSSION OF DEPOSITIONAL SEQUENCES IN THE "GRAY GROUP"

Vertical distribution of lithofacies

Each of the six depositional sequences in the "Gray group" displays a consistent vertical succession of facies consisting of—from bottom to top—LP-SH, SH, PW, BPW, and IP. Figure 3 displays these lithofacies and their interpretation in the context of a simplified "Gray group" sequence. The basal portion of the sequence, consisting of facies LP-SH, is interpreted to represent a deepening-upward succession from a basal transgressive lag into a condensed section. Condensed sections may form during transgression as a result of ponding of siliciclastics in source areas (Heckel, 1989) and because carbonate production is reduced by nutrient excesses. Nutrient excesses may result in both reduced clarity of the water column (and light penetration) (Neumann and Macintyre, 1985; Hallock and Schlager, 1986) and the development of an oxygen minimum zone (Wetzel, 1991). Upon maximum inundation, condensed sections may continue to form as a result of both reduced light levels and retardation of carbonate production under dysoxic or anoxic conditions resulting from development of a thermocline (Heckel, 1977, 1986, 1990). Climate change during glacioeustatic rise such as during the Pleistocene-Holocene transition may have contributed nutrients, encouraging organic productivity. Also, freshwater runoff may have assisted in stratifying the water column, promoting preservation of organic matter (Calvert et al., 1987; Coveney et al., 1991; Hatch and Levanthal, 1992; Heckel, 1991).

Carbonates (PW and BPW) may have begun to accumulate above the condensed section in response to either a decrease in the rate of rise of relative sea level, a stillstand, or a drop in relative sea level. Depending on water depth, depositional topography, clarity of the water column, siliciclastic influx, and marine circulation, shoaling upward facies indicate that carbonate sedimentation rates were greater than the rate of relative sea-level rise or that there was a fall in relative sea level.

Facies IP that caps each sequence represents an abrupt

basinward shift from subtidal carbonates below to subaerially exposed carbonates of the same facies above. This indicates that sea level fell abruptly relative to carbonate deposition rates, resulting in an attenuated section that lacks intertidal and supratidal facies. The abruptness of sea-level fall is supported from several observations: (1) no evidence of peritidal facies exists, such as relict clasts, to suggest that erosion may have removed this facies; (2) no clastic wedges exist on the mid- or lower-shelf that can be attributed to a prolonged period of erosion during falling sea level; and (3) no incised valleys are associated with these subaerial surfaces such as might be anticipated if erosion had been significant.

Parasequences. The shoaling-upward pattern of the basic "Gray group" sequence (Fig. 3) is interrupted by minor deepening events in sequences *f, h, i,* and possibly *j* (Fig. 2). These flooding surfaces, below which an abrupt basinward shift in facies did not occur, are interpreted to represent parasequence boundaries. They are recognized by the abrupt termination of the shoaling-upward pattern in facies BPW. Parasequences divide the basic depositional sequence into several smaller-scale shoaling-upward cycles.

In sequence *h* the presence of a parasequence can be detected on wireline logs because of the presence of shale in facies SH (Fig. 4). However, it is more common for deeper-water carbonates to overlie the flooding surface and to sit directly on top of shallower-water carbonates. The superposition of these carbonate facies makes the parasequence boundary difficult to establish with wireline logs alone.

Regional distribution of lithofacies within "Gray group" sequences

Sequence boundaries identified in the Schauf core (Fig. 4) were traced throughout the eastern Hugoton embayment using cross sections constructed from gamma-ray and neutron-density wireline logs. Lateral facies transitions within each depositional sequence were analyzed from three reference points along a depositional profile: the lower-shelf, mid-shelf, and proximal shelf (Fig. 5).

Lower-shelf sequences. Wireline-log characteristics of depositional sequences *f* through *m* in the Anadarko Production #1-A Milhon (Fig. 6) are interpreted to represent typical lower-shelf sequences. "Gray group" lower-shelf depositional sequences range from 3 to 10 m in thickness. The base of each sequence is marked by elevated radioactivity in a 1.25- to 3-m-thick black shale or limestone. These facies thin shelfward, grading into less radioactive dark-gray shales (Fig. 6). They correlate to the thin black shales of facies LP-SH in the Schauf core. The lower-shelf black shales intertongue shelfward with mid-shelf limestones.

Most black shales grade vertically into nonradioactive limestones 1.25 to 6 m thick. Cross sections tied into cores indicate that these limestones thicken shelfward up to 25 m and grade into phylloid algal to bioclastic wackestones and packstones. In sequences *g* and *h,* black shales grade vertically

through shaley limestone before passing into nonradioactive dense limestones. These shaley carbonates also thin and grade shelfward into the overlying limestone facies.

Carbonate production in the lower-shelf environment probably began when water circulation improved, leading to better-oxygenated water at the sediment-water interface. This process accelerated when the sediment-water interface was in the photic zone. Lower-shelf limestones are interpreted to have accumulated in response to relative sea-level falls that culminated in subaerial exposure of correlative mid-shelf limestones. Lower-shelf sequences do not vary significantly throughout the basin.

Mid-shelf sequences. Sequences *f* through *i* in the #1 Schauf core are considered typical of mid-shelf sequences. Mid-shelf sequences differ from lower-shelf sequences in that they are thicker, contain a greater percentage of carbonate, and are separated from one another by subaerial exposure surfaces (sequence boundaries). Well-developed subaerial exposure surfaces and a lack of thick black shales reflect the decrease in accommodation space for mid-shelf sequences compared to lower-shelf equivalents.

High gamma spikes (greater than 150 API units) may occur locally at the top of some mid- and proximal-shelf limestones. Unlike lower-shelf sequences, these "hot" limestones are rare and generally restricted to less than 0.25 km^2. They are developed immediately below subaerial exposure surfaces and probably reflect local uranium concentrations from pedogenic or groundwater processes (Carlisle, 1983; Chung and Swart, 1990).

Proximal-shelf sequences. Proximal-shelf sequences are thin, contain peritidal facies, and are heavily overprinted by processes associated with subaerial exposure. These characteristics reflect further decrease in accommodation space for sequences deposited higher on the flanks of the Central Kansas uplift. Proximal-shelf sequences are commonly preserved in incised valleys, where pedogenic processes have significantly altered them but postdepositional erosion has not removed them.

The #1 Harris core (Clark County, Kansas; Fig. 1), contains a vertical succession of sequences that illustrate a range of proximal-shelf facies. This core is located on the edge of a valley incised into Mississippian carbonates. The Harris core is described below from the top down.

Sequence *i* in the #1 Harris consists of facies IP and BPW with the presence of fenestral fabrics. A well-washed 15-cm-thick bioclastic packstone forms the base of the sequence in place of facies LP-SH (Fig. 7).

The absence of a condensed section in sequence *i* indicates that water depth was insufficient for the development of a thermocline or for the sediment water interface to drop below the photic zone. The lack of black shale also suggests that deposition on the proximal shelf began sometime after the point of maximum rate of sea-level rise and before the turnaround point on the relative sea-level curve (e.g., because of its higher shelf position). With a slower rise in sea level on the

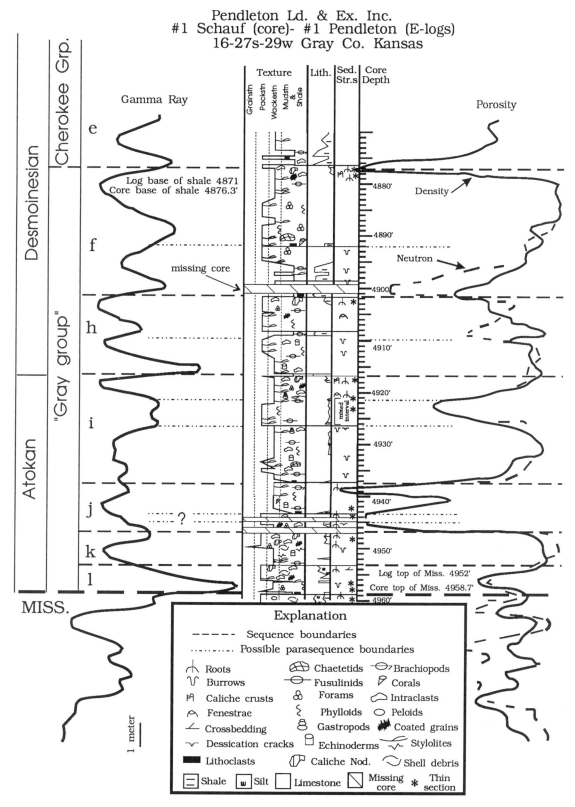

Figure 4. Core description and wireline log of "Gray group" type section.

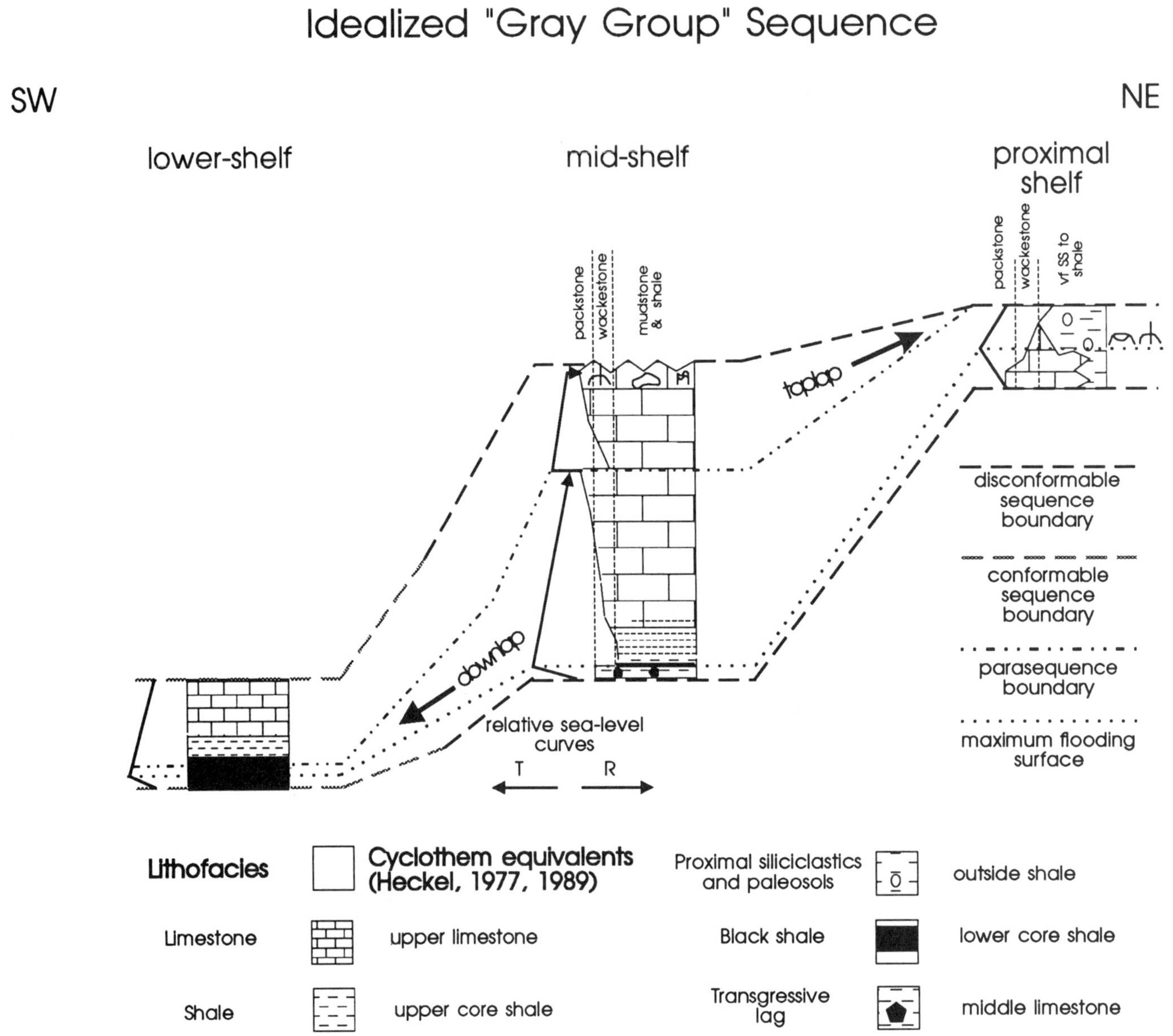

Idealized "Gray Group" Sequence

Figure 5. Generalized distribution of lithofacies in "Gray group" sequences and comparison of idealized sequences to classic "Kansas" cyclothems.

proximal shelf, carbonate production was not interrupted, and carbonate sedimentation continued through both a rise and fall in relative sea level. Transgression is represented by the gradation from a well-washed bioclastic packstone into subtidal wackestones. Regression is evidenced by the gradation from bioclastic wackestones into overlying peritidal carbonates. The exact turnaround point of the sea-level curve is difficult to establish; it occurred somewhere within the bioclastic wackestones that separate the basal packstone from overlying fenestral carbonates. Locally, in the absence of well-defined parasequences, the relative sea-level profile of proximal-shelf sequence may appear symmetrical (Fig. 5).

Two relatively well preserved limestone beds (60 and 120 cm thick respectively) are present about 60 cm below the base of sequence *i*. Despite the karsting within these carbonates, fossils of stenohaline open-marine organisms are present. The limestones are separated by about 1 m of green blocky shale with slickensides, caliche nodules, intraclasts, lithoclasts, and disoriented chaetetid heads interpreted as filling karst features. The two limestones and intervening shale are correlated as proximal equivalents to sequence *k* limestones in the Schua core (Fig. 7).

Below sequence *k* are two beds of calcareous siltstone, 3 and 45 cm thick, respectively. Both siliciclastic beds contai

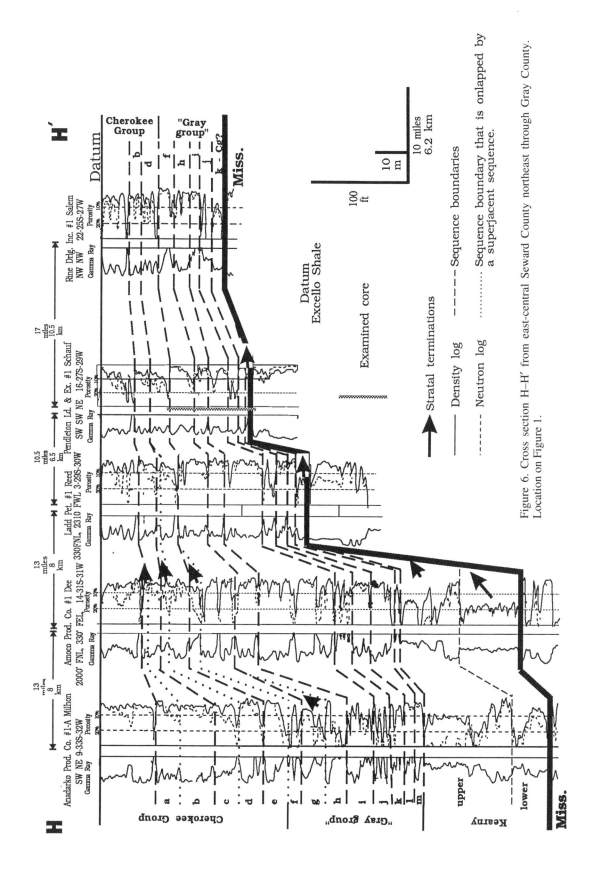

Figure 6. Cross section H–H′ from east-central Seward County northeast through Gray County. Location on Figure 1.

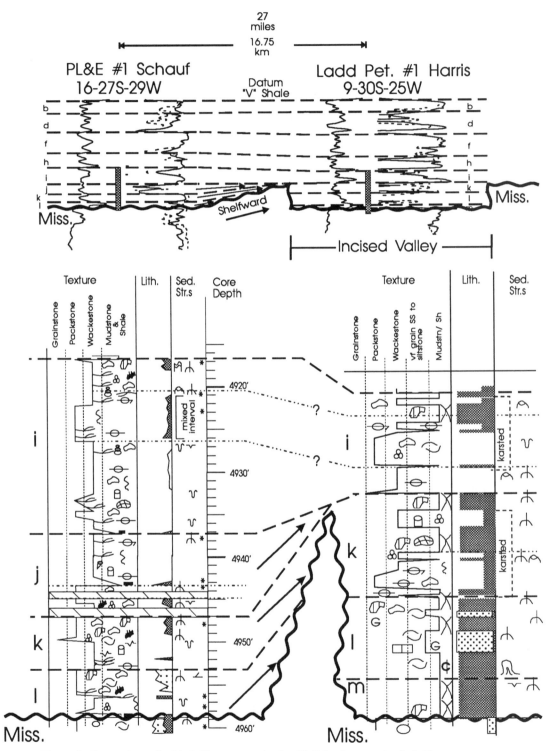

Figure 7. Comparison of mid-shelf sequences in the #1 Schauf to proximal-shelf sequences preserved within an incised valley in the #1 Harris. See Figure 4 for key.

minor lithoclasts and abraded shell fragments as well as display root traces at their tops. The beds are separated by 60 cm of blocky shale with slickensides and caliche nodules interpreted to be a paleosol. The siltstones are interpreted to represent low-energy coastal equivalents of sequence/carbonates in the Schauf core. In local incised valleys, sequences *m, k, l,* and *i* contain estuarine sandstones up to 18 m thick (Youle, 1992). The lowermost siltstone grades down into about 1 m of medium-gray, slightly silty shale at the base of sequence *l*.

Below sequence *l* lies a green and red mottled, slightly silty, blocky shale with root molds, caliche nodules, and, locally, shell fragments. This shale is interpreted as a paleosol representing sequence *m*. Well log correlations indicate that sequence *m* onlaps the sub-Pennsylvanian unconformity surface southwest of the #1 Schauf (Fig. 6).

Comparison of the #1 Harris core with the #1 Schauf core indicates that mid-shelf carbonates grade shoreward into thin subtidal to upper-intertidal carbonates. These proximal-shelf carbonates grade further shoreward into siliciclastic strand or estuarine units, eventually lapping out to undifferentiated soil profiles.

Figure 5 displays a generalized "Gray group" sequence along depositional dip. Lower-shelf portions of sequences represent continuous deposition but are thin as a result of prolonged sediment starvation. Sequences thicken toward the mid shelf because of the higher rates and longer times of carbonate deposition. Proximal-shelf sequences are thin from a lack of accommodation space and lack of deposition during subaerial exposure and possible erosion.

Internal architecture of depositional sequences

Parasequences. Mitchum et al. (1977) identified six types of stratal terminations based upon reflection seismic records. Similar stratal terminations are apparent cross sections of sequence *i* that extend from the distal Hugoton embayment to the flanks of the Central Kansas uplift (Figs. 8 and 9). Progressive changes in the thicknesses of the correlative intervals within sequence *i*, traced along depositional slope, strongly suggest that they delineate parasequences, some of which tie to those found in the wireline logs and cores of the Schauf and Harris wells (Fig. 7). Furthermore, gradual facies changes within the correlative intervals indicate that they are genetically linked, not simple lithostratigraphic beds. The stacking patterns of these parasequences delineate basic systems tracts within sequence *i* (Figs. 8 and 9).

Development and preservation of parasequences are a function of shelf position (Fig. 5). In mid-shelf sequences, older parasequences merge down dip into condensed sections where deeper water and a distal position led to sediment starvation. Similarly, younger mid-shelf parasequences toplap shelfward as a result of a lack of accommodation space or erosion.

Comparison with classic Kansas cyclothems

Within each depositional setting, "Gray group" sequences display a repetitious and predictable suite of facies. It is instructive to compare them with classic cyclothems, from which they differ depending on their depositional position (Fig. 5).

Lower-shelf "Gray group" sequences lack distinctive transgressive ("middle") limestones and regressive ("outside") shales. The base of each lower-shelf sequence is marked by a condensed section (black shale) equivalent to the "core shale." The black shales grade vertically into a limestone equivalent to the regressive ("upper") limestone. However, in lower-shelf sequences the regressive limestone may be conformably overlain by the black shale of the succeeding sequence.

Mid-shelf sequences contain all the major components of the "Kansas" cyclothem, but the "transgressive limestone," "core shale," and "outside shale" equivalents are attenuated. In these localities the basal transgressive lag would be equivalent to the "transgressive limestone," and the condensed section is equivalent to the "core shale." The shoaling-upward carbonates that overlie condensed sections in mid-shelf sequences are similar to "regressive limestones." The subaerial exposure surfaces and associated paleosols that cap these sequences may be considered roughly equivalent to the "regressive shale."

Proximal-shelf sequences differ from "Kansas" cyclothems because they do not contain core shales. Transgressive ("middle") limestones grade into overlying regressive ("outside") limestones without developing an intervening core shale. The turnaround point of relative sea level in a proximal-shelf cycle occurs within the single proximal-sequence carbonate unit. Proximal-shelf sequences are similar to the "Kansas" cyclothem in that the regressive limestones may be overlain by thick soil profiles equivalent to "outside shales" of Heckel (1977).

DEPOSITIONAL HISTORY OF THE "GRAY GROUP" AND LOWER CHEROKEE GROUP IN THE EASTERN HUGOTON EMBAYMENT

Fourth-order depositional sequences

Depositional sequences in the #1 Schauf core are similar in thickness to Missourian and upper Desmoinesian cyclothems described by Heckel (1977, 1986, 1991). Heckel (1986) estimated the duration of most Pennsylvanian cyclothems to range from 235,000 to about 400,000 yrs and that of "minor" cycles to range from about 40,000 to 120,000 yrs. Some recent workers suggest that the estimated duration of the Pennsylvanian Period should be reduced by 45% and that cy-

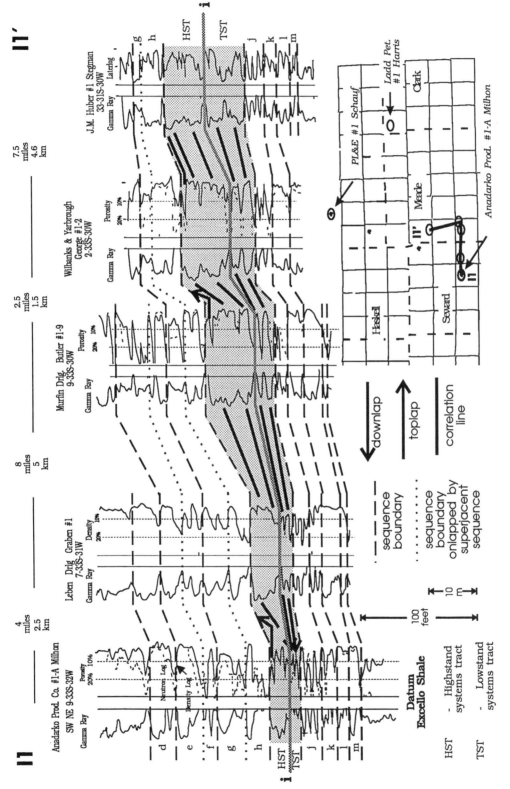

Figure 8. Cross section I1–I1′ displaying intrasequence *i* correlations from lower-shelf to mid-shelf.

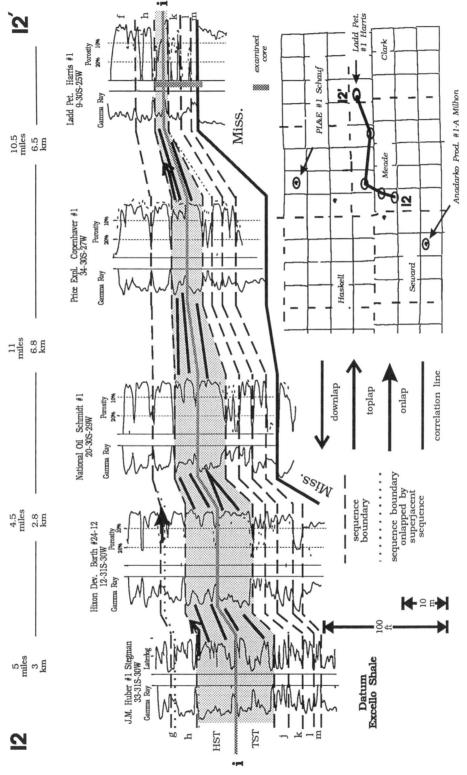

Figure 9. Cross section I2–I2′displaying intrasequence *i* correlations from mid-shelf to proximal-shelf.

clothem duration may be considerably less than Heckel estimated (Klein and Kupperman, 1992; Klein, 1990). Veevers and Powell (1987) estimated that glacioeustatically driven Pennsylvanian cycles averaged about 400,000 yrs in duration.

Biostratigraphic information from the Pendleton #1 Schauf core constrains the duration of these depositional sequences. The Atokan-Desmoinesian boundary is located at the base of sequence *h* (Fig. 2). Sequences *i* through *l* are included in the zoned of *Fusulinella,* indicating that these sequences are from the approximate latest one-third of the Atokan. The duration of this upper Atokan succession is approximately 1 m.y., using the time chart of Haq and Van Eysinga (1987). Four sequences are present in this interval. Thus, the average duration of a single sequence is approximately 0.25 m.y. Desmoinesian sequences *f* through *h* at the top of the Gray Group include the lower two subzones of *Beedeina* and most likely represent approximately the lower one-fourth to one-fifth of the Desmoinesian. The approximate duration of these zones ranges from 1.2 m.y. to 1.5 m.y. (Haq and Van Eysinga, 1987). Three sequences are contained in this interval, including sequence *g,* which laps out along the lower shelf. The average duration of these sequences is estimated to be between 0.4 and 0.5 m.y. These average and approximate times indicate that both the Atokan and Desmoinesian sequences are fourth-order cycles (0.1 to 1.0 m.y. of Goldhammer et al. [1991] or 0.08 to 0.5 m.y. of Vail et al., [1991]).

Third-order sequence

Regional wireline-log correlations reveal subtle vertical changes in the character of facies, geometries, and stacking patterns of the thirteen fourth-order "Gray Group" depositional sequences. This integrated change in character records the influence of a third-order (1 to 10 m.y. of Goldhammer et al. [1991]) relative sea-level cycle. At least two scales of relative sea-level change affected "Gray group" deposition, with each depositional sequence recording one high-frequency relative sea-level cycle.

Transgressive phase. The transgressive phase of a sea-level cycle is indicated by an overall increase in accommodation space through lower "Gray group" sequences *h* through *m* in the Schauf core. (1) Exposure surfaces are common and closely spaced at the base of the section but become more widely spaced up section (Fig. 2). (2) Facies LP-SH and SH, interpreted as the deepest-water facies, are absent in the basal two sequences. They appear and become progressively thicker in sequences *j* through *h.* (3) Proximal-shelf lower-shoreface deposits (facies SP) are present only at the base of the "Gray group." (4) The condensed section at the base of sequence *h* produces about five times more conodonts per kilogram (5,000 to 8,000c/kg) than the other condensed sections. Assuming a constant background population of conodont animals, this suggests that the condensed section at the base of sequence *h*

spanned the longest interval of time. It follows that sequence *h* also represents the maximum flooding interval in the third-order relative sea-level cycle.

Regional cross sections also indicate the presence of a third-order rise in relative sea level during lower "Gray group" deposition. Cross sections show younger sequences overstepping older sequences as the lower "Gray group" (*h* through *m*) onlaps the Central Kansas uplift (e.g., Figs. 6 and 10). The vertical succession of facies in the Schauf core and the regional geometries of "Gray group" sequences depict these units as cyclic backstepping or retrogradational transgressive units. They are interpreted to represent the transgressive phase of a third-order relative sea-level cycle.

Regressive phase. The wireline log of the Anadarko Production Co. Milhon #1-A (Fig. 6) illustrates changes in the distribution of upper "Gray Group" facies. This reflects a third-order fall in relative sea level during upper "Gray group" through lower Cherokee Group deposition. In the Milhon #1-A, sequences *a* through *c* in the lower Cherokee Group lack the thick radioactive shales that occur in underlying sequences *f* through *m.* Sequences *a* through *c* are also thicker and contain a greater percentage of limestone than sequences *f* through *m.* Wireline-log characteristics of sequences *a, b,* and *c,* in the Milhon #1-A, resemble the wireline-log characteristics of mid-shelf sequences *f, h,* and *i* in the #1 Schuaf (Fig. 6). Sequences *d* and *e* have wireline-log characteristics that are transitional between sequences *f* through *m* and sequences *a* through *c* (Fig. 6). In the #1-A Milhon, the vertical decrease in black shales and concomitant increase in limestone indicate that mid-shelf facies prograded basinward from upper "Gray group" through lower Cherokee Group deposition, reflecting a third-order sea-level regression.

Regional cross sections also indicate a third-order regression. Sequences *a, c, e,* and *g* onlap subjacent sequences and are restricted to distal portions of the eastern Hugoton shelf (Figs. 6 and 10). This indicates a decrease in accommodation space from "Gray group" through lower Cherokee Group deposition. The decreases in accommodation space on the shelf and progradation of mid-shelf facies basinward from "Gray" through lower Cherokee Group deposition supports a third-order regression (Fig. 10).

Third-order composite sequence

The third-order relative sea-level cycle is interpreted to represent a composite sequence (Mitchum and Van Wagoner, 1991), subdivided into three sequence sets. Each sequence set contains four or five fourth-order depositional sequences. Based on similar geometries, stacking patterns, and facies distributions within the fourth-order sequences, third-order transgressive, early highstand, and late highstand sequence sets are identified

Transgressive sequence set. Transgressive sequence sets are deposited during maximum rates of a third-order relative

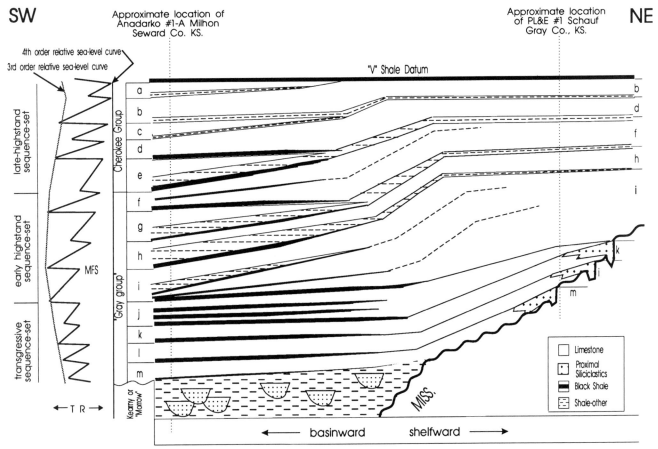

Figure 10. Conceptual cross section from Hugoton embayment northeastward toward Central Kansas uplift.

sea-level rise (Mitchum and Van Wagoner, 1991). Lower "Gray group" sequences *j* through *m* are interpreted to make up a transgressive sequence set because: (1) younger sequences successively overstep older sequences toward the shelf (Figs. 6, 8, 9, and 10), (2) younger sequences contain deeper-water facies than do older sequences (Fig. 2), and (3) none of the sequences more than double in thickness between the lower-shelf into the mid-shelf (Figs. 6, 8, 9, and 10). Related to this lack of thickening is an absence of internal toplapping and downlapping stratal terminations indicative of well-developed parasequences.

Incised-valley-fill estuarine sandstones are best preserved within the sequences that comprise the transgressive sequence set (Youle, 1992). Preservation of these proximal siliciclastics may in part be a function of the relatively brief period of time during which these depositional sequences were subjected to subaerial exposure and erosion prior to subsequent inundation.

Early-highstand sequence set. An early-highstand sequence set is deposited when the rate of sea-level rise slows, stops, and then falls slowly. Because third-order rates of sea-level change are minimal, it is probable that higher-frequency

relative sea-level fluctuations may be preserved in the rock record with greater fidelity than is possible during deposition of other sequence sets. Sequences *i* through *f* increase in thickness up to five times from lower-shelf to mid-shelf settings. These depositional sequences display internal toplapping and downlapping stratal terminations, suggesting thick progradational to aggradational parasequences are present (Figs. 8 and 9).

Late-highstand sequence set. The late-highstand sequence set is deposited on the falling limb of the third-order sea-level curve. Sequences *a* through *e* (lower Cherokee Group) thicken basinward of older sequences and display a distinct progradational pattern (Figs. 6 and 10). Half of the lower Cherokee Group sequences onlap subjacent sequences and are restricted to distal portions of the eastern Hugoton shelf. The vertical facies changes in sequences *a* through *e* in the Milhon #1-A also indicate mid-shelf facies prograded basinward. Toplapping and downlapping stratal terminations in late-highstand depositional sequences may be absent. When third-order fall in sea level occurs at high rates, high-frequency, low-amplitude relative sea-level changes may be damped out.

CONCLUSIONS

Sequence stratigraphic and biostratigraphic analyses provide independent means to establish and correlate a hierarchy of cycles in the rock record. These types of observations can provide important temporal and process information instrumental in refining and applying climate models and paleogeographic reconstructions.

"Gray group" through middle Cherokee Group strata (mid-Middle Pennsylvanian) in the Hugoton embayment represent a third-order composite depositional sequence built of thirteen fourth-order sequences. Four to five fourth-order sequences with similar facies distributions and stacking patterns comprise the third-order transgressive, early-, and late-highstand sequence sets. Each fourth-order sequence has a sigmoidal geometry because of changes in facies character and degree of conformity along the depositional profile. Largely conformable contacts characterize thin lower-shelf sequences made up of "starved" facies. Thick mid-shelf sequences are separated by diastemic surfaces and may consist of several well-developed parasequences. More pronounced unconformity (nondeposition and erosion) separate the resulting thin upper-shelf sequences composed of shallow subtidal to coastal facies. Lithologic successions within fourth-order sequences vary along depositional slope and may possess all or portions of the components in the classic Kansas cyclothem.

ACKNOWLEDGMENTS

We thank Tony Walton, Continental Exploration, Inc., and KTEC, Inc. for supporting this research with encouragement and funding. Special thanks to Evan Franseen and John French at the Kansas Geological Survey, Pius Weibel at the Illinois Geological Survey, and Jim Markello at Mobil for many helpful suggestions and insights. Shannon Rudine assisted in preparing oriented fusulinid thin sections. Appreciation is extended to Lea Ann Davidson for word-processing support.

REFERENCES CITED

Boardman, D. R., and Heckel, P. H., 1989, Glacioeustatic sea level curve for early Late Pennsylvanian sequence in north-central Texas and biostratigraphic correlation with curve for Midcontinent North America: Geology, v. 17, p. 802–805.

Boardman, D. R., Mapes, R. H., Yancey, T. E., and Malinky, J. M., 1984, A new model for depth-related allogenic community succession within North American Pennsylvanian cyclothems and implications on the black-shale problem: Tulsa Geological Society Special Publication 2, p. 141–182.

Calvert, S. E., Vogel, J. S., and Southon, J. R., 1987, Carbon accumulation rates and the origin of the Holocene sapropel in the Black Sea: Geology, v. 15, p. 918–921.

Carlisle, D., 1983, Concentration of uranium and vanadium in calcretes and gypcretes, in Wilson, R.C.L., ed., Residual deposits: Geological Society of London Special Publication 11, p. 185–195.

Chung, G. S., and Swart, P. K., 1990, The concentration of uranium in freshwater vadose and phreatic cements in a Holocene ooid cay: A method of identifying ancient water tables: Journal of Sedimentary Petrology, v. 60, p. 735–746.

Clopine, W. W., 1992, Lower and Middle Pennsylvanian fusulinid biostratigraphy of southern New Mexico and westernmost Texas: New Mexico Bureau of Mines and Mineral Resources Bulletin 143, 67 p.

Coveney, R. M., Jr., Watney, W. L., and Maples, C. G., 1991, Contrasting depositional models for Pennsylvanian black shale discerned from molybdenum abundance: Geology, v. 19, p. 147–150.

Goldhammer, R. K., Oswald, E. J., and Dunn, P. A., 1991, Hierarchy of stratigraphic forcing: Example from Middle Pennsylvanian shelf carbonates of the Paradox basin, in Franseen, E. K., Watney, W. L., Kendall, C.G.St.C., and Ross, W., eds., Sedimentary modeling: Computer simulations and methods for improved parameter definition: Kansas Geological Survey Bulletin 233, p. 361–415.

Hallock, P., and Schlager, W., 1986, Nutrient excess and the demise of coral reefs and carbonate platforms: Palaios, v. 1, p. 389–398.

Haq, B. U., and Van Eysinga, F.W.B., 1987, Geologic time chart (fourth edition): New York, Elsevier, Plate.

Hatch, J. R., and Leventhal, J. S., 1992, Relationship between inferred redox potential of the depositional environment and geochemistry of the upper Pennsylvanian (Missourian) Stark Shale Member of the Dennis Limestone, Wabaunsee County, Kansas, U.S.A.: Chemical Geology, v. 99, p. 65–82.

Heckel, P. H., 1977, Origin of phosphatic black-shale facies in Pennsylvanian cyclothems of midcontinent North America: American Association of Petroleum Geologists Bulletin, v. 61, p. 1045–1068.

Heckel, P. H., 1986, Sea-level curve for Pennsylvanian eustatic marine transgressive-regressive depositional cycles along midcontinent outcrop belt, North America: Geology, v. 14, p. 330–334.

Heckel, P. H., 1989, Current view of midcontinent Pennsylvanian cyclothems, in Boardman, D. R. II, Barrick, J. E., Cocke, J., and Nestell, M.I.K., eds., Middle and Late Pennsylvanian chronostratigraphic boundaries in north-central Texas—Glacial-eustatic events, biostratigraphy, and paleoecology: Texas Tech University Studies in Geology 2, p. 7–34.

Heckel, P. H., 1990, Evidence for global (glacial-eustatic) control over upper Carboniferous (Pennsylvanian) cyclothems in midcontinent North America, in Hardman, R. F., and Brooks, J., eds., Tectonic events responsible for Britain's oil and gas reserves: Geological Society Special Publication 55, p. 35–47.

Heckel, P. H., 1991, Thin widespread Pennsylvanian black shales of Midcontinent North America: A record of cyclic succession of widespread pycnoclines in a fluctuating epeiric sea, in Tyson, R. V., and Pearson, T. H., eds., Modern and ancient continental shelf anoxia: Geological Society Special Publication 58, p. 259–273.

Joeckel, R. M., 1991, Palosol stratigraphy of the Eskridge Formation; early Permian pedogenesis and climate in southeastern Nebraska: Journal of Sedimentary Petrology, v. 61, p. 234–255.

Klein, G. deV., 1990, Pennsylvanian time scales and cycle periods: Geology v. 18, p. 455–457.

Klein, G. deV., and Kupperman, J. B., 1992, Pennsylvanian cyclothems Methods of distinguishing tectonically induced changes in sea level from climatically induced changes: Geological Society of America Bulletin v. 104, p. 166–175.

Lambert, L. L., 1992, Atokan and basal Desmoinesian conodonts from central Iowa, reference area for the Desmoinesian Stage, *in* Sutherland, P. K., and Manger, W. L., eds., Recent advances in Middle Carboniferous biostratigraphy—A symposium: Oklahoma Geological Survey Circular 94, p. 111–123.

Lambert, L. L., and Heckel, P. H., 1991, The Atokan/Desmoinesian boundary in North America: Preliminary considerations for selecting a boundary horizon, *in* Brenckle, P. L., and Manger, W. L., eds., Intercontinental division and correlation of the Carboniferous System: Frankfurt, Courier Forschungsinstitut Senckenberg [imprint 1990], v. 130, p. 307–318.

Merriam, D. F., 1963, The geologic history of Kansas: Kansas Geological Survey Bulletin 162, 317 p.

Meyers, D. A., 1988, Stratigraphic distribution of fusulinid foraminifera from the Manzano Mountains, New Mexico: U.S. Geological Survey Professional Paper 1446-A, p. 3–21.

Mitchum, R. M., 1977, Seismic stratigraphy and global changes of sea level. Part 1: Glossary of terms used in seismic stratigraphy, *in* Payton, C. E., ed., Seismic stratigraphy applications to hydrocarbon exploration: American Association of Petroleum Geologists Memoir 26, p. 205–212.

Mitchum, R. M., and Van Wagoner, J. C., 1991, High-frequency sequences and their stacking patterns: Sequence stratigraphic evidence of high-frequency eustatic cycles: Sedimentary Geology, v. 70, p. 131–160.

Mitchum, R. M., Vail, P. R., and Thompson, S. III, 1977, Seismic stratigraphy and global changes of sea level. Part 2: The depositional sequence as a basic unit for stratigraphic analysis, *in* Payton, C. E., ed., Seismic stratigraphy applications to hydrocarbon exploration: American Association of Petroleum Geologists Memoir 26, p. 53–62.

Moore, G. E., 1979, Pennsylvanian paleogeography of the southern Mid-Continent, *in* Hyne, N. J., Pennsylvanian sandstones of the Mid-Continent: Tulsa Geological Society Special Publication 1, p. 2–12.

Moore, R. C., 1936, Stratigraphic classification of the Pennsylvanian rocks in Kansas: Kansas Geological Survey Bulletin 22, 256 p.

Neumann, A. C., and Macintyre, I., 1985, Reef response to sea-level rise— Keep up, catchup or give up, *in* Proceedings, Fifth International Coral Congress, International Coral Reef Symposium, Tahiti, volume 3: Bedford Park, South Australia, Flinders University, p. 105–550.

Posamentier, H. W., Allen, G. P., and James, D. P., 1992, High-resolution sequence stratigraphy—The East Coulee delta: Journal of Sedimentary Petrology, v. 62, p. 310–317.

Rascoe, B., Jr., and Adler, F. J., 1983, Permo-Carboniferous hydrocarbon accumulations, Midcontinent, U.S.A.: American Association of Petroleum Geologists Bulletin, v. 67, p. 979–1001.

Suchy, D. R., and West, R. R., 1991, Genetic stratigraphy of the Fort Scott Limestone (Pennsylvanian, Desmoinesian), southeastern Kansas, in Franseen, E. K., Watney, W. L., Kendall, C.G.St.C., and Ross, W., eds., Sedimentary modeling: Computer simulations and methods for improved parameter definition: Kansas Geological Survey Bulletin 233, p. 207–231.

Thompson, M. L., 1944, Pennsylvanian Morrowan rocks and fusulinids of Kansas: Kansas Geological Survey Bulletin 52, p. 409–431.

Vail, P. R., Audemard, F., Bowman, S. A., Eisner, P. N., and Perez-Cruz, C., 1991, The stratigraphic signatures of tectonics, eustasy and sedimentology—An overview, *in* Einsele, G., Ricken, W., and Seilacher, A., eds., Cycles and events in stratigraphy: New York, Springer Verlag, p. 617–659.

Van Wagoner, J. C., 1985, Reservoir facies distribution as controlled by sea-level change [abs.]: Society of Economic Paleontologists and Mineralogists Mid-Year Meeting Abstracts, Golden, Colorado, August 11–14: Tulsa, Society of Economic Paleontologists and Mineralogists, p. 91–92.

Van Wagoner, J. C., Mitchum, R. M., Campion, K. M., and Rahmanian, V. D., 1980, Siliciclastic sequence stratigraphy in well logs, cores and outcrops: American Association of Petroleum Geologists Methods in Exploration Series 7, 55 p.

Veevers, J. J., and Powell, C. MCA., 1987, Late Paleozoic glacial episodes in Gondwanaland reflected in transgressive-regressive depositional sequences in Euramerica: Geological Society of America Bulletin, v. 98, p. 475–487.

Wanless, H. R., and Weller, J. M., 1932, Correlations and extent of Pennsylvanian cyclothems: Geological Society of America Bulletin, v. 43, p. 1003–1016.

Watney, W. L., French, J. A., and Franseen, E. K., 1989, Sequence stratigraphic interpretations and modeling of cyclothems: Kansas Geological Society, 41st Annual Field Trip Guidebook, 211 p.

Watney, W. L., Wong, J. C., and French, J. A., 1991, Computer simulation of Upper Pennsylvanian (Missourian) carbonate-dominated cycles in western Kansas, *in* Franseen, E. K., Watney, W. L., Kendall, C.G.St.C., and Ross, W., eds., Sedimentary modeling: Computer simulations and methods for improved parameter definition: Kansas Geological Survey Bulletin 233, p. 415–430.

Wetzel, A., 1991, Stratification in black shales: Depositional models and timing—An overview, *in* Einsele, G., Ricken, W., and Seilacher, A., eds., Cycles and events in stratigraphy: New York, Springer Verlag, p. 508–524.

Youle, J. C., 1991, Sequence stratigraphy of the lower Middle Pennsylvanian in the eastern Hugoton embayment, southwestern Kansas, in Integrated Studies of Petroleum Reservoirs in the Midcontinent, Midcontinent Core Workshop, American Association of Petroleum Geologists section meeting, Wichita, Kansas: Kansas Geological Survey Open-File Report, p. 142–172.

Youle, J. C., 1992, Sequence stratigraphy of the lower Middle Pennsylvanian and distribution of selected sandstones, eastern Hugoton embayment, southwestern Kansas [Masters thesis]: Lawrence, University of Kansas, 205 p.

MANUSCRIPT ACCEPTED BY THE SOCIETY MAY 14, 1993

Index

[Italic page numbers indicate major references]

A

Acadian orogeny, *85*
accretion, 1, 182, 255
 Greater Pangea, 248
acid rain, 182
Adirondack Massif, *163*
advection, 141
Afghanistan, 217
Afghanistan block, 96
Africa, 19, 120, 146, 147, 173, 174
African craton, 175
African plate, 176
aggregate grains, 231
Aghdarband, Iran, 257
Alaska, 230, 244
albedos, 44, 46, 65, 69, 70, 95, 118, 143
algae
 calcareous, 253
 coralline, 253
 green, 231, 236
 phylloid, 272
 symbiotic, 250
Alleghanian/Hercynian orogeny, 163
Alleghanian orogeny, 85
Alleghanian thrust fault zone, 175
Alleghany-Mauritanides, 170
Alleghany Orogen, 86
Alleghany-Variscan deformation, 177
Allegheny Mountains, 160
allochems, 272, 273
Alps, 221, 256, 258
alteration, 210, 213, 224
 hydrothermal, 209
Amazonia, 125
American craton, 174
American plate, 176, 177
Amery Group, 192
Amman, Jordan, 182
Ammovertella, 236
amphibian, phytosaurid, 113
Anapiculatisporites, 201
Andes, 76, 79
Angaran flora, 110
anhydrite, 237
animals, marine, 193
anomaly
 heat, 14, 17
 negative, 217
 thermal, 189
Antarctic ice, 208
Antarctic ice sheet, 86, 87
Antarctic Peninsula, 18
Antarctic region, 231
Antarctica, 19, 72, 86, 113, 146, 189, 192
anthracite, *161*
Anthracite district, 164
anthracite region, 163
Anthracoporella, 236

Anthracoporellopsis, 236
Anti Atlas, 174
Antler orogeny, 160
Antoinette Formation, 235, 237
Aoujgalia, 236
apatite, 17
Apatopus, 201
aphelion, 48, 53
Appalachia-Hercynian chain, 29
Appalachian Basin, 161, 162, 163, 165
Appalachian Mountain chain, 86
Appalachian Piedmont, 173
Appalachians, 31, 78, 171, 173, 174, 175, 176, 182
Apterrinella, 236
aragonite, 208, 209, 211, 213, 217, 225, 231, 233, 236, 237, 253
arc, magmatic, 189, 191
Archaeolithoporella, 236
Archaeolithophyllum, 236
Arctic-Alaska-Chukotka terrane, 95
Arctic Archipelago, 229
Arctic Canada, 217
Arctic Ocean, opening, 230
Arctic region, 231
Argentina, 19, 113, 192
arid regions, *119, 129*
aridity, 25, 29, 50, 72, 92, 113, 119, 122, 123, 127, 129, 131, 132, 137, 145, 151, 154, 177, 179
 defined, 120
Armenia, 221, 224
Artinskian, *237*
Asia, 86, 120, 248
Asselian and Sakmarian interval, 235
assemblages
 Lesser Pangea, 248
 palynfloral, *200*
Assistance Formation, 239, 240
associations
 benthic, *230, 234*
 limestone, 7
 skeletal, 7
asteroid impact hypothesis, 36
asthenosphere, 164, 177
Atacama Desert, 120, 122
Atlantic, central, *173*
Atlantic extensional basins, 182
Atlantic margin, 177
Atlantic passive margins, 174
Atlantic provinces, Canada, 174
atmosphere composition, *182*
Australia, 17, 18, 19, 122, *139*, 150, 189, 190, 192, 223, 233, 239
Australian sector, 96
Austria, 221, 223, 249
Avalon suture, 175
Avalon terrane, 175
Awaba Tuff, 190

B

Bahamas fracture zone, 172
Balmoral Coal Seam, 151
Baraker Formation, 150
Barbados, 209
Barents Sea, 244
barnacles, 231
basalt, 182
 flood, 178, 182
 flows, 189, 203
 horizons, 197
basement, orogenic, 16
Bashkirian and Gzhelian interval, 235
basin filling, *176*
basins
 clastic, 177
 climate drainage (arid), 126
 drainage, 134
 evaporite intraplate, 177
 extensional, *174*, 177
 intermontane transtensional, 174
 intracratonic, 248
 intramontane, 174
 lacustrine, 176
 pull-apart, 174
 rift, *174*, 178, 179, 180, 182, 197, 198, 229
 sabkha, 177
 Scotian, 179
 sedimentary, 233, 242
 strike-slip, 177
 temperate, 182
 transtensional, 177
 wrench-formed, 173
 wrench-related, 176
bauxite, 6, 178, 182
 deposits, 92
Beaufort Group, 189, 192
Beaufort volcaniclastic sediment, 189
beds, lacustrine, 238
Beedeina, 269, 282
 insolita, 269
Beekmantown Group, 162
Belcher Channel, 235
Bengal fan, 78
Benguela Current, 120
Benoue Trough, 96
bentonites, 163
Bermuda, 211
Berner curve, 68
Bevocastria, 236
bicarbonate, 209
bioclasts, 231, 232
bioerosion, 250
biogeography, *12*
biomass, floral, 21
biopolarity, *65*
Biosphere-Atmosphere Transfer Schome (BATS) model, 93

biota, 26, *193*, 237, *244*, 248
   climate change, *36*
   migration, 260
biotite, 189, 190
bioturbation, 272
Bjornoya, 244
Black Jack Formation, 189
Bloody Bluff fault, 175
Bonaparte Basin, 150
Borup Fiord Formation, 235, 237
boundaries, sequence, 268
Bowen Basin, 150
brachiopods, 211, 213, 214, 215,
   217, 225, 253, 272
   shells, 213, 214, 215, 220, 225
Brachychirotherium, 201
Brazil, 150, 189
brecciation, 273
British Columbia, 256
Brook Street magmatic arc, 189
Brookneal fault, 174
Bryomol, 231
Bryonoderm associations, 234, *237,
   239*
bryozoans, 231, 253
burial ratios, 59, 71
Buru-Seram-Janimbar terrane, 96

C

cadophytes, 152
calcification, 250
calcisponges, 255, 256
calcite, 162, 208, 210, 211, 213, 223,
   233, 236, 237, 238, 239, 253
   compensation depth, 76
calcrete, 6, 149, 179, 182, 222
caliche, *237, 238*
   crusts, 273
   nodules, 276, 279
Canadian Arctic, *229*
Canadian Shield, 95
Canary hot spot, 176
Canyon Fiord Formation, 235, 237
Cape Fold Belt, 19, 189
carbon, *207*, 224
   burial, 27, 71, 72
   changes, 27
Carbon County, Pennsylvania, 163
carbon cycle, 26
carbon dioxide, 15, 16, 22, 31, 33, 34,
   37, 44, 47, 53, 76, 77, 80, 93,
   94, 118, 134, 140, 141, *142,
   146, 148*, 159, 188, 192, 194
   atmospheric changes, *20*, 27
   flux, 2
   Phanerozoic levels, *57*
carbonate organism, 210
carbonates, 7, 11, 76, *142*, 163, 175,
   178, 208, 209, 211, 222, 223,
   229, 230, 232, *235*, 236, 239,
   240, 241, 244, 259, 273
   altered (diagenetically), *212*
   biogenic, 208
   buildup, 249
   minerals, 208, 210, 213
   platforms, 248
   production, 274, 276

carbonates (continued)
   ramp, 151
   sedimentation, 276
   sediments, 211
   shallow-water, 233
   shelf, 232, 233, 236, 237, *247*,
   253
   shelf deposits, 238
   skeletal, 211
   temperate, 231, 232, *233*
   tropical, 229, 231, 232
Carboniferous, *18*, *207*, *215*
Carnarvon basin, 151
Carnian, *111, 113, 200*
Carnian event, *257*
Carnian map, 98
Carpathian Mountains, 258
Cassiar orogeny, 160
Caucasian Range, 257
cements, 236
   aragonite, 217, 233
   carbonate, 249
   hematite, 151
   marine, 212, 215, 223, 225
   meteoric, 209
   silica, 152
   smectite, 151
   submarine, 237, 238
Cenozoic, *71*
Central Kansas uplift, 268, 269, 274,
   279
chalcedony, 240
chalcopyrite, 161
Chasmatosaurus, 151
Cherokee Group, 268, 284
   Lower, *279*
chert, 179, 211, 230, 233, 235, 240,
   241, 242
China, 19, 190, 191, 192, 194, 221,
   223, 256, 257
Chinese stratotype, 189
chlorite, 151
Chloroforam associations, 234, *235*,
   237
Choiyoi province, 189
Choristites, 215
Chortis block, 95
chron, magnetic, 22
circulation
   atmospheric, 159
   changes, *48*
circum-Arctic regions, 230, 233, 244
Clark County, Kansas, 274
clastics, 174, 178, 182, 229, 230
   coaly continental, 108
   sediments, 211
clasts, 239
Clavaporella, 236
claystones, 200
climate, *159, 164, 169*, 177, 192,
   230, 238
   arid, 122
   benthic associations, *230*
   change predictions, *152*
   changes, 1, 2, 37, *52*, 72, 77, 178,
   230, 244
   classification, *50*
   control, *44*

climate (continued)
   cooling, *229*
   evolution, *139, 243, 258*
   feedbacks, 136
   global, 2, 76, 83, 99
   greenhouse, 2, 16, 20, 44, 58, 75,
   159, 178, 192, 259
   icehouse, 2, 15, 20, 75, 159, 178,
   259
   indicators, *6, 230*
   models, *4*, 27, 32, 34, 36, *41, 43*,
   53, 77, *139, 143*
   non-icehouse, 72
   orbital change, *41*
   Pangea breakup, *169*
   Pangean, *25, 41*
   Permian, *229*
   polar, 243
   processes, *4*
   rain-forest, 179
   savannah, 179
   semiarid, 243
   supercontinent, *28*, 94
   Triassic, *91, 177*
   tropical-like, 243
climatic indicators
   Carnian, *111*
   proxy, *103, 111*
   Scythian, *103*
climatology, soil moisture, *124*
cloud cover, 120
cloud formation, 123
cloud parameterization, 93
coal, 7, 92, 111, 113, 148, 149, 150,
   151, 152, 154, 178, 193, *239*,
   244
   deposition, 104, 150, 151, 154
   deposits, 31, 87, 108, 111, 113,
   134, 136, 149, 151
   formation, 26
   gap, 21, 72, 87, 190, 191, 192,
   193, 194
   high-latitude, 11
   low-latitude, 11
   measures, 21, 188, 189, 194
   temperate, 11
   Tethyan, 11
coaly bed, 192
coaly seam, 240
coelobites, 254
collapse
   orogenic, *169*
   Variscan-Alleghanide orogenic, *169*
collisions, 97, 174
Community Climate Model (CCM), *43*,
   92
composita, 212
compression, 174, 176
   plate-boundary, 173
conchostracans, 108, 113
conformities, 230, 235, 237, 239
conglomerates, 174, 235, 237
conifers, 152
Connecticut rift basin, 111
contact, Mississippian-
   Pennsylvanian, *271*
continental crust, 16, 61, *62*, 77, 78,
   174

continentality, *179*
continents, dispersed, *17*
convection, 93
convergence, 170, 176, 182
   continental, 78
Converrucosisporites, 201
cooling, 189, 243
   global, 182
   Permian, 244
   progressive, 229
   surface water, 258
   winter, 28, *33*, 36, 37, 108
Cooper Basin, 19, 150
corals, 209, 213, 223, 231, 250, 251,
   253, 256, 257, 258
Coralville Formation, 215
Cordilleran belt, 160
cores
   Harris, 274, 279
   Milhon, 274, 282, 283
   Schauf, 269, 271, 274, 279, 282
Corollina, 200, 201, 205
   meyeriana, 200
Crockerland, 230
Crurithyris, 212, 215
crust
   algal, 249, 255
   brittle, 182
   continental, 16, 61, *62*, 77, 78, 174
   cratonic, 17
   lower, 176
   micritic biogenic, 250
   microbial, 249
   orogenic, 171
   rift stage, 174
   rifted, 16
   rifted-continental, 174
   thin, 16
   thinning, 14
   unroofing, 162
Culpepper rift basin, 111, 198, 201
Cuneiphycus, 236
currents, oceanic, 248
Cürük Dag section, 222
cycles
   diurnal, 93
   dry, 106, 108
   glacial-interglacial, 41
   hydrological, 117
   lacustrine, *198*, 203
   precession, 42, *48*, 134
   sand-patch, 198
   seasonal, 28, 41
   sedimentary, 205
cyclicity, *198*
   sedimentary, *200*
cycling, chemical, 92
cyclothems, 268
   Kansas, *279*

D

Dan River, 174, 175, 198
Danville basin, 175, 198
Dead Sea, 180
Dead Sea rift, 180, 182
Deerfield basin, 200
deformation, 170, 173, 176, 177

degassing rates, mantle, 58, 59, 68,
   72, 77, 80, 87
Degerböls Formation, 239, 240
degradation, 99
Delta Plain facies, 189
deltaic deposits, 7
Deltoidospora, 201
Dempsey Formation, 190
denudation, 79
Des Moines Supergroup, 269
deserts, *119*
   modern, *117*, *119*, 122, 129
   Pangean, *117*
   polar, 229
detrital deposits, 176
detritus, 177
Devonian, post-, *163*
diagenesis, 163, *210*, *213*, 224
diagnostics, GCM hydrological, *117*
Dicroidium, 109, 110, 113, 151, 190,
   191
Dictyophyllidites, 201
Dictyophyllum, 113
dinosaurs, 26, 37
Diplopora, 236
discharge, 101
   catastrophic, 20
disconformity, 190
dispersal, Pangea, 248
displacement, 174
dolomite, 162, 259
dolostones, 162, 221, 239
Donezella, 236
dropstones, 20, 72, 190, *239*, 244
drought indices, *127*
drying, 26
Dundee Rhyodacite, 189, 190
Durham Basin, 174
Dvinella, 236

E

earthquake, 164
East African Rift System, 97, 180
East Antarctica, 18
echinoderms, 213, 231, 253, 272
ecosystems, 248
Ellesmere Island, 237, 238
Ellesmerella, 236
Ellesmerian Orogeny, 230
Ellsworth Mountains, 19
emergence, continental, 68, 69, 70,
   71, 77
Emmaville Volcanics, 189, 190
energy
   solar, 16
   surface, 43
England, 150
Eniwetok Atoll, 211
environment
   changes, 1
   history, *187*
   sedimentary, *13*
eolian deposits, 6, 92, 129
eolian dune deposits, 131
epeirogeny, 160, *163*
   causes, *164*
   intraplate motions, 164

Epimastopora, 236
Epimastoporella, 236
Epistachoides, 236
Eridmatus, 212
erosion, 18, 21, 78, 159, 160, 163,
   176, 271
eruption, 188, 189, 191, 194
Estrada Nove Formation, 189
Eugonophyllum, 236
Euramerica, 17
Eurasia, 28, 34, 35
Europe, 18, 19, 113, 145, 192
Eurydesma, 150
evaporation, 118, 121, *123*, 132, 134,
   208
   potential, 128, 132, 136
   rates, 145
evaporites, 2, 7, 92, 98, 103, 104,
   111, 129, 131, 148, 149, 154,
   175, 177, 178, 182, 229, 230,
   235, *237*, *238*, 240
   formation, 26
evapotranspiration, 121, 123, 124,
   127
   potential, *128*, 132
   rates, 143
evolution
   climatic, *139*, *243*
   late Paleozoic, *243*
   Pangea, *207*
   record, 3
   supercontinent, *13*
Exeter Village section, 201
Exmouth Plateau, 96
exposure, subaerial, 271
extension, 14, 16, *18*, 174, 176, 177,
   179, 188
   Late Triassic, *20*
extinction, *12*, 26, 36, *164*, 177, 194,
   197, 203, 248, 252, 255, 256,
   258
   Late Triassic, *197*

F

facies
   marine, 14
   nonmarine, 14, 17
fault systems
   sinistral, 177
   South Atlas, 174
faulting, wrench, *171*
faults
   border, 174, 175
   detachment, 177
   dextral, 174
   extensional, 182
   listric, 176, 177
   normal, 175, 176
   reverse, 175
   sinistral, 173
   strike-slip, *172*, 176, 182
   thrust, 175
   transcurrent, 174
   transfer, 175
   wrench, 175
fauna, 2
feldspar, 79, 80, 150

feldspar (continued)
    microcline, *162*
fern spikes, 205
ferns, 152
fish
    dipnoid, 106, 113
    semionotid fossil, 105, 113
Fitzroy Basin, 150
flooding, 61, 72
flora, 2, 149, 155, 232
    Euramerican, 110
fluvial deposits, 7
foldbelts, 18, 19
foraminifers, 231, 236, 253
forcing
    greenhouse, 47
    insolation, 29
    Milankovitch, 31, 37, 92, 107, 113
forcing factors
    astronomical, 2
    biological changes, 2
fossils, *104, 113*
    semionotid, 105, 113
Fourstonella, 236
Fundy basin, 174, 175, 179, 201, 203
Fusulina, 236
Fusulinella, 236, 282

G

galena, 161
Gamburtsev Sub-glacial Mountains,
    18
Gebel Um Shomar, 164
Gettysburg basin, 172, 198, 201
Gigantoproductus, 211, 215
Ginkophytes, 152
glacial deposits, 6, 244
glacial effect, 209
glaciation, 25, 27, 37, 76, 149, 182,
    209
glaciers, 31, 215, 233
glass, volcanic, 162
glauconite, 231, 239, 241
global warming, 117, 182
Glossopteris, 21, 149, 150, 151, 154,
    190, 191, 192
Gobi Desert, 120
Gondwana, 25, 35, 70, 95, 109, 141,
    144, 145, 146, 148, 149, 152,
    244
    basins, 19, 152
    glaciations, *31*
Gondwana fold belt, 20
Gondwanaland, 14, *17*, 190
    platform, 14
Gondwanan Plateau, 147, 148
Goochland terrane, 174, 175
Gorni Karabach, Azerbaidzhan, 257
grabens, 20
gradient averaging, latitudinal, *66*
grains, nonskeletal, *236, 238*
grainstones, 237, 238
Grand Banks, 98, 179
granite, 177
granitoids, 189
    magmatism, 189
Granulatisporites, 201

gravitational slip, 174
Gray Group, *268*, 284
    depositional history, *279*
    depositional sequences, *273*
Great Artesian Basin, 20
Great Bear Cape Formation, 237, 238
Great Bear Cape shelf, 239
Greater Pangea accretions, 248
greenhouse climate, 2, 16, 20, 44, 58,
    75, 159, 178, 192, 259
greenhouse effect, 58
greenhouse forcing, 47
greenhouse warming, 33, 47, 58
Greenland, 208
Greenland Sea, 241
Gregory rift, 175
Grist Mills, 201
groundwater, 118
Gryhus, 213
Guizhou, China, 257
Gulf of Mexico, 174
Gulf Rim Fault System, 95
Gulf Stream, 33
Gunnedah basin, 189
Gunnedah biotites, 190
Gwyneddichnium, 201
gymnosperms, 26
gypsum, 103, 237

H

Hadley cell, 120, 144
half-grabens, 174, 175, 198, 230,
    235, 237
halite, 98, 103, 209, 237
    deposits, 111
Hamilton Group, 164
Hare Fiord Formation, 235
Hartford basin, 175, 182, 200, 201
Hartford-Deerfield basins, 175
Harz Mountains, 97
heat
    accumulation, 14
    anomalies, *17, 18*
    flux, 43, 95
    storage, 118
    transport, 33, 44, 108
Hedraites, 236
Hercynian-European plate, 173
Hercynian orogeny, 160
Hercynians, 182
High Atlas, 174
High Atlas basins, 177
Himalaya block, 96
Himalaya Orogen, *86*
Himalaya-Tibet region, 22
Himalayan orogeny, 85
Himalayan-Tibetan system, 176
Himalayas, 76, 78, 79, 86, 150, 152,
    176
Holder Formation, 212
Horquilla Limestone, 217
horsts, 248, 258
Hugoton embayment, 268, 269, 274,
    279, 284
    eastern, *279*
Hunstein-Jimi-Bismark terrane, 96
Hunter Valley, 151

Hyalosponge assemblage, 233, 234
Hyalosponge associations, 234, *240*
hydrocarbon reservoirs, 11
hydrologic budget equations, 43
hydrology, *118, 131*
Hylas fault, 174
Hylas fracture zone, 175
hypsometric province, *17*
hypsometry, *16*, 59, *67*

I

ice, 85, 208, 244
    continental, 76, 83
    crystals, 151, 154
    glacial, 208
    land, 143
    nucleation, 84, 85, 86
    rafting, 70, 71
    volume, 217
ice age, 192
ice caps, *67*, 69, 70, 71, 72
ice cover, 31, 67, 241, 242
ice-sheet formation, continental, 84,
    85, 86
ice-sheet initiation, continental, *75*
ice sheets, 20, 31, 67, 77, 164
    continental, 76, 83, 86
ice shields, 259
icehouse climate, 2, 15, 20, 75, 159,
    178, 259
icehouses, 67, 83, *84*, 86, 87, 88
    decay, 88
    defined, 76
icesheet deposits, continental, 143
ichnofossils, 197, 201
ignimbrites, 21, 189
inclusions, 209
India, 19, *139*, 192, 221
India Block, 96
Indo-Burman Range terrane, 96
Indochina block, 97
Indus Fan, 78, 79
inertinite, 151, 152
inertodetrinite, 151, 154, 155
insolation, *182*
    forcing, 29
    orbital, 33, 34
    seasonality, 48, 53
    solar, 93, 140
    solar changes, 32
insulator, 14
Inter-Tropical Convergence Zone
    (ITCZ), 29, 100, 122, 144
intraclasts, 272, 273, 276
intrusions, 176
invertebrates, marine, 197
Ipswich Coal Measures, 20
Ipswich Microflora, 151
Iran, 221, 224, 257
Iran block, 96
isotopes
    carbon, *209*, 225
    environmental indicators, *208*
    geochemistry, 8
    oxygen, *208*, 225
    ratios, 92
    stable, *21, 208*

isotopic composition, *210*
isotopic record, Pangea, *215*
Ivanovia, 236

J

Jacksonwald basalt, 201
Jacksonwald Syncline, 201
Japan, 248
Jerusalem, Israel, 182
jet streams, 99, 145
Jurassic, *151*
  Early, *129*, *131*, *200*
  mid-, *139*, *148*

K

Kalkberg tephra, 163
Kanimblides/proto–New England
    Foldbelt, 19
Kansas, 217, *267*
kaolinite, 151, 152
Kapp Starostin Formation, 221
Karoo Basin, 19, 189
Karoo tectonosedimentary terrain, 19
karst, 6
karstification, 178
karsting, 276
Kazanian, *239*
  post-, *240*
Kazanian-Norian interval, 9
Kearny Formation, 268
Keeneia, 150
Kerguelen, 194
Koeppen climate, *50*
  classification, *50*
Kolyma Block, 244
Kungurian, *239*
Kyrtomisporis, 201

L

labyrinthodont locations, 113
lacuna, 14, 17, 18
lacustrine deposits, 6
Lake Tanganyika, 175
lakes
  deposits, 182
  Gondwana, 36, 37
  levels, 29
  rift, 180
land distribution, 71
landmass, 28, 33, 59, 65, *70*, 82, 142,
    143, *144*, 147, 150, 170, 171,
    179, 182, 230, 252, 260
  large, *66*, 70
Laramide Orogeny, 95
Last Glacial Maximum, 59
Latemar platform, 259
Laurasia, 14, 17, 95, 144, 149
Laurasian province, 17
Laurentide Ice Sheet, 31
lavas, 174, 177, 194
  tholeiitic, 176
leaching, 21
Leigh Creek Coal Measures, 20
Lesser Pangea assemblage, 248
Lhasa block, 96

lignin, 87
limestone, 221, 223, 235, 239, 257,
    274, 276, 279
lithification, submarine, 250
lithoclasts, 272, 276
lithofacies, *271*, *273*
logs, preserved, 113
luminosity, 27, 28, 31, 32, 34, 37,
    59, *67*
lungfish, 151
Lystrosaurus, 151

M

Macroporella, 236
Madagascar, 19
Madagascar Block, 96
magnetite, 162
mantle
  degassing, 72, 77
  plumes, 16, 164, 194
  processes, 1
Marathon Mountains, 160
marine deposits, 222
marine facies, 14
Martinia, 211, 215
Maurice Ewing Bank, 96
Meguma suture, 175
melting, 20, 177, 233
Melvillian Disturbance, 230, 237,
    239
mesetas, 174
Mesogean Sea, 248
Mesozoic, *71*
metabentonites, 163
metagenesis, 161
metamorphism, 18, 176
microcline, 162
Microreticulatisporites bitriangularis,
    189
Middleton basin, 175
migration, *70*, 177
Milankovitch cycles, 36, 67
Milankovitch fluctuations, 26, *28*
Milankovitch forcing, 31, 37, 92,
    107, 113
Minas Geofracture, 172, 174
Minas Geofracture system, 177
mineralogy, *236*, *238*, *239*, *240*,
    253
minerals
  iron-bearing deposits, 8
  metallic resources, 12
  phosphate, 211
  silicate, 142
  siliceous, 240
Mississippi Valley Type (MVT)
    deposits, 163
Missouri, 164
Mobile Belt, 229
models
  Arthaud and Matte, 172
  atmospheric general circulation,
    141
  Biosphere-Atmosphere Transfer
    Schome (BATS), 93
  carbon dioxide, 142
  Carnian, 111, 113

models (continued)
  cavitating-fluid, 93
  circulation, 92, *93*
  climate, *4*, *27*, 32, 34, 36, *41*, *43*,
    53, 77, *95*, 105, *139*, *143*
  community climate, 141
  detachment, 177
  energy balance (EBMs), *27*, 37,
    107, 140
  general circulation (GCMs), *27*, 37,
    77, *117*, 124, 125, 126, *129*,
    134, 140, 144
  general circulation simulations, *91*
  GENESIS, 92, *93*
  geochemical, 58, 94
  GISS GCM, *118*, 122, 123, 124,
    125, 126, 127, 132
  global, 194
  global climate (GCMs), 92, *93*,
    114
  ground hydrology, 136
  land-surface transfer, 93
  mass-balance, 142
  NCAR Community Climate, 139,
    141, 143, 144
  numerical, 129, 140
  ocean, 32
  orogenic, *87*
  orogenic collapse-tectonic escape,
    176
  Pangean, *15*
  qualitative, 140
  reefs, *252*
  Scythian, 104, 105, 113
  seasonal cycle general circulation,
    140
  simulation, 260
  six-layer soil, 93
  six-layer thermodynamic, 93
  spectral climate, 141
  surface temperature maintenance,
    59
  tectonic, 92, *95*
  three-layer thermodynamic, 93
  two-dimensional energy-balance,
    140
  weathering, *80*, 87
moisture, missing, *134*
Mojave-Sonoma Megashear, 95
molasse basins, 177
molasse sequence, 174
mollusks, 213, 231, 253, 272
monsoon, 29, 41, *42*, 49, 71, 113,
    134, 141, 145, 154, 179, 198
Monte region, 120
Moonbi Plutonic Suite, 190
Moroccan plate, 177
Morocco, 174, 175, 176, 256
Morrowan-Atokan boundary, 217
Mt. Algonquin, 164
Mount Bayley, 235
Mount Bayley Formation, 237
Mt. Marcy, 164
mountain building, 160, 164
mountain ranges, active, *176*
mountains, fold-belt, 160
mud mounds, 249
mudstones, 150, 179, 224

N

Namib desert, 120, 122
Nansen Formation, 235
Nansenella, 236
Narrabeen Group, 189, 190
Narragansett Basin, 174
Neoanchicodium, 236
Neognathodus caudatus, 271
Neospirifer, 212, 217
Neotethys, 248
Network basin, 198
Nevada section, 217
New England, 174
New England Foldbelt, 19
New England magmatic arc, 189
New Madrid, Missouri, 164
New Mexico, 212, 215, 217, 220
New South Wales, 151
New York, *163*, 217
Newark basin, 113, 172, 175, 177,
    182, 198, 201, 205
Newark-Gettysburg basins, 175
Newark Supergroup, *197*
Newcastle Coal Measures, 189, 190
nonmarine facies, 14, 17
Norfolk Basin, 174
North America, 192, 197, 248
North American craton, 160, 174,
    225
North Carolina, 175
North China Block, 97
North 40°-Kelvin Lineament, 171,
    175, 177, 182
North German Basin, 97
North Greenland, 244
North Mountain basalt, 201
North Sea Basin, 97
Northwest Territories, 150
Nova Scotia, 162
Nutbush Creek fault, 174

O

Oaxaca Block, 95
obliquity, 42
ocean
    changes, *33*
    currents, 44
oceanography, *179*
oncoids, 233, 237
Onslow Microflora, 151
Ontong Java, 194
ooids, 231, 233, 237, *239*
ophiolites, 209
Orange Mountain basalt, 201
orbital change, *41*
Orinoco River, 79
    sediments, 80
orogenic collapse, *169*, 182
orogens, 80, 82, *86*
    continent-continent collisions, *78*
    standard, *78*, 85, 86
    strongly cooling, *84*, 86
    Variscan-Alleghanian, *173*
    weakly cooling, 86
orogeny, 81
    defined, 160
Ortonella, 236

Osprey Salt, 98
Otterdale Formation, 200
Otto Fiord Formation, 235, 237
Ouachita Mountains, 160, 163
Ouachita orogenic belt, 160
outgassing, volcanic, 142
oxygen, *207*

P

packstone, *272*
Pakistan, 221
Palaeoaplysina, 233, 236, 261
Paleoarctic Ocean, 95
paleobiogeography, 8, *97*
paleoclimate, 2, *4*, *13*, 92, 103, 104,
    111, 113, *117*, 123, 137, 139,
    140, *148*, 150, 151, 159, *247*,
    259
    changes, *190*
    controls, 11
paleoclimatology, 261
paleocommunities, 8
paleocurrents, 18
paleoecology, 8
paleoenvironments, 213
paleogeography, *5*, *141*, 145, 148,
    179
    changing, *57*, 72
    maps, *5*
paleolatitudes, *61*, 68, 77, 95, *179*,
    233, 252, *259*
paleomap, 260
paleo-Pacific, 31
paleosols, 6, 151
paleotemperature, 217
Paleotethyan region, 217
Paleotethyan Seaway, 221
Paleotethys, 32, 248
paleotopography, *97*
Paleozoic, *70*
    late, *232*, *243*
Palisades sill, 201
palynofloras
    Early Jurassic, *200*
    Late Triassic, *200*
palynology, *197*
palynomorphs, 189, 197
Pangea, *140*
    breakup, 2, 22, 26, 71, 72, 129,
        142, *169*
    environmental history, *187*
    isotopic record, *215*
    northern, *243*
    resources, 2, *11*
Pangean, *25*, *41*, *117*, *159*, *164*, *187*,
    247
Panthalassa Ocean, 33, 248
Panthalassan, 15, 217
Panthalassan margin, 189
Paraepimastopora, 236
Parana basin, 95, 189
Patagonian region, 120
path, polar wander, 36
Patinasporites densus, 201
patterns, sea-level pressure, *144*
peats, 12
    accumulations, 134

peats (continued)
    deposition, 129
    deposits, 132, 134, 136
Pee Dee formation, 208
Peera Peera Formation, 20
Peidmont suture, 175
peloids, 231, 233
Pennsylvanian, *163*
    Middle, *267*
Pensacola Mountain, 19
perihelion, 41, 42, 44, 48, 52, 53
permafrost, 101, 113
Permian, *19*, *20*, *149*, *163*, *187*, *217*,
    229, *247*
    Late, *19*, *139*, *143*, *146*
Permian-Triassic event, 20
Permian/Triassic boundary, 21, *187*,
    220
Perth Basin, 19, 152
Peruvian Desert, 120, 122
Petrified Forest, 111
Phanerozoic, *57*
phosphate, 239
Phosphoria Formation, *241*, 244
phosphorites, 7, 11
photosynthesis, 209
Planetary Boundary Layer (PBL)
    thermals, 93
planktonic organism, 210
plant debris, 161
platform lacuna, 15
plutonism, 174
plutons, 19
podzols, 151
polar regions, ice-cap-free, 113
polar wander curve, 95
polarity, magnetic, *194*
Ponperaug basin, 198
Porcellispora, 201
porosity, 239
Portugal, 256
potassium, 163
potassium feldspar, 162
precipitation, *29*, *46*, 52, 76, 79, 93,
    98, 101, 105, 113, 114, *121*,
    123, 126, *128*, 131, 132, 137,
    141, 144, 146, 148, 179, 182,
    198
    changes, *48*
    global mean, 99
    global mean annual, 122
    model-predicted pattern, 144
    rates, *47*, 118, 122, 131, 132
    summer monsoonal, 145
Project Pangea, *1*
    objectives, *3*
Pseudofusulina, 236
Pseudofusulinella, 236
Ptilophyllum, 152
pyrite, 161
pyroclastics, 189

Q

quartz, 150
    layers, 205
    shocked, 203, 205
quartz arenites, 152, 155

R

Raanes Formation, 237
radiation, 16
  balance, 159
  equations, 118
  solar, 41, 48, 93, 120, 143, 259
rain, acid, 182
rain forest, 52
rainfall, 49, 53, 151, 154, 176, 178,
  182
rainshadows, 120
  effects, 123
Raleigh belt, 174
Ramapo border fault, 175
Raniganj Formation, 150
reconstruction, Pangean
  paleoclimates, *148*
red beds, 21, 148, 149, 151, 179, 188,
  190, 191, 192, 194, *237, 238,*
  242, 248
  deposits, 92
Reef Complex, 212
reefs, 7, 149, *236, 238*
  algal, 229, 236, 237, 255
  ancient, 259
  biota, *253*, 255, 260
  biota changes, 256
  biodetrital, 249
  bivalve, 254
  bryozoan, 236, 254
  calcisponge, 255
  carbonates, 248, 257
  cement, 255
  chaetetid, 255
  communities, 259
  construction, *253*
  coral, 250
  crest, 254
  crises, 256
  cryptic habitats, *254*
  dasycladacean, 254
  dramatic crises, *251*
  ecologic, 253
  evolution, 248, 252, *254*, 258
  facies, 2
  gap, 255, *257*
  guilds, 256
  hydromechanical, 249
  Lithiotis, 254, 256
  low-water, 250
  medium-lived, 255
  mixed, 236
  models, *252*
  modern, 248, 253
  mounds, 248, 255
  Norian Lime Peak, 249
  Palaeoaplysina, 255
  Pangean, 248
  pelecypod, 254
  Permian, *247*
  Rhaetian Steinplatte, 249
  short-lived, 254
  sites, 248
  sponges, 255
  stromatolite, 249, 254
  Triassic, *247*
  types, *248*, 254
regression, 271, 276

Reguibat Promotory, 173
reptiles, therapsid, 106
reservoirs, constant-depth, 118
residence times
  in-situ, 80
  in-transit, 79, 80
respiration, 209
  rates, 209
Reticulatisporites, 201
Richmond basin, 174, *200*
Richmond-Taylorsville basin, 175
ridge, mid-ocean, 16
rift basin, 111
rift controls, *175*
rift oceans, 16, 17, 20
rift phase, 235
rift system, 92
rift uplift, 92
rift valley, 111
rifting, 16, 72, 95, 97, *98*, 174, 176,
  177, 179, 182, 230, 255, 258
  continental, 20
rifts
  intramontane, 19
  volcanic, 15
Rio Bonito Formation, 189
river runoff, *126*, 136
Roanoke basin, 175
rocks
  basement, 174
  calcalkaline, 189, 190
  carbonate, 162
  igneous, 78, 79
  sedimentary, 162, 209
  source, 11
  volcanic, 142, 190
Rot event, 92
rotation pole, 95
runoff, 43, 47, 52, 53, 76, 79, 93,
  100, 101, 105, 106, 108, 113,
  118, 121, 123, 136, 152, 178
  changes, *48*
  river, *126*, 136
  surface, *124*, 132, 134, 137
Russia, 217, 257

S

Sabine Bay Formation, 239, 240
Sabine plate, 174
sabkhas, 177
sags, 14, 19
Sahara Desert, 120, 122
St. Helena hot spot, 176
Sakmarian, *235*
Salado basin, 95
salinity, 208, 231, 233, 258
salt deposits, 179
Salt Range, 189
salts, 98
Samba terrane, 96
San Jorge Basin, 95
sand deposits, 92
sands, 79, 80, 150
  carbonate, 250
sandstone, 79, 149, 150, 151, 152,
  178, 189, 201, 230, 235, 237,
  239, 240, 241, 283

Santa Katarina, 164
Schwagerina, 236
Scotsburg basin, 175
Scythian, *103, 113*
sea ice, 102, 113
  fractional cover, 102
  seasonal, 143
sea level, *16, 193*, 224
  change, 2, 41, 252
  curve, 274
  fluctuations, 182, *258*
  lower, 62
  pressure, *46*
  pressure patterns, *144*
  rise, 20, 26, 283
seafloor, 17
seafloor diagenesis, 210
seafloor spreading, 14, 15, *20*, 68, 77,
  142, 179
seasonal cycles, 28, 41
seasonality, precession cycle, *48*, 53
seawater, 208, 209, 210
  changes, 21
  composition, 2, 21, 41
  isotopes, *193*
  stable isotopes, 21
seaways, 146, 152, 154
  epeiric, *179*
sedimentary record, 1, 2, *5*
sedimentation, 180, 182, 197, 212
sediments
  accumulation, 92
  bioclastic, 249
  carbonate, 212, 231
  clastic, 230
  marine, 209
Serpukhovian, *235*
serpulids, 231
shales, 8, 11, 149, 152, 182, 193,
  237, 238, 240, *272*, 274
shallow-water associations, 235
shelf carbonates, Pangean *247*
shell
  altered, 212
  aragonitic, 212
  fragments, 279
  preserved, 212
shortening, 14, *18*, 170
  Carboniferous, *18*
  Early Triassic, *19*
  Late Permian, *19*
  Middle Triassic, *19*
Siberia, 144, 145, 149
Siberian Traps, 21, 22, 188, 189, 193,
  194
siderite, *239*
Sierra de la Ventana Foldbelt, 19
silica deposits, 7
silicate enhancement rates, 83
silicates, 58, 78
  weathering, *58*, 67
siltstone, 150, 200, 237, 238, 240,
  276, 279
Simple Biosphere Model (SiB), 93
simulations, *114*
  carbon dioxide, 152
  climate model, 140
  GCM, 121, *131*

simulations (continued)
    Jurassic, 153
    Late Permian, *143*, *146*, 152
    Late Triassic, *147*, 153
    mid-Jurassic, *148*
Sinai subplate, 164
slab, thermodynamic, 93
slickensides, 276, 279
smectite, 151
snow cover, 31, 32, 33, *46*, 93, 100
snow cover, changes, *48*
snowmelt, 43, 100
soil layer, 101
soil moisture, 43, *46*, 49, 100, 113,
    118, 121, 123, *124*, 132, 137
soil properties, 95
soil water, 102
soil-ice fraction, 101
solar processes, *1*
South Africa, 19, 150, 189, 192
South America, 120, 189
South Atlas fracture zone, 172, 175,
    176, 177, 182
South Carolina, 208
South China Block, 97
South Pole, 141
Spain, 217, 256
sphalerite, 161
sphinctozoans, 257
spicules
    monotaxon, 240
    sponges, 231, 241
spikes
    gamma, 274
    Triassic, 21
splays, 240
sponges, 223, 238, 253, 256, 258
    spicules, 231, 241
spores, 200, *201*
    spike, 201, 205
Stacheia, 236
Stacheoidella, 236
Stacheoides, 236
Steinplatte complex, 223
steppe, 52
Stony Coal Facies, 189
storm systems, cyclonic, 145
storm tracks, *145*, 150, 153, 154,
    155
    mid-latitude, 145
strata
    carbonate, 163
    coal-bearing, *163*
    fluvial, 198
    lacustrine, 198
    post-Devonian, *163*
    vanished, *163*
stratal hierarchy, *267*
stratal terminations, *279*, 283
stratigraphy, *9*
    sequences, *15*, *267*
stress
    reversal, *176*
    shared, 110
strike-slip shear zones, 173
stromatolites, 162
strontium, 21, 236
stylolites, 272

subduction, 16, 77, 97, 177
submergence, *17*
subsidence, 14, 19, 72, 120, 122, 162,
    164, 174, 230
    stages, *14*
sulfur, 21
sulphates, 103
superchron, 194
    magnetic, *22*
supercontinents, 2, 25, *28*, *33*, 37, 42,
    71, 92, *140*, 146, 188
superocean, 15
supracontinent, 182
Svalbard, 244
Sverdrup Basin, 150, 220, *229*, 238
    benthic associations, *234*
    climatic evolution, *243*
    climatic indicators, *234*
    succession, 230, 244
swamp deposits, 178
Sydney Basin, 150, 189, 190
symbiosis, algal, 250, 251, 253
synchroneity, global, *5*, *9*
synthesis, 12

T

Taconian orogeny, 85
Taconic Orogen, 85
Taklimakan Desert, 120
Tanquary, 235
Tanzania, 111
Tasmania, 103, 233
Tasmanian coal measures, 20
Taylorsville basin, 200
tectonics, *1*, *5*, *176*
tectonism, 177, 230, 244
tectono-sedimentary stages, *18*
temperature, *27*, *33*, 35, 36, 37, 41,
    44, 52, 113, 118, 140, *144*, 147,
    148, 152, 154, 179, 210, 213,
    217, 231, 259
    ambient air, 81
    changes, *48*
    global, *46*, *57*, 85, 117, 188
    polar, 68, 70, 71, 84, 85, 86
    regional, *46*
    sea-surface, 35, 144
    surface, *146*
    surface air, 98
tephra, 162
tephra beds, *163*
terranes
    biotite, 177
    displaced, 260
    exotic, 248, 257
    metamorphic, 177
    suspect, 260
Tethyan margin, 144, 145
Tethyan regions, 244
Tethys, 248, 251
Tethys coast, 46, 49, 51, 147
Tethys Ocean, 43, 132
Tethys Ocean basin, 97
Tethys Sea, 44, 140, 142, 144, 147,
    150, 154, *248*
tetrapods, 191, 193, 197, 201, 203
Texas, 217

therapsids, 109
Thinnfeldia callipteroides, 191
Tibetan Plateau, 76, 176
Tien Shan, 176
tile, axial, 43
tillites, 149, 244
Timan-Petchora Basin, 244
Timor, 217
Timor terrane, 96
Todisporites, 201
topography, *179*
trace elements, *213*
Transantarctic Mountains, 189
transgression, 17, 237, 272, 276
transport, larval, 260
transpression, 18, 173
Trappers Cove Formation, 237
Trepeilopsis, 236
Triassic, *20*, *91*, *147*, *151*, *176*, *177*,
    187, *197*, *200*, *207*, *220*, *247*,
    257
    Early, *19*, *257*
    Late, *197*
    Middle, *19*
Triassic-Jurassic boundary, 36
Triassic/Jurassic boundary sections,
    201
Trold Fiord Formation, 239, 240
Tuberitina, 236
Tubiphytes, 236, 253, 255, 256
Tuckahoe Formation, 200
tufa, 179
tuff, 182, 189, 190, 191
turbidites, 79
turbidity, 182
Turkey, 221, 222, 224
Turkey Branch Formation, 200
Tuscany, Italy, 203, 205

U

unconformities, 230, 235, 237, 239,
    252, 268, 284
Ungdarella, 236
uplifts, 67, 76, 79, 86, 113, 162, *164*,
    177, 230
    Carboniferous, *18*
    Early Triassic, *19*
    epeirogenic, *159*, *160*, *163*, *164*
    Late Permian, *19*
    Middle Triassic, *19*
    orogenic, 21, *159*, *160*
    Pangean, *159*, *164*
    Permian, *163*
    thermal, 14, *98*
Ural Orogen, *86*
Uralides, 170
Uralla Suite, 190
Urals, 86
Urey reactions, 58, 59

V

Vallasporites ignacii, 201
valley incision, 271
Van Hauen Formation, 240
Variscan orogen, 174, 175
Variscan-Alleghanian orogen, 176

Variscan-Alleghanide orogenic
    collapse, *169*
Variscides, 19
vegetation, 92, 93, 94, 114, 132
    albedo, 120
    distributions, 118
    shifts, 26
    types, *118*, 132, 143
    winter, 118
Vendian supercontinent, 17
venting, 15, 16
Verrucosisporites, 201
vertebrates
    amphibian-dominated, 26
    reptile-dominated, 26
Vesterisbanken Seamount, 241
Virginia, 175
vitrinites, 161
volatiles, 194
volcanic activity, 164
volcanics, 19, 20, 229
volcanism, 203
Volvotextularis, 236
Voltzia flora, 191

W

wackestone, *272*
Waldheimia, 213
Waltonia, 213
warming
    global, 117, 182
    summer, 26, 31, 34, 107, 110
water vapor, 93
water-balance equations, 124
water-balance feedbacks, 143
wave base, 235
waves, surface, 150
weathering, *75*, 192, 209
    categories, 83
    chemical, 72, 76, 77
    continental, 76, 79
    extreme, 191
    mechanical, 76, 78, 79
    silicate, 76, 78, 79, 80, 81, 85, 86,
        87
weathering rates, 58, 68, 78, 80, *81*,
    83, 86, 209
    chemical, 76

weathering rates (continued)
    silicate, 87
West Irian–Jaya terrane, 96
West Spitsbergen, 220, 221
White Nile, 134
wind fields, 98, 99
winds
    mid-tropospheric, 99
    surface, *46*
Wordian shelf, 240

Y

Yangtze area, 223
Yaqui Block, 95
Yucatan Block, 95
Yugoslavia, 217, 221
Yukon territories, 249

Z

Zambezian rifts, 19
zeolites, 162

Typeset by WESType Publishing Services, Inc., Boulder, Colorado
Printed in U.S.A. by Malloy Lithographing, Inc., Ann Arbor, Michigan